Western Europe in the Old Stone Age

The stations whose names are underlined were first used by de Mortillet to delineate the stages of

K. D. Pōpert

The Science of Man

The

Holt, Rinehart
and Winston, Inc.
New York, Chicago,
San Francisco, Toronto

MISCHA TITIEV

Science of Man

Revised and Enlarged

Library of Congress Catalog Card Number: 63-13943
Printed in the United States of America
28468-0313

Second Printing, May, 1964

This book is most
affectionately dedicated
to my wife Estelle
and our son Bob

Whenever I have studied human affairs, I have carefully labored not to mock, lament, nor condemn, but only to understand.

1676 Spinoza

Preface to the Second Edition

The revised text has been rewritten and expanded to cover more material than did the first edition and includes recent findings and up-to-date points of view without slighting traditional teachings. Nevertheless, the principal objective remains the same—"to introduce to the science of man, or anthropology, those college students and other interested readers who have had no previous experience with the subject."

As with the first edition, this book strives to cover all the major facets of anthropology and to achieve a balance between physical anthropology, archeology, and cultural anthropology. Each of these subdivisions is different from the others, but when integrated, they combine to increase our understanding of man and his behavior.

It is the author's contention that *Homo sapiens* resulted from the play of the same evolutionary forces that produced all other creatures. The writer is also of the opinion that man promptly and proudly set himself apart from all other animals by developing and adding to his biological resources those nonbiogenetic factors that play a vital part in all patterns of culture. But, it is important to keep in mind, man could never have developed culture had not his body been properly constituted for this great achievement.

Indeed, a leading physical anthropologist, Sherwood L. Washburn, believes that man's use of tools—a cultural practice—may even have aided his bodily evolution;[1] and, in his latest book, the famed geneticist, Theodosius Dobzhansky, writes that human evolution is not a purely biological process. Instead, he maintains, human evolution represents an interaction of biology and culture, with a steady feedback between them.[2] It is this constant intermingling of biological and cultural

[1] S. L. Washburn, "Tools and Human Evolution," *Scientific American*, Vol. 203, 1960, pp. 3-15.

[2] T. Dobzhansky, *Mankind Evolving*, New Haven and London, 1962, p. 18.

elements that provides the basis for what is here called "biocultural behavior."

Anthropology is a vigorous and ever-changing discipline. Fresh discoveries are constantly being made, and new interpretations and methods of analysis are constantly being offered. As a result, no author can prepare a new text without considerable help. The writer has been fortunate in getting much valuable assistance from others; but he, alone, is responsible for all deficiencies.

Many important suggestions and criticisms were made by George A. Agogino, Donn V. Hart, and Marshall T. Newman. Much help was also received from James B. Griffin, James N. Spuhler, and Frank B. Livingstone. Gabriel W. Lasker read the first part of the manuscript, Chester S. Chard read Part Two, and Robert J. Miller read the entire typescript. Each of the readers made numerous comments, pointing out flaws and offering suggestions, many of which have been incorporated into the text. For their aid the author is deeply grateful.

It is a pleasure to acknowledge the cheerfully given help of June Crockett, Nancy Bates, and Brenda Richardson, who did the bulk of the needed typing and retyping. It is also a pleasure to thank Frances Mannard, who prepared many of the line drawings in the book. Finally, I must record my gratitude to my wife and son.

Mischa Titiev

Ann Arbor, Michigan
March 1963

FROM THE

Preface to the First Edition

. . . the present volume is an introduction to Anthropology, rather than a summary of all it teaches. . . .

While the various departments of the science of Man are extremely multifarious, ranging from body to mind, from language to music, from fire-making to morals, they are all matters to whose nature and history every well-informed person ought to give some thought. It is much, however, for any single writer to venture to deal even in the most elementary way with so immense a variety of subjects. In such a task I have the right to ask that errors and imperfections should be lightly judged.

Edward Burnett Tylor

February 1881

It is sometimes whispered in academic circles that a teacher writes a textbook more to impress his colleagues than to instruct his pupils. Exactly the reverse is true in this instance. The major purpose of this book is to introduce to the science of man, or anthropology, those college students and other interested readers who have had no previous experience with the subject. While trying to reach his goal, the author sought to write simply yet effectively, to integrate related facets of the topic wherever possible, and to explain and interpret his material at every step of the way.

This textbook, then, is not designed to be a more or less comprehensive encyclopedia of anthropological facts and speculations, nor will the reader be left to puzzle out for himself such inferences as may logically be drawn from the data. On the contrary, every effort will be made to derive meanings from the facts, meanings which, it is hoped, will help students to understand what anthropology is all about and also to recognize more fully the significance of many things that they say and do in their daily lives. . . .

At different times in the past, various schools of anthropology rose to prominence. The author does not consciously belong to any one of them, although he willingly acknowledges some indebtedness to all. This book is intended not to advance the viewpoint of any school or branch of the science of man, but is written to demonstrate that all phases of man's biological and cultural behavior form an integrated theme that legitimately makes up a single discipline. Many topics are lightly touched upon, so that teachers may have ample opportunities to elaborate whatever they wish. For the benefit of those who may want to delve more deeply into some aspects of anthropology a number of selected references have been placed at the end of each chapter.

Readers will find that the bulk of the material incorporated into this volume is drawn primarily from American, and secondarily from British, sources. This is due to the circumstance that the amount of anthropological writing in English far outweighs what has been printed in other languages, and is more readily available to students in the United States. Moreover, the very definitions of basic terms, as well as the objectives and methods of our foreign colleagues, often differ markedly from American usage, and cannot fail to confuse a newcomer to the science of man. As it is, the self-imposed limitation on source materials will not prevent a reader from being served an ample feast that should be enough to satisfy his intellectual hunger.

If Tylor felt the need of apologizing in 1881 for the magnitude of the task he was undertaking, an author in our time must feel even more overwhelmed with a sense of humility. The science of man has grown so vast and diversified since Tylor's day that no one can truthfully claim to have mastered it all. Only the compelling hopes of introducing a better sense of order than is yet available into the scattered data, and of offering some fresh viewpoints and original interpretations, have led the author to undertake the audacious and arduous task of writing a new text.

M. T.

Ann Arbor, Michigan
February 1954

Contents

The Science of Man

Introduction

CHAPTER 1

Anthropology, or the science of man, deals with everything pertaining to human beings. Since men and women are highly complicated organisms, and since they do a great many different things, it follows that the study of mankind must pursue a large number of lines, and must appear in a wide variety of forms. As a matter of fact, anthropology is so diversified that it reminds one of the classical figure of Proteus. Proteus, it will be recalled, had the power, whenever he wished, of instantaneously changing his shape. This made him exceedingly hard to seize and overcome. So it is with the science of man. It deals with so many fields and it appears in so many shapes that it is very hard to master. Yet, just as Proteus was regarded as a single personage, so too is anthropology considered to be a single subject of study.

It was just over 100 years ago, largely under the stimulus of Charles Darwin's writings on evolution, that anthropology entered its modern phase. It should not be forgotten that his work was part of the intellectual ferment that accompanied England's Industrial Revolution. The nature of the times encouraged men to seek out and hold ideas that often challenged long-established beliefs. Even before Darwin's day there had been a number of important efforts to find out how the human body had come to assume the form it had, exactly how it was constructed, how it compared with the bodies of other living things, and how it functioned. However, so few facts were available and sacred dogmas were so thoroughly accepted that an objective and scientific study of man was almost impossible.

In the light of what has happened since his works were issued, it seems hard to believe that Charles Darwin was a shy and sickly man who had little taste for stirring up a world-shaking controversy. Indeed, it is said that it took a good deal of persuasion on the part of his friends and colleagues to get him to publish *The Origin of Species* in 1859. This book, which set forth his theory of evolution for all living things, was followed in 1871 by *The Descent of Man*. Both of these works were written in such a straightforward manner and contained such an unparalleled wealth of examples and calm reasoning from the facts that together they inspired a detached view of man's bodily construction and of his evolution from earlier members of the animal kingdom. At the same time, Darwin's concept of natural selection provided the first effective (and still the most valuable) clue toward an understanding of the mechanisms by which the process of evolution worked. It is no exaggeration to say that Darwin's works aroused, among other things, an undying interest in man's origins and past history, and that a great deal of present-day anthropology still reflects that interest.

Nevertheless, we must not forget that when the science of man first began to assume modern form there was no blueprint available *in advance* to channel material into a coherent framework. Nor could the earliest workers possibly have had the advantages of training and studying under experienced teachers. The pioneer anthropologists perforce, had to be amateur students of man, usually recruited from the ranks of scholars who had already undertaken one or another of the older, established disciplines.

Thus Adolph Bastian, who became Berlin's Curator of Ethnography in 1868, and who founded the world-famous Museum für Völkerkunde in 1886, was a doctor of medicine; while Pierre P. Broca, one of the founders of *physical anthropology*, who in 1889 established in Paris the first European anthropological society, was a brilliant neurosurgeon. Trained as lawyers were Johann J. Bachofen, author in 1861 of the still-debated *Das Mutterrecht*; Henry J. S. Maine, whose *Ancient Law* came out in 1861 and may be said to have inaugurated the study of comparative jurisprudence; John F. McLennan, who published his essay, "Primitive Marriage," in 1865; and the famed American, Lewis H. Morgan (1818–1881), whose voluminous writings provided a great many stimulating and significant contributions to our subject. Moreover, the renowned Edward B. Tylor (1832–1912), another of anthropology's early giants, was a privately educated businessman who never received a university degree.

Brilliant though they were, the pioneers of anthropology moved along many paths, partly because they were following their own disciplines, skills, and inclinations, and partly because they had no one to tell them where to go nor what to do when they got there. Some inquired into the origins and evolution of man's physical or bodily (*somatic*) characteristics; many sought to describe and classify the living varieties of mankind; others were busy searching out and analyzing relics of human workmanship (*artifacts*) from times past; and still others traveled far afield to report and interpret the customs of their primitive contemporaries. Almost invariably the first students of man failed to recognize or to understand the relationship of their findings to the material that was being made available by their coworkers, who were laboring in different branches of the same subject.

Nevertheless, whether they realized it or not, the work of the first modern anthropologists had much in common. In viewpoint, they practically all defined man as a member of *Homo sapiens* on biological grounds, regardless of when or where he happened to live. In method, they quickly came to realize that a true science of man could be achieved only if their data were accurately and objectively gathered, and dispassionately analyzed; and with regard to basic aims, they were convinced that man and his past and present activities were legitimate objects of scientific study. Within this framework, all anthropologists have been and still are motivated to discover new and significant facts about some aspect of man's body or behavior.

As for systematic anthropology in the United States, it was as far back as 1885,[1] within the short span of fourteen years following the publication of *The Descent of Man,* that the new subject found a place in the curriculum of Harvard. Soon after, Franz Boas,[2] himself originally trained as a physicist and mathematician, began to teach anthropology at Clark University in Worcester, Massachusetts; and in 1892 that institution awarded the first American[3] doctorate in anthropology to A. F. Chamberlin.[4] By the turn of the present century, many students who became outstanding American anthropologists studied for higher degrees, often under Boas after he had transferred to Columbia, and a few of them are still active. It may be hard to realize, but the bulk of today's mature students of man belong only to the third or fourth generation since Darwin.

Even though the science of man was gradually taking its present shape in the United States, it remained rather limited in scope until

[1] Even before this date, as early as 1881, the Anthropological Society of Washington, D.C., had been founded, with John W. Powell as its first president.

[2] For a recent evaluation of Franz Boas' contributions to anthropology in the United States of America, see W. Goldschmidt, ed., "The Anthropology of Franz Boas," *Memoir 89, American Anthropological Association,* Menasha, Wis., 1959.

[3] In this text book America will often be used interchangeably with the United States.

[4] E. W. Voegelin, "Anthropology in American Universities," *American Anthropologist,* Vol. 52, 1958, p. 350.

Chamberlain is probably meant. In later years he became a student of primitive folklore and mythology.

after 1900. Up to that time most of its practitioners joined the American Anthropological Association and the American Folklore Society, and published their material either in the *American Anthropologist*,[5] or in the *Journal of American Folklore*. Thereafter, horizons widened and a marked tendency toward segmentation and specialization set in, with each major subdivision of the subject threatening to become an independent science. This trend may be seen from a review of anthropological periodicals in the United States. The revitalized American Ethnological Society, specializing in *ethnology*, or *cultural anthropology*, began to issue monographs in 1906;[6] the *International Journal of American Linguistics*, with its interest in aboriginal American languages, first appeared in 1917; and 1918 saw the inauguration of the *American Journal of Physical Anthropology*, which dealt with topics pertaining to the body. This subject was amplified when *Human Biology* began to appear in 1929. In 1935 *American Antiquity* started, to provide an outlet for those interested in American *archeology*, or the record of past events in the New World; and in 1941 there took place the inception of *Applied Anthropology* that became *Human Organization* in 1955. This periodical deals with *applied anthropology*, or efforts to put anthropological concepts to practical use in handling certain contemporary situations. The *Southwestern Journal of Anthropology* (1945) opposed fractionalism by printing essays in the entire field, and *Current Anthropology*, similarly oriented, started in 1960. The latest journal to date, *Ethnology*, appeared in 1962, and again showed the tendency toward fragmentation, by being limited to cultural anthropology. In addition, anthropologists currently publish many books and monographs, to say nothing of articles in a wide variety of nonanthropological periodicals.

Nevertheless, this text, while fully recognizing the powerful trend toward separatism, is designed to show that all parts of anthropology belong and work together.

DEFINING ANTHROPOLOGY'S SUBDIVISIONS

Nowadays, large numbers of men and women are being trained early in their college careers to become professional anthropologists. As is to

[5] Those who wish further details regarding the early days of anthropology in America, and those who are interested in the establishment of the American Anthropological Association, are advised to consult G. W. Stocking, Jr., "Franz Boas and the Founding of the American Anthropological Association," *American Anthropologist*, Vol. 62, 1960, pp. 1–17.

[6] Actually, the American Ethnological Society was founded in New York as far back as 1842, about 17 years before the appearance of Darwin's *Origin of Species*.

be expected they do not deal equally with the entire field, but respond to the pressure for specialization by concentrating in one or another of its many branches. Such diversity is neither the result of blind adherence to precedents established in the days of anthropology's uncharted period, nor is it a matter of sheer whim. Instead, it stems directly from a sophisticated awareness of the great diversity of anthropology, and particularly of the two-sided nature of all human beings. Even the greenest of novices quickly discovers that in matters of body build and function *Homo sapiens* is an animal whose physical structure and physiological behavior closely resemble those of many other animals. In other respects, though, such as in his development of clothing, houses, tools, languages, esthetics, philosophies, religions, and ethical or moral systems of values, a beginner soon learns that man differs from all other animals. He alone seems to have the ability and desire to practice those extrabiological, or extrasomatic, forms of behavior that anthropologists call *cultural.* This is true not only in "advanced" societies, but in "primitive" societies as well. Man is everywhere an animal with culture.

On the basis of the fundamental distinction between *human biology* and *culture* the major division in anthropology takes place. Those who specialize in any of the problems connected with the evolution, shape, skeletal structure, genes, fleshy parts, muscles, fluids, appearance, functions, comparisons or variations of the human body are classified as *physical (biological) anthropologists.* They frequently work as natural scientists, in conjunction with geologists, paleontologists, anatomists, primatologists, physicians, dentists, geneticists, and the whole range of investigators who may, in general, be called biologists. What unites all physical anthropologists, regardless of their special interests, is the conviction that whatever they study is connected with biogenetic inheritance.

On this score the tasks of the biological anthropologists differ fundamentally from those of their colleagues who study culture, since culture is not believed to be biogenetically transmitted. Again, unlike physical anthropologists, all of whom are classified together, cultural anthropologists are divided into two broad categories. Those who deal with the evidence of man's handiwork in times past are known as *archeologists* and, by a sort of informal convention that has gradually developed, they are expected to deal with human affairs in any area of the world before the emergence of writing at the spot under investigation. In practice, of course, many archeologists continue their studies well beyond the appearance of written documents; but, on the whole, writing represents the point at which historians, linguists, and numerous other humanists and social scientists step in. To the extent that most of their efforts are devoted to the study of preliterate peoples and cultures, archeologists may properly be called prehistorians. It must also be realized that archeologists usually delve so far into the past that there are no representatives left alive of the cultures they are investigating. Hence, it is also proper to refer to archeologists as *students of extinct cultures.* Furthermore, they cannot recover nontangible or perishable items; and this lack, coupled with the absence of living informants, confronts archeologists with many severe obstacles that prevent them from obtaining and presenting completely rounded accounts of ancient or extinct cultures. Yet they have exercised tremendous ingenuity in facing up to their difficulties, and were it not for their efforts we would have no reliable information at all about the origins of culture or about its subsequent developments in times before the appearance of writing.

Different from their colleagues are those anthropologists whose primary concerns are with living cultures, particularly with those of so-called primitive peoples who reside in far-flung societies that are not extinct and which have never devised any form of writing. Investigators of the customs that prevail in these kinds of societies are variously known as *ethnographers, ethnologists, cultural anthropologists,* or *social anthropologists,* but in this volume they will usually be designated as ethnologists or cultural anthropologists. A word must be said, however, about how they may differ.

Not long ago, ethnographers and ethnologists were rather carefully set apart. Students of the ways of living mankind who felt that their principal function was to provide accurate descriptions of various cultures were known as ethnographers. Somewhat different were those who investigated living cultures in order to discover their underlying principles. Together, all those who dealt with basic processes, universal laws, or analyses and theories of culture, came to be known as ethnologists. Today it is recognized that no large-scale generalizing or theorizing about culture is likely to be valid unless it is based on close familiarity with the details of many particular ways of life. Consequently, the division between ethnography and ethnology appears to be old-fashioned and is rapidly disappearing. Today theories, analyses, and descriptions of culture are likely to go hand in hand.

As to the distinction between social and cultural anthropologists: the former tend to emphasize the social institutions or patterns of interrelationships that prevail among the people who form a society; the latter may stress the customs or learned modes of behavior that are noticeable among those who live together. These two factors are as closely interrelated as a teacher and his curriculum, but they are not necessarily identical under all conditions. For instance, an individual's social relationships are bound to change markedly after he is married and begets children; but many of his cultural customs, including his occupation, place of residence, times and methods of eating, and clothing habits, may remain relatively unchanged. On the other hand, if a married man shifted his line of work from farming to teaching, let us say, his way of life would be greatly altered, but his social interrelationships might remain basically the same.

Such cases make it altogether likely that something of value might be gained by keeping the two approaches apart. However, since no human society exists without a patterned way of life, or culture, and since no pattern of culture can possibly exist without a society of men and women,[7] the distinction is often hard to maintain. For this reason, "culture" and "society" are frequently used interchangeably. In the last analysis ethnographers, ethnologists, and social and cultural anthropologists are all deeply interested in the standardized forms of behavior that prevail wherever living groups of *Homo sapiens* dwell together in societies. Indeed, some cultural anthropologists have recently begun to investigate peasant or "folk" communities, whose members are "backward" when compared to some of their fellow citizens; and others have ventured to apply some of their techniques to the study of cultures of large, industrialized modern nations.

A simple way of calling attention to the differences of aims and methods that exist among the major subdivisions of anthropology would be to consider the question of food. The physical anthropologist might well regard the need for food as a biological phenomenon, and might properly analyze hunger in terms of stomach contractions. If an archeologist found numbers of sweet-corn cobs in a ruin that he was investigating, he would be justified in assuming that sweet corn had once been used at that place to satisfy the pangs of hunger. And a cultural anthropologist would be able to determine such things as how sweet corn was prepared and by whom; when and how it was eaten; and how much of a part it played in a person's life.

At the present time there is much concern in the profession about the proper placement of *linguists*. There are some who regard students of language as workers in a subdivision that is as distinctive as physical anthropology and just as vital for an understanding of the totality of

---

[7] It should also be kept in mind that various animals below man, including a number of insects, may have complicated social structures without culture. That is to say, whatever activities particular nonhumans carry out arise, presumably, from their genetic inheritance, and not through some process of learning or training at the hands of others. It is, therefore, possible to have a society of interacting individuals but no culture. Further details on this point may be found in A. L. Kroeber, *Anthropology*, rev. ed., New York, 1948, pp. 36 ff.

human behavior. Without denying the validity of such a viewpoint, others feel that *linguistics* should not be treated as a separate topic, but should be integrated with studies of culture and should be part of the equipment of every cultural anthropologist. The writer inclines toward the latter view. He also believes that it is far less important to be able to make exact delineations of the subdivisions of anthropology than it is to keep in mind constantly that the joint aim of all students of man is to acquire an ever-increasing understanding of the full range of body types and forms of behavior that are to be found among the members

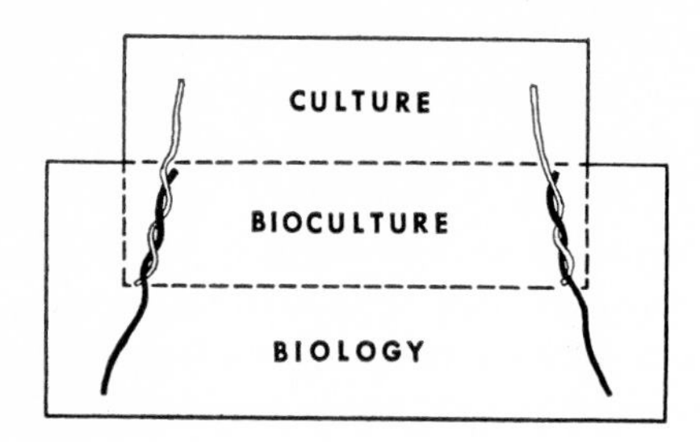

FIG. 1-1. Biology, bioculture, and culture. Culture and biology operate according to different principles, yet culture may be said to rest on a foundation of biology. Between them there is a sphere wherein biological forces intertwine with cultural forces to produce biocultural behavior.

of *Homo sapiens.* Furthermore, the growing realization that so much of man's culture is intertwined with human biology (Fig. 1-1) serves to unite all specialists in the manifold aspects of physical and cultural anthropology as coworkers in one vast field.

How anthropology resembles and differs from other social sciences

For the present it seems best to look upon anthropology as a social science, in the sense that its subject matter concerns aggregates of people who generally occupy a single region and share a common mode of life. Even those anthropologists who deal with the physical attributes of the human body and who work most closely with natural scientists are more interested in the characteristics prevailing among clusters of people that make up a race or population than they are in the details of a single person's anatomy or physiology. Moreover, no anthropologist feels that he must confine his interests to the bodily forms and activities of one group of people in one time and place. Instead, he prefers to feel free to investigate any or all groups of mankind in all times and places.

With respect to the scientific method, most scientists have come to realize that science implies not only the use of techniques that call for precision, objectivity, control, and reproducible experiments, but also a search for universal reactions that are always the same wherever identical conditions prevail. Once the universals are recognized and described, they provide a basis for sound predictions. Obviously, the more accurately one can predict a future course of events, the better can one plan ahead and establish controls where necessary. It is when they are on the quest for universal and predictable forms of human structure and behavior that anthropologists most nearly resemble other scientists.

Students of culture, too, are more interested in groups or societies than they are in individuals. On the whole, they are far less concerned with the behavior of a single person than they are with the repetitive ways in which numbers of people interact when they live together.

Human sociocultural behavior may be studied in a large number of ways. Underlying such divergent approaches as those of anthropology, sociology, geography, economics, political science, and psychology, is the basic assumption that we could not behave as proper human beings unless we had contact, at least occasionally, with other members of our species. This statement clearly implies that to an individual who is destined to become a normally functioning person a society is not a secondary or trivial matter, but is even more fundamental than are limbs or eyes. One who is blind or crippled may be a badly handicapped member of his society, but it is doubtful that a child could become human at all if it were somehow reared in total isolation from its fellows.

Although anthropologists are commonly classed as social scientists, their training serves to set them apart from their colleagues in related disciplines. Students are expected to master the broad principles of the entire discipline before they begin to specialize. Just as no one is permitted to become a specialist in any branch of medical practice before he has received a thorough grounding in general medicine, so it is with the anthropologist. Not until he has demonstrated his grasp of the whole field is he permitted to concentrate on the specialty of his choice.

The anthropologist develops a distinctive viewpoint as the result of such a program. This does not necessarily mean that other social scientists always neglect or disregard the matters that concern him most. Not at all. Sometimes the only real distinction is more a question of emphasis or degree than it is of kind. There are many cases where the differences between anthropologists and other students of human behavior are slight or subtle.

On the other hand, an anthropologist is a distinctive kind of social scientist. One of the attributes that serves to distinguish him is his required knowledge of the human body. Every anthropologist must learn to know, and never to disregard, the biological factors that play so fundamental a role in shaping a good portion of man's conduct. So little of his basic biology is truly unique to *Homo sapiens,* and so much, apparently, was bequeathed to him by his forerunners, that it behooves each anthropologist to learn as well as he can the story of organic evolution.

There can be no denying the fact that biology must precede culture in every instance. It is earlier with respect to the beginnings of all *hominid*[8] life, whether we are dealing with the entire species of *Homo sapiens,* or with single individuals. Insofar as his species is concerned, scientists can trace the beginnings of life and the many antecedents of man for about one-and-a-half billion years *before* the first recognizable signs of culture ever make their appearance. As to individuals, students of man believe that no shred of culture can possibly reach an embryo during its nine months in the womb, unless a cultural stimulus, such as an insult, is somehow first converted to a biological factor within a pregnant woman's body. One cannot hope to understand the totality of human behavior without knowing something of human biology.

Another attribute of the American anthropologist is a required knowledge of archeology. He should not only have a detailed grasp of man's activities from the time of his first appearance on the face of the earth, but he should also know the sequence in which various traits of culture were formed, the reasons for their start and subsequent development, their relationship to one another, and the various patterns of culture exhibited in different parts of the world. Simultaneously, he should be prepared to recognize whatever universal trends or processes appear to underlie the evolutionary progress of all human culture as one stage grows out of another.

Equally distinctive is the anthropologist's concern with the manifestations of body and behavior shown by members of *Homo sapiens* anywhere, regardless of race, place of residence, or degree of development when compared to the institutions of Western societies. To him, primitive men and women are not second-class citizens of mankind, and their activities are as much grist for his mill as are the doings of people in the Western, Judeo-Christian, industrialized world. The anthropologist tries in every conceivable way to override the particular values and outlooks that he learned in his own culture, and to call him *ethnocen-*

[8] Unless it is otherwise stated, "hominid" will be used throughout this book for manlike or mannish, in the sense of approaching or approximating the condition of *Homo sapiens.*

tric, or unable to see things except in terms of his own way of life, is to hurt him to the quick.

Up to now the universities that train professional anthropologists have usually insisted that each student make at least one field trip before he is awarded his doctorate. This requirement generally applies to everyone, regardless of his particular interest. To the cultural anthropologist, this requirement generally means that an advanced student must go to live and study among a people, usually a primitive group, whose ways of life are entirely different from his own. Such an experience, it has been found, generally has a profound and lasting effect on everyone who has gone through it; and it serves to set anthropologists apart from those social scientists who are not required to do field work.

A modern anthropologist is taught to view a pattern of culture as a composite of interdependent, interacting, interrelated, and mutually adjusted parts. He does not look upon economic activities, for example, as unrelated to interpersonal relationships or religious practices.[9] Thus, for example, he is not at all surprised to discover that a society of hunters worships game deities, whereas farmers pray to agricultural gods and goddesses. This obvious statement has a deeper implication, for it means that economic pursuits are related to religious practices.

Similarly, because they believe that close connections exist between all parts of any pattern of culture, anthropologists hold that even the introduction of a new and perhaps helpful technological device may have tremendous repercussions on every other phase of a group's way of life.[10] Anthropologists do not claim to know all the fine details of every social science, and they may have trouble in explaining just how all the parts of a complicated pattern of culture are fitted together; but the very search for interrelationships gives their work a distinctive quality.

The biology of man

The time has come to explain more precisely what is meant by the term "human biology." Without attempting to go into technical details, human biology is here used to comprise the entire corpus of what a newly

---

[9] Compare the recent statement by the British anthropologists G. and M. Wilson, as it appears in *The Analysis of Social Change,* Cambridge, England, 1954, p. 13: ". . . we seek the relation between this type of belief [in magic and witchcraft] and the form of society."

[10] For numerous examples that illustrate this point, see E. H. Spicer, ed., *Human Problems in Technological Change,* New York, 1952.

conceived infant does or develops solely on the basis of whatever materials he gets from his parents. This takes in all the chemical and physical ingredients that enable a child to live, grow, and ultimately reproduce his kind. It includes all the initiating substances, in their proper arrangement and environment, that make up his gross anatomical structure, his entire cerebroneuromuscular system, and the complete range of his physiological organs, as well as their manner of working and interacting.

All of the nuclei for these body components are received by each child-to-be at the exact moment of conception, and at no other time, directly as the result of sexual intercourse on the part of the male and female who are becoming its parents. No other individual can, at this instant, introduce anything whatsoever for the about-to-be-formed embryo to acquire. At this stage, too, the ripe egg cell of the prospective mother can exercise nothing but some little known *biophysicochemical*[11] choice in the selection of the genetic materials it is receiving from the sperm cell contributed by the father.

When a newly born child, or *neonate*, emerges from its mother's womb, it has no resources of its own for coping with life except for those things arising from the nuclear ingredients it has inherited. Taken by themselves, these are not enough to guarantee the successful formation of a human body. Interaction with a suitable physical environment is equally vital. Realistically speaking, insofar as human beings are concerned, neither the fertilization of an egg cell nor gestation can occur unless there is a suitable environment within a female's reproductive system. Moreover, a fertilized human egg is never self-sufficient and cannot possibly mature unless it has a chance to draw what it needs from its immediate setting. Inherited biological factors determine what elements a developing embryo will take from its intra-uterine environment and how this shall be done. Inherited biological factors will also delimit, at the very outset of postnatal life, what interactions a baby is going to establish with its new, external environment.

There is little in the realm of sheer biological behavior to differentiate a member of *Homo sapiens* from an individual belonging to many other species of *mammals*, particularly to the large *Primates* such as *orangutans, chimpanzees,* and *gorillas.* Given a favorable environment, human beings can carry on a wide range of activities with nothing but their inherited, genetically determined, biological equipment. Nevertheless, man's biology, under unfavorable conditions, is woefully inadequate. Human infants are notoriously helpless at birth and have no bio-

[11] For the sake of convenience, the single word "biological" will frequently be used interchangeably with the compound term "biophysicochemical." It should also be made clear that in this text biology includes physiology as well as anatomy.

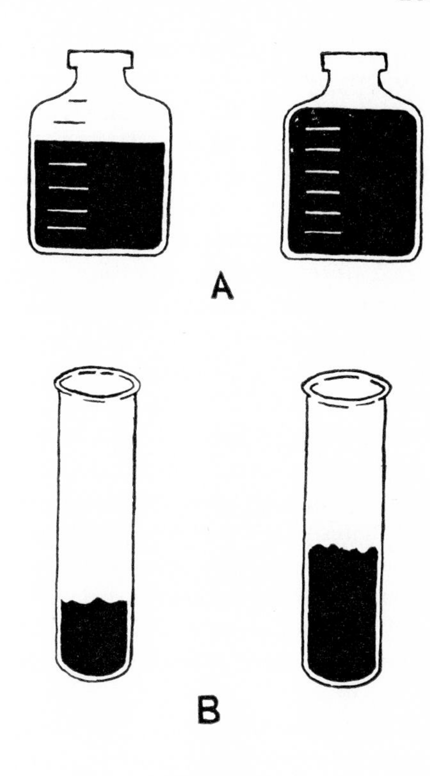

FIG. 1-2. Biological adaptation in man. The short, stocky type of Andean Indian pictured in (C) lives at a very high altitude. (A) shows that such Indians have about seven quarts of blood, compared to the five quarts of the average Indian who lives at low altitudes. (B) shows how much more hemoglobin highlanders have as compared with lowlanders. These are but two of the biological adaptations made by the Andean Indians who live in the higher reaches of Peru. Usually, man's biological adaptations are masked or replaced by cultural devices. (After M. T. Newman, "Man and the Heights," *Natural History,* Vol. 67, No. 1, 1958, p. 13. Courtesy of the author and editor.)

logical means of escaping enemies or of getting nourishment unaided; nor are they equipped with any means of distinguishing palatable from unpalatable or even poisonous substances. Left to themselves, human babies would soon die of starvation or poisoning. Once again, we see how essential other people are to the very existence of a newly born child.

Even adults are biologically unfit to cope with such things as winter weather. We speak of ourselves as being *warm-blooded,* and we sometimes dwell on our possession of various mammalian devices, such as shivering and the contraction of blood vessels, that help us to resist cold. But the sad truth is that all of us would quickly freeze to death in very cold weather if we had nothing to rely on but genetically inherited mechanisms for remaining warm.

It is here that human beings and other animals come to a parting of the ways. Other creatures, when faced with a problem that their inherited biology cannot solve, must somehow change their biological mechanisms before they become extinct. Ordinarily, this process is slow, uncertain, and terribly expensive in terms of individual lives. Man, and man only, when he finds his biology inadequate, escapes extinction—not by readjusting his biology—but by turning to an entirely different kind of behavior. This is what underlies the nonbiologic or extrasomatic form of activity that anthropologists call cultural. Only on the rarest of occasions, within the past thousands of years, have human beings changed their biologies when challenged by drastic changes of environment or other factors that seriously threatened their abilities to survive (Fig. 1–2). Instead, they have again and again met challenges by altering their cultures. Indeed, it has been the diversity of his cultural mechanisms that has enabled *Homo sapiens,* as a single species, to dwell in any environment on earth and to outlive many other animal groups that once seemed more capable of survival.

Culture and bioculture

The term "culture" is commonly used in at least two different senses. It may refer to the nonbiological aspects of mankind's behavior as a whole, or it may pertain only to the way of life of one particular group or society of men and women. In either case, anthropologists use it to describe the entire range of man's nongenetically acquired implements, as well as all other facets of his postnatally learned behavior. There is not a single respect in which culture fails to differ from human biology. Culture is not composed only of biophysicochemical ingredients; it is not passed along by sexual intercourse; it is not transmitted at a single moment of time; it is not received exclusively from the two people who are becoming one's parents; and, in theory, it does not have to be retained for life but can be modified or dropped at the will of an individual. For practical reasons human beings seldom volunteer to make radical changes in the cultures they learn from their mentors, but surely it cannot be denied that theoretically it is easier to change one's language or religion than the shape of one's head or the color of one's eyes.

Because man's culture and biology differ in every essential regard and because they operate according to totally different principles, it is not surprising that they should sometimes serve different purposes or have different standards of value. Thus, it can be said with assurance that when *Homo sapiens* began to develop cultural behavior, he began to abide by some new and nonbiologic concepts of value. Now, human beings no longer considered it proper to breathe, eat, drink, excrete, or reproduce simply in conformity to the requirements and dictates of biology. Instead, each society differentiated culturally right from wrong ways of carrying out these functions, and so laid the basis for a moral or ethical code. For example, breathing is everywhere a biological necessity for man, but in our culture it is considered improper to rush into a room for an important interview while one is gasping for breath. Similarly, in our society, biological pangs of hunger do not justify the theft of food, nor does a compelling sexual urge excuse rape. An indefinite number of teachers contribute to a neonate's education along the lines of cultural values, and it takes a long while for a child to learn all of the approved and disapproved ways of conduct that prevail in his social unit. The process of *socialization* or *enculturation*[12]—that is, becoming adjusted to one's culture—is by no means easy, for it compels each infant to fit his innate, genetically determined ways of acting to the established cultural practices of his group. There are good grounds for believing that the length and difficulty of the process of adjustment are the basic factors that prevent all but the most persevering from readily changing whatever patterns of culture they learned in youth.

Human societies are the only groups in the entire animal kingdom to have devised forms of culture that exert powerful modifying influences on the inherited mechanisms of their individual members. Sometimes the biologic and cultural elements coincide or reinforce each other in seeking the same objective; sometimes they have no effect on one another; and sometimes they actually work at cross purposes and clash or

[12] The anthropological meaning and use of the term "enculturation," may be found in M. J. Herskovits, *Man and His Works,* New York, 1948, pp. 40–41. In general, it refers to the process whereby a neonate is taught the cultural ways that his society expects him to follow. Herskovits introduced this term to anthropology.

oppose each other. So it is that if a pattern of culture calls for the wearing of a sweater in cold weather, the culture trait is "logical" insofar as it helps the wearer to conserve his body heat as a biological necessity. On the other hand, if a wearer feels that maroon is preferable to crimson in an otherwise identical sweater, the cultural preference for the darker sweater is "nonlogical" in this context, since it neither helps nor retards the workings of biology. But, should a way of life forbid the wearing of sweaters or other covers in cold weather, the refusal to wear a sweater, where one was available, would be "illogical" because it opposed the biological welfare of the potential wearer.[13]

The possibility that a society's culture might demand such "illogical" behavior makes it no easy matter to live like a human being. For mankind everywhere takes pride in the cultural structures that it has reared, and wherever the values of biology and culture clash man is likely to give preference to the cultural, just short of the point where it may cause the extinction of individuals or societies. In fact, the English-speaking world frequently expresses contempt by making slighting references to cultureless creatures. How often, when we want to insult someone, do we resort to the names of animals. A list of terms like "Crab!" "Skunk!" "Rat!" and "Pig!" can be extended indefinitely, and seems to express a feeling that beasts, which lack culture, are somehow objects of contempt. Like ourselves, the denizens of the primitive world may also show distaste for noncultural creatures. Sometimes they knock out teeth to make themselves look different from other members of the animal kingdom; sometimes they pluck face and body hair to emphasize their unique humanity; and occasionally they blacken teeth because "white teeth are no better than a dog's."[14]

At this point we are led to seek the reasons for man's universal willingness to run the danger of glorifying culture at the possible risk of clashing with biology. "Why," it may well be asked, "is *Homo sapiens* unwilling to live according to the dictates of biology, as do other species of animals?"

It would be a mistake to think that man has developed culture out of sheer whimsy. He has gained many real advantages from extrabiological

---

[13] Words like "logic" can have a host of meanings in English. Moreover, a comparative analysis of various cultures reveals an amazing variety of "logical" relationships. To an American Christian, the wearing of shoes may have no "logical" connection with Christianity. To a group of barefooted, pagan natives, however, among whom a Christian missionary family was the only one to wear shoes, it might appear perfectly "logical" to connect Christianity with the wearing of shoes.

[14] W. H. Furness III, *The Home-Life of Borneo Head-Hunters,* Philadelphia, 1902, p. 157.

devices. Of these, none is more important than flexibility in coping with his external environment. Should a cold climate turn hot, as has occasionally happened in times past, or should a society of human beings happen to migrate from the Arctic to the Equator, men and women would have it within their control to shut off cultural heating devices or to give up the wearing of heavy garments. Other creatures, which might have grown heavy pelts or made other biogenetic adjustments to cold, would lack man's flexibility and would face extinction whenever their environments were radically altered.

There are also some situations wherein culture interferes with the workings of sound biology. This is the case whenever religious regulations forbid hungry people to eat available nutritious foods, or whenever cultural conventions prohibit individuals from eating some of the edible substances to be found in their physical environment, as when we refuse to eat ants or locusts. Man is thus the only creature in the animal kingdom who might go hungry in the midst of biological plenty. Cultural factors usually strike a balance with biological necessities, but it is dangerous to overlook the fact that biology can exist without culture, whereas culture cannot exist without biology. A social scientist should never allow himself to forget that no cultural device has yet been perfected that can completely take the place of biology. Not even the best of eyeglasses can give sight to a person lacking an optic nerve; nor can the finest of iron lungs make a corpse breathe. True enough, there have been times in the history of mankind when it was the fashion to belittle things of the body, to claim that man was not an animal, and to pretend that he was not bound to observe the laws of biology; but we know that such conventional statements did not express the truth, for men and women could not have lived and maintained their species had they actually refused to breathe, eat, drink, digest, excrete, and reproduce according to biological principles.

In each expression of voluntary activity,[15] we find that some aspects of culture intertwine with some features of biology. This concept accords with anthropological observations, made in all sectors of the globe, that the vast majority of voluntary actions performed by human beings are the blended products of two different forces that operate simultaneously to produce a single activity. So it is that whenever an individual manufactures a stone tool, digs edible roots with a pointed stick, plays the piano (Fig. 1–3), makes a speech, hits a tennis ball, milks a cow, or

[15] As it is used here, "voluntary" refers to any aspect of human behavior that calls for a measure of conscious control. It is used in contrast to such involuntary actions as breathing or the beating of the heart, which may be carried on without any conscious control at all.

drives an automobile, he is employing some genetically inherited body parts in certain ways and for particular purposes that are determined by the culture of his society. It is for this entire category of human activity that I propose to use the term *biocultural behavior.*

To some extent the dichotomy between biology and culture has long been recognized, as the old arguments over nature or nurture imply, but today it is more than ever necessary to define each of these factors as accurately as possible and to show that they frequently intertwine,[16] particularly if one is interested in trying to solve pressing social problems. If one is concerned about a sterile couple, for instance, biological correctives will have to be applied if the failure to have offspring arises from biological causes. If, however, to cite a farfetched, hypothetical situation, the failure to have children results from a cultural convention that prevents a married couple from having sexual intercourse, then the remedy will have to involve a change of culture.

When it comes to the interweaving of the two elements we might ask ourselves why prostitutes are always feminine. Part of the answer is firmly rooted in biology, for only females have reproductive systems that are capable of repeated acts of intercourse without desire. We also know that so great a variety of cultural reasons induces various women to take up prostitution that the activity may properly be called biocultural. If that be so, another question promptly comes to mind. Why should we try so hard to separate biology from culture if they so often work together to produce biocultural behavior? This time the answer is concerned with the scientific method, for the biological universality enables us to predict something about culture. In other words, if a presently unknown society were to turn out to have prostitution, we could predict that all of the prostitutes would be females.[17]

In the normal course of our daily lives we see so many things happening as single actions that we are seldom aware of the basic distinction between human biology and culture and of their interplay, but every now and then, perhaps without conscious thought, we do find ourselves recognizing all three elements. Let us imagine that early on each working day we hear someone singing, and that on one occasion we make a special

[16] T. Dobzhansky, *Mankind Evolving,* New Haven, Conn., and London, 1962, discusses the interaction between man's biological and cultural components as a key to his evolution.

[17] Readers should bear in mind that words have many meanings. Male prostitutes have been reported in anthropological literature, but the reference is not to common prostitutes. It is just as impossible for a male to engage in frequently repeated acts of sexual intercourse as it is for a man to conceive a child or to suckle an infant. This provides an excellent illustration of the fact that cultures and cultural conditioning can never go beyond the limits established by biology.

A

FIG. 1-3. Biocultural behavior. With practically the same anatomical equipment, a young Australian woman wields a digging stick (A) and a concert pianist plays the piano (B). In each case biogenetically inherited mechanisms are being used, in ways dictated by culture, to produce biocultural behavior. (A. H. Basedow, *The Australian Aboriginal.* Adelaide, 1925. Courtesy of F. W. Preece. B—Courtesy of Eck Stanger, *The Ann Arbor News,* Ann Arbor, Mich.)

B

effort to see and hear what is going on. If it turns out that the singer is a Negro man, and that his song is the familiar spiritual, "Swing Low, Sweet Chariot," we can quickly make an analysis in terms of biology, culture, and bioculture. We know at a glance that the individual is a Negro because of the color of his skin, the form of his hair, the breadth of his nose, and the thickness of his lips. These features, we may be sure, could have been acquired only through genetic transmission at his conception, without any reference to the man's will and with very little likelihood of fundamental change throughout his lifetime. On the other hand, with regard to culture, we may be equally sure that the singer could not possibly have learned the words and tune of his song until some time after he had been born, and that it is within his voluntary control to sing something else or to refrain from singing altogether.

The case of the Negro singer also enables us to reaffirm that much of human behavior is based on the interaction of biology and culture to produce a single activity. Without lungs, larynx, pharynx, mouth, tongue, teeth, and lips, it is unlikely that anyone could produce either words or a tune. Yet, even the possessor of the best biological song-producing mechanism in the world could not sing the notes and lyrics of the particular spiritual, "Swing Low, Sweet Chariot," unless through cultural training he had learned the correct text and melody. This is an example of that channeling of inherited biology into particular ways that may well be called "biocultural behavior."

The central thesis of this introductory chapter explains the arrangement of the material in the rest of the book. The biogenetic considerations that apply to man will make up the first part. The second will deal with the origin and development of culture in the past; and the third part will be devoted to various aspects of cultural and biocultural behavior as they appear wherever groups of human beings reside in societies. Taken jointly, the three parts make up an introduction to anthropology, and our contribution to a better understanding of the complex science of man.

Selected References

Daniel, Glyn E., *A Hundred Years of Archaeology*, London, 1950.

Goldschmidt, Walter, ed., "The Anthropology of Franz Boas," *Memoir 89, American Anthropological Association,* Menasha, Wis., 1959.

Haddon, Alfred C., *History of Anthropology*, rev. ed., London, 1934.

Kluckhohn, Clyde, "Cultural Anthropology," in L. White, Jr., ed.,

Frontiers of Knowledge in the Study of Man, New York, 1956, pp. 33–47.

Linton, Ralph, "The Scope and Aims of Anthropology," in R. Linton, ed., *The Science of Man in the World Crisis,* New York, 1945, pp. 3–18.

Lowie, Robert H., *The History of Ethnological Theory,* New York, 1937.

Mead, Margaret, and Bunzel, Ruth L., eds., *The Golden Age of American Anthropology,* New York, 1960.

Mitra, Panchanan, *A History of American Anthropology,* Calcutta, 1933.

Montagu, M. F. Ashley, *An Introduction to Physical Anthropology,* rev. ed., Springfield, Ill., 1961, "Introduction."

Penniman, T. K., *A Hundred Years of Anthropology,* New York, 1935.

Sears, P. B., *Charles Darwin: The Naturalist as a Cultural Force,* New York, 1950.

Spicer, Edward H., ed., *Human Problems in Technological Change,* New York, 1952.

Tax, Sol, ed., *After Darwin,* Chicago, 1960.

Voegelin, Erminie W., "Anthropology in American Universities," *American Anthropologist,* Vol. 52, 1950, pp. 350–391.

PART ONE

The Biology of Man

Spineless Creatures

CHAPTER 2

Reading the Geological Timetable

Normal human behavior results from a complicated interweaving of the forces within man's own body and others relating to his environmental and social setting. In former times it was widely believed that man's mind and body were separate entities that could operate independently. At present, the mind and body are thought to be in a state of continuous interaction. Formerly, too, the belief prevailed that man had acquired his body rather suddenly, in fairly recent times, by an act of special creation. Today, scientists favor the concept that the human body is the result of an exceedingly lengthy, evolutionary process, during the course of which a variety of animal structures were formed and handed on until they came into the possession of *Homo sapiens.*

Much of the data on which the framework of the evolutionary hypothesis rests are presently studied by *geologists,* who investigate the earth's structure and history, and by *paleontologists,* who concentrate on the remains of ancient forms of life, practically all of which are now extinct and are popularly termed *fossils.* The two groups of scientists work together, because remnants of ancient organisms are frequently found embedded in the mud and ooze that formed many old rocks and layers of earth. These specialists have provided a chronological scale, based on various ways of estimating the ages of rocks, that serves as an approximate timetable of the events in which students of man's origins are keenly interested (see Fig. 2–1). Since the soil layers containing relics that come ever closer to human configurations are, in many cases, piled above those that hold remains far removed from *Homo sapiens,* there is scientific as well as figurative reason to use phrases like "higher evolution" when speaking of the creatures that most resemble man, and terms like *infrahuman* ("below human") for animals that preceded hominids.[1]

The very earliest rocks known on earth, dating back some two billion years or so B.P. (before the present), are called *Azoic,* which means that they are literally "without life." That is, they contain not the slightest trace of anything that was once alive. Thereafter, successively higher layers of rock are named in the order in which they are believed to have been formed: *Archeozoic* ("ancient life"); Proterozoic ("former life");

Era	Period	Epoch	Approx. Beginning Date	Highest Animal Group
Cenozoic	Quaternary	Holocene	12,000 B.P.	*Homo sapiens*
		Pleistocene	1,000,000 B.P.	Extinct hominids
	Tertiary	Pliocene	13,000,000 B.P.	Man-apes?
		Miocene	30,000,000 B.P.	Apes
		Oligocene	40,000,000 B.P.	Monkeys
		Eocene	60,000,000 B.P.	Lemurs, Tarsiers
		Paleocene	70,000,000 B.P.	Tree shrews

FIG. 2-1. Chart of Primate evolution. The higher forms of animals do not ordinarily appear in the lower strata of rocks. This chart is simplified, and the dates are not precise.

Paleozoic ("old life"); *Mesozoic* ("middle life"); and *Cenozoic* ("recent life"). These six great eras, together with the fossils contained in the rocks of the later five, yield the evidence on which the theory of evolution is based. Since our concern is with man, we shall move incompletely and irregularly over the material, spending our time on the organisms closest to *Homo sapiens,* emphasizing the traits that are thought to have been handed on to man, and entirely omitting such important but collateral groups as plants, insects, and birds.[2]

---

[1] The great biologist, Julian S. Huxley, states that in biological terms "higher" means an increase of complexity, integration, and efficiency. He also believes it possible to rank moral ideas as "higher" or "lower" in terms of adaptation for change. He refuses to consider as equals all surviving or contemporaneously existing oganisms. Huxley feels that while all currently living organisms have adapted to their present environments, not all of them are equally suited to adapt to whatever the future might bring. For further details see J. S. Huxley, "Cultural Process and Evolution," in A. Roe and G. G. Simpson, eds., *Behavior and Evolution,* New Haven, Conn., 1958, pp. 437–54.

[2] It should also be remembered that our story of man's evolution is expressed in general, not particular, terms. Specialists know of specific exceptions to many of the broad statements that are here made.

THE LIFELESS EARTH

In order to understand the physical composition of man, as well as something of its importance to his behavior, an anthropologist must go back to the very origin of the earth, for the human body is made up of chemical substances derived from the earth. About four billion years ago, one theory holds, a stupendous mass of solar material somehow became detached from the sun, and when this mass had cooled a bit it became the planet that we call "Earth."[3]

For an incredibly long time, estimated at around two-and-a-half billion years, the chemical ingredients that make up our planet probably remained lifeless. But this is not to say that they were still or motionless. On the contrary, they are thought to have been made to move by a number of physical forces. Thus, whenever temperatures fluctuated, winds blew, or moisture came and went, and whenever altitudes and atmospheric pressures differed as hills and mountains were uplifted, the original elements were moved about in space and underwent many alterations. Sometimes various chemicals changed their structures, and sometimes brand new combinations of elements came into being. Of these, the most important for our purposes, was *deoxyribonucleic acid,* commonly abbreviated DNA.[4] This nucleic acid, which has the amazing quality of self-duplication, became a part of protein, a complex material consisting of hydrogen, nitrogen, oxygen, and carbon, together with small amounts of other substances.

Up to this point, it must be emphasized, the highest level of anything's structure was chemical or physical and all responses that may be called behavioral, such as the formation of crystals, were dictated exclusively by physicochemical laws. In other words, for about two-and-a-half billion years the basic chemical elements on earth made changes, adjustments, and recombinations only when they were acted upon by physical forces, such as those of heat, light, gravity, magnetism, radioactivity, natural electricity, humidity, or atmospheric pressure.

Although these factors reach back very far in time, it does not follow that they have little or no effect on contemporary man and his behavior. All of us know that our bodies are made up of chemical ingredients, that we have glands that are veritable manufacturing plants of

---

[3] H. F. Blum, *Time's Arrow and Evolution,* Princeton, N. J., 1951, pp. 8–12, estimates the age of the earth to be about three billion years. If anything, the modern tendency is to assign even greater age to our planet's origin.

[4] For a discussion of DNA, see J. H. Taylor, "The Duplication of Chromosomes," *Scientific American,* Vol. 198, June 1958, pp. 36–42.

those complex chemicals known as hormones, and that a person acts very differently if his body contains too much or too little of a substance produced, let us say, by the thyroid gland.[5]

We are less likely to have a conscious awareness of the effects of physics. However, if we stop to think about it, we know that it is the pull of gravity that helps make us tired when we stand. Since our muscles relax when we sit or lie down, all chairs, stools, mats, sofas, cots, and beds could in this way be interpreted as cultural responses to a physical force.

It is important to note that at the level of physicochemical behavior there is no emotion, no volition, and no self-directed or voluntary locomotion of any kind. Furthermore, whatever may be thought to correspond to later processes of reproduction must be understood to represent nothing more than fixed responses or purely physiocochemical interactions. Nor is there a sharp and basic distinction between life and death. All reactions are believed in times past, present, or, presumably, future, to be invariable; and there is such a complete absence of choice or decision making, that a scientist thoroughly familiar with the laws of chemistry and physics can predict with unfailing accuracy and mathematical precision how a given element will behave under given conditions. Certainty and exactness diminish as material becomes subject to change in the course of time, and as the capacity for choice and voluntary action increases.

THE EMERGENCE OF LIFE: PROTOZOA

With the formation of protein, the stage was set for the appearance of living matter. It is generally believed that about one-and-a-half billion years ago many chemicals combined with protein to form an entirely new substance called *protoplasm*, which is thought to be the first material on earth to show, beyond doubt, the properties of life, in addition to having retained the capacity for self-duplication. Protoplasm is the key material out of which the bodies of all plants and animals, including men, are

---

[5] The relationship of his chemical ingredients to man's body and behavior has been explored by R. J. Williams in "Chemical Anthropology—An Open Door," *American Scientist*, Vol. 46, 1958, pp. 1–23.

It has been found, for instance, that muscular dystrophy can be induced in monkeys by withholding vitamin E, essentially a complicated chemical, from their diets. The connection of chemicals and mental illness in humans is so probable that there is now a flourishing new field of interdisciplinary investigation, known as *psychopharmacology*.

made. It exhibits certain characteristics that set it apart from any previous combination of chemical elements. Its most important characteristic is that under one set of conditions it is alive, but that under another set of conditions it is dead. In the case of protoplasm, as is equally true of all organisms made from it, death means that it has reverted to the chemical elements of which it is composed, and is once more subject only to the unchanging forces of chemistry and physics.

Anything that is made up of protoplasm can remain alive only so long as it is able satisfactorily to observe a new set of regulations, conveniently labeled *biological imperatives.* As a minimum, these require that protoplasm must be able to secure oxygen and food from its external environment. From the very outset of life to the latest child of man, protoplasmic material has never had a built-in reservoir for the storage of food and oxygen, so that these basic ingredients have had to be replenished constantly, although at different time intervals. So it is that a human being can go without fresh oxygen for only a few minutes before he faints or dies; but he may live without water for several days, and he can last without solid food for many weeks.[6]

Since each living person must continuously satisfy the biological imperatives, all societies and their patterns of culture must show some regularities. Thus, there must always be opportunities for such things as breathing and excreting, access to food and housing, and provision for mating, if the social group is to survive. No enduring culture pattern can disregard either the rules of biology or the laws of physics and chemistry.

In order to meet their requirements, all living things must have at least a tiny potential, much more evident in animals than in plants, for self-initiated motion. Coupled with its search for oxygen and food, one usually finds a system that enables an animal to move away from a stimulus that irritates or endangers it, and to move toward a stimulus that the animal interprets as favorable. This implies the existence of something that corresponds to a nervous system, which in the earliest forms of life is thought to have been spread throughout an entire organism instead of having been centered in, and controlled by, one brain.

In addition, there is always a process of reproduction that is closely connected with growth. Whenever a unit of protoplasm reaches a given size it divides in two. At this stage the matter of reproduction is no more than a mechanical, automatic action, entirely devoid of the subjective

[6] There is, of course, a considerable amount of individual variation in the details by which particular organisms meet the demands of the biological imperatives. See R. J. Williams, *Biochemical Individuality,* New York, 1956.

and emotional connotations that human beings associate with the choice of a mate and the begetting of children.

After the formation of protoplasm it becomes necessary to speak of a higher level of organization, for while protoplasm continued to observe the laws of chemistry and physics, it had, in addition, to satisfy the requirements of the biological imperatives. Thus do we find ourselves in the realm designated as biophysicochemical, a realm in which all organic creatures belong. Workers in this field cannot achieve the mathematical precision and predictability that is possible for chemists and physicists, because even the slightest exercise of choice or of self-initiated movement cannot be mathematically anticipated. The merest fleck of protoplasm occasionally thrusts a bit of itself away from the main body as it reacts to a stimulus or seeks nourishment, and there is no way of foretelling exactly when it will act, or the precise angle of its thrust.

The new substance seems to have appeared, from the outset, not as great sheets or formless lumps, but organized into tiny units called *cells*. As far as is known at present, each cell initially constituted a microscopic little animal, the whole group being collectively termed *Protozoa*. All the activities of eating, digesting, excreting, breathing, moving, growing, and reproducing, had to be performed by a cell that must have been a marvelous jack-of-all-biological-trades.

When studied under a microscope each cell that makes up a protozoan animal can be seen to consist of several different parts, of which the most distinctive is called the *nucleus*, while the rest may be comprised under the term *cytoplasm*. Within the nucleus are tiny grains of fairly solid matter that can readily be colored or dyed. It is the nucleus that is most clearly concerned with reproduction. Although various protozoa may reproduce in numerous ways, including some sexual mating,[7] there is a general pattern of events that is consistent for almost all. For each species a fixed number of rodlike bodies or *chromosomes* cluster together in the center of the surrounding cytoplasm. There the chromosomes split into two identical parts, with one full portion going to the nucleus of a daughter cell and the other remaining with the parent (Fig. 2–2).

Virtually all experts hold that a chromosome is primarily an aggregate of very tiny, submicroscopic particles called *genes*. There is universal agreement that the genes and chromosomal matter in the nucleus of every reproductive cell have always conveyed the chemical ingredients of biological inheritance from parent to child, and that the process has

[7] It has been found that certain strains of bacteria reproduce sexually. The evidence is summarized in E. L. Woolman and F. Jacob, "Sexuality in Bacteria," *Scientific American*, Vol. 195, No. 1, 1956, pp. 109–18.

remained essentially the same from the time of primordial Protozoa to the present.[8]

Somehow, even in the matter of asexual reproduction, where only a single, one-celled parent is involved, and where offspring seem to have inherited exact duplicates of the ancestral genes and chromosomes, descendants do not inevitably duplicate their parent (Fig. 2–3). This factor of variability, which becomes even more noteworthy among more com-

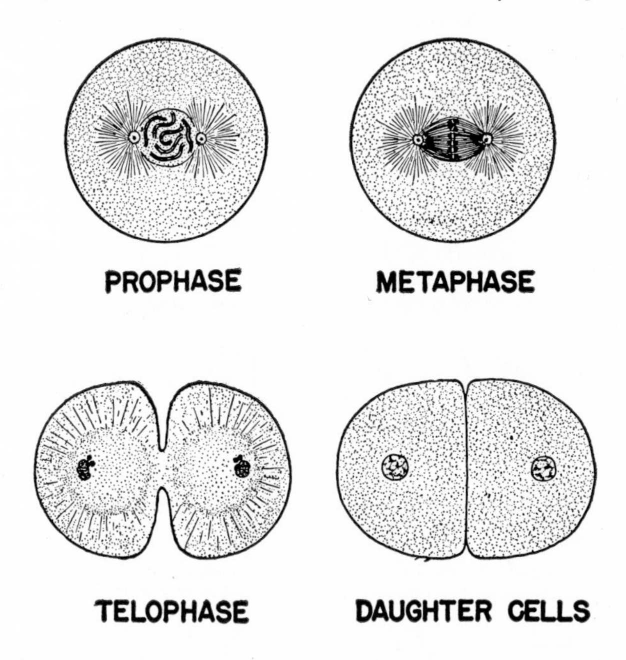

FIG. 2-2. Principal stages of cell division. The steps shown sum up the main stages of the reproductive process in Protozoa. Biologically, cell division is much alike in all living things. (Douglas Marsland, *Principles of Biology,* 3d ed., New York, 1957.)

plex animals with bisexual modes of reproduction, provides one of the major keys to biological evolution.

Let us repeat that most often the genes involved in reproduction make exact copies of themselves, but sometimes offspring do not inherit exact copies of ancestral genes. Changes may take place within a gene, often for reasons that are presently unknown to scientists. These appar-

[8] Those who wish further information about chromosomal or genetic transmission are advised to read R. B. Goldschmidt, *Understanding Heredity,* New York, 1952. A more scholarly treatment is given in C. Stern, *Principles of Human Genetics,* San Francisco, 1949.

ently random or spontaneous, internal but transmittable cellular changes are known as *mutations*. For the most part they are lethal, which means that an organism may die off before it can reproduce, so that its lethal

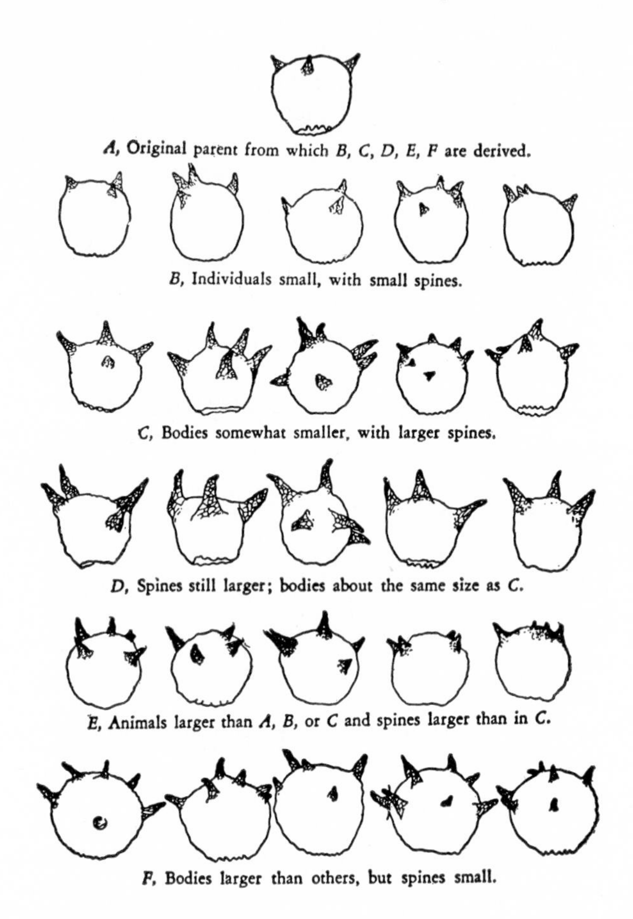

FIG. 2-3. Creation by evolution. A single parent, in the course of asexual reproduction, may give rise to greatly varied offspring. When two parents join in sexual reproduction—each one's body comprising millions of cells and countless genes—the chances of creating new forms by evolutionary changes, which utilize variation, are infinitely greater. (F. B. Mason, *Creation by Evolution*, New York, 1928. Courtesy of The Macmillan Company.)

(deadly) mutation fails to be perpetuated. However, in the long stretch of time that the recognizably hominid line has been evolving, it is estimated that there have been about two million generations, among whom some 20,000 favorable mutations might have taken place and been transmitted. These diversities have given nature a range of variation within which to make selections, and it is assumed that natural selection will operate to preserve favorable traits in a population, rather than in an individual, since he may or may not reproduce.

It now appears that the course of evolution is one part of a three-branched process. Starting with a common ancestor, there is one branch that indicates a path of extinction, which some populations of creatures inevitably take in the course of time; a second path represents the way of successive generations of descendants who never wander far from the ancestral condition; and the third is the road taken by some offspring

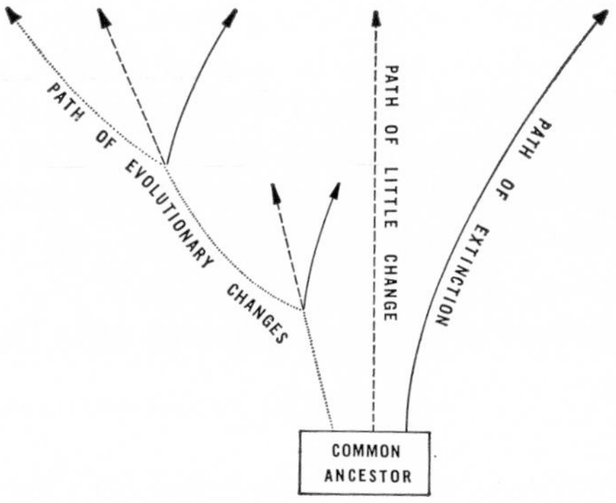

FIG. 2-4. The paths of evolution. Some offspring, in the course of successive generations, follow a road that leads to ultimate extinction. Others change hardly at all over the years; but some descendants change drastically as time goes on.

who, in later generations, come to differ so much from the original ancestor as to form a different species (see Fig. 2–4).

Needless to say, although man is faced with the same biological imperatives as are the protozoans, and although he resembles them in some details of reproduction, he is so vastly different in size and complexity that we must seek his immediate forebears among animals who traveled far on the path of divergence from some ancestral Protozoa.

Multicelled metazoa at sea

The next major step on the road leading from Protozoa to man was taken when offspring cells adhered to their parent instead of severing all ties and going free. This evolutionary stage is known as *colonialism,* and seems to have led to the evolution of *Metazoa,* which are multicellular organisms characterized by the fact that each of their adhering cells is no longer capable of answering to all of the biological imperatives. Instead, some cells are specialized only for breathing, others just for locomotion, and so on. The result is a single creature made up of a large number of interdependent, specialized cells. Gone is the biological jack-of-all-trades cell that independently and alone makes up the body of a protozoan.

As we come a bit closer to the ultimate emergence of human beings we are led to consider the marine metazoans, no one of which possessed a backbone. Together they are classed as *invertebrates,* but various groups show a tremendous diversity of forms. Worms, clamlike mollusks, sponges, jellyfish, small lobster-shaped trilobites, squids, snails, and many others lived in the seas during the vast stretch of time that extends for over a half a billion years from the days of the earliest protozoans.

Altogether, the major contribution made by the invertebrates to later forms of animal life stems from the fact that some of them had well-developed specialized organs associated with full-fledged systems for respiration, circulation, digestion, excretion, locomotion, and reproduction; as well as mechanisms for visual, nervous, and muscular behavior. There are numerous indications that by a series of evolutionary steps the first *vertebrates* descended from invertebrate ancestors.

Recapitulation

The whole story of organic evolution on earth starts with four basic assumptions. First, we must assume that in the beginning there were chemical elements. No one knows where they came from or how they got their characteristic properties, but once they came into existence they seem to have had fixed ways of acting and reacting.

Second, it must be assumed that at the outset there was space, for the original elements do not seem to have occupied one and the same spot. Instead, they seem to have been distributed in space, so that some were higher or lower than others, or else to the right or left. Third, physical forces, such as gravity, must be assumed to have been in operation, and to have caused some elements to shift about in space. Fourth, we must assume that as they approached or touched one another, certain chemicals changed their shape or internal composition, or entered into various new combinations. Perhaps we should also postulate that time existed from the beginning, since these changes seem to have taken place at different times.

It is in some such way, we think, that DNA was formed, and ultimately joined in the composition of protein, which then became basic to the formation of living substance or protoplasm. At first, it is believed, protoplasm took the shape of one-celled animals or Protozoa. Generally, Protozoa are thought to have appeared during the Archeozoic era, which is estimated to have begun one-and-a-half billion years ago and to have lasted for half a billion years. No complete remains of living organisms have been preserved in Archeozoic rocks, but the indirect evidence of imprints left in what was originally soft mud, and the occurrence of minute quantities of animal carbon, presumably deposited by very tiny creatures, make it appear likely that Protozoa were then present. Indeed, one outstanding authority, Richard S. Lull, goes so far as to call the Archeozoic era the Age of Unicellular Life.[9]

During the succeeding Proterozoic time span, considerable evolutionary progress was probably made. Only a few actual fossils, chiefly spicules of ancient sponges, have been found, but enough recognizable tubes and burrows have been identified to establish the existence of marine worms, and there are other indications that suggest the presence of jellyfish. Inasmuch as these are multicelled animals, the evidence strongly implies that the great advance from Protozoa to Metazoa had already been accomplished in Proterozoic times. Very likely, most of these fauna were small invertebrates, but by the next era there were such numbers and varieties of all kinds of spineless animals that experts believe some of them must have originated earlier. In line with such reasoning, Lull refers to the latter part of the Proterozoic as the Age of Primitive Marine Invertebrates.

During the extent of the Paleozoic era, the evidence of continuing evolution becomes increasingly detailed and conclusive, partly because some invertebrates were secreting lime that formed hard shells or covers that resist disintegration and so provide abundant material for contemporary scholars to examine and interpret. Thanks to the great quantities of animal hard parts that have been discovered in Paleozoic rocks, it can be shown that there were then in existence flourishing populations of many sorts of invertebrates. By the middle of the Paleozoic era, too, there is proof of the emergence of true vertebrates in the form of fishes; and with their formation a great forward stride was taken in the direction of man's body arrangement.

W. W. Howells, of Harvard, has made an interesting analogy between the process of evolution and a house with only one staircase but with many rooms on every floor.[10] As animal groups reach each level most of them rush into the rooms, but a few remain near the stairway

[9] R. S. Lull, *Organic Evolution,* rev. ed., New York, 1947, p. 74.
[10] W. W. Howells, *Mankind in the Making,* New York, 1959, p. 32.

and ultimately climb (evolve) to a higher stage. This procedure seems to have been repeated over and over again until *Homo sapiens* emerged at the topmost level.

Elman R. Service has pointed out that those animals that in Howell's analogy took to rooms, may have continued to develop within the confines of their environments and may have produced some extraordinary specializations as they adapted themselves to their immediate surroundings. But as they did so they sacrificed their total evolutionary potential. Meantime, some of their unspecialized and more generalized relatives continued to climb the stairs of evolutionary progress to new forms.[11] Thus, according to Service, evolution is discontinuous and proceeds from the lowlier members of one group after another, instead of being continuously progressive and going from the highest level of one group to the highest level of another. It is a well-known biological rule of thumb that greatly specialized creatures are unlikely to play a part in higher (later) stages of evolution.

Biologists who deal with the proper classification of organisms are known as *taxonomists.*[12] Theoretically, creatures which show numerous resemblances are supposed to be related and to have a common ancestry. Resemblances may be of several kinds, but taxonomists feel safest when they deal with those resemblances of structure that are known as *homologies.* Organisms that are grouped together into such large divisions as *kingdoms* or *phyla* need show only a few structural similarities, but the number of close homologies should increase as we delimit the groupings called *classes, orders, families, genera,* and *species.*

Selected References

Blum, H. F., *Time's Arrow and Evolution,* Princeton, N. J., 1951.

Carlson, Anton J., and Johnson, V., *The Machinery of the Body,* rev. ed., Chicago, 1941.

Carter, George S., "The Theory of Evolution and the Evolution of Man," in *Anthropology Today,* A. L. Kroeber, ed., Chicago, 1953, pp. 327–42.

Dobzhansky, Theodosius, *Evolution, Genetics, and Man,* New York, 1955.

———, *Mankind Evolving,* New Haven, Conn., 1962.

[11] M. P. Sahlins and E. R. Service, *Evolution and Culture,* Ann Arbor, Mich., 1960, p. 97.

[12] The outstanding paleontologist, George Gaylord Simpson, has published an insightful discussion of this topic in *Principles of Animal Taxonomy,* New York, 1961.

Goldschmidt, R. B., *Understanding Heredity,* New York and London, 1952.
Meggers, Betty J., ed., *Evolution and Anthropology: A Centennial Appraisal,* Washington, D. C., 1959.
Pearse, A. S., *The Emigrations of Animals from the Sea,* New York, 1950.
Raymond, Percy E., *Prehistoric Life,* Cambridge, Mass., 1939.
Roe, Ann, and Simpson, George G., eds., *Behavior and Evolution,* New Haven, Conn., 1958.
Simpson, George G., *The Meaning of Evolution,* New Haven, Conn., 1949.
Stern, Curt, *Principles of Human Genetics,* San Francisco, 1949.

Vertebrate Contributions to Man

CHAPTER 3

BEFORE THE TRUE FISHES

All through the millions and millions of years that make up the Archeozoic and Proterozoic, a vast quantity of living organisms had evolved, but not one of them possessed a real spine. Then, quite early in the Paleozoic era, a number of aquatic creatures appeared that were of prime importance from the standpoint of human ancestry. These were the *chordates*, a group of animals whose structures typically include a *notochord*, which is an elongated rod running the length of the body, and supposedly the forerunner of a true backbone. Another distinguishing trait of chordate anatomy is the occurrence of *gill slits*. They appear to have served not only as breathing mechanisms for taking oxygen from water, but also as devices for straining particles of solid substances that were utilized for feeding. Although adult men and women do not have gill slits, it is interesting to observe that at one stage of their embryological development human infants do have recognizable gill slits.

Beginning with chordates and present in all the succeeding lines that lead to *Homo sapiens*, there is a distinctive cigar-shaped body, containing a head end and a tail end, with the head end leading all forward movements of the body of the organism. It was the front end of a creature that first came into contact with every new feature of the environment, and as vertebrate evolution progressed, the nervous system moved forward. In the course of time, distance receptors were developed that were capable of informing an organism about the conditions that it was going to encounter. Thus, creatures began to learn something about what lay ahead and became increasingly concerned with the future, instead of being occupied chiefly with what had happened in the past or with what was going on in the present. A few scientists also believe that evolution of a cigar-shaped body may have been a prior stage leading to the later development of stereoscopic vision.

Gifts from true fishes

As we approach the Devonian period of the great Paleozoic era, we find abundant evidence of a remarkable variety of fishes, some of which had real, bony, internal skeletons and were beyond doubt true vertebrates. All of these had segmented and flexible backbones, and many other anatomical traits that have persisted on into *Homo sapiens*. So much is this the case that there is more than a grain of truth in the jesting remark that man is nothing but a made-over fish.

Examination of some of the details of the general vertebrate ground plan should help to clarify the relationship of men to fish. All vertebrates exhibit the phenomenon of *bilateral symmetry*, which means that each side of the body is a mirror image of the other. Thus, in man, we find right and left nostrils, eyes, ears, arms, breasts, ribs, lungs, testes or ovaries, legs, and so on. From the torso there extend right and left, or paired, fins or limbs; with one pair situated forward near the head or neck, and the other pair located at the hind end, close by the pelvis. Our own marked tendency toward bilateral symmetry cannot be denied, even though a few vital organs, such as the heart and liver, are not duplicated on each side of the body.

All vertebrates have bony heads that cover and protect a multipart brain and contain most of the important sense organs, corresponding to human noses, eyes, and ears. In fish, the nostrils may be little more than a pair of pockets that hold cells sensitive to odors, and the ears may contain a connected series of fluid-filled sacs or canals used for balance. Even though greatly modified, these structures and their functions have persisted in all succeeding vertebrates. Far more important than the dropping or addition of parts is the evolutionary conversion of old parts, as in the formation of the human ear, as well as shifts of emphasis, such as the fish's reliance on smell as opposed to the importance of sight in later forms.

Vertebrate heads come to be associated with movable mouths and jaws, especially the lower jaw, which is known as the *mandible*. Movable mouths and jaws are useful for seizing prey, fighting enemies, or taking in relatively large morsels of food. In vertebrates, food enters at the mouth and passes into a digestive system within the main body cavity. Waste matter is always excreted at the tail end.

We come now to the important matter of reproduction. From fish to man the reproductive organs have always been closely linked to the organs of excretion. Among fishes the two sexes retain permanently the feminine function of laying eggs, or the masculine activity of producing sperm. As everyone knows, fish eggs are like tiny specks of gelatin that are laid in water outside a female's body[1] and are fertilized by independently deposited sperm. Not only is it true, as Ogden Nash has put it, that a fish "hardly ever sees its mates," but it is only by accident that a mother ever sees her offspring.

Leading a double life

Even if we grant that the main outlines of the forthcoming human body were foreshadowed in fishes, we still must consider the biological distinctions that set man apart from water dwellers. Strange as it may seem, some of these factors were begun, not without a degree of success, by certain fishes.

So many varieties of fish were in evidence during the Devonian period, about halfway through the Paleozoic era, nearly 350 million years ago, that it is often termed the Age of Fishes. But the climate in Devonian times was not always well suited to fish life, for there were violent alternations of rainy and dry seasons. Many bodies of water probably dried out during stages of drought, leading to overcongestion of fish populations in those that remained. As a consequence the supply of available oxygen would have tended to become exhausted, a contingency that would have put the highest of biological premiums on an ability to gulp atmospheric oxygen from the air.

Close to the direct line of man's ancestry, in the opinion of some authorities, were species of the lobe-finned *crossopterygian* fishes,[2] which combined a capacity to take atmospheric oxygen into air sacs with the possession of strong, muscular, paired fins whose firm flesh rested on a bony framework (Fig. 3-1). These fins were strong enough to serve as limbs whenever the animal found itself forced to progress on dry ground.

[1] As is true of most general statements, there are exceptions to this "rule." Some fish give birth to live babies.

[2] It used to be thought that all the crossopterygians had become extinct long ago, but since 1939 a number of coelacanths, one variety of crossopterygian fish, have been caught off the African continent. Some scientists regard crossopterygians as playing no part in later evolution and refuse to consider them as remote ancestors of man.

Because of their distinctive features, crossopterygians were capable of living out of water for reasonably protracted lengths of time, and it is believed that they transmitted their special qualities to the *amphibians* who were the next animals to evolve.

In the course of time, amphibian limbs became suited for movements on dry soil, and their air sacs came to function more and more as

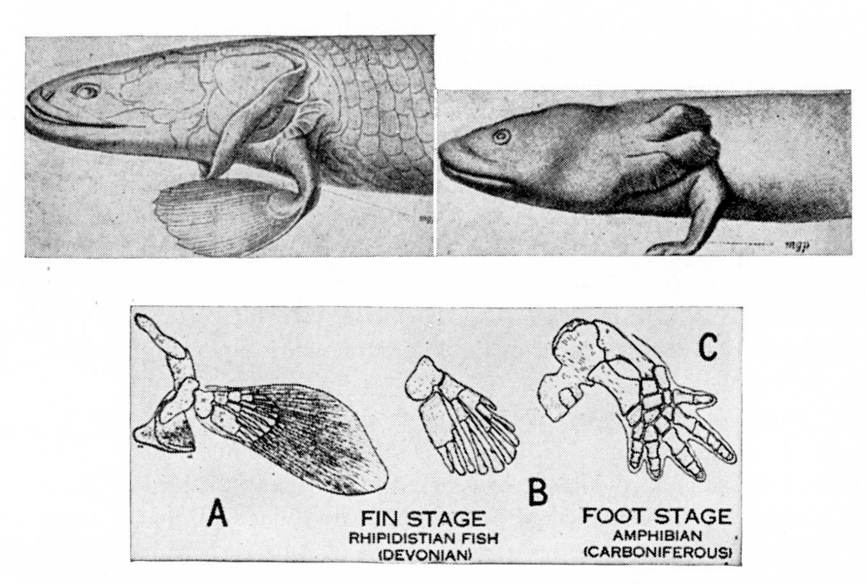

FIG. 3-1. Toward the evolution of land legs. (Above) Students should note the close resemblance between a crossopterygian fish (left), and an early amphibian (right). (Courtesy of the Buffalo Museum of Science.) The postulated evolution of land legs from such powerful fins as those of crossopterygian fishes is worthy of careful study. (Below) The five-digited amphibian foot is thought to have evolved from the underlying skeletal structure of the fins of some fishes. (Courtesy of the Museum of Anthropology, the University of Michigan.)

true lungs. Thus equipped for terrestrial existence, amphibians avoided the congestion to which fishes were being subjected and sustained themselves by eating land-dwelling substances, such as ferns, mosses, and insects.

An amphibian life process can be carried out only under conditions where the females are able to find wet places for the safe deposit, fertilization, and hatching of their eggs. When severe droughts are greatly prolonged, or when amphibians wander into an arid region, a new adaptation whereby eggs can be laid and hatched on dry land becomes necessary. Such a major evolutionary change was accomplished before the close of Paleozoic times by the *reptiles*, who became completely emancipated from living in or close to water.

Reptiles rule the land

The earliest of the Paleozoic reptiles resemble some of the amphibians very closely. But, as the succeeding Mesozoic era progressed, reptilian forms underwent several significant changes. Internal organs like the heart and lungs were improved to carry out their functions more adequately; the spinal column became bonier and sturdier without losing its suppleness; the limbs were strengthened, elongated, attached more firmly to the trunk, and brought into a better position to hold up and move the body; the number of face and head bones was reduced; and in the brain there appeared the first traces of a new development, the *cerebral cortex* (*neopallium*), made up of gray matter that overlies the forward hemisphere or *cerebrum*. It was the cerebral cortex that was destined to become the locus of the higher mental functions in succeeding vertebrates.

Some of the greatest contributions paving the way for man are concerned with changes in the manner of reproduction. The key is to be found in the development of a new kind of egg, called an *amniote egg*, which is large and covered with a hard but porous shell that protects a developing embryo without cutting off its supply of atmospheric oxygen. It also contains an assortment of membranes and liquids that provide nourishment.[3] Not until natural selection favored reptilian females who had acquired the biological mechanism for laying amniote eggs on dry land could the ties with bodies of water have been severed.

If a female is to deposit a hard-shelled egg within which an embryo is to develop, the egg must of necessity be fertilized before its discharge from her body. This was achieved by the reptiles through copulation, the method of sexual reproduction in which the male genital member must be capable of penetrating a pocketlike female organ, in order to intromit spermatozoa. The basic reptilian mode of reproduction, which demands extremely close contact between a male and a female, is still to be found in man, albeit with important modifications.

Throughout the long, long span of about 130 million years that the Mesozoic lasted, the varieties and quantities of reptilian types were so great that this era is suitably named the Age of Reptiles. There is no

---

[3] The size of an amniote egg is delimited by the size of a female's laying apparatus and, in turn, the size of the egg determines the size of a fetus at birth.

need for an anthropologist to describe or even to summarize the diverse kinds of reptiles that flourished in the Mesozoic, but as the era drew to a close an overwhelming majority became extinct, and those that have survived to our day shrank to a few varieties and sank into comparative insignificance.

As is well known, reptiles may be provided with coverings that range from scales to plates of heavy bone, but the entire class lacks a heat-regulating mechanism and the type of hairy or furry growth that serves to retain the warmth produced by the body. Since all members of this class of animals have absolutely no way of conserving the body's heat, they are *cold-blooded,* which really means that they reflect whatever temperature prevails in their immediate surroundings. When cold weather comes they tend to freeze until they become sluggish in their movements or resort to the inactivity of hibernation. By contrast, *warm-blooded* animals can maintain constantly high body temperatures that are much less responsive to external conditions, and so they are able to remain energetic and active in all seasons.

Mammals take over

Even while the big hulking dinosaurs were the most prominent animals on earth, some of their less conspicuous relatives were already beginning to initiate *mammalian* traits. These reptiles began to show the earliest known method of regulating internal body heat (warm-bloodedness), and, in addition, featured a new technique for the mastication of food. Most reptiles are provided with peg-shaped teeth that are alike from front to back (*homodont*), continuously replaceable if lost, and utilized primarily for seizing prey and tearing food. There are no grinding teeth, so that when food is swallowed the grinding process takes place not in the mouth but in the stomach. Unlike the more orthodox members of their class, the promammalian reptiles evolved a varied assortment of teeth (*heterodont*) including, from the front center of the mouth to the back along each side, sharp-edged incisors for biting and shearing, pointed canines for piercing, and comparatively broad and flat premolars and molars for crushing and grinding. This dental arrangement persists in man. With the help of *heterodontism* an animal can better cut its food into small bits that can be quickly converted to energy.

In mammals, at least, warm-bloodedness is maintained with the aid of a thermostatic device that is probably controlled in the thalamus region of the brain. Whenever body temperature falls dangerously below what is normal for a given species, shivering and the contraction of blood vessels attempt to provide and conserve additional heat. Conversely, sweating and dilated blood vessels make efforts to cool the body when its temperature rises too high. Much of the retention of body heat in mammals is made possible by the insulation provided by skin covers of fur or hair. Heat and energy production are closely integrated, and it is their high metabolic rate that keeps mammals active and energetic in all seasons.

Smelling, seeing, tasting, and hearing abilities improved as mammals became more fully evolved, and a new sensory device—a sensitive skin—sent innumerable contact impressions to the brain, where judgments based on the sense of touch became highly exact and discriminating. The cerebral cortex developed deep folds, and expanded with the upward and backward growth of the cerebral hemispheres that it overlies. It is estimated that the human cortex alone lodges in its intricate folds and convolutions more than nine billion cells. Coupled with its increase in size among the higher mammals is the brain's development as an extraordinary sense-combiner. Within the neopallium impressions sent in from various sources are blended and stored, thereby providing a basis for memory, the association of ideas, foresight, planning, and all the so-called higher mental faculties that reach their greatest peak in man.

Certainly it is hardly to be expected that the great gap between fully evolved mammals and their reptilian forebears should have been bridged in one great leap. Much more probable is the likelihood that the changes occurred in a series of steps, each one favored by natural selection. Even if one searches only among the relatively few forms that still survive, he may find representatives of what seem to be transitional stages. Lowest of the extant mammals, in the sense of having the smallest number of typically mammalian features, is the subclass called *Prototheria* (Fig. 3–2). At present they are found only in Australia, where they are represented by the duckbill (platypus) and the spiny anteater (echidna). These Prototheria have some reptilian skeletal traits and exhibit other nonmammalian characteristics in that they are toothless; and the females lay fairly large, shelled, prefertilized eggs, outside their bodies. On the other hand, Prototheria, like other mammals, have furry covers and warm blood (though some say that their warmth is unstable). Females have breastlike glands from which their young lick, rather than suck, a milky fluid. It may be that the Prototheria are so specialized that the later mammals did not pass through an actual Prototherian stage. In that case these animals would merely serve to indicate some of the ways in which the gap between reptiles and true mammals could have been bridged.

A

B

FIG. 3-2. Surviving Prototherian mammals. A. The duckbill or platypus. B. A spiny anteater or echidna. Both creatures are found in Australia. They bear little external resemblance to the higher mammals, and the females lay prefertilized eggs externally. Yet they feed their offspring with milk. They are believed to indicate an early stage in the evolution of placental mammals. (Courtesy of Zoological Society of Philadelphia.)

Considerably closer to full-fledged mammals is the subclass of *Metatheria,* or pouched mammals, best known from fauna living in Australia and its environs, including kangaroos, wombats, wallabies,

FIG. 3-3. A metatherian mammal. This picture shows a wallaby mother and child. Wallabies are closely related to kangaroos, and live in Australia. The baby, locally known as a "Joey," is shown secure in its mother's pouch. (Courtesy of Zoological Society of Philadelphia.)

koalas, and others, but more widely represented throughout the world by the *opossum*. Metatherian females produce tiny eggs, which are retained within the mother's body even after fertilization, but the eggs contain small yolks and so make little provision for the feeding of embryos. Hence, the offspring are born after a brief pregnancy, alive but very little and immature. For shelter and nourishment they crawl up the mother's body and enter an abdominal pouch where they are kept secure, protected from the elements, and given ready access to teats from which they draw milk (Fig. 3–3).

The fullest expression of mammalian development occurs in the subclass of *Eutherian* or *placental* mammals, to which man belongs. Reproduction involves the internal fertilization of a tiny egg and its

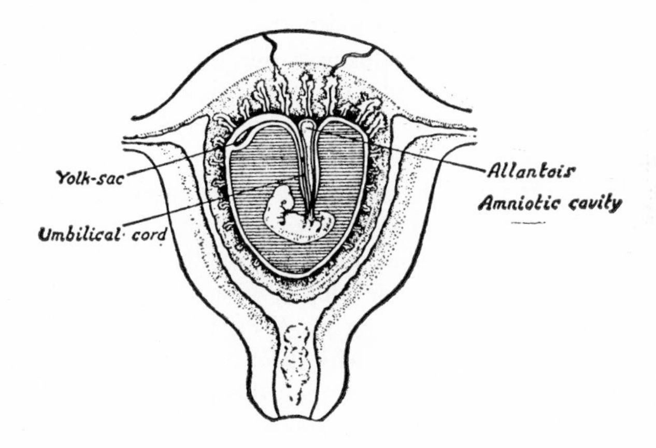

FIG. 3-4. The human placental arrangement. The manner in which an embryo, during its mother's pregnancy, is carried, nourished, and sheltered, is very similar for all placental (eutherian) mammals. (E. A. Hooton, *Up from the Ape,* rev. ed., New York, 1946. Courtesy of the author and The Macmillan Company.)

retention within the female's body for an extended length of time. During this period the embryo is provided with membranes, many of which are just like those in the reptilian amniote egg. Soon after conception, a number of these membranes combine with part of the mother's uterine lining to form the *placenta.* Thereafter, maternal and embryonic blood are brought close together and may occasionally mix a bit, but the two blood streams do not merge into one (Fig. 3–4). Pregnancy terms vary in different species of *Eutheria,* but run to six months or more in large animals. Gestation is always long enough to enable the embryo to reach a far greater degree of maturity than is possible in nonplacentals. Such a protracted pregnancy is to be found only among creatures whose metabolic rate is high enough to provide mother and embryo with a good supply of energy. Among the Eutheria, the placenta is discharged as the afterbirth soon after an infant has emerged, and a new placenta originates with each succeeding pregnancy. Shortly after her delivery, the mother's breasts fill with milk with which a baby can be fed for many months.

It is in the matter of reproduction that we come upon one of the most profound differences distinguishing placental mammals from all the animals that preceded them. Females of all nonmammalian species have, as a rule, vast numbers of offspring, very few of which survive to maturity.[4] Furthermore, such mothers seldom have contact with their children after their eggs are laid and hatched. Mammalian mothers, in contrast, give birth to relatively few offspring, most of which grow to adulthood. They have intimate internal contacts with their babies throughout pregnancy, and through the device of suckling remain closely attached to them for long periods of time. It is obvious that man has retained the mammalian pattern of mother-child relationships.

Constituted as they were, the Eutherian mammals ultimately took over the dominant position formerly held by reptiles, and during the Cenozoic era they set out on a career of widespread, adaptive radiation. Most of them were four-footed and lived on the ground (as is true today); but some, like the bats, developed wings and spent much of their time in the air. Others, including sea cows, whales, dolphins, and walruses, adjusted themselves to marine life; at least one, the mole, went underground; and several types, among them insect-eating shrews, took to the trees. The Eutheria that became adapted to life in the air, at sea, or beneath the ground, tended to become highly specialized and lost their evolutionary potential. Others, particularly the ones that climbed into the trees, retained what may be called a generalized mammalian condition. It was from among the generalized arboreal placental mammals that the Primates are believed to have evolved.

MAMMALIAN EVOLUTION IN BRIEF REVIEW

It is important for the student of anthropology to know the story of mammalian evolution so that he will understand when and, to some extent, why and how various aspects of man's body structure and biological behavior were developed. With these objectives in mind, it may be well to review some of the salient facts so far presented.

Even the most casual of observers knows that man's body contains systems of cells that are specialized for breathing, digesting, excreting,

[4] Readers are reminded that this brief synopsis is highly selective and is couched in broad terms to which there may be particular exceptions.

reproducing, and so forth. Associated with the organs that make up these systems are sets of muscles, which require nerve mechanisms to regulate and direct their activities. Among the early invertebrates the nerve cells were dispersed in scattered units throughout the body, every unit acting almost independently to control muscular activity in its own area. Later, as may be seen in jellyfish, the disparate nerve units were merged into a coordinated nervous system that functioned as a central receiving and dispatching center for the entire organism. This scheme was improved in various Paleozoic invertebrates.

With the emergence of elongated bodies among chordates—and, more significantly, among truly vertebrate bony fishes—a pattern was devised that included clearly marked head, body, and tail divisions; bilateral symmetry; paired appendages; and permanent distinctions of sex. Among vertebrates, all of the sense organs and their associated nerve cells were connected with a brain, which was lodged in a bony head that thereafter led the way forward while it directed the movements of an animal. Fish bodies are so specialized for speedy movement that their responses to external impressions are very quick and in the nature of automatic or reflex actions. Thoughtful behavior, based on the recollection of past happenings, is something that lies beyond the capacity of fishes; and they are also incapable of any activity (such as first-degree murder) that requires premeditation. Above all, they lack a good sense-combiner for merging sense impressions received from various sources into a composite whole. Without such an arrangement a creature cannot function mentally, as a human.

Following in the footsteps, as it were, of some Devonian fishes that were able to crawl on dry soil while they gulped atmospheric oxygen, came the ambitious amphibians who led the way to partially terrestrial life by contributing adult lungs and limbs to the vertebrate theme composed by fishes. As their paired fins became changed to legs, the amphibians required alterations in those parts of the brain and nervous system devoted to locomotor controls. After the necessary changes came about, adult amphibians could use their legs either to walk on land or to swim. The senses of sight and smell likewise became adapted to air or water; in addition, the amphibians were the earliest in the line of mammalian evolution to develop a genuine sense of hearing.

Pioneer reptiles showed the first suitable adjustments for carrying out the vertebrate theme entirely on land. They underwent numerous changes of body, limbs, and lungs; but even more vital was the initiation of a new mode of reproduction. This included the development of an amniote egg and internal fertilization by copulation. Certain reptiles exhibited a cerebral cortex, a new element in the brain that was ultimately to play a major part in the life of man; and the conversion of teeth from homodont to heterodont is also found among some reptiles. In this class of animals, too, there sometimes occurs that internal system of regulating body temperatures that is conventionally termed warm-bloodedness. All these features, however, are much better represented in the mammals.

Although mammalian evolution probably had its beginnings well over 70 million years ago, it did not reach a climax until the Cenozoic era had begun. Supposedly lowly members of the class, it is sometimes assumed, comprise the egg-laying Prototheria; and the somewhat more advanced, pouched Metatheria. But fully mammalian body forms and behavior are restricted to the Eutheria. The females of these warm-blooded, air-breathing, hair- or fur-covered animals give birth to limited numbers of relatively mature, living offspring. These are first nourished within the mother's body during a prolonged pregnancy by means of a deciduous placenta, and after birth they are fed on milk from the mother's breasts. There is thus provided a long stretch of time during which an infant is dependent on its mother.

As far as their anatomical structures go, the subclass of placental mammals quite generally provides the prototype for man, but there are many specific features of the human body that can better be understood by investigating the particular order of Primates, which is a subdivision of the Eutheria.

Selected References

Colbert, E. H., *Evolution of the Vertebrates,* rev. ed., New York, 1955.
Dunbar, Carl O., *Historical Geology,* New York, 1949.
Gregory, William K., *Evolution Emerging,* New York, 1951.
———, *Our Face from Fish to Man,* New York and London, 1929.
Hall, T. S., and Moog, F., *Life Science,* New York, 1955.
Romer, Alfred S., *Man and the Vertebrates,* rev. ed., Chicago, 1941.
———, *The Vertebrate Body,* Philadelphia, 1949.
Simpson, George G., *Tempo and Mode in Evolution,* rev. ed., New York, 1953.
Snider, L. C., *Earth History,* New York and London, 1932.
Tilney, Frederick C., *The Master of Destiny, a Biography of the Brain,* New York, 1930.

Prosimians and Monkeys

CHAPTER 4

PRIMATE ANATOMY AND ITS ORIGINS

An anthropologist's interest in the long lines of animals that preceded mankind indicates his belief that form and function are intimately connected. As this applies to human beings, it means an awareness that we could not possibly act like men and women if we were not built like men and women.

By this time it should be clear that man's anatomical building blocks were obtained by inheritance or modification of parts first developed by many infrahuman creatures. Although man's body, beyond the shadow of a doubt, is that of a placental mammal, it is equally evident that some of his structural features are different from the general run of Eutheria. A few of his body specialties are unique to him, but several of his most typical body parts are duplicated, sometimes with startling exactness, among creatures belonging to the *Primate* order, a subdivision of Eutherian mammals that consists of *lemurs, tarsiers, monkeys, apes,* and *men.*

Take, for instance, the customary way in which a man throws a baseball (Fig. 4–1), or holds a tennis racket, hammer, or a canoe paddle. In each case, the same anatomical structures, shared by the lower Primates and man, are brought into play (Fig. 4–2). No fine control, tight hold, or prehensile grip, would be possible to an animal that lacked strong and flexible fingers capable of wrapping firmly about an implement. It should also be noted that in order to get a really tight grasp on something, the thumb must wrap around it in the opposite direction

FIG. 4-1. Throwing a curve. It would be impossible to grasp a baseball properly for throwing a curve if man's anatomy did not include strong, separable fingers, an opposable thumb, and a flexible wrist. (Courtesy of Eck Stanger, *The Ann Arbor News,* Ann Arbor, Mich.)

from the other digits. Technically, this Primate mechanism is known as the *opposable thumb* and is usually taken to mean that the ball or tip of the thumb can be touched (*opposed*) to the tips of the other four fingers.[1] Some believe that the Primate development of flat nails, rather than claws on the five digits of each hand and foot, is likewise associated with grasping functions, in the belief that nails are less likely than claws to get in the way. A few writers have gone so far as to attribute the ridges on the insides of the fingers to the firm purchase they provide for picking up or holding things.

Then, again, the movements involved in the strenuous use of implements call for the firm attachment of fingers, hands, wrists, and arms to the shoulders. This implies the need of a sturdy shoulder

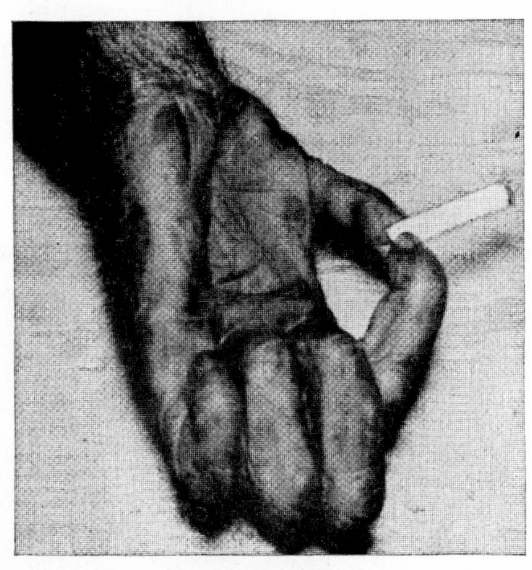

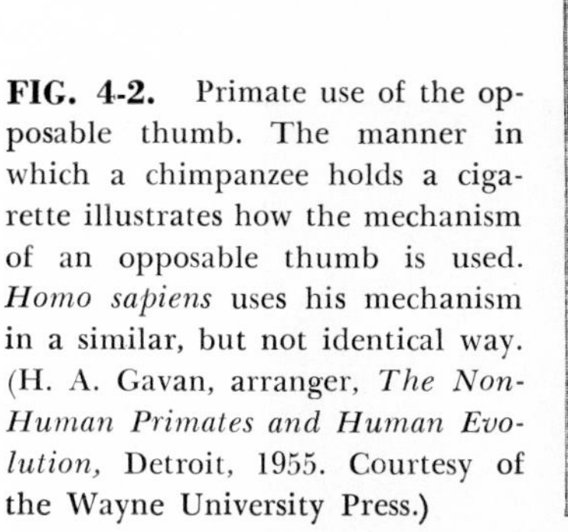

FIG. 4-2. Primate use of the opposable thumb. The manner in which a chimpanzee holds a cigarette illustrates how the mechanism of an opposable thumb is used. *Homo sapiens* uses his mechanism in a similar, but not identical way. (H. A. Gavan, arranger, *The Non-Human Primates and Human Evolution,* Detroit, 1955. Courtesy of the Wayne University Press.)

girdle, in which the collarbone (*clavicle*) must play an important part. Without a strong and firmly knit clavicle, violent motions of the arms to the sides and rear are next to impossible. So, were he not a Primate, a baseball player could not swing hard enough to hit a home run and no tennis player could develop a powerful stroke.

Another distinctive trait of human and Primate behavior is made possible by the fact that the two long bones of the forearm can be rotated so that the outer one (*radius*) moves over the inner (*ulna*). (See Fig. 4–3.) This makes it a simple matter for the hand and arm below the elbow to be turned so that the palm may face up, down, or to either side. Firm,

---

[1] Unlike man, most other Primates have prehensile feet as well as prehensile hands, and opposable great toes as well as thumbs.

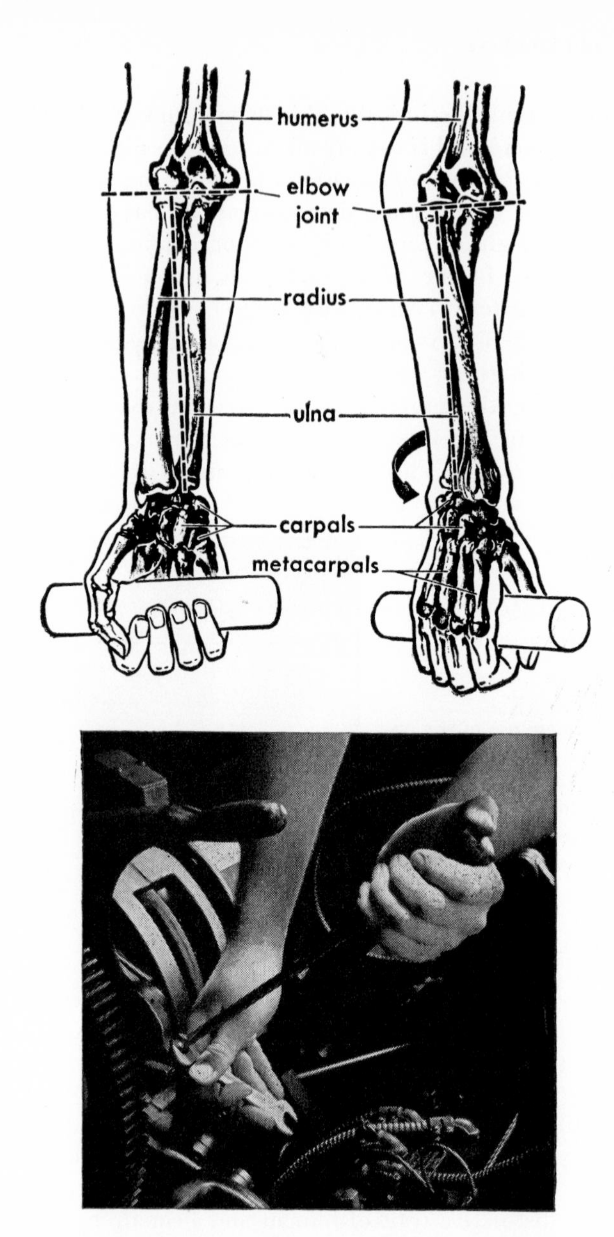

FIG. 4-3. Man's rotating forearm. The structural (anatomical) features here shown demonstrate the way in which the outer bone, or radius, slides over the inner bone, or ulna, to make possible a rotating forearm. Below: It is the mechanism of the rotating forearm, coupled with a prehensile grip, that makes it possible for a human being to use all kinds of tools. So is form related to function. (Above: J. S. Rogers, T. Hubbell, and C. F. Byers, *Man and the Biological World*, Rev. Ed., New York, 1952, Courtesy of the authors and the McGraw-Hill Book Company, Inc. Below: Courtesy of Eck Stanger, *The Ann Arbor News*, Ann Arbor, Mich.)

mobile, opposable digits, a flexible wrist, and a rotating forearm attached to a strong shoulder girdle, together with their associated muscles, nerves, ligaments, and tendons, provide the biological potential for such divergent activities as digging post holes, playing the accordion, throwing a swift forward pass, steering an automobile, knotting a necktie, rolling out bread dough, or using a screwdriver.

Other anatomical features commonly regarded as typical of Primates include: a large, deeply convoluted brain covered with a much-wrinkled cortex; a greatly intensified increase in the sense of sight, coupled with stereoscopic vision; an attendant decline of keen smell; a tendency for females to bear only one young at a time; possession, as a rule, of only two breasts, situated high on the chest; and a bony wall, penetrated by the optic nerve, that shuts off the eye socket at the side and rear. Not all of these body traits are newly evolved formations. For instance, studies of early mammals have revealed that skeletal features such as the clavicle and rotating forearm occurred long ago, but among none of the Eutherian mammals save Primates are they still functionally important.

From time to time, efforts have been made to explode the notion that there may be a cause-and-effect relationship between arboreal life and Primate anatomy. Opponents object to the idea that increased reliance on the sense of sight, prehensile grip, flexible wrist, rotating forearm, and expert hand–eye coordination, may be associated with their usefulness to tree dwellers. There is even a theory, not to be lightly dismissed, that man's ancestors have always been ground dwellers, who never abided in trees. However, since all Primates, with the exception of man and the man-apes, are to some extent arboreal, it is probable that a connection does exist and that some aspects of Primate structure were selected because they were so well adapted to life in the trees. On the other hand, the fossil record makes it plain that at the beginning of the Cenozoic era Primates went through a tremendous outburst of adaptive radiations that continued on into *Homo sapiens,* who appears in a great many diversified forms.

The reader may have noticed how few specialized traits are attributed exclusively to Primates. Indeed, one may go so far as to say that the very lack of specialization is the most distinguishing aspect of the entire order. Thus, the search for Primate origins inevitably leads one to consider highly generalized Eutherian mammals. An almost universal consensus has been reached to the effect that the parent group was most likely tree-dwelling and insect-eating, and is represented today by certain *tree shrews* (Fig. 4–4), but it should not be thought that the

FIG. 4-4. A Philippine tree shrew. Although this creature is very far from the hominid branch of Primates, it has five digits on each hand and foot, separable thumbs, and a differentiation of hind and fore limbs. It is generally regarded as indicating the ancestral line of the Primate order. (Courtesy of the New York Zoological Society.)

higher Primates evolved from any surviving creatures. Scientists do not believe that the Primates descended from any living animals, but they do feel that extant tree shrews suggest the kind of group from which the Primates might well have started.

The dubious lemurs

Although a few scientists refuse to classify lemurs as Primates, most of them admit these creatures to the ranks but assign them to the separate infraorder of *Lemuroidea*.[2] Others prefer to treat tree shrews, lemurs, and tarsiers as lower Primates, and put all three into the Primate sub-order of *Prosimii.*

Many kinds of lemurs are still to be found in Madagascar and the vicinity, but during the Eocene epoch they were widely spread through other parts of the world, including the Western Hemisphere. They are, on the whole, small animals about two feet long, with fur-covered bodies and long tails. Most varieties have pointed, projecting snouts and big, round eyes that peer to the sides and fail to provide overlapping, stereoscopic vision. They live in trees and are most active at night, when they feed busily on a mixed diet of insects, bird eggs, fruits, leaves, buds, and shoots.

Lemurs are generally quadrupedal, but both the thumb and great toe are well developed and capable of being turned to touch the inner tips of the other digits. They are, accordingly, equipped with prehensile hands and feet and can secure a tight grasp on a branch by wrapping either organ around it. They also have rotating forearms which, in conjunction with powerful upper arms and shoulder girdles, permit them to perform such operations as grasping things at any angle, hanging or swinging by the arms, pulling the body upward or forward, pouncing and seizing on prey, conveying food to the mouth, and handling objects in a prehensile manner. Whenever they reach for new holds, lemurs tend to use their arms and hands, temporarily throwing the weight of the body on the rear limbs (Fig. 4–5). These are somewhat elongated, stable, and incapable of being rotated. Such a separation of the structure and function of front from hind limbs is an important Primate characteristic that becomes increasingly marked as we run the range from lemur to man.

While Lemuroidea have enough Primate aspects to be admitted, somewhat grudgingly, to that order, they also exhibit some anatomical traits of lower evolutionary status. Their eyeballs are suspended by membranes within rings of bone, whereas the eyeballs of higher Primates

[2] Some physical anthropologists separate from lemurs a closely related animal called loris; see M. F. Ashley Montagu, *An Introduction to Physical Anthropology,* rev. ed., Springfield, Ill., 1951, pp. 30–39. W. W. Howells, *Mankind in the Making,* New York, 1959, p. 65, also differentiates the galagos, or bush babies, who are related to true lemurs.

FIG. 4-5. Ring-tailed lemur. Lowly though this Primate may be, it has a five-digital arrangement, flat nails on fingers and toes, strong and flexible fingers and wrists, opposable thumbs and great toes, rotating forearms, and clearly differentiated front and hind limbs. (Courtesy of the New York Zoological Society.)

are set in bony cups with solid back walls; their tear ducts lie on the facial surfaces outside the eye cavities, instead of being enclosed within the eye sockets; they are not believed to possess stereoscopic vision, and it is therefore unlikely that they can perceive depth or third dimension; and their brains are poorly developed and give much prominence to the sense of smell. The latter is regarded as a backward condition, because tree dwellers require agility and coordination that are better served by increased visual, tactile, kinesthetic, and motor areas in the brain.

The Curious Tarsiers

Somewhat more progressive than lemurs in various biological respects, but unique and overspecialized in others, is the Primate subdivision of *Tarsioidea*. Today *tarsiers* are found only in a few of the islands in Indonesia, including the Philippines, but, like the lemurs, they had a much wider distribution in Eocene times. Their bodies average well under two feet in length, but they have bare, ratlike tails that may be longer. They are covered with reddish-brown fur, and are characterized by rounded heads and short, blunt snouts. Feeding and other essential activities take place at night. Grasshoppers, small lizards, and other little fauna are eaten, but vegetable or plant foods are neglected.

Tarsiers are so named because of a greatly enlarged tarsus bone that in all Primates helps form the arch of the foot. To this unusual development must be added the further circumstance that the long bones of the lower leg (*tibia* and *fibula*) are merged together at their bottom. These specialties of the ankle region, coupled with the retention of very flexible

FIG. 4-6. A tarsier. Far removed from the structure and appearance of *Homo sapiens* is this lowly Primate, which is specialized for rapid hopping. Yet, its eyes are in a frontal position, and it has prehensile hands and rotating forearms. The front and hind limbs are differentiated in form and function. (Courtesy of McGraw-Hill Book Company, Inc.)

toes, seem to enable tarsiers to make prodigious hops at lightning speed. When they employ this mode of progression in the trees, where they habitually reside, they are aided by still another specialty, for the balls of all the digits are extended into roughened, disklike pads that are thought to prevent slipping when a fresh hold is obtained.

Other distinctive anatomical peculiarities of Tarsioidea are concerned with the visual apparatus. Being nocturnal of habit they do not like strong light and have big round eyes, so large that only a small space separates them, and while the fields of vision appear to overlap somewhat, it is uncertain whether truly stereoscopic vision is produced. The eyes are set within tremendous bony sockets whose back walls, unlike those of lemurs, are complete. Tear ducts are large, beginning within the eye cavity but extending out to the face. When it wishes to observe something above and behind it, a tarsier is said to be able to swivel its head around 180 degrees and so look directly backward without turning the rest of its body.

Despite their strange appearance and body specialties, tarsiers show various advanced Primate features. The fundamental differentiation of front and hind limbs is more advanced. Hands and arms measure less than half as much as feet and legs; all ten digits have rather sharp and narrow nails but no claws; and there is a much greater tendency to use the hands in feeding (Fig. 4–6). Tarsier brains show an increase of space devoted to sight and the olfactory area is correspondingly reduced. In general, the forward region of the brain (cerebrum) extends up and back to overlie the cerebellum at the rear. Only one offspring is normally born at a time and female tarsiers, unlike lemurs, have monthly discharges of blood at the vagina, somewhat like menstrual periods.

Wood Jones, a highly competent primatologist, holds the opinion that the line of higher evolution culminating in man branched off from a tarsioid stage of development,[3] but other biologists regard tarsiers as forerunners only of the next rank or so of the Primates.

Monkeys
of the New World

Within the forests of the more tropical parts of Central and South America there live a great many varieties of monkeys. Together they are known as *Ceboidea* or *Platyrrhini*, a term that refers to broad fleshy noses within which the nostrils are widely separated and may be located at

---

[3] F. W. Jones, *Hallmarks of Mankind*, Baltimore, 1948, p. 33.

the sides so that they open outward to left and right, instead of downward. These monkeys, together with Old World monkeys, apes, and men, comprise the Primate subdivision of *Anthropoidea.*

Ceboidea have been in existence since Oligocene days, and while their ancestry is unclear, it is thought that they are related to the tarsiers. They are divided into two families, one of which is restricted to the little monkeys commonly called *marmosets.* As a rule these are considered to be the least highly evolved of the New World monkeys. Except for marmosets, the Platyrrhini belong to the *Cebidae* family, of whom the best known are the *cebus* (organ-grinder), *howler,* and *spider monkeys.* As a group they are bigger than tarsiers, and they have larger and more convoluted brains, with considerable space devoted to the sense of sight. Their eyes are set in completely frontal positions within reduced sockets with bony back walls; their tear ducts are entirely contained in the eye cavities; and they have overlapping, stereoscopic vision, capable of discerning depth as well as height and width. In addition, the Cebidae have flat-nailed digits without disklike pads; opposable great toes and thumbs; and legs and feet well suited for climbing and jumping but not specialized for hopping on both feet. They are most active by day instead of at night.

The better nervous organization of all the Anthropoidea is reflected in the growing independence of the hands, which can be directed to carry out certain tasks that are different from those assigned to the feet. Thus the hands and front limbs only, aided by the eyes, are used to grasp moving objects, such as insects.

When they proceed along the boughs of trees, Western monkeys sometimes go on all fours, but occasionally they swing from branch to branch, using their hands, arms and shoulder girdles in the manner of gymnasts performing on rings or trapezes. This method of progression, in which the body is carried upright by the forelimbs, is termed *brachiating,* and is best developed in the Cebidae division of the Platyrrhini by the spider monkeys, who are sometimes regarded as typifying the most highly evolved monkeys in the Western World. They have slender bodies, long and narrow heads, chests that are not rounded but flattened from front to back, arms that greatly exceed the legs in length, and well-knit collar bones and shoulder girdles. Spider monkeys have no restricted breeding season, and females menstruate regularly for 72 hours or more every 24 to 27 days.

Perhaps in conjunction with their brachiating habits, their thumbs are reduced to mere vestiges. Another spider monkey specialty is the prehensile tail. True, such tails are common among the Cebidae, even if they are not universal, but in the spider monkeys they are extra-

FIG. 4-7. American spider monkey. Use of the long, powerful, prehensile tail as an extra limb and hand is well illustrated. Spider monkeys belong to the platyrrhine subdivision. (Courtesy of New York Zoological Society.)

ordinary. They are nearly twice as long as the body, sturdy enough to hold the animal suspended (Fig. 4–7) yet so sensitive that the tail can make feeling and exploratory movements and can grasp food and bring it to the mouth.

All in all the Platyrrhini, especially the large division of Cebidae, make up the highest forms of Primates to have evolved in the Western Hemisphere. It is believed that the Platyrrhini became separated in Eocene or Oligocene days from the stem that later produced the main body of anthropoids. They are much further advanced than the tarsiers who preceded them in geological time, yet they are far removed from apes and man. For reasons that are not yet understood, evolution failed to go beyond the Platyrrhini in the New World, and it was not until members of *Homo sapiens* penetrated this continent from Asia that higher Primates became known to any of the Americas.

OLD WORLD MONKEYS

Somewhat more highly evolved and often larger than the monkeys of the New World are their Old World relatives who, together with apes

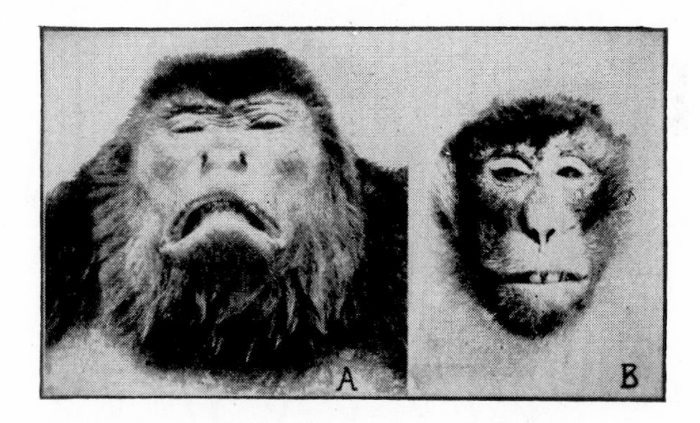

FIG. 4-8. New and Old World monkeys. A. Howler monkey. This is an American platyrrhine type with widely spaced, laterally directed nostrils. Its swollen appearance is caused by its prodigious sound mechanism, from which it gets its name. B. A catarrhine (Macaque) monkey from the Old World. It has narrowly spaced nostrils that open downward. This configuration approaches man's much more nearly than does the platyrrhine nasal structure. (A. H. Schultz, "Man as a Primate," *The Scientific Monthly,* 1931.)

and humans, are called the *Cercopithecoidea* or *Catarrhini*. The latter term refers to a narrow nose in which the nostrils are close together, centrally located, and pointed downward (Fig. 4–8). Exactly how they are related to the monkeys of the New World is not known, but specialists distinguish many catarrhine varieties, among the best known of which are *baboons, mandrills,* and *macaques* or *rhesus* monkeys, which are widely used in medical laboratories. All of them are sufficiently alike to be grouped, for our purposes, into a single family. Members of this group are the first to have the identical dental formula of man. Customarily, it is written

$$\begin{matrix} I & C & PM & M \\ \frac{2}{2} & \frac{1}{1} & \frac{2}{2} & \frac{3}{3} \end{matrix}$$

which means that from front to back there are in each side of the upper and lower jaws two incisors, one canine, two premolars, and three molars, including the wisdom teeth, making a total of thirty-two (Fig. 4–9).

Most of the Catarrhini also anticipate human characteristics because they are active by day and sleep at night and because they have relatively large brains, completely stereoscopic vision, thoroughly differ-

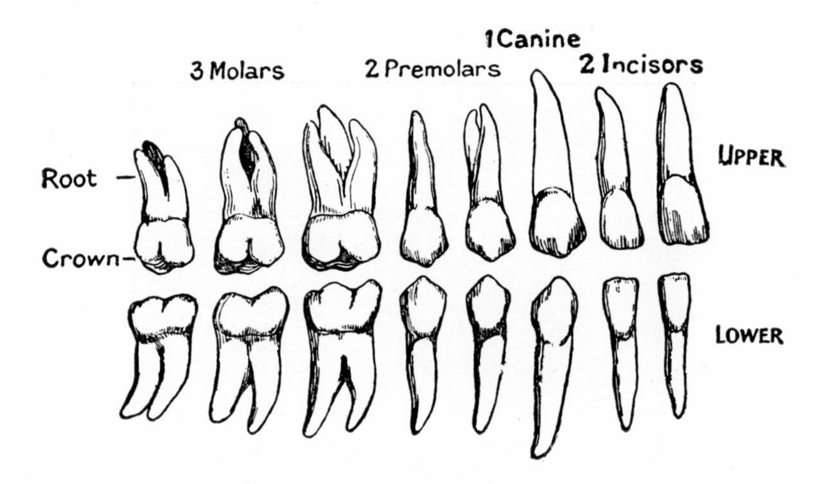

FIG. 4-9. Dental formula of man. The same kinds and numbers of teeth are found in the jaws of all higher Primates, from catarrhine monkeys to *Homo sapiens.* No other animals have this combination.

entiated front and hind limbs, flat nails on all the digits, and a breeding system that very nearly approaches man's in that it is not limited to one season of the year. They differ from man in that nearly all of them are arboreal, and many of them have cheek pouches for the temporary storage of food. Also common are hard, calloused areas (*ischial callosities*) on the buttocks; tails that may be short or long but are never prehensile; and in some species patches of skin on the buttocks that may periodically become vividly colored, particularly in females.

Of all the catarrhine monkeys of the Eastern Hemisphere, baboons and mandrills are the most unusual because they have forsaken the trees and adapted themselves to life on the ground. Although they go on all fours, they still have opposable great toes and thumbs (Fig. 4–10), and they often sit up and use their hands when feeding. Their facial areas project as snouts in a fashion that gives them a kind of doglike appearance, and they have sharp, powerful canines that protrude beyond the limits of the other teeth. All the same, with the exception of a few structural peculiarities thought to be connected with their quadrupedal pos-

FIG. 4-10. Hamadryas baboon. The raised front left leg shows the separated and opposable thumb that this animal has retained in spite of its quadrupedal posture and its life on the ground. It is sometimes held that terrestrial life has given baboons a doglike muzzle. As is true of all Old World monkeys, the tail is not prehensile. (Courtesy of the New York Zoological Society.)

ture on the ground, baboons and mandrills have bodies typical of Old World monkeys.

The ancestry of the Catarrhini may be tentatively traced back to the early Oligocene period because a level of soil of that date from the Fayum basin near Cairo, Egypt, has yielded a lower jawbone and a few teeth, which some scientists regard as the oldest known remains of a catarrhine monkey. This fossil specimen has been named *Parapithecus*.[4]

Its small size suggests that the original cercopiths were considerably smaller than their present-day descendants, but its relationship to later Primates is an open question. Even if we admit that analysis of a single, fragmentary specimen may not provide convincing evidence, the discovery of Parapithecus has demonstrated the possibility that as far back as the early Oligocene the Catarrhini had already branched off from their ancestors in a direction different from that taken by the Platyrrhini.

SUMMARY OF LESSER PRIMATES

As early as 1758, the great Swedish naturalist and taxonomist, Linnaeus, gave the name "Primate" to the order of Eutherian mammals that includes lemurs, tarsiers, monkeys, apes, and men. Only a few positive traits of anatomy characterize the Primates but, taking the order as a whole, these include opposable thumbs and great toes, flexible but strong five-digited hands and feet, flat nails on the digits, breasts located on the chest, bony eye sockets, keen (generally stereoscopic and color) vision, large and wrinkled brains with decreasing emphasis on smell, well-differentiated front and hind limbs, excellent coordination between hands and eyes, and a tendency toward an omnivorous diet, including a variety of proteins. By nearly every test of biology, man is a Primate; yet he is sufficiently different to make it evident that he belongs to a separate category.

There are several suborders of Primates, the lowliest of which is that of the Prosimii, which contains tree shrews, lemurs, and tarsiers. All three groups are thought to have emerged in the Paleocene, at the start of the Cenozoic era, and their great diversity bears witness to a period of intense evolutionary activity. They seem once to have roamed far and wide throughout both hemispheres, but in our day their range is restricted to a few spots in the Old World.

When they first appeared, the lesser Primates probably resembled some of the modern tree shrews, although it must be realized that none of the living prosimians and monkeys is ancestral to any of the present-day creatures to which it is thought to be related. The earliest Primates were probably alert, active, and agile little animals that lived in the tops

---

[4] The man who found Parapithecus has described and analyzed his discovery in M. Schlosser, "Beiträge zur Kenntniss der oligozänen Landsäugtiere aus dem Fayum," *Beiträge zur Paläontologie und Geologie Oesterreich-Ungarns,* Vol. XXIV, 1911.

of trees and depended on the sense of smell somewhat less than did their predecessors.

When we arrive at the Oligocene epoch, we find that natural selection and evolution have gone beyond the prosimians in the direction of man, and have produced a monkey known as Parapithecus. There is still much dispute about the proper identification and placement of Parapithecus, since so little of him has survived, but the best guess is that he was a little, four-footed, catarrhine monkey, who differed from his New World platyrrhine relatives.

Monkeys, especially those of the Old World, are so much closer to human configurations that most authorities link them with apes and men in the suborder of Anthropoidea. Today it is generally recognized that there is a large gulf between man and monkey, but that *Homo sapiens* shows many close resemblances to various apes. It is for this reason that monkeys and prosimians are treated together in this chapter as lesser Primates, while the apes are reserved for later treatment.

Selected References

Clark, W. E. LeGros, *History of the Primates,* rev. ed., London, 1950.
———, *The Antecedents of Man,* Chicago, 1960.
Gregory, William K., "On the Classification and Phylogeny of the Lemuroidea," *American Geological Society Bulletin,* Vol. XXVI, 1915.
Howells, William W., *Mankind So Far,* New York, 1944.
———, *Mankind in the Making,* New York, 1959.
Jones, F. Wood, *Man's Place Among the Mammals,* New York, 1929.
Mayr, Ernst, *Systematics and the Origin of Species,* New York, 1942.
Schultz, Adolph H., "Primatology in its Relation to Anthropology," in W. L. Thomas, Jr., ed., *Yearbook of Anthropology,* New York, 1955.
Simpson, George G., "Studies on the Earliest Primates," *American Museum of Natural History Bulletin,* Vol. LXXVII, 1940.
Straus, William L., Jr., "Primates," in A. L. Kroeber, ed., *Anthropology Today,* Chicago, 1953.

Apes, Man-Apes, and Man

CHAPTER 5

LESSONS FROM THE FOSSIL APES

The outburst of evolutionary activity that we noted during the early stages of the Cenozoic did not end with the emergence of monkeys. Indeed, there is reason to believe that apes also came on the scene at about this time, for the same Oligocene layer of earth in Egypt's Fayum basin that produced the fragments of Parapithecus has also yielded the remains of a fossil ape that glories in the name of *Propliopithecus.* By the next epoch, the Miocene, so many forms of extinct apes abounded that it is impossible to tell which were directly ancestral to man and which were not. But dubious as they may be with respect to human origins, the remnants of ancient apes indicate at least two lines of future development; for one branch points in the direction of modern gibbons, smallest by far of the living apes; and the other line seems to lead in the general direction of the large-sized apes.

Propliopithecus, known from two lower jaws and some teeth, is generally considered to be a forerunner or ancestor of two other gibbon-like fossils. One of these, called *Limnopithecus,* belongs to the early Miocene of East Africa; and the other, *Pliopithecus,* originally came from a later Miocene deposit in Europe. Some experts believe that a type like Limnopithecus may have given rise to forms like Pliopithecus, which they claim existed in Asia as well as in Europe. In its turn, Pliopithecus in Asia is thought to indicate how the ancestors of the gibbons of our day were probably constructed. There is thus established a tentative line running from Propliopithecus to Limnopithecus, and from Limnopithecus to Pliopithecus and the modern gibbon. And the start of this ape line seems to take off from quadrupedal, presumably monkeylike creatures that resembled Parapithecus.

The branch that culminated in the large apes of our own day may well have begun with creatures like the fossil known as *Proconsul.* The bones of Proconsul were discovered in Early Miocene soil layers of east Africa by L. S. B. Leakey and his wife. Proconsul represents a genus, with three species that range in size and appearance from what looks like a pygmy chimpanzee to a very large gorilla. Its dentition approximates those of the big apes, but in various ways it suggests connections with cercopith monkeys on the one hand, and with hominids on the other. It had neither big bony ridges over the eyes, nor a *simian shelf* (see Fig. 5–1).[1] Most commonly Proconsul is grouped with other large Miocene apes, as an unspecialized forerunner of the specimens sometimes called *Dryopithecus-Sivapithecus.* Dryopithecus is the common name for such a variety of fossil apes that specialists group them into many genera and species. Dryopithecus is best known for the cusp arrangement of its molars. These cusps come in sets of three and two, with a Y-shaped fissure between them. The Dryopithecus pattern, or a variant thereof, is found in the big apes and man, but appears most prominently in chimpanzees and gorillas. In Miocene days, Dryopithecus animals wandered widely throughout the Old World, including the European continent, which has never been inhabited by extant apes; but Sivapithecus is known only from specimens obtained in the Siwalik Hills of India.

We come now to the heart of the matter. Why should an anthropologist study fossil apes? Primarily because it is assumed that the ape and human lines began to diverge in the Miocene or earlier. Thereafter each went its own way, with the consequence that the living apes developed specialties far different from those of *Homo sapiens.* Accordingly, none of the present-day apes is an ancestor of man; and if we want to know something about mankind's ancestry from the beginning we must examine the fossil apes.

From our inspection several facts emerge. Even though the *pongid* (ape) and hominid lines are thought to have become separated by Miocene times at least, each group retained enough features from their

[1] A simian shelf is a transverse outgrowth of bone, located at the inner center of the lower jaw, "opposite" where the chin is located in *Homo sapiens.* It is regularly found in apes, but does not occur in the human mandible. In March 1962, Leakey announced the discovery of jaw and teeth fragments that may pertain to a presumed common ancestor of apes and men. The finds were made in Kenya, East Africa, and Leakey thinks the remains may be 14 million years old, of Pliocene date. He named his discovery *Kenyapithecus wickeri.* It is not a hominid, and Leakey places it between Proconsul and Zinjanthropus.

common ancestors to show that they were once closely related. However, since only fragments of fossil ape bones come to light, and then but seldom, we are forced to get at many additional aspects of anatomy and behavior by observations made on our distant cousins, the surviving apes.

It is from the study of fossil apes that we hope ultimately to get answers to such puzzling questions as the problems of brachiation and upright posture among man's forerunners. *Homo sapiens* does not brachiate; did his ancestors? Moreover, of all the Primates, only man and a few other varieties, such as baboons and mandrills, customarily live on the ground. Hence, the question arises, were man's forebears arboreal or terrestrial? There are some who claim that those portions of man's body that seem adapted to brachiation in trees result from the fact that the ancestors of *Homo sapiens* were partial brachiators at least; whereas others point out that even terrestrial quadrupeds, when in tall grass, occasionally rear up and so become temporarily bipedal.

Then, further, as we study the ancient records we cannot fail to note that the fossil apes came in several genera and assorted sizes. Propliopithecus and his fellows were small, but the series from Proconsul to Dryopithecus-Sivapithecus was larger. This size division has persisted into later times. Modern gibbons are small, but other apes are big and, as we shall see later on, some hominids are pygmies, most are of average size, and a few extinct types appear to have been large. What is true of apes and humans is equally true of many other creatures. So many animals have appeared in various shapes and sizes that one can only conclude that natural selection has played the field in this regard, at least, and did not consistently favor one size and build over all others. Man appears to have been *polytypic* (of many types) rather than *monotypic* (of one type) from the start, and it should not be surprising that today *Homo sapiens* is greatly varied.

MEET THE LIVING APES

Laymen regularly confuse monkeys with apes, but students of anthropology must learn to tell them apart. With few exceptions, apes are larger than monkeys, have bigger and more wrinkled brains, show much more of a tendency to carry the body upright from time to time, and are completely devoid of external tails. Apes and hominids so closely resemble each other in numerous anatomical details that they are generally classed together in the superfamily, *Hominoidea*.

Although all of the apes may be known as pongids, a way is usually found to separate the large forms, terminologically, from the small gibbons. Another manner of grouping the four varieties of living apes is to divide them on the basis of the closeness of their ties to tree life; but the most common division is based on geographical range, for gibbons and orangutans inhabit portions of southeast Asia, whereas chimpanzees and gorillas live in a zone that extends across a good part of central Africa. This geographic arrangement has an additional advantage since, on the whole, the apes from Asia are somewhat further from modern human configurations and those from Africa more nearly resemble ourselves.

According to W. W. Howells, the basic adaptation of the Hominoidea, carrying the body upright, is part of a general Primate trend. He notes that monkeys sit rather erect when they are not on the move, and that the apes are typically upright at all times, except when they take to the ground. Coupled with the habit of carrying the body erect, in Howells' opinion, is the manner in which the internal organs are arranged. In pongids and hominids the arrangement is much alike, but it is vastly different in monkeys that go about on all fours.[2]

The brachiating gibbon

Of the four groups of extant apes, the gibbons are thought to be furthest removed from modern man. Most gibbons belong to the Hylobates genus, of which several species are to be found in the dense forests of southeastern Asia. Rarely do they exceed 3 feet in height, and adults of either sex commonly weigh about 20 pounds. Ischial callosities, not unlike those of Old World monkeys, are frequently found on the buttocks, but gibbons do not have such cercopith traits as external tails or cheek pouches. Their heads show low foreheads and large oval eye sockets with thick rims of bone, and their jaws protrude and contain jutting canine teeth that interlock, instead of meeting edge to edge, at the corners of the mouth. All apes with interlocking canines must have spaces, known as *diastemas,* on the jaws to accommodate the projecting teeth (Fig. 5–1). So closely are these two features related, that if a jawbone is found with a diastema it is assumed that its owner had projecting canines.

The cranial capacity, a term that denotes the size of the skull chamber in which the brain is lodged,[3] is limited in gibbons to 90 cubic centi-

---

[2] W. W. Howells, *Mankind in the Making,* New York, 1959, p. 75.

[3] To get an approximate measure of the amount of brain that any vertebrate has, anthropologists fill the hollow cranial vault of a skull with a free-flowing material, usually mustard seed, and pour the contents of the vault into a measuring glass or graduate. The resultant reading, expressed in cubic centimeters, is known as the cranial capacity and provides a convenient measure of gross brain size.

meters, a figure greatly below that of the big apes and man, but far in excess of the average for most monkeys.

Nothing is more characteristic of gibbons than their enormous and exceedingly elongated arms (Fig. 5–2), which are more than twice as long as the body. Figuratively speaking, a gibbon can pick a dime from the floor without stooping. The greater part of this excessive length is in the forearms rather than the hands and may be related to the gibbons' brachiating habits. A light, slender body, coupled with powerful

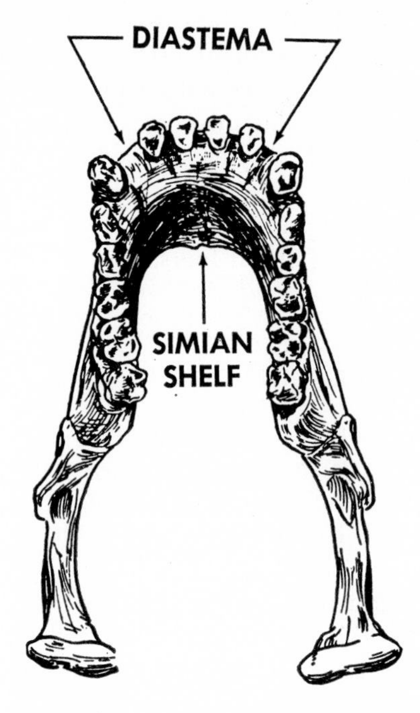

FIG. 5-1. Two features of an ape's mandible. Inside a typical ape's lower jaw there is found, "opposite" where the chin would be, a bony plate called a simian shelf. Moreover, there is a space (diastema) between the incisors and the canine tooth, presumably for the accommodation of an interlocking or projecting canine.

arms that culminate in long-fingered hands with short thumbs, seems to be especially well-suited for brachiation. With the greatest of ease and nonchalance a gibbon moves among the trees with a free-swinging, pendulum motion, rapidly shifting its hold from one hand to another. Distances of many feet are readily covered with each graceful swing by young and old; and mothers with infants clinging to them do not hesitate to make prodigious leaps. Such skill in brachiating and hurtling through space implies that gibbons must have excellent eyesight, acute judgment of distance, accurate and instantaneous perceptions of depth and size, extraordinary coordination of hand and eye, splendid motor controls, and fast reaction speeds. All this requires adequate representation in the brain.

Gibbons are so well adjusted to an arboreal environment that they

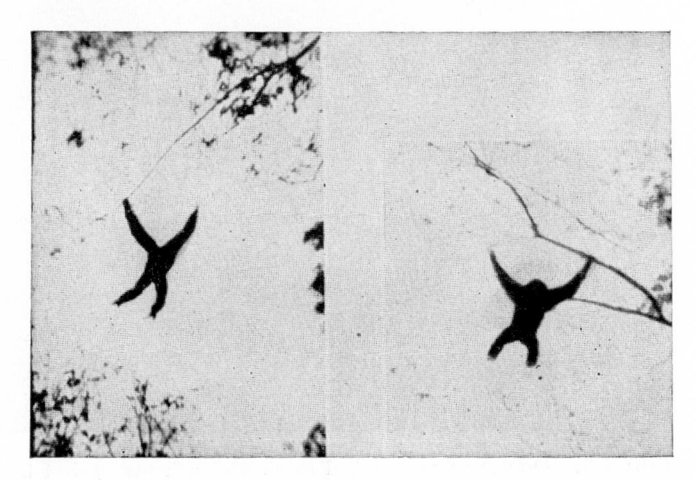

FIG. 5-2. Gibbons in action. Above: Note the easy swing and prehensile hands and feet. (Courtesy of the New York Zoological Society.) Below: Brachiating in the wild. Powerful long arms contrast with very short legs and feet. (Courtesy of the editor of *Comparative Psychological Monographs*.)

seldom descend to earth, but in the course of their daily wanderings in search of food they occasionally find it necessary to walk or run over open ground. At such times they rise up on their hind legs, keeping their bodies vertical, and getting their big arms out of the way by lifting them above their heads or holding them out at the sides.

THE DELIBERATE ORANGUTAN

Orangutans inhabit portions of Sumatra and Borneo off the coast of southeastern Asia (Fig. 5–3). They stand nearly 5 feet high and adult

FIG. 5-3. Orangutan mother and child. Although possessed of long and powerful arms, the adult orangutan is too bulky to leap across wide stretches of open space. As the illustration shows, it has a strong, prehensile grip and rotating forearms, and uses its feet in the same manner as the hands. (Courtesy of Zoological Society of Philadelphia.)

males weigh from 165 to 200 pounds. In brain size, too, they show a great advance over the gibbons, for their cranial capacities may reach up to 400 cubic centimeters. Big and bulky though they are, the orangutans are still arboreal, but they are by no means such expert and graceful brachiators as gibbons. They move cautiously and ponderously through the trees, and although they sometimes swing by the hands and arms, they never attempt to leap across wide stretches of open space. Their arms are long and strong, but less elongated than the gibbons'. To use another figure of speech, an orangutan can tie its shoes laces without bending over.

When they are compared to the size and strength of the forelimbs, the legs and feet of an orangutan are singularly small and weak; the feet are long and narrow; the great toes are stunted, devoid of nails, and held at right angles to the main axis of the foot; the toes are perpetually curved and bent so that they cannot be straightened out; and the heel is poorly developed. Such feet resemble hands in structure and are ill-suited for supporting the weight of a heavy creature. Consequently, it is not surprising that orangutans do not walk upright when they come to earth. Instead, they either go on all fours or rest their knuckles on the ground and swing their bodies between hands and arms, as if on crutches. Neither method seems to be comfortable, and orangutans prefer to remain aloft.

Orangutans, or Simia, tend to have dark brown skins and extensive coverings of long, reddish hair. The eye orbits are large and set closely together, and above them occurs a fairly prominent brow ridge of bone (*supraorbital torus*). The tooth-bearing portion of the upper jaw juts forward (*alveolar prognathism*), all the front teeth are large, and the lower jaw is massive but chinless. Like gibbons, orangutans are not thought to be very close to the line of human evolution, and their specialties are considered to have been acquired after the divergence of the hominid and pongid lines. In one particular or another the Asiatic apes may make a close approximation to man, but on the whole the differences outweigh the resemblances.

CHIMPANZEES FROM AFRICA

Because they can be more readily raised and trained in captivity, and because they are more frequently exhibited in public than other apes, it is popularly believed that chimpanzees are nearly human. Such a judgment is only partially confirmed by primatologists, and it would be an error to accept it uncritically. Under natural conditions, chimpanzees reside only in those parts of equatorial Africa that are drained by the Congo and Niger rivers. They are divided into several species, all of which are of the genus Pan. Bodily proportions approximate those of man, with full-grown males standing just over 5 feet high and weighing around 110 pounds. As a group chimpanzees have round, low-vaulted heads, and their cranial capacities average about 400 cubic centimeters. With the approach of adolescence, a male develops a solid, transverse

FIG. 5-4. Chimpanzee in walking posture. This animal's hind limbs and feet are poorly adapted for walking upright or for supporting the body in an orthograde position. The great toe is opposable, the arch of the foot is low, and the heel is rudimentary. Much weight, when the animal walks, is placed on the elongated front limbs, which rest on their knuckles. The opposable thumb is high on the hand. Compare with Fig. 5-5, lower picture. (Courtesy of Peabody Museum, Harvard University.)

supraorbital torus, and his big chinless jaws bulge forward. The front teeth are big and strong, with interlocking canines, but the back teeth are apt to look quite human.

Chimpanzees are fine climbers and expert brachiators. They swing easily from one limb to another, but observers have noticed that they never travel for long distances without resorting to the ground for part of the way. This is somewhat unexpected, because they have long, narrow, prehensile feet, with massive but opposable great toes, rudimentary heels, and partially webbed outer toes. Ordinarily, a grounded chimpanzee uses the crutchlike stance of the orangutan and has an ungainly, waddling, sidewise gait (Fig. 5–4); but under special conditions, as when the ground is wet or cold, a chimpanzee may walk erect for a few paces.

Manlike gorillas[4]

Largest by far of all the Primates is the African ape genus of Gorilla (Fig. 5–5). These beasts may grow to prodigious sizes, with adult males standing up to 70 inches high and weighing from 300 to as much as 600 pounds. Although gorillas comprise only a single genus, two major types are customarily distinguished. One is a lowland group that inhabits the Cameroon district, and the other is the mountain gorilla that lives in what was the Belgian Congo. Particularly noteworthy among full-grown males is a massive skull, with a great bony *sagittal* crest on top running from front to back, and an enormous supraorbital torus of solid bone that goes from left to right above the eye openings. Cranial capacities go to 500 cubic centimeters, but may run a little higher in exceptional cases. This is the greatest amount reported for any of the living apes, but it is surprisingly little in relation to the overall size of the skull. Most of the big cranium consists of thick, solid bone, and there is comparatively little hollow space to contain a brain. Truly may the gorilla be described as a big bonehead!

Heavy though they are, gorillas spend much time in trees and are good swingers and climbers. When they come to the ground, as they apparently do more frequently than other apes, they have a tendency to stand erect from time to time. They have even been observed to take a few strides forward, placing the feet flat on the ground and moving ahead in a fairly straight line. On such occasions the knees are flexed and the hands dangle at the sides. As is true of the other big apes, gorillas have proportionately long forearms, but in their case the fingertips come only to the knees when the animal is standing. They have short,

---

[4] Not much is known of gorilla behavior in the wild. The scientific world is eagerly awaiting the findings of a small group of workers who have, for a long time, been observing gorillas in their natural habitats in Africa. Niels Bolwig, John T. Emlen, and George B. Schaller are variously engaged on the project. More information is available in R. A. Dart, "The Kisoro Pattern of Mountain Gorilla Preservation," *Current Anthropology*, Vol. 2, 1961, pp. 510–11.

but thick, stumpy legs; broad, short feet that are proportioned somewhat like man's; great toes that are massive but shorter than those of the chimpanzee; and a heel that projects backward and is fairly well developed to help support the body in an upright position. Webs of skin may reach to the middle joints of the lesser toes, and the big toe is opposable to the others. This suggests that the foot is a prehensile rather than a supporting organ, yet it is said to be only infrequently used for lifting

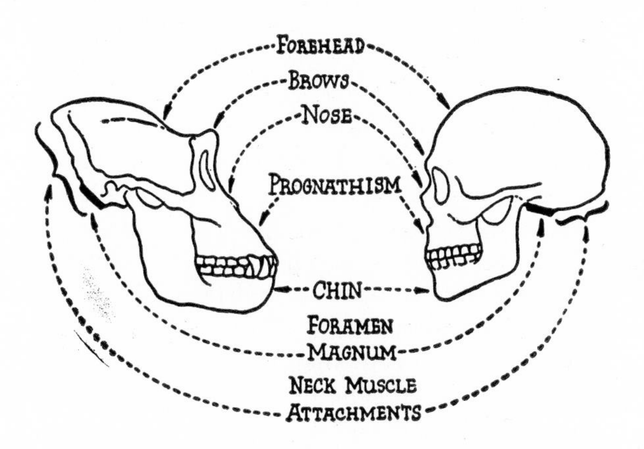

FIG. 5-6. Comparison of a gorilla's and a human skull. Many essential distinctions are plainly indicated. (W. W. Howells, *Mankind So Far*, New York, 1944. Courtesy of Doubleday & Company, Inc.)

or carrying things. The hands are readily differentiated from the feet and their proportions are not too unlike the human.

Among the least humanoid of gorilla features are the face and jaws. The latter are particularly massive in adult males, forward protruding, and devoid of chin. The huge jaws contain formidable incisors, great tusklike, projecting, and interlocking canines that call for a diastema, and molars that are large but of manlike shape. The nose is long, and is narrow at the root but broad at the nostrils. It is not elevated above the rest of the facial plane and the nasal bones that underlie the fleshy parts are flat and low (see Fig. 5–6).

FIG. 5-5. Two gorillas. Above: Gorilla in sitting position. The huge supraorbital torus and low forehead are plainly revealed. Although the feet can be differentiated from the hands, their prehensile structure is noteworthy. Below: A grounded gorilla. The quadrupedal stance of a walking gorilla resembles that of a chimpanzee. (Above: Courtesy of New York Zoological Society. Below: Courtesy of Newton W. Hartman and Zoological Society of Philadelphia.)

THE TROUBLESOME MAN-APES OF AFRICA

Within the last three or four decades, Africa has been the focus of a vexing evolutionary problem of world-wide significance. It stems from the rapid-fire discovery of a great number of man-ape fossils, scientifically known, when they are grouped together, as the *Australopithecinae* ("Southern Apes").[5]

The story begins in 1925 at Taungs, now spelled without an "s," in Bechuanaland, where Raymond Dart came across the remains of a skull that he called *Australopithecus africanus*.[6] It pertained to a youngster, facetiously named "Dart's baby," about 6 years old at the time of its death, with some of its milk teeth and its first molars intact. The "Taungs skull" was apelike in most ways, but the teeth were remarkably human except for their large size. Then, in 1936, Robert Broom collected the relics of several adults that had been blasted out of a cave at Sterkfontein.[7] These were named *Plesianthropus* (Fig. 5–7), and again they proved to have a combination of apelike and manlike characteristics. The year 1938 brought to light, at Komdraai, portions of skeletons from an adult male and a 3- or 4-year-old baby. They were labeled *Paranthropus* and once more disclosed a previously unsuspected assortment of human and simian aspects. Many experts now consider the Paranthropus specimens to be somewhat older than other Australopithecinae, and to reflect habituation to a different environment.

In 1947 Broom was back at Sterkfontein in time to discover more parts of Plesianthropus individuals who were of varying age and both sexes. At about the same time his colleague, Dart, came across a new type of fossil that he called *Australopithecus prometheus*, because he believed it to be associated with the use of fire. Not everyone is in accord with Dart, but he is of the opinion that *Australopithecus prometheus* was a small, upright-walking creature, capable not only of utilizing fire,[8] but also of hunting game, smashing skulls, and splitting bones.

Many additional discoveries have been made in Africa between

---

[5] L. S. B. Leakey, a very prominent anthropologist from Nairobi, Africa, and much concerned with Australopithecine discoveries, prefers the term, "near-men."

[6] R. A. Dart, "Taungs and Its Significance," *Natural History*, Vol. 26, 1926, pp. 315–27.

[7] Since the retirement of Dart and the death of Broom, their work has been carried on by such men as J. T. Robinson, C. K. Brain, and others. One of the foremost authorities on the tools that the Australopithecines might have used is Van Riet Lowe.

[8] The association of *Australopithecus prometheus* with deliberately made fires has recently been seriously questioned.

1948 and the present, and while no two are identical, the most extraordinary ones probably pertain to *Paranthropus crassidens* and *Paranthropus robustus.* The former, first found at Swartkrans, may be described as very large, and with a good number of hominid features in the jaw and teeth. He probably walked in fairly erect fashion, yet there

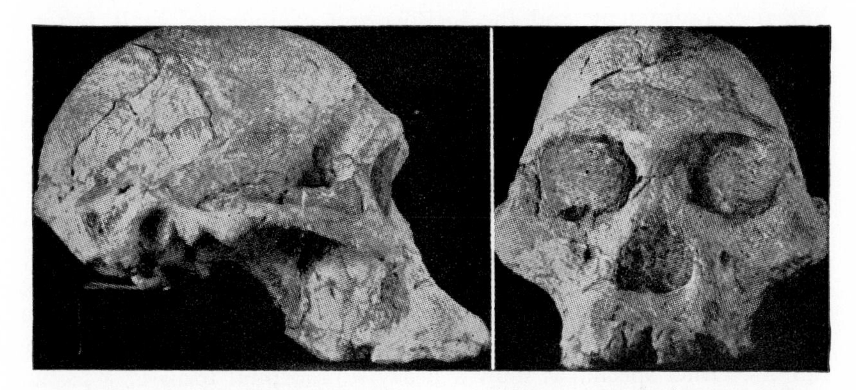

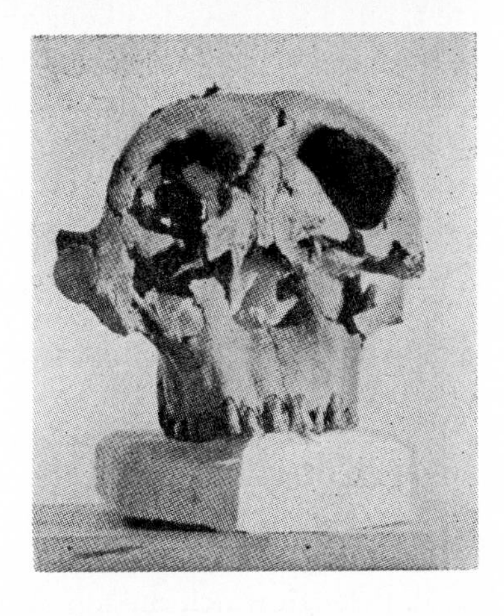

FIG. 5-7. Man-ape specimens. Top: Plesianthropus. It looks hominid, especially from the front; but it has a big supraorbital torus, an exceedingly projecting jaw, low-lying nasal bones, and a diastema in the upper jaw. Bottom: Zinjanthropus, reputedly a very early Australopithecine. It has extremely flaring cheekbones, strange low nasal bones, a markedly low forehead and cranial vault, and a small sagittal crest. (Top: from M. F. A. Montagu, *Introduction to Physical Anthropology*, rev. ed., Springfield, 1951. Courtesy of the author and Charles C Thomas, publisher. Bottom: Museum of Anthropology, the University of Michigan.)

are enough simian attributes in the skull, including a bony crest along the mid-line of the cranial vault,[9] to make the proper classification of this fossil a matter of grave uncertainty. Latest in the series is *Zinjanthropus boisei* found by Mrs. and Dr. L. S. B. Leakey on July 17,

[9] This feature is common among the large apes and is often cited as a simian characteristic of certain Australopithecinae. However, LeGros Clark warns that the sagittal crest is not a separate genetic trait, but part of a general skull configuration. He does not regard the crest as diagnostic for judging apish resemblances. He, and others, argue that the sagittal crest in the Australopithecinae is anatomically quite different from the formation commonly found on ape skulls.

1959, at the base of Olduvai Gorge in Tanganyika (see Fig. 5–7).[10] This fossil, too, has a sagittal crest on top of the skull and is reminiscent of Paranthropus. Thus, it belongs to the general category of Australopithecines, but Leakey thinks that Zinjanthropus represents the earliest hominid yet found in South Africa. The teeth are set in a perfectly human arrangement, and the incisors and canines are small, but the premolars are large and the molars are about twice as big as in modern man.

The discoveries of the numerous and astoundingly diversified Australopithecinae have posed many baffling problems for students of human origins. It will take years of hard work before experts will be in a position to make reasonably acceptable hypotheses of the proper placement of these assorted fossils in the animal kingdom. Some authorities feel that all the Australopithecinae are variants of one genus, but Broom maintains that they represent several distinct types. Some forms have chinless jaws but human dentition, with no indication of projecting canines. Other specimens show a heavy supraorbital torus or a sagittal crest, but a few have less bone above the eye openings than modern man. It is no wonder that the experts are puzzled when it comes to classifying the material from Africa. Taken as a whole, though, the Australopithecinae have slanting foreheads and low cranial vaults. Their faces protrude and help give the skulls a generally apelike appearance, although the shape of the skull and, perhaps, the shape of the brain are more human than apish. The lower jaw also tends to be massive and chinless, but there is no simian shelf. Furthermore, the dentition and dental arcade are usually hominid, and so too is most of the remaining skeletal structure.

Almost as soon as detailed accounts of the Australopithecinae began to appear in scientific journals it became likely that the creatures had used an upright posture. This deduction was based on the shape and location of the foramen magnum, the large opening at the base of the skull, through which the top of the spinal cord enters the head. Close inspection of the foramen magnum showed that the skull was well-balanced on the backbone, which implied good poise, a trait that generally accompanies upright posture. These scientific guesses were vindicated

---

[10] An account of this discovery is given in L. S. B. Leakey, "A New Fossil Skull from Olduvai," *Nature*, Vol. 184, 1959, pp. 491–93. More recently, Leakey has found several additional fragments that belong, presumably, to Zinjanthropus, and also some skeletal remains that appear to resemble Asiatic forms of very early man.

The Olduvai Gorge, where Zinjanthropus was found, contains the fossilized remnants of many animals of gigantic size. They include the bones of a pig that was as large as a contemporary rhinoceros.

when a number of Australopithecine hipbones (pelves) were found.[11] Their wide and rounded forms so nearly approached modern human configurations, especially those of African Bushmen, and differed so greatly from the narrow, cylindrical pelves of extant apes, that it is universally conceded that the man-apes ran or walked upright on their hind legs. Since there is no reason to believe that they had ever been accustomed to tree life, it is unlikely that they or their immediate ancestors were arboreal apes who had come to adopt an orthograde stance on the ground.

One of the key problems centering on the African man-apes relates to their use of tools. Almost as soon as they were discovered, most of them came to be associated with caves, in which were found numerous animal bones, including broken baboon skulls. Some of these were so fractured that it came to be maintained by some specialists that the Australopithecines used thigh bones (femurs) or arm bones (humeri) to crack open skulls from which brains could be extracted and presumably eaten. Others held, not always on good evidence, that it was an unsettled question whether the man-apes were hunters or victims. Dart is of the opinion that the Australopithecines used bones and teeth as tools, and that these materials comprised an *osteodontokeratic* industry that flourished before hominids consistently used stone for fashioning tools.[12] Then, beginning in 1957, an assemblage of pebble tools in Africa came to be linked with the man-apes; and it became customary to admit that Australopithecines could probably *use* tools, but it was widely held doubtful if they could *make* tools. Now Leakey has found crude stone tools associated with Zinjanthropus, and he is of the opinion that they could have been manufactured by man-apes. Several additional authorities believe, nowadays, that the Australopithecines were capable of making crude pebble tools.

The dates during which the Australopithecinae flourished are still unsettled, but they will have to be firmly established before the position of the man-apes with regard to later forms of man can be ascertained. If they prove to be of fairly recent date, it will have to be acknowledged that they cannot be regarded as direct ancestors of any of the more

[11] Various Australopithecine pelves have been found and described by several writers. One of the best accounts is given in R. Broom and J. T. Robinson, "Notes on the Pelves of the Fossil Ape-Men," *American Journal of Physical Anthropology,* Vol. 8, 1950, pp. 489–94. See also R. A. Dart, "Innominate Fragments of Australopithecus prometheus," *American Journal of Physical Anthropology,* Vol. 7, 1949, p. 301.

[12] Those interested in following up this topic should consult R. A. Dart, "The Bone Tool-Manufacturing Ability of Australopithecus prometheus," *American Anthropologist,* Vol. 62, 1960, pp. 134–43. See also R. A. Dart, *Adventures with the Missing Link,* New York, 1959, pp. 163–64, *et passim.* Abbé Breuil supports Dart's opinion.

modern varieties of man. Unfortunately, the shattered remains of the man-apes have frequently been found after blasting, or else as the result of some equally unscientific procedure. This helps to explain why there is so little consensus when it comes to dating the Australopithecines. In recent years it has often been demonstrated that the man-apes were associated with plants and animals of *Villafranchian* date. Villafranchian, it is widely agreed, belongs to the earliest phases of the Pleistocene, about one million years B.P., and that is where the Australopithecinae are often placed.[13]

Despite the great diversity of the African man-apes, and despite the dangers of lumping together young and adult specimens, males and females, it is possible to bring some order out of chaos by treating all the Australopithecinae as a unit. The suggestion has even been made that all of them were sufficiently hominid and sufficiently alike to warrant their grouping into a single taxonomic category, to be known as *Homo transvaalensis.* By way of a general summary, Broom[14] is of the opinion that it has been conclusively shown that there once existed in south Africa, and remained on the scene for many thousands of years, a family of higher Primates that were practically human. Although they had relatively small brains, he is certain that they moved about on their hind feet and that their hands were too delicate to have been used for walking on the ground. We thus have a picture of little Primates with protruding jaws and small-sized brains, going about in a fairly erect posture in Africa in very early Pleistocene times.

Turning to the problem of human origins, it is no longer necessary in the light of the African material to rely entirely on the older notion that man has derived his distinctive body from some arboreal, brachiating simian who may have grown too heavy for tree life and began walking upright on earth. Instead, the Australopithecinae give additional

[13] Leakey accepts a date, established by the still unperfected potassium-argon method of 1,750,000 years ago. This appears to be too early for any presumed hominid, and should not be uncritically accepted. See "More Time for Evolution," *Scientific American,* Vol. 205, No. 3, 1961, p. 86.

The date has been formally and seriously challenged in G. H. R. von Koenigswald, W. Gentner, and H. J. Lippolt, "Age of the Basalt Flow at Olduvai, East Africa," *Nature,* Vol. 192, 1961, pp. 720–21. The discussion is continued in a series of letters to the editor by Leakey, von Koenigswald, Curtis, and Evernden. See "Age of Basalt Underlying Bed 1, Olduvai," *Nature,* Vol. 194, 1962, pp. 610–12. The dispute is summarized in F. C. Howell, "Potassium-Argon Dating at Olduvai Gorge," *Current Anthropology,* Vol. 3, 1962, pp. 306–08.

Regardless of how this scientific controversy is finally settled, it seems likely that the start of the Pleistocene and, possibly, the beginnings of hominids will have to be dated much earlier than the conventional 600,000 to 1,000,000 years ago.

[14] R. Broom, "The Ape-Men," *Scientific American,* Vol. 181, No. 1, 1949, pp. 20–24.

support to the hypothesis that the human line may have begun veering away from the ape direction starting from some catarrhine, ground-walking, quadrupedal ancestral cercopith, such as Parapithecus, or fossil ape, such as Propliopithecus.[15] At the moment, it seems best to look upon the man-apes as representatives of a hominid branch that was moving slowly and incompletely in the direction of modern man, while elsewhere in the Old World some of their contemporaries were approaching and perhaps crossing the threshold of humanity.[16] It is not at all incredible to postulate that incomplete hominids could have existed at the same time as more complete forms of man.

THE GENUS HOMO EMERGES

In Pliocene times there lived a kind of animal—known only from lignite deposits in Tuscany, Italy—that is called *Oreopithecus.* When fragments of Oreopithecus were first found about a century ago, the remains were regarded as pertaining to a variety of Old World, cercopith monkey. More recently, the old finds were re-examined by Johannes Hürzeler. Taking these findings in conjunction with fresh discoveries, Hürzeler has come to the opinion that, chiefly on the basis of various features of the jaws and teeth, Oreopithecus was a primitive hominid. Even the few anthropologists who accept Hürzeler's views are likely to insist, however, that while Oreopithecus may show some manlike traits, he is not to be regarded as in the direct line of human ancestry.[17]

Not until Pleistocene times do we find abundant evidence of un-

---

[15] J. T. Robinson, "The Evolutionary Significance of the Australopithecines," in G. W. Lasker and J. L. Angel, eds., *Yearbook of Physical Anthropology,* New York, 1950, pp. 38–41.

[16] Most anthropologists, including Washburn, who deal with Africa disagree. They are inclined to view the Australopithecines as being in the direct line of human ancestry. There is a growing body of evidence that tends to relate the Australopithecinae with early forms of Asiatic hominids who are considered to represent forerunners of *Homo sapiens.*

[17] In the period between 1956 and 1958 nearly a complete skeleton of Oreopithecus was found. Hürzeler thinks that the animal was about 4½ feet high, and that it is between ten and eleven million years old. Dr. Hürzeler is reported to believe that it resembled neither modern man nor the modern apes, but that it may represent the common ancestor of both lines. Who its own progenitors may have been is not known. Further details may be found in W. L. Straus, Jr., and M. A. Schön, "Cranial Capacity of Oreopithecus bambolli," *Science,* Vol. 132, 1960, pp. 670–72. The authors set the cranial capacity of Oreopithecus at a minimum of 276 and a maximum of 529 cubic centimeters. These figures place it well within the company of the manlike apes, and remind us again that man's large brain is a recent phenomenon.

doubted mannish forms, some of which may be directly ancestral to *Homo sapiens.* W. E. LeGros Clark has provided a checklist of traits that separate pongids from hominids.[18] Among other things, he notes that hominids go about in an upright posture and have legs that are long with relation to the length of the trunk, whereas pongids do not go about at all times in a bipedal position and it is their arms that are long,

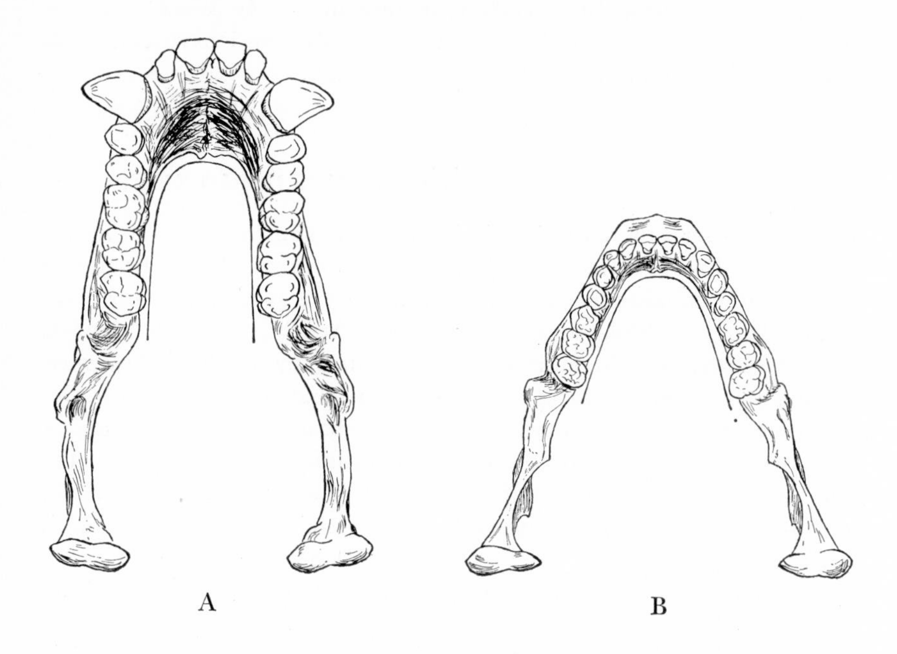

FIG. 5-8. Dental arcades. There is a noteworthy contrast between an ape's and a human mandible, particularly with respect to the dental arcades. An ape (A) tends to have a long, narrow, U-shaped configuration, whereas a man (B) is likely to have a short, broad, parabolic formation. The latter splays out at the rear, presumably for attachment to a big brain case.

relative to the trunk. Furthermore, pongids have interlocking canines, wide incisors, and back teeth all set in nearly parallel rows, whereas hominids do not have overlapping canines, possess small incisors, and have their teeth set in a more rounded arcade (Fig. 5-8).

For all that has been written on the subject, no one really knows precisely how or when the immediate ancestors of *Homo sapiens* ac-

[18] W. E. LeGros Clark, *The Fossil Evidence for Human Evolution,* Chicago, 1955, pp. 13 ff.

quired their most distinctive body traits. Most often it is assumed, despite the evidence of the Australopithecinae, that the process was set into action while big, basically quadrupedal Primates were forsaking tree or forest life and were changing to terrestrial bipeds who could get along on open ground.

If such assumed prehominids were to succeed in the habit of going upright it is apparent that their feet would have had to be changed from flexible, prehensile organs to stabilized, supporting members capable of bearing the weight of the body. Likewise, the bone of the heel (*calcaneum*) would have increased in size, extended backward, and with its attendant soft parts become the main lever employed in lifting the leg from the ground whenever steps were taken. Altogether the structure of the foot became compact and sturdy enough to support the body, at the same time that upraised arches made it sufficiently flexible to permit a springy stride in which only the heel and the ball of the foot touch the ground.

As man's ancestors came to walk habitually upright, so the hypothesis continues, the bones running from knee to ankle (*tibia* and *fibula*) became longer and stronger than in other Primates, and the calf muscles (*gastrocnemius*), which some men delight to observe in females, were enlarged and utilized to help raise the legs and feet when in motion or to hold them steady while standing still. Similarly, the thigh bone became elongated and straight of contour, and the muscles attached to it became larger and more powerful in order to extend the leg fully and to give it strength for walking. With the attainment of these modifications in the lower limbs, the body was given firm support or flexibility as needed, and the distinction of forelimbs from hindlimbs received its greatest emphasis. A biological curiosity deserves attention here. Virtually every student agrees that the capacity for upright posture while walking or running is an absolute essential for any form of Homo. Yet, this trait has never become fixed in man's biogenetic inheritance, with the consequence that every human child must go through the difficult procedure of learning to walk erect.

On the assumption that the human body represents a changeover from an original quadrupedal to a bipedal form, modifications are to be expected in the trunk and pelvic regions. By comparison with other Primates, man's pelvis seems to have been rotated forward and downward; and appears to have become considerably shortened and broadened. Wide hips may not be stylish, but the wider they are the more human they are. Simply stated, it appears as though the pelvic girdle was transformed from a long, narrow, horizontally placed cylinder in a pronograde body to a short, wide, flat, vertically situated basin that was firmly articulated to the thigh bones and spinal column.

In terms of the hypothesis being developed, changes of trunk and backbone above the pelvis also took place. Within the rear space between the lowest rib and the upper margin of the pelvis the lumbar vertebrae form the *lumbar curve,* a configuration restricted among Primates to human beings. Correspondingly, in the area at the back of the neck, between the head and shoulders, a *cervical forward curve* is found. These curves are thought to play an important part in keeping the head, trunk, and lower limbs in line, and in serving as springs to make the spinal column more pliant than a perfectly straight shaft.

A great number of highly significant alterations are thought to have taken place above the shoulders and are believed to be related to the manner in which the head is balanced on top of the spine. In quadrupeds, or in animals that only infrequently walk erect, like some of the apes, the spinal column is held horizontally or nearly so, and the spinal cord enters the skull through an opening (*foramen magnum*) near the rear bone (*occiput*). Such an arrangement necessitates a set of strong ligaments or *nuchal muscles* at the back of the head, in order to hold the poorly poised head firmly in place. These nuchal muscles require sturdy points of attachment, which are provided by a rugged area of bone in the occipital region of the skull, in conjunction with elongated bony projections that protrude backward from the cervical or neck vertebrae. Such a set of structures may be readily observed in the skeleton of a gorilla (Fig. 5-9). When one of these beasts is seen in the flesh, its neck appears to be exceedingly thick, short, and muscular, while its head gives the impression of being sunk between the shoulders.

To the simian arrangement of neck, head, and upper spinal column, the body of an orthograde being, such as man, provides a marked contrast. A human carries his spine vertically with the cord entering a foramen magnum that is centrally situated at the base of the skull. Thus, the head is neatly balanced and poised on top of the vertebral column, and neither the occiput nor the backward projections of the cervical vertebrae are particularly rugged, for only a slight nuchal musculature is needed to bind the head securely in place. Man has, as a result, a good deal of free space between the shoulders and head, so that his neck appears long and slender when compared with an ape's.

Although it must be admitted that the cause-and-effect relationships of the changes discussed in this section are not properly known, it certainly seems reasonable to assume that modifications of feet, legs, pelvis, visceral attachment, spine, neck, and head, were somehow connected with the attainment of bipedal, terrestrial locomotion. Simultaneously, while these presumably functional adjustments were going on, another series seems to have been taking place that has little or no direct connection with the position in which the body is held and carried. Of these the most significant, in the light of man's later development, pertain to the size and form of the bony braincase and its contents.

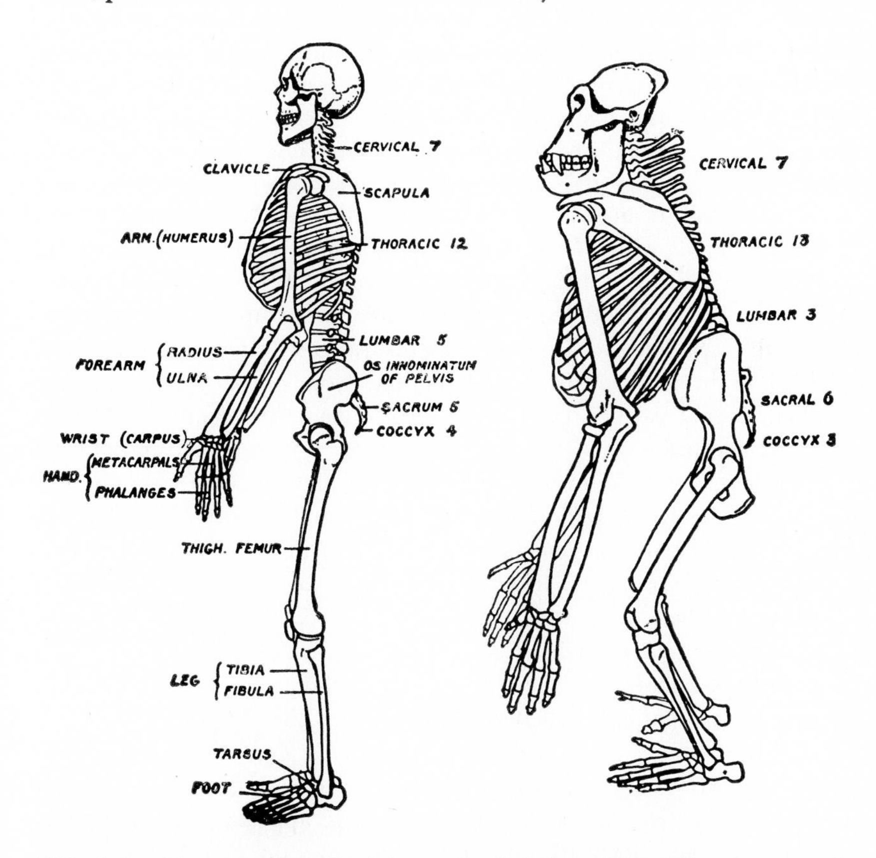

FIG. 5-9. Human and gorilla skeletons. Particularly striking differences are to be found in the configurations and carriage of the skulls, the number and form of the vertebrae, the curves of the spine, the rib cage, the limb lengths and proportions, and the feet and stances. (E. P. Stibbe, *Introduction to Physical Anthropology,* London, 1930. Courtesy of Edward Arnold & Co.)

In most species of apes, but best exemplified by the gorilla, the eye sockets are crowned in adult males, it should be recalled, by a great, thick, transverse supraorbital torus. Such an ape, as was explained, is likely to have a great deal of rugged bone at the back of the skull to provide attachment for ligaments and powerful nuchal muscles. Compressed between the front and rear areas of solid bone the thick cranial vault has only a small hollow chamber in which the brain may lodge. It may be that it is such an arrangement that limits the cranial capacity of the gorilla to an average of about 500 cubic centimeters, or less.

Very important, indeed, are the differences to be noted in all these respects among living humans. The heavy bars of bone over the eye orbits have diminished almost to the vanishing point; and with the attainment of an evenly poised head on the upper end of the spine, the nuchal muscles and ligaments have become so delicate that they do not require massive areas of bone for attachment. The cranial vault, made up of thinner bones, gives the appearance of having expanded upward, backward, and from side to side, increasing threefold the size of the hollow chamber which holds the brain. These conditions seem to make possible an average cranial capacity of around 1450 cubic centimeters for European men, and the upper limit may even run considerably over 1600 cubic centimeters. Some of the cultural consequences of man's expanded brain will be discussed later, but from any point of view the swollen cranial vault is one of the most outstanding features of man's physical evolution.

Whereas the braincase is thought to have grown larger among hominids, the facial region was becoming smaller and more delicate, while the forehead was getting higher and broader, and the brow ridges and jaws were shrinking. In particular, the lower jaw (mandible) looks as though it had diminished in bulk and receded in position. At the same time the rear branches (*ascending rami*), which join the skull near the temples, had to become splayed out if they were to accommodate themselves to man's broadened braincase (see Fig. 5-8).

Development of a prominent, bony *chin* is another exclusively human feature of the lower jaw. When viewed in profile, the outer line of almost any nonhuman Primate's mandible appears at the center to curve under and away like the arc of an old-fashioned rocking chair. Conversely, the same region in man shows a very pronounced forward bulge (Fig. 5-10). No adequate explanation for this phenomenon has yet been offered, but a prominent, forward-projecting, bony chin is one of the most distinctive traits of the human body, in spite of the fact that a few lower animals show traces of a chin.

Although jaw dimensions have decreased, the mouths of living men contain the same dental formula as in the higher Primates. There has been a reduction in the over-all size of human teeth; the canines neither project beyond the other teeth nor interlock; differences of spacing and in length-to-breadth proportions have come about; and there are variations of cusp pattern on the molars that are peculiar to man. On the whole, though, human teeth do not differ radically from those of the higher Primates. Some students attribute the difficulties often attendant on the eruption of man's third molars (wisdom teeth) to the circumstance that the jawbones have been reduced without a corresponding lowering of the number of permanent teeth from 32.

Few things contribute as much to the distinctive appearance of the human countenance as do thick, fleshy, and sometimes everted or outrolled lips that expose the reddened, mucous portions to view; and a

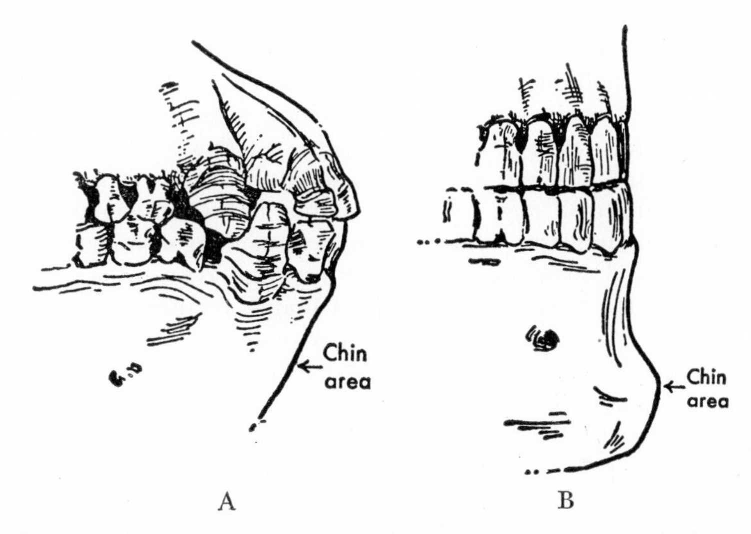

FIG. 5-10. Ape and human chin areas. Lower jaws of ape and man (after Hooton). An ape's lower jaw (A) protrudes and shows prognathism, but is entirely without a chin. Man's lower jaw (B) is far less protrusive, but the chin area juts prominently forward.

nose that rises well above the rest of the face. Since other Primates generally have thin, taut lips that seem to be tightly stretched over bulging mouths, it has been suggested that the recession of the human jaws has left behind a considerable amount of slack tissue that has somehow become furled into lips. This hypothesis is not quite satisfactory; nor has any likely theory been advanced to account for the uniqueness of the human nose. Reference is made only to the underlying nasal skeleton, and not to the soft parts that rest on it. Simians have low-lying and flat nasal bones that scarcely rise above the rest of the facial skeleton. To possess high, elevated nasal bones, therefore, is to show one's self to be a true representative of modern man.

MAN STANDS ALONE, AND PAYS A PRICE

Physical anthropologists think it likely that man has retained a highly generalized and typical form of Primate body, except for his expanded braincase; long, straight, hind legs; and stabilized feet. His other organs and members are neither exceedingly large nor exceptionally small, and their usefulness is not confined to a restricted environmental range nor a sharply delimited kind of function. Humans make up the only species of Primates that customarily walks or runs on the ground in an upright posture. Some think that the acquisition of this ability was such a gradual, slow, and difficult process that it has not yet been successfully completed even in our own day. A surprising number of adjustments remain imperfect, and until they are perfected they will continue to plague mankind. Without stopping to dwell on the frequency of flat feet, degenerate small toes, and fallen arches, let us consider the stress imposed on the circulatory system which, in upstanding men and women, must pump blood, sometimes against the force of gravity, to such distant extremities as the fingers, toes, ears, and brains. In their minor manifestations the difficulties of circulation may cause no greater discomfort than cold feet or readily frostbitten ears or finger tips, but in extreme cases they may contribute to the grave ailments that are lumped under the phrase, "heart failure."

In upright posture the heart is about 4 feet above the ground, with the result that the veins of the legs sometimes fail adequately to overcome the necessary gravitational pull, and so become swollen and result in the condition known as *varicose veins*.[19] Furthermore, there is a tendency for the lower end of the intestine to become congested, a tendency that sometimes results in hemorrhoids.

A heavy burden is also imposed by the force of gravity on the mesenteries that help hold some of the internal organs in place. When the wall muscles weaken, as they not infrequently do, a rupture or tear may occur that permits an organ to slip out of place. Abdominal hernias are the most common of these displacements, but various other forms of rupture are known to surgeons.

In a four-legged vertebrate animal the skeleton is built on the principle of a cantilever bridge, with an arched backbone that rests on the four limbs. When the backbone becomes upended a distressing mechanical imbalance results. Again, as in the case of upright posture

[19] More details on this topic are given in W. M. Krogman, "The Scars of Human Evolution," *Scientific American*, Vol. 185, 1951, pp. 54–57.

and walking, human infants are born without the necessary adjustments, which have to be acquired in post-natal life. The single-arched spine is gradually converted to the form of an "S," with the development of the cervical and lumbar curves, but many a backache develops if the lumbar vertebrae press on one another.

On the score of behavior, too, there are some resemblances and some startling contrasts between monkeys, apes, and men. In all three groups females are subject to menstrual cycles, there is no particular breeding season, there is protracted maternal care of the young, and adult masculine dominance is readily apparent. In striking contrast, however, infantile dependence lasts much longer in humans than it does in monkeys or apes, simian groupings are much smaller in numbers and range of territory than are human societies, hominids consume a far greater intake of varied proteins, and among infrahumans, adult males neither provide food for their dependents nor do they ever build anything corresponding to permanent houses. It is clear that neither in anatomical structure nor in behavior are human beings just like monkeys or apes.

THE RELATIONSHIP OF MAN TO OTHER PRIMATES

Although scientists disagree on the details of man's immediate ancestry, they stand firm in the belief that the long list of distinctively human features is matched by an equally impressive list of biological resemblances shared by man and higher Primates. If the arrangement of evolutionary lines shown in Fig. 2–4 approximates the truth, it indicates that two related but different paths appear close together when they are just starting to separate, but become more widely divergent with the passage of time. The figure of a caret, $\wedge$, demonstrates the basic idea in simple fashion. The top represents the start of divergence from a common ancestral point, and the bottom shows separation at a much later date. As we trace the two lines backward in time (upward), the less far apart they are. Such is the case with the living simians and modern man. Today they seem very far apart but we can discover their common ancestry by tracing their evolutionary lines back in time.

Not many decades ago the quest for predecessors of modern man used to be spoken of as a search for "missing links." Such a description has fallen into disuse partly because it may give the impression that there once existed crosswise connections between other Primate and human branches, as if ape mothers had once given birth to human children. Anthropologists do not believe in the existence of such fanciful crossties, but they do believe that if man's line is followed back it will lead to creatures less hominid than living men and women.

Remains of so many partially manlike forms have been discovered that a figure like a caret is greatly oversimplified and fails to show the multiplicity of lines that actually exists. Far from having too few remains to guide them, anthropologists occasionally find themselves embarrassed with riches. Out of the mass of early hominids already found they do not know which ones belong in the direct path leading to modern man, and which represent side branches that culminated only in dead ends. They do not know with certainty where each of these hominids originated, and they cannot recite the entire cast in the order of its appearance. Moreover, they are forced to deal with the vagaries of asymmetrical evolution.[20] According to this concept, the course of evolution proceeds irregularly, with some body parts evolving at different times than others. Only with such a concept in mind can we understand why some specimens of early hominids, as is actually the case, have human thighbones but apish skulls, or simian jaws containing hominid teeth. Confronted with such assortments, who is to say whether a particular example should be classed with man or with some other Primate?

Selected References

Brain, C. K., "The Transvaal Ape-Man–Bearing Cave Deposits," *Transvaal Museum, Memoir No. II,* Pretoria, Union of South Africa, 1958.

Broom, Robert, "The Genera and Species of the South African Fossil Ape-Man," *American Journal of Physical Anthropology,* Vol. 8, 1950, pp. 1–13

———, and Robinson, J. T., "Notes on the Pelves of the Fossil Ape-Men," *American Journal of Physical Anthropology,* Vol. 8, 1950, pp. 489–94.

———, and Schepers, G. W. H., "The South African Fossil Ape-Men, the Australopithecinae," *Transvaal Museum, Memoir No. 2,* Pretoria, Union of South Africa, 1946.

Clark, J. Desmond, *The Prehistory of Southern Africa* (Pelican), 1959.

Clark, W. E. LeGros, *The Fossil Evidence for Human Evolution,* Chicago, 1955.

Dart, Raymond A., *Adventures with the Missing Link,* New York, 1959.

[20] E. A. Hooton, "The Asymmetrical Character of Human Evolution," *American Journal of Physical Anthropology,* Vol. 8, 1925, pp. 125–41.

———, "Taungs and Its Significance," *Natural History,* Vol. 26, 1926, pp. 315–27.

Gavan, James A., ed., *The Non-Human Primates and Human Evolution,* Detroit, 1955.

Hooton, Earnest A., *Man's Poor Relations,* New York, 1942.

———, "The Asymmetrical Character of Human Evolution," *American Journal of Physical Anthropology,* Vol. 8, 1925, pp. 125–41.

Krogman, Wilton M., "The Scars of Human Evolution," *Scientific American,* Vol. 185, No. 1, 1951, pp. 54–57.

Morton, J. Dudley, *The Human Foot,* rev. ed., New York, 1937.

Schultz, Adolph H., "Man as a Primate," *Scientific Monthly,* 1931, pp. 385–412.

Yerkes, Robert M. and Ada W., *The Great Apes,* New Haven, Conn., 1934.

Extinct Forms of Man[1]

CHAPTER 6

In spite of the confusion that prevails in respect to particular details of human origins, the main outlines of the story may be seen with some clarity. A long time before our species had achieved its present body forms there lived on earth a large number of hominids who are assumed to have been less completely evolved than *Homo sapiens.* No one of these partially mannish forms, with the dubious exception of Oreopithecus, appeared before the earliest phases of the Pleistocene; and the great majority, except for the Australopithecinae and one or two others, go back only to mid-Pleistocene times or less, roughly from 600,000–500,000 B.P. on. Not one of the early kinds of man has survived to our day in its original form. It is believed, however, that the remnants of the extinct Pleistocene hominids suggest the path or paths that contemporary man's forebears took as they moved away from the simian line. Ancient forms of man may also reveal the times and places where some hominid features first appeared. It is for such reasons that *paleoanthropologists* concerned with human origins devote so much time and effort to the study of extinct varieties of man.

Before a reader gets too impatient with the uncertainty that prevails in these matters he should recall that even as late as 1871, when Darwin published *The Descent of Man,* very few specimens of Pleistocene forms of man had been found and described. In contrast with this

[1] In other anthropological textbooks the phrase "fossil men" is commonly used in place of "extinct forms of man." Unfortunately, this customary usage, although quite old, is not entirely accurate. Not all of the remains to be discussed are fossilized, in the usual sense of having been mineralized or turned to stone. Hence, "extinct forms of man" seems to be more precise than "fossil men."

state of affairs, a tremendous number of extinct hominids have come to light within the last ninety years, particularly from parts of Europe, Asia, and Africa. At the outset, each newly discovered relic so impressed its finder with its uniqueness that he usually took it for a new genus or species and enthusiastically assigned it a name, generally without regard for established taxonomic usages. Thus, there came into being a bewildering hodge-podge of terms that had little real significance and that made it harder than ever to work out the probable relationships of one specimen to another or to establish presumed connections with *Homo sapiens.*

One of the earliest efforts to bring order into this chaotic situation was made by Franz Weidenreich. He grouped the remains of extinct forms of men into three large categories, which he named *Archanthropinae* ("ancient hominids"); *Paleoanthropinae* ("old hominids"); and *Neoanthropinae* ("new hominids").[2]

A somewhat more widely accepted arrangement was utilized by the late A. L. Kroeber, among others. Like Weidenreich, Kroeber was impressed by the fact that some remnants approach modern man's structure far more nearly than do others. Accordingly, he arranged them into three successive divisions, called *Protoanthropic* ("first human"), *Palaeoanthropic* ("old human"), and *Neanthropic* ("newer human").[3]

Terms such as those employed by Weidenreich and Kroeber have been severely criticized.[4] Following suggestions made by Ernst Mayr[5] and W. E. LeGros Clark,[6] a new scheme for grouping together some of the best-known forms of extinct men will here be proposed and followed. It rests on the central idea that all hominids, extinct or extant, belong to the single genus of Homo. This genus and its forerunners

---

[2] F. Weidenreich, *Apes, Giants, and Man,* Chicago, 1946, pp. 29–31. Weidenreich's scheme has aroused objections, partly because it appears to be based on a concept known as morphological dating. This concept wrongly assumes that a more apelike trait *must* be older than a comparable feature which is more manlike. For a discussion of this method of dating, see T. D. Stewart, "The Development of the Concept of Morphological Dating . . . in America." *Southwestern Journal of Anthropology,* Vol. 5, 1949, especially pp. 15–16.

Weidenreich's categories were used in the first edition of this text, which was published in 1954.

[3] A. L. Kroeber, *Anthropology,* rev. ed., New York, 1948, pp. 80 ff. In fairness to Kroeber it should be pointed out that he realized that the successions were not clear-cut, and that there was a great deal of overlap, especially in matters of time. The translations in parentheses are Kroeber's.

[4] W. E. LeGros Clark, *The Fossil Evidence for Human Evolution,* Chicago, 1955, p. 9.

[5] E. Mayr, "Taxonomic Categories in Fossil Hominids," *Cold Spring Harbor Symposium in Quantitative Biology,* Vol. 15, 1950, pp. 109 ff.

[6] W. E. LeGros Clark, *op. cit.,* pp. 6 ff.

have always been highly variable. It should be no surprise, therefore, that a number of differing forms are grouped into each of the designations that follow.

1. Homo erectus—giant size and regular

In this category are to be found the earliest relics that are customarily regarded as men.[7] Their ancestors are unknown, but they seem to have lived in east Asia, for their principal remains have been discovered on the island of Java and in China. Only a few remnants have been found, often in a fragmentary condition, so that our account must necessarily be incomplete and tentative.

The type specimen for this variety of early man is the famous relic called *Pithecanthropus erectus* ("Ape-man erect"), also known as Java or Trinil Man. Taxonomically, this creature might properly be dubbed *Homo erectus erectus*. Parts of several Pithecanthropoids have now been found. They form a curious assortment, ranging from some that are very large to others that approximate the human dimensions of today.

(a) Pithecanthropus erectus

The manner in which this extinct hominid was discovered makes an interesting and amazing story. Less than ten years after the death of Charles Darwin, a young and energetic Dutch surgeon named Eugene Dubois applied for colonial service in the Netherlands East Indies. He was a zealous student of organic, including human, evolution, and so great was his faith in the truth of the evolutionary theory that he publicly proclaimed his intention of finding the remains of an ape-man. He spent many years on the islands of Sumatra and Java, searching for the bones of those simianlike hominids that he was convinced had once roamed the warmer stretches of the earth. Despite the overwhelming odds against him Dubois persisted until, in the years 1891 and 1892, his diligence and faith were rewarded.

One day, while he was collecting animal fossils along the banks of an ancient channel that the Solo River had cut in Pleistocene times near the village of Trinil in central Java, Dubois picked up, in September of

[7] It was previously pointed out that the suggestion has been made that all of the African man-apes (Australopithecinae) should be grouped together under the heading of *Homo transvaalensis*. However, as long as their status is still debatable, it may not be wise to class them as men.

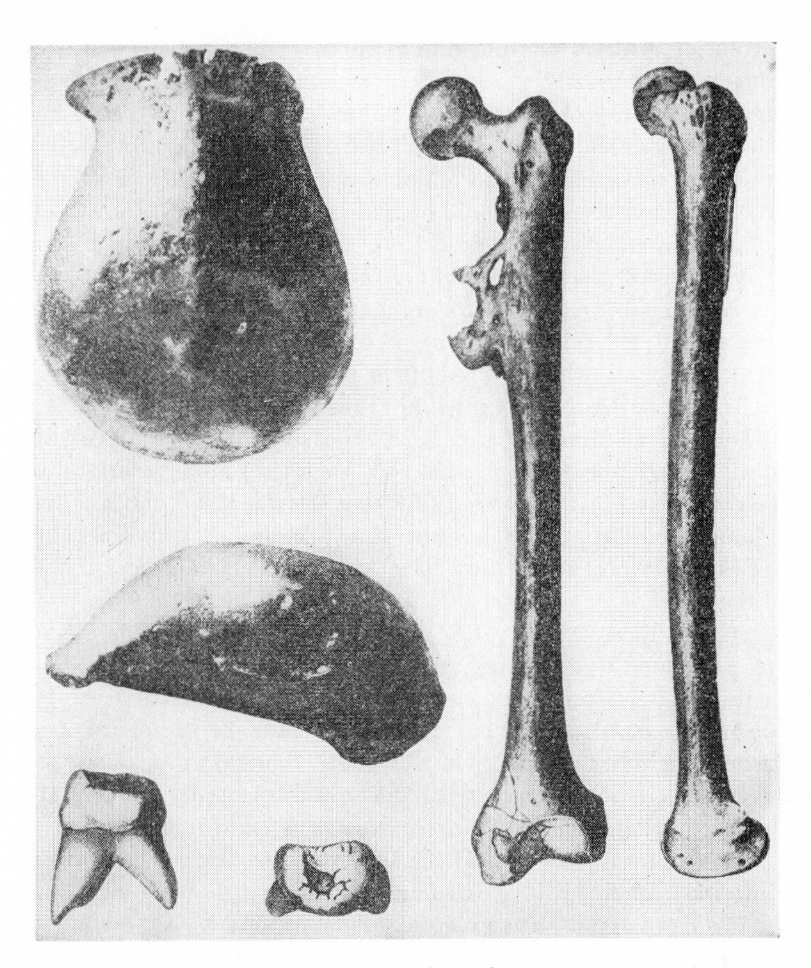

FIG. 6-1. The principal remains of *Pithecanthropus erectus.* The skull cap, pictured from above and in profile, is about one fourth its natural size. The thigh bone (femur), front view and profile, is about one fifth its natural size; the tooth, which is a third upper molar, shown in profile and from above, is approximately one fourth its natural size. (After Dubois. From M. Boule and H. V. Vallois, *Fossil Men,* rev. ed., New York, 1957. Courtesy of H. V. Vallois and the Musée de l'Homme.)

1891, an unusual kind of tooth. Three feet away, in the month that followed, he came across the upper part of a skull; and in August of 1892, nearly 50 feet further off, he located a left thigh bone, or femur. Before he was through, two more teeth and a piece of a lower jaw, found in a more distant spot, were added to his collection (Fig. 6–1).

From his knowledge of comparative anatomy and from his studies of evolution, Dubois became convinced that all the skeletal fragments belonged together and pertained to an apish kind of man whom he designated *Pithecanthropus erectus.* As can readily be imagined, a heated discussion arose when Dubois published his findings in 1894. Scientists of the time were reluctant to admit the former existence of a creature whose anatomy seemed to combine simian and hominid traits. Cautious scholars insisted, not without reason, that the remnants had been so widely scattered that they might originally have belonged to several different animals, instead of to one and the same individual. Perhaps, it was argued, the simian portions were the remains of an ape, possibly a gigantic gibbon, whereas the human parts came from a long-deceased man. In reply it has been pointed out that many of the combined simian and hominid features are to be seen on a single bone, the skull vault; that all of the bones, though scattered, occupied similar positions in the same geological (Trinil) layer of soil; that fluorine tests[8] indicate that all the bones are of approximately the same age; and that more recent discoveries of Pithecanthropoids have supported Dubois' original contentions.

Today there are very few skeptics, although the teeth are sometimes attributed to an orang, and the authenticity of the thigh bone is still in dispute. More than one anthropologist believes that the femur came from a modern man but got shuffled into the geological stratum that held the other remains. On the whole, though, the majority favors the view that Dubois' first interpretation was essentially correct.[9] If this be granted, what, then, was *Pithecanthropus erectus* like?

Judged by the remains of the skull cap, the ancient hominid from Trinil was rather apish, particularly resembling gibbons or chimpanzees. His cranial vault was exceptionally thick and heavy; a solid torus of bone protruded above the eye orbits; the forehead was very low, narrow, and greatly constricted just behind the eye cavities; the foramen magnum was placed toward the rear; and the nuchal area was so ex-

---

[8] The fluorine test has been most fully developed and utilized by the great English scientist, K. P. Oakley. Simply stated, the test rests on the assumption that all bones lying in similar soil will gradually accumulate similar amounts of fluorine. Thus, bones lying in one stratum, and showing the same proportions of fluorine, are assumed to be of about the same age. Details of this technique may be found in K. P. Oakley, "The Fluorine-Dating Method," *Yearbook of Physical Anthropology,* New York, 1949, pp. 44–52.

[9] It is strange that Dubois, who first fought to persuade the world of science that *Pithecanthropus erectus* was a hominid, later changed his mind and argued that he had found the remains of a large gibbon. As he advanced in age, Dubois became increasingly isolated and eccentric. He hid the fragments of *Pithecanthropus erectus,* and would let no one see or examine them.

tensive and the muscle attachments for the back of the head ran so high up on the occipital bone that the head must have been poorly poised on the top of the spine. Consequently, the face and jaws must have jutted far forward. This is a simian characteristic. Moreover, this extinct hominid has a diastema in the upper jaw, presumably for the accommodation of an interlocking lower canine.

Several competent specialists, building on the fragment that was actually found, have reconstructed the entire skull and measured its cranial capacity. Their results vary somewhat, but an average of about 925 cubic centimeters is fairly representative of all the estimates. This is nearly twice the figure for a large ape; it is considerably above man-ape amounts; but it is only about two thirds the cranial capacity of an average human of today. Looked at in this fashion, Pithecanthropus may be said to occupy a sort of midway position between the apes and *Homo sapiens.* Such an appraisal is supported by the jaw fragment, which is presumably of the same time period, and which indicates a big, chinless jaw, comparable to an ape's, but without a simian shelf.

Markedly different from the other remains is the disputed femur. Although it has an excrescence of bone that may have been the result of a disease, it is quite modern in every way. The shaft is big and strong, and it has such a straight contour that its owner must have had upright posture. Insofar as such things can be judged from a single bone, the ape-man from Java stood around 5 feet 7 inches high, and had a weight of about 150 pounds.

When the remnants are put together, they give the impression that *Pithecanthropus erectus* had a modified ape's head mounted on an essentially human body. If all the fragments do belong together, they lead to the conclusion that upright posture was developed before man's brain had reached its present size. This conforms to a hypothesis that is supported by the Australopithecinae, and which is upheld by Sherwood L. Washburn and many other anthropologists.

(b) Homo modjokertensis and Skulls I, II, and III

Had all our knowledge of *Pithecanthropus erectus* been limited to the fragmentary and widely scattered discoveries made by Dubois, all conclusions would have been forever tentative and open to question. Luckily, later investigators persisted in searching on Java for other remains that might support or contradict the conclusions originally reached by Dubois. An early expedition, sponsored by Madame Selenka in 1909, got no results; but in the years between 1936 and 1939 G. H. R. von Koenigswald, a Dutch paleontologist, was fortunate enough to locate, in early to middle Pleistocene formations, a shattered cranium. This remnant was named *Homo modjokertensis,* after the place where it was found. It has been carefully studied, and it is now generally held to represent a very young Pithecanthropoid. It is from an older soil layer (Djetis), than *Pithecanthropus erectus,* and may even have been a contemporary of some of the African man-apes.

Von Koenigswald made several additional discoveries in Java. These include parts of two adult crania that are known as *Skulls II* and *III.* All of them show affiliations with *Pithecanthropus erectus.* Above all, Skull II is so much like the latter that the two are reported to resemble each other "as closely as one egg another."

(c) *Pithecanthropus robustus*

Somewhat bigger and different from the Pithecanthropoid remains so far discussed, is the fragment usually called *Skull IV* or *Pithecanthropus robustus.* It was also found by von Koenigswald in 1939, this time in the vicinity of Sangiran, Java. It consists of a brain case, with only the front quarter missing, together with an upper jaw that still contains most of its teeth. (Further details are given in Appendix A.)

From the description of *Pithecanthropus robustus,* it seems apparent that the Pithecanthropoids came in various sizes.[10] Some approached the averages of contemporary human beings, but others may have been larger. This statement is supported by the specimen called *Meganthropus,* which will be discussed next.

(d) *Meganthropus paleojavanicus*

Meganthropus paleojavanicus ("Giant man from old Java") was discovered by von Koenigswald at Sangiran in 1940–1941.

As the Japanese were taking over Java at the time, and as von Koenigswald foresaw an indeterminate break in his scientific investigations,[11] he sent this find to Weidenreich. In this way, the welcome task

[10] The occurrence of large-sized Pleistocene hominids formerly aroused greater surprise and discussion than it does today. It was once held that the large specimens represented separate species, but modern scholars tend to regard them as belonging to the bigger ranges of distribution among hominids. In other words, the giant sizes may represent no more than large individuals of the same species. Moreover, it has now been established that one part of a creature may grow to a large size, while the animal itself remains rather small.

[11] Von Koenigswald's premonition was borne out. When, in the course of World War II, the Japanese took Java, he was confined in a concentration camp for about four years.

It will be remembered that the United States and her allies declared war on Japan of studying and publishing an analysis of Meganthropus fell to von Koenigswald's old friend and colleague.

The remains of Meganthropus consist of two jaw fragments which still hold in place some of the original teeth. The main fragment was a good-sized part of a large mandible with three teeth. Both von Koenigswald and Weidenreich agreed that the relic was hominid (see Fig. 6–2). Weidenreich found the mandible to be chinless, thicker, and higher than the corresponding portions of any Primate jaw known to science. On the

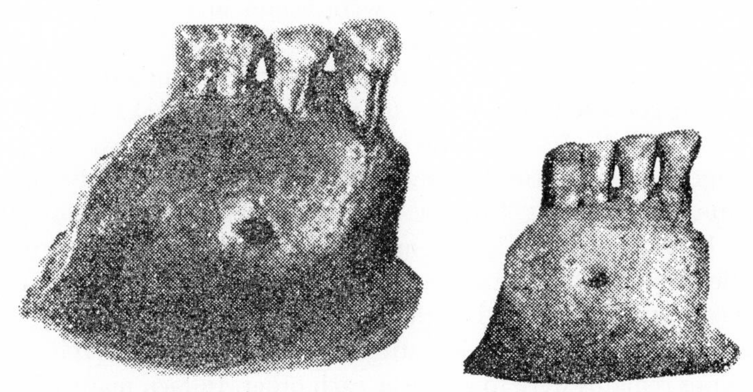

FIG. 6-2. Meganthropus relic, after Weidenreich. Left: A fragment, with teeth in place, of the lower jaw of Meganthropus. An idea of its size may be gained by comparing it with the same portion of a modern man's mandible at right. The pictures of both specimens are about one half of natural size. (From F. Weidenreich, *Apes, Giants, and Man,* Chicago, 1946. Courtesy of the University of Chicago Press.)

other hand, he judged that the contours of the dental arch were intermediate between those of apes and men. But the thing that really led him to classify Meganthropus with Homo, was the fact that the teeth, though large, were identifiably hominid.

From so small a sample, especially in the light of the vagaries of asymmetrical evolution, nothing can be said of the body size and shape of Meganthropus. Nevertheless, Weidenreich ventured to guess that this ancient hominid from Java was bigger than any living gorilla. As a matter of fact, he firmly believed that human beings were gigantic before they shrank to the familiar sizes of today.[12]

---

early in December, 1941. World War II lasted until Japan surrendered in the summer of 1945.

[12] It was formerly believed that such a conclusion was partially supported by a relic called *Gigantopithecus* ("Giant ape"). All that was known of this creature were fragments of three molar teeth that von Koenigswald had purchased about thirty years ago. They came, of all unlikely places, from the drawers of a Chinese apothecary shop

On the basis of the notion that the various kinds of *Homo erectus* must have had ancestors with even smaller brains and bigger jaws than their own, one school of thought would link some of the Australopithecinae with Meganthropus. However, most authorities think that Meganthropus was a large variant of *Pithecanthropus erectus.*

(e) Sinanthropus pekinensis

About thirty years after Dubois had made his first discovery of *Pithecanthropus erectus,* excavations were begun in a limestone quarry situated at Chou Kou Tien, 40 miles southwest of Peking, China. Up to 1927 the best sign that caves in the quarry contained remnants of extinct forms of man consisted of a single tooth. Davidson Black, then of the Peking Union Medical School, was led to the conclusion that the tooth had belonged to a hitherto unknown type of creature which he named *Sinanthropus pekinensis* ("Chinese man from Peking"). In subsequent years Black's risky assumption seemed to be vindicated, for more and more skeletal material came to light from Chou Kou Tien, and all of it that was mannish pertained to the same kind of hominid.

Unlike the assorted and scattered Pithecanthropoid relics, the Sinanthropus remains were found near each other. In fact, many of them were even embedded in the same block of stone, in such fashion as to leave no doubt of their belonging together. Up to 1939, portions of approximately forty different individuals had been recovered from the mid-Pleistocene deposits at Chou Kou Tien.

By this time, Franz Weidenreich had replaced Davidson Black, who had died in 1934. Weidenreich did not possess a single complete skeleton available for study, but he did have a big collection of parts that included a dozen or more skulls, numerous jaws and thighbones, a great many teeth, one armbone, and other fragments. These remains are

---

on the island of Hong Kong. Several authorities feel that the teeth pertain to a hominid rather than to an ape, but most of them regard the teeth as simian.

More recently, the remains of extremely large apes have been reported from China and elsewhere, especially by Wen-chung Pei. Some of his claims have been challenged, but it is quite certain that many kinds of gigantic animals existed at various times and places in the past. It is not now thought that human beings started out as giants and later shrank to modern sizes.

Kwang-chi Chang, of Yale, has published an important article called "New Evidence on Fossil Man in China." *Science,* Vol. 136, No. 3518, 1962, pp. 749–60. Among other things, Chang believes that Gigantopithecus "can be removed from the family tree that leads to modern man"; that true hominids in China began with *Sinanthropus pekinensis*; that some relics show Neandertaloid characteristics; and that China has now yielded a typologically complete series of hominid fossils, ranging from *Homo erectus* to *Homo sapiens.*

somewhat variable in character, but it is possible to arrange them into one composite picture.

As a rule, Sinanthropus skulls (Fig. 6–3) are provided with heavy, bony brow ridges or supraorbital tori; the foreheads are low and retreating; the jaws massive, protruding, and relatively chinless; and the nuchal areas are as rugged and extensive as in *Pithecanthropus erectus*. Cranial capacities vary, but run to 1000 cubic centimeters or more. The teeth

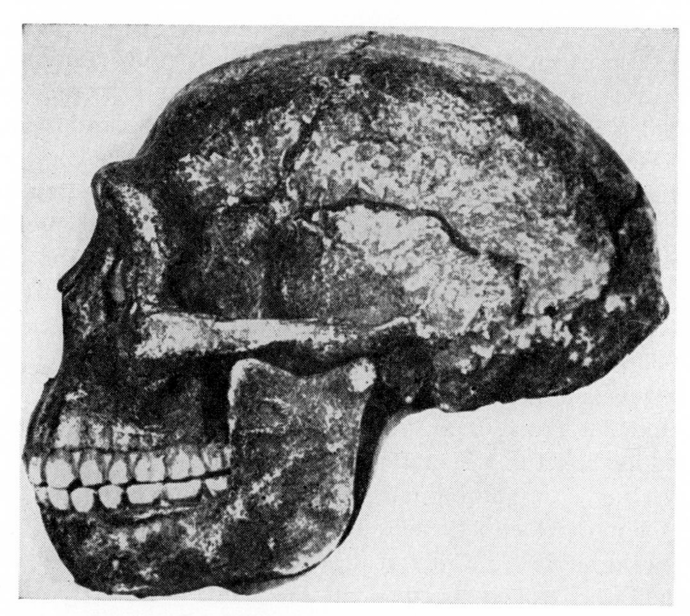

FIG. 6-3. Side view of *Sinanthropus pekinensis*. The reconstructed skull of a female Sinanthropoid is pictured. Sinanthropus is between modern man and ape with respect to the size of the torus, the height of the skull vault, degree of prognathism, and other features. (Courtesy of H. V. Vallois and the Musée de l'Homme.)

are far from uniform, and some of the molars show an enlargement of the pulp cavities that is known as *taurodontism*, a condition that sometimes occurs in *Neandertal man* (to be described later in this chapter). Nevertheless, the teeth are only moderately large, the canines neither project nor interlock, and, on the whole, they approach the condition of *Homo sapiens*.

The thighbones show that the Chinese men of Peking walked upright and stood about 5 feet 2 inches. This means that their forelimbs must have been emancipated, so that they could have handled tools.

That is why almost all students of human evolution, even though they realize that they are dealing with a biological problem, like to cite as supporting evidence of Sinanthropus' hominid nature many cultural objects that have been found reliably associated with the skeletal remains.[13] These objects indicate that the mid-Pleistocene hominids who had once occupied this part of China had lived in caves, used fire, hunted and eaten game animals, in addition to plant foods, and probably had fabricated and used stone and bone tools. These people are commonly held to have been cannibals, and it is true that the crania were usually broken at the base—as though to permit the brains to have been extracted, and presumably eaten. Some of the long bones are also cracked, as if someone wanted to get at the marrow.

The proper placement and relationships of Sinanthropus have always been matters of great concern. The problems are complicated by the fact that the original materials disappeared during the Second World War and were never again found. Luckily, we have Weidenreich's extensive reports, and numerous reproductions to go on.[14] Many experts believe that the Sinanthropus people were somehow ancestral to Neandertals, and Weidenreich felt that they were the forerunners of the present-day Chinese. However, the best tie-ins appear to be simply with other members of *Homo erectus.*

Although Black, soon after the first discoveries were made, had ventured the belief that Sinanthropus might have been related to *Pithecanthropus erectus,* nothing much was done about classifying them together for more than a decade. Then, in 1939, Weidenreich and von Koenigswald published a joint article in which they stated their conviction that, when taken together, all the remains of *Pithecanthropus erectus* and of *Sinanthropus pekinensis* established a close relationship between these two types of extinct hominids.[15] This opinion has been widely accepted. Neither of these forms is conclusively more highly evolved than the other, but Sinanthropus may be a little closer to *Homo*

---

13 Man is the only creature known to have culture and to use cultural equipment regularly. It is assumed, therefore, that wherever manufactured tools or other cultural objects are found, they *must* have been made or used by hominids. For an able article along these lines, see S. L. Washburn, "Tools and Human Evolution," *Scientific American,* Vol. 203, pp. 3–15.

14 Weidenreich has published a number of detailed and profusely illustrated studies of various parts of *Sinanthropus pekinensis.* See, for example, F. Weidenreich, "The Skull of *Sinanthropus pekinensis:* a comparative study on a primitive hominid skull," *Paleontologia Sinica,* No. 127, 1943.

15 G. H. R. von Koenigswald and F. Weidenreich, "The Relationship between Pithecanthropus and Sinanthropus," *Nature,* Vol. 144, 1939.

sapiens because it has a greater cranial capacity, more suggestion of a chin, a higher forehead, and no sign of a diastema.

(f) Atlanthropus

As recently as 1954, Camille Arambourg, a paleontologist from Paris, found two hominid jaws and some of their teeth in north Africa. Although he named them *Atlanthropus mauritanicus,* he recognized a resemblance to other types of *Homo erectus,* particularly to Sinanthropus and Meganthropus. (Further details are given in Appendix A.)

(g) Solo Man (Homo soloensis)

Just as there is no certainty about the ancestry of the various forms of *Homo erectus,* so no one can speak with assurance about their descendants. Actually, *Homo erectus* may have become extinct without issue. Yet, in some quarters, there persists a belief that these forms gave rise to the men called *Neandertaloids.* One of the alleged links is known as *Homo soloensis* or *Solo man.*

Homo soloensis refers to a cluster of ancient hominids, whose bones lay in Upper Pleistocene gravels at Ngandong, Java, a scant half-dozen miles east of Trinil, where Dubois had located the remains of *Pithecanthropus erectus.* The finder of these bones was W. F. F. Oppenoorth, of the Geological Survey of Java. In the five years between 1931 and 1936, he discovered portions of eleven crania and fragments of several other bones. In keeping with the custom of the time, Oppenoorth took the remnants from Ngandong to represent a new hominid species.

All of the remains were so badly shattered and so many parts were missing that it is impossible to judge the proper evolutionary position of *Homo soloensis.* Suffice it to say that the skull vaults are low pitched, with receding foreheads and huge brow ridges.[16] At the same time, the skulls are quite commodious, for their cranial capacity has been estimated at 1200 cubic centimeters.

Those who believe that forms like *Homo soloensis* provide a link between *Homo erectus* and *Homo neandertalensis* sometimes recall that when Oppenoorth first reported his discoveries, he drew attention to the resemblances between Solo man and Rhodesian man, often considered to be a Neandertaloid from Africa. Tentatively, while it may be admitted that the Solo material bears some resemblance to *Homo erectus,*

---

[16] For further details see F. Weidenreich and G. H. R. von Koenigswald, "Morphology of Solo Man," *Anthropological Papers, American Museum of Natural History,* Vol. 43, New York, 1951.

the evidence for its supposed ties with Neandertal man is very doubtful. When it is remembered that the Solo remains lay in Upper Pleistocene gravels, whereas Neandertaloids are usually regarded as mid-Pleistocene, it is impossible to see how the later forms could have been ancestral to earlier kinds of men. Leakey is one of those who consider Solo man too young to have been an ancestor of Neandertal man. He favors the theory that Solo man was one contemporary variant of Neandertal man, and that Rhodesian man was another.

2. Homo neandertalensis

Long ago, in 1856, a faceless skull cap was found in a gravel pit in the beautiful Neander valley, near Düsseldorf, Germany. It was massive and exceedingly low browed, yet there seemed to be something human about it. Contemporary scholars were puzzled by this find, and some of them made "explanations" that strike us as ludicrous. In the course of time this specimen acquired the name of Neandertal man, and came to be recognized as belonging to a group of middle to late Pleistocene hominids.[17]

As the years went by, more and more Neandertaloid remains were discovered in various countries of western Europe, and it began to dawn on students of man that these people had lived through a bitter phase of the Ice Age. At first only assorted fragments were found, but shortly after the turn of the century a fairly complete skeleton was unearthed at La Chapelle-aux-Saints, in Dordogne, France. Around 1912 this skeleton was painstakingly described by the late Marcellin Boule, and soon became the standard for descriptions of Neandertal man (Fig. 6–4). Unfortunately, the individual from La Chapelle-aux-Saints was quite old, in the neighborhood of 50; and a recent re-examination of his bones by two exceedingly competent anatomists, W. L. Straus, Jr., and A. J. E. Cave, has revealed that he had suffered badly from arthritis. It is forever to be regretted that our most widespread account of Neandertal man is based on the faulty evidence of an arthritic old man's skeleton.

Even if we grant the dangers of erroneous description there was little reason to doubt, until thirty years ago, that the western European specimens were recognizably distinctive and typical of all Neandertaloids. Then, in 1931–1932, an expedition headed by one of Britain's

[17] Actually, a relic, now judged to have been Neandertal, was found at Gibraltar as early as 1848. At that time, however, no one knew what to make of it. Today it is estimated that the remains of about 100 Neandertaloids of various kinds have been discovered.

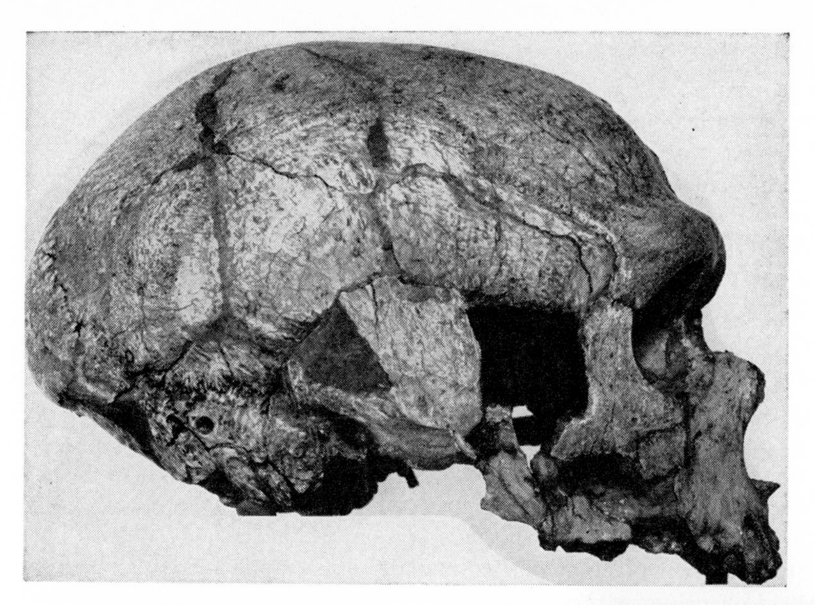

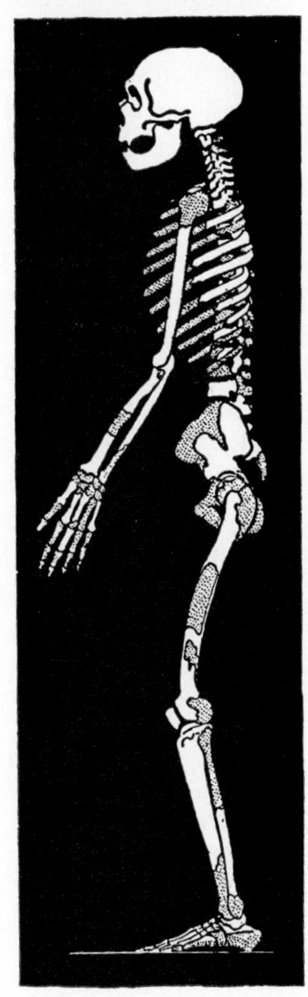

FIG. 6-4. Classic Neandertal man. Above: The skull from La Chapelle-aux-Saints (after Boule). Parts of the facial area have been restored, but the skull shows the big brow ridges, low cranial vault, and occipital "bun," that have long been thought to be typical of Neandertal man. (Courtesy of H. V. Vallois and the Musée de l'Homme.) Right: Restoration of the Neandertal skeleton from La Chapelle-aux-Saints (after MacCurdy). This is the skeleton that once provided the basis for descriptions of Neandertal man. Noteworthy are the poorly poised skull, the bent knees, the bowed (curved) femur, and the poorly developed spinal curves. (Courtesy of the Peabody Museum, Harvard University.)

leading archeologists, Dorothy Garrod, made some startling discoveries. In two caves on the slopes of Mt. Carmel in Palestine, her workers found no less than twelve Neandertal skeletons, some of them virtually complete. From a cave locally known as et-Tabun ("The Oven"), came two relics. One of these, a female, closely resembles the Neandertaloids of western Europe. At the opposite extreme, one of the males from es-Skhul ("The Kids") cave, is practically indistinguishable from *Homo sapiens.*

All students of these remains agree on the great variability of the Mt. Carmel specimens,[18] but what is the explanation for the avowedly Neandertal Tabun woman, and the modern-looking man from Skhul? Two opinions have prevailed widely. According to one, there was a local evolution from Neandertal through intermediate forms (which are present), to those that closely approximate *Homo sapiens.* According to the other theory, the modern type migrated full-fledged to Palestine from some unknown place of origin, mated with Neandertals and produced hybrid offspring. A theory along these lines has received strong support from Joseph Weckler.[19] Recently, it has been pointed out that not all of the Palestinian remains are from exactly the same soil levels. Hence, not all members of this assorted population were necessarily living at the same time, and they might have had no opportunity to interbreed. Then, too, F. Clark Howell, who has carefully studied all known Neandertal remnants, thinks that the bulk of them fall into two distinct categories.[20] One of these, found primarily in western Asia, he calls *Early*; and the other, represented chiefly in western Europe, he calls *Classic.* Howell is of the opinion that the Early forms were incipiently Neandertaloid, and that they became the ancestors of the Classic people. As for the Classic Neandertals, Howell, together with many another anthropologist, believes that they represent an isolated dead end, specialized in western Europe for life under Ice Age conditions. He does not believe that the Classic Neandertalers evolved into *Homo sapiens,* nor does he think that they interbred with more modern forms of man. Carleton S. Coon holds a different point of view, and is convinced that in one way or another, Classic Neandertal traits have been transmitted to many Europeans whose descendants still live among us. It is, indeed,

---

18 By far the fullest description of the Mt. Carmel remains is to be found in T. D. McCown and A. Keith, *The Stone Age of Mount Carmel,* Vol. 2, London, 1939.

19 J. Weckler, "Relations between Neandertal Man and *Homo sapiens,*" *American Anthropologist,* Vol. 56, 1954, pp. 1003–25.

20 F. C. Howell, "The Evolutionary Significance of Variation and Varieties of 'Neanderthal' Man," *The Quarterly Review of Biology,* Vol. 32, 1957, pp. 330–47, and F. C. Howell, "The Place of Neanderthal Man in Human Evolution," *American Journal of Physical Anthropology,* Vol. 9, 1951, pp. 379–416.

hard to deny that some members of *Homo sapiens* today exhibit characteristics that resemble traits shown by Classic Neandertal man, but it is impossible to say how they got that way.

(a) Early Neandertaloids

In accordance with Howell's thinking, these forms lived prior to the Classic Neandertals of western Europe. He believes that they were distributed from central Asia to parts of Europe, and he would include under this heading remnants from Uzbekistan (central Asia), et-Tabun (Palestine), Krapina (Croatia, Yugoslavia), Ehringsdorf (Germany), Saccopastore (Italy), and others. He is not sure that one ought to place here the African specimens known as *Rhodesian man, Saldanha,* and *Florisbad.*

As a rule, Early Neandertaloids have rather delicate jaws and teeth, but rugged occiputs (backs of heads). Their long bones are generally straight and gracile; there are traces of projecting chins; and though the brow ridges may be bony and massive, they are usually divided into two parts instead of forming one, unbroken torus. Adult males may have reached 5 feet 10 inches in stature, and bodies are thought to have been fairly light. Although the Early specimens differ from the Classic in many respects, there are enough resemblances to warrant the hypothesis that the Early forms were incipiently and perhaps ancestrally Classic. Nor must we forget the belief that some of the Early Neandertaloids may have evolved into sapiens varieties.

(b) Classic Neandertaloids

These Ice Age people, presumably adjusted to and isolated by glaciers, are the prototypes of the cave men so dear to the hearts of popular writers and cartoonists. They are best known to anthropologists from a number of European relics found at Düsseldorf (Germany), Gibraltar (Spain), La Quina (France), Le Moustier (France), Spy (Belgium), La Chapelle-aux-Saints (France), and elsewhere. These specimens indicate that Classic Neandertal men stood in adulthood only 2 or 3 inches above 5 feet. Conventionally, this short stature, accompanied by a slouching posture, was believed to have been caused in part by failure to have achieved a fully upright posture. Leg bones are generally massive but short, with curved shafts. These have been interpreted as having prevented full extension of the legs when standing upright. Consequently, the Classic Neandertaloids are believed to have walked with a perpetual dip at the knees, a mode of progression sometimes referred to as "the bent-knee gait." It may well be that such a description exaggerates this condition, which is found in extreme form in the skeleton from La Chapelle-aux-Saints (Fig. 6–4, right). Nevertheless, other Classic Neandertal thigh and shin bones also show some curvature or bowing, so that it is probably correct to say that these people could not stand completely erect; but, on the whole, they were not as bestial as they have sometimes been pictured.

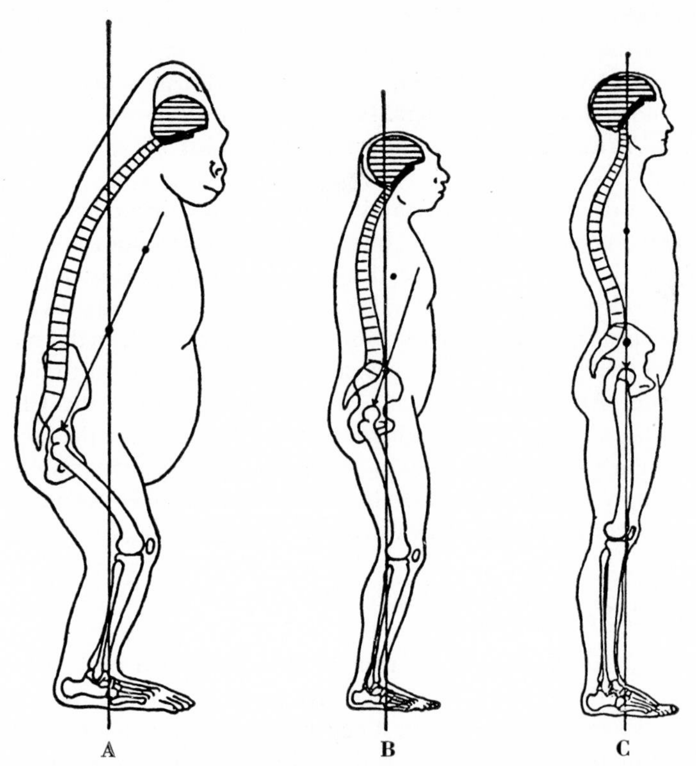

FIG. 6-5. Upright posture and spinal curves (after J. Dudley Morton). A comparative view of (A) a gorilla, (B) Neandertal Man from La Chapelle-aux-Saints, and (C) *Homo sapiens*.

The feet seem imperfectly adjusted to orthograde locomotion. Ankle arches are low, the great toes are set apart from the others, and scholars believe that the weight of the body was transmitted mostly to the outer borders of the feet (Fig. 6–5).

Generally speaking, Classic Neandertal man appears to have been stockily built. He had a rather high and narrow pelvis, a rounded (*Homo sapiens* has a flattened) chest, a poorly developed lumbar curve, and long and prominent processes at the backs of the cervical vertebrae—that is, in the neck region. These are associated, it should be remembered, with a heavily developed nuchal musculature; and this feature is found when the head and jaws project forward and the skull is poorly poised on top of the spine. Such a conclusion is justified, because the spinal cord of Classic Neandertalers passes through a foramen magnum that is located toward the rear of the skull base. All these signs indicate that the Classic Neandertaloids had short, thick necks and outthrust faces and jaws. Mandibles are inclined to be large, but teeth are hominid, even when they show taurodontism.

Classic Neandertal skulls are quite distinctive. Brow ridges are always prominent and may merge into a single supraorbital torus; and there is often a bun-shaped projection at the rear. The facial area is large, with big, rounded eye orbits and large nasal openings. Curiously enough, while it is felt that these hominids could not stand fully erect their cranial capacities were high, ranging from about 1300 to about 1600 cubic centimeters. This large brain size should not hastily be compared with sapiens' averages. It may be that in terms of over-all complexity of development and in respect to the size of several important parts, the brains of Neandertalers were far removed from the conditions of contemporary men. For instance, it has been argued that there was only a poor development of the frontal and upper lobes, where most of modern man's higher faculties are supposedly lodged. Most experts are unimpressed with the gross size of Neandertaloid brains.

Nevertheless, while the bent-knee gait may, to some extent, have interfered with speed and agility, the Classic Neandertaloids are not considered to have been significantly below *Homo sapiens* in general fitness. In western Europe they are known to have lived on into a bitter Ice Age (*Würm*), and to have survived in spite of the harsh arctic or subarctic environment. They were advanced enough to have employed a wide variety of cultural devices, such as cave homes, fireplaces, a kit of stone tools and weapons, and, presumably, clothing. We shall meet Classic Neandertal man again when we take up the Mousterian phase of culture in western Europe.

3. HOMO NEANDERTALENSIS —CERTAIN AND DUBIOUS

Since the beginning of this century a large number of so-called Neandertaloids have been found in various parts of the world. Some of them are too fragmentary to be classified properly; some resemble Classic Neandertal man; some are comparable to Early Neandertaloids; some appear little different from *Homo sapiens*; and some are interpreted to be mixtures of Classic Neandertaloids with more modern types of men. Most of these assorted specimens will be briefly treated in this section.

(a) The Heidelberg Jaw: Years ago a geologist named Otto Schoetensack, from the University of Heidelberg, was in the habit of making regular visits to a deep sandpit at Mauer, about six miles southeast of his school. Here, in 1907, Schoetensack was shown the amazing relic that is now known as the *Heidelberg jaw* (Fig. 6–6). Only a

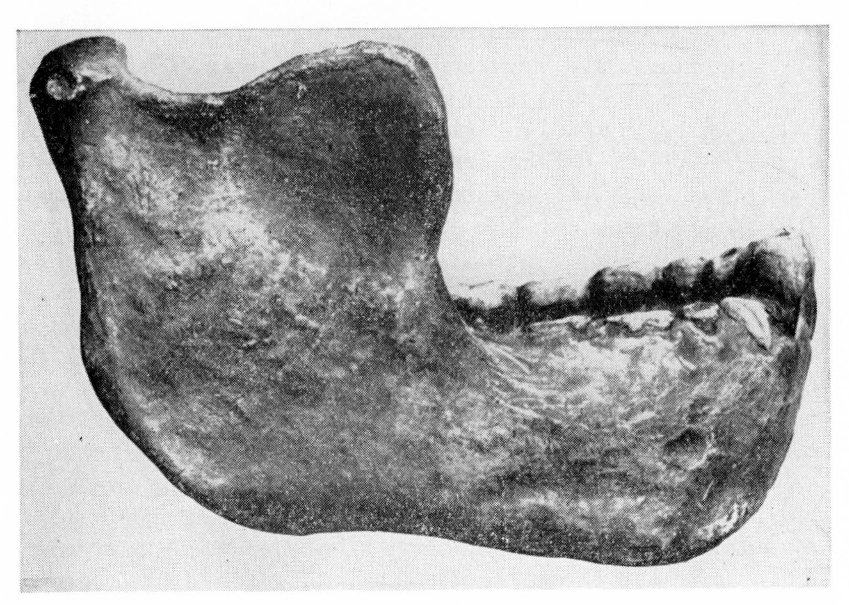

FIG. 6-6. The Heidelberg Jaw (after Schoetensack; shown about three fourths of natural size). This large, chinless jaw contains unexpectedly human teeth. (Courtesy of H. V. Vallois and the Musée de l'Homme.)

lower jaw with most of its original teeth in place was recovered, but it came from a layer about 80 feet below the surface of the pit. The mandible is stupendous in size, lacks all semblance of a chin, and exhibits several apish characteristics. Yet, within this big, apelike jaw there is no simian shelf, and the implanted teeth are entirely human in size, proportion, number, arrangement, and projection. Thus do these enigmatic remains help to document the theory of asymmetrical evolution.

Because the molar teeth are taurodont, it used to be argued that the man with the Heidelberg jaw was ancestral to the Classic Neandertaloids. This theory has been abandoned, since it has been shown that taurodontism may turn up in many kinds of subhuman Primates, as well as in many forms of hominids.

So little of Heidelberg "man" was found that it is unwise to try to guess how the rest of him was built, how he stood and walked, or what his cranial capacity might have been.

(b) Rhodesian Man: Almost no hominid relic caused more excitement than the skull and other skeletal parts that were found in 1921, after a blasting operation at the Broken Hill mine in Southern Rhodesia, Africa. Conservative anthropologists, headed by the late Aleš Hrdlička, flatly refused to believe that all the fragments pertained to the same individual, but even when the skull is examined by itself the Rhodesian cranium is amazing. Above a pair of big, high eye sockets there projects a stupendous bony torus, equal in magnitude to that of a large, fully grown, male gorilla. Coupled with this is an exceedingly retreating forehead and a very low-roofed cranial vault. These features give *Rhodesian man* (Fig. 6–7) a singularly bestial appearance.

In other regards the skull conforms to recent human standards. Its cranial capacity is estimated at 1300 cubic centimeters; the nasal bones are not quite as developed as in men of today, but they are by no means simian; the palate is huge in dimension but hominid in shape; and the teeth are large but of human proportions. No one mentions Rhodesian man without calling attention to his poor health, for his teeth are badly decayed, he had trouble with his mastoids, and he probably suffered from arthritis.

No matter how it is to be interpreted, the Rhodesian skull is an astonishing relic. Within itself it provides a striking illustration of asymmetrical evolution, for the stupendous torus and apelike face are accompanied by a cranial capacity and a set of teeth that fall well within the range of contemporary human averages. There is room for argument in regard to its relations with other extinct hominids, but it shows resemblances both to Solo man and to some of the Classic Neandertaloids from western Europe. It is frequently regarded as an irregular specimen of an African Neandertaler. Later finds on the scene of the original discovery have supported this conclusion.

(c) Saldanha Man: At Hopefield in South Africa, around Saldanha Bay, about 90 miles south of Capetown, there were found in 1953 a hominid skull cap and a fragment of a mandible. The skull cap is a little smaller than Rhodesian man's, but in shape the two are virtually identical. This establishes the probability that Rhodesian man was

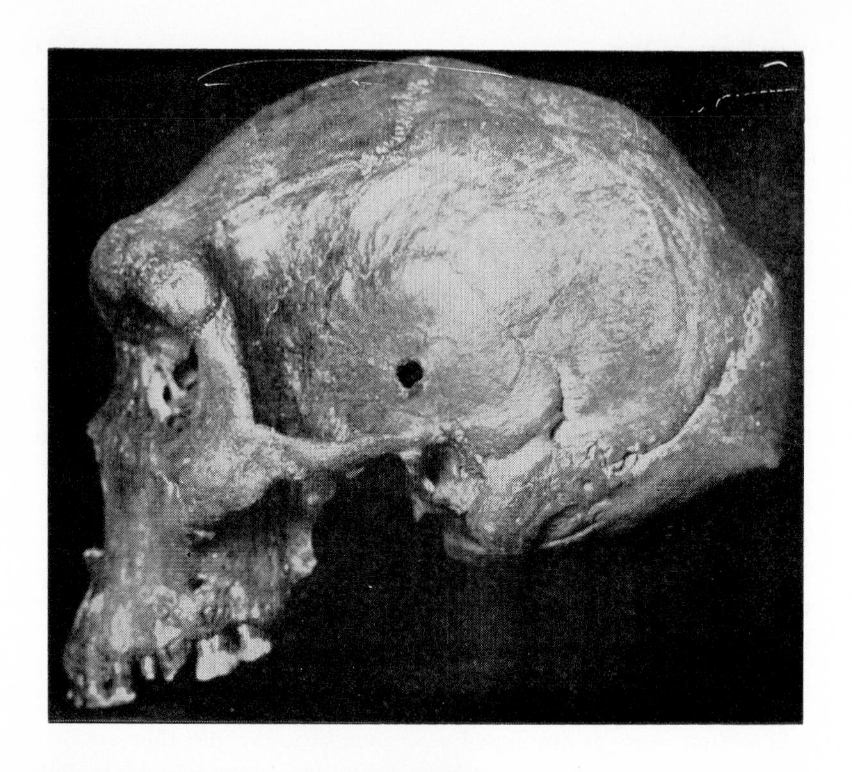

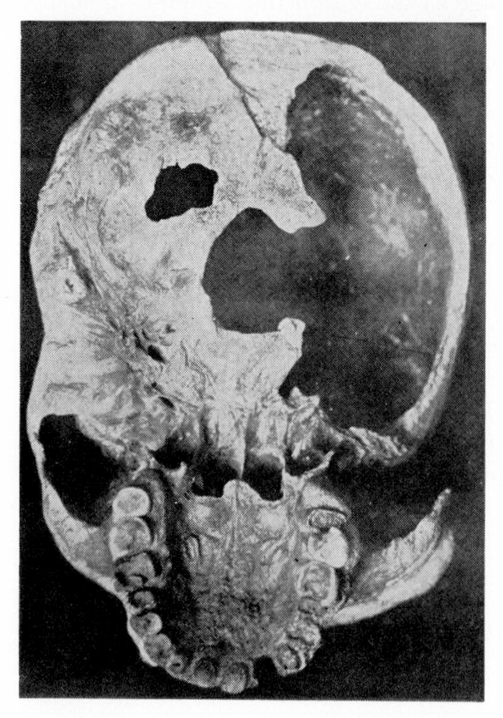

FIG. 6-7. The skull of Rhodesian man. Above: Despite its stupendous supraorbital torus and low-arched skull vault, the cranial capacity of this extinct hominid was well up to modern standards. Asymmetrical evolution is also apparent from the slightly elevated nasal bones and the hominid teeth. Left: The base of the Rhodesian skull. This view brings out the contrast between the huge palate and the hominid teeth. (Courtesy of the Museum of Anthropology, The University of Michigan.)

not a solitary freak, but that Rhodesianlike Neandertaloids were once rather widespread in Africa.[21]

(d) Shanidar: Since 1957, R. Solecki, an anthropologist now at Columbia University, has found the skeletons of about seven Neandertaloids who had lived and died in the Kurdistan hills of northern Iraq. In general, the *Shanidar* folk resemble the Classic Neandertals of western Europe, but they differ in some details, such as in the possession of divided brow ridges. A few experts think that the Shanidar people—together with assorted specimens from Mt. Carmel, the northern shore of the Sea of Galilee, and Behistun—should be placed into a separate category to be known as the Southwest Asiatic Neandertals. These hominids were probably contemporaneous with Europe's Classic Neandertals and emphasize the great variability of *Homo neandertalensis.*

(e) Ehringsdorf and Steinheim: Back in 1925 an important Neandertaloid skull was excavated at Ehringsdorf, near Weimar, Germany. The *Ehringsdorf skull* is fragmentary, but it shows some modern features such as thin bones and a high forehead, associated with large brow ridges. Because of its more highly evolved features, some anthropologists call it a progressive Neandertaloid, and feel that it was progressing toward a sapiens type; but others regard it as a mixture between Classic Neandertal and a more advanced kind of hominid.

Virtually all that has been said of the Ehringsdorf skull applies to *Steinheim man.* This specimen was found in Germany in 1933. Judged by the soil in which it lay, and by the animal bones with which it was associated, this form may be earlier than the Classic Neandertaloids further west. Nevertheless, although the cranium is low and has huge brow ridges—Classic traits—in other regards it is modern or progressive. Generally speaking, the Steinheim relic combines a Neandertaloid face with

[21] For a report on Saldanha man, by one of its finders, see R. Singer, "The Saldanha Skull. . . . ," *American Journal of Physical Anthropology,* Vol. 12, 1954, pp. 345 ff.

A discussion of this specimen, and of its links with Rhodesian man, may be found in W. L. Straus, Jr., "Saldanha Man and His Culture," *Science,* Vol. 125, 1957, pp. 973–74.

Other famous discoveries in Africa include the *Florisbad Skull,* a fragmentary specimen of an ancient but relatively modern hominid with some Neandertaloid traits; *Boskop man,* a massive-skulled late Pleistocene type that has been associated both with Negroid and Australoid forms of man; and *Oldoway man,* found by Leakey at Gamble's Cave, Elementeita, Kenya. Oldoway man has been interpreted as a very tall, late Pleistocene hominid who may have been ancestral to some of Africa's present varieties.

A number of anthropologists feel the African finds alone provide links running all the way from the apes to *Homo sapiens.*

an essentially sapiens brain case. Needless to say, there is great uncertainty about its proper placement and interpretation. No one knows whether it was evolving into a modern type of man, or whether it was a hybrid between a Classic Neandertal and a member of *Homo sapiens.* There is also a possibility, as LeGros Clark has indicated, that anthropologists of a few decades ago used to assign Neandertaloid affiliations to any skull that had massive, bony brow ridges. Possibly, too much significance has been read into this anatomical feature.

4. Homo modernus[22]

The author introduces the term *Homo modernus* with some trepidation. It may be that zoological taxonomists will find fault with it, but there is need in anthropology for some term to denote a category of Pleistocene forms of man that seem to have evolved more in the direction of *Homo sapiens* than any of the specimens treated so far. At present it is commonly believed that some varieties of *Homo modernus* are at least as ancient as some types of *Homo neandertalensis.*

So far the evidence is scant and a bit shaky, but there do seem to have been varieties of early Pleistocene man whose forms closely resemble those of *Homo sapiens.*

(a) Swanscombe Man or Woman

A long time ago, far back in the Pleistocene era, perhaps 200,000 or 300,000 years B.P., the Thames in southern England deposited a layer of gravel that is 100 feet above the river's present level. This stratum is

22 At one time, as an examination of older textbooks will reveal, it used to be customary for anthropologists to include *Galley Hill man* and *Piltdown man* in their discussions of Pleistocene forms of hominids with modern traits. Galley Hill man, it has been proved, was a member of *Homo sapiens* whose body happened to be laid in a stratum of Pleistocene soil. For this story consult M. F. Ashley Montagu and K. P. Oakley, "The Antiquity of Galley Hill Man," *American Journal of Physical Anthropology,* Vol. 7, 1949, pp. 363–84.

Piltdown man, on the contrary, seems to have been a deliberate hoax. An ape's mandible, and a sapiens upper skull were stained and otherwise treated alike and then buried together. After more than forty years of puzzlement over this "specimen," careful, scientific detective work revealed the true nature of this fraud. For a fascinating and detailed account of this entire episode, see J. S. Weiner, *The Piltdown Forgery,* New York, 1955.

Other specimens from England that have been dismissed from serious consideration include the London skull, the Bury St. Edmunds relic, the Baker's Hole remains, and a few others.

widely known as the 100-foot terrace of the Thames. In 1935 and 1936 an English dentist and amateur archeologist, A. T. Marston, found embedded there portions of a skull that fitted perfectly together and comprised the occiput (rear) and left parietal (side wall above the temple) of an early Pleistocene hominid. Anthropologists, with the help of fluorine analysis, are agreed that the fragments belong together; and that they come from a youthful, probably a female cranium (Fig. 6–8). The

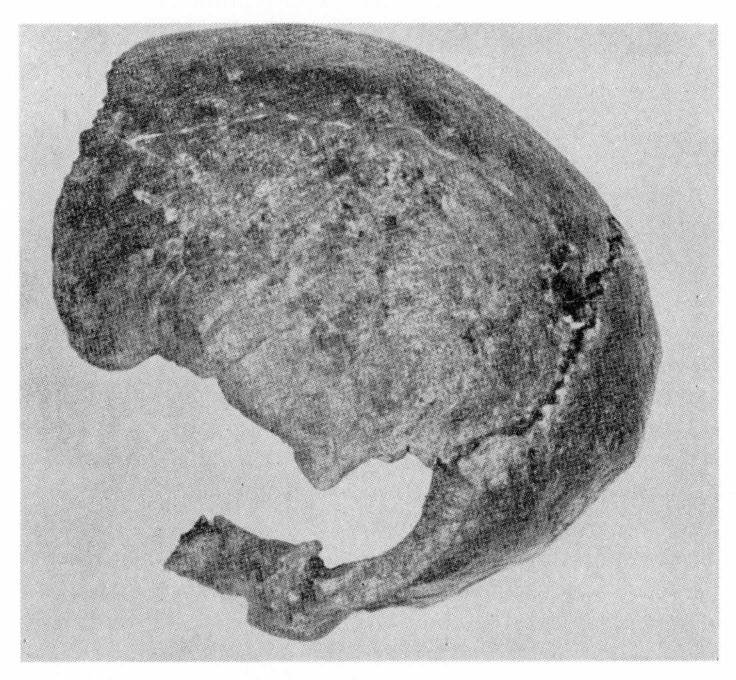

FIG. 6-8. Swanscombe bones (after Morant; about five ninths of natural size). The parietal and occipital bones first discovered at Swanscombe. Except for their thickness, they are quite modern. (Courtesy of H. V. Vallois and the Musée de l'Homme.)

remnants cannot be said to provide anywhere near a complete picture of *Swanscombe man*. The bones are thick and broad but modern, and the cranial capacity has been estimated at about 1325 cubic centimeters. There is something surprisingly sapienslike about these fragments, and neither in thickness nor in cranial capacity do they fall outside the range of living mankind.

So important were the meager remains of Swanscombe man that when their discovery was announced the Royal Anthropological Institute of Great Britain and Ireland appointed a commission of highly trained experts to look into the entire matter.[23] They agreed that the finds were authentic, that the remnants belonged together, and that the bones pertained to an early Pleistocene hominid, whose skull was virtually modern. It was further noted that the skeletal material probably belonged to the warm Interglacial period that preceded the third (*Riss*) major advance of Pleistocene ice; and that it was directly connected with the Middle Acheulian hand-ax culture. This comes before the Mousterian culture which is conventionally linked with Neandertal man. All this indicates that Swanscombe man lived in earlier times than the Neandertalers.

Twenty years after Marston found the left parietal and occipital bones of Swanscombe man, John Wymer and Adrian Gibson came across a right parietal about 50-feet from the spot of the original discovery. Everything indicates that the new find belongs with the others, but it is too soon to know what light it will shed on Swanscombe man's appearance.[24]

(b) The Fontéchevade Skulls

At Fontéchevade in southern France, Mademoiselle Henri-Martin in 1947 dug parts of two hominid skulls from a spot just outside the present mouth of a cave. Apart from the bone fragments, two things about the discovery are of great interest. In the first place, it is entirely likely that the original cave formerly covered the place where the finds were made; and in the second place, the hominid remnants were found together with Tayacian tools in a level underlying Mousterian implements. It is felt therefore that the Fontéchevade skulls belonged to hominids that roamed the area before it was dominated by Classic Neandertaloids.

As for the bone fragments, they are very thick, yet of sapiens type. Unfortunately, only portions of the Fontéchevade skulls were found, and it would be reckless to infer too much from them. It is enough to say that they strike most observers as modern; that they were found together with the remains of animals that love warmth; that they were presumably earlier than Classic Neandertalers; and that their relation to Swanscombe man has not yet been worked out.

---

[23] The Swanscombe Committee included among its members LeGros Clark, Mourant, and Oakley. For the full details of their conclusions, see the "Report on the Swanscombe Skull," *Journal of the Royal Anthropological Institute,* Vol. 68, 1938, pp. 17–98.

[24] Announcement of the new discovery was made by John Wymer in *Nature,* Vol. 176, September 3, 1955, pp. 426 ff.

(c) The Coming of Cro-Magnon

Although some of the geologically early specimens of *Homo modernus* are questionable, it cannot be denied that modern men appeared in force late in the Pleistocene, perhaps 35,000 B.P. The best known of these forms, in Europe, are called *Cro-Magnon*. The name is taken from a spot in Dordogne, France, where Louis Lartet, in 1868, first discovered parts of an old man's skeleton. A short distance away Lartet found the remains of four other individuals. These comprise the original Cro-Magnon men, but the name has come to be used for a wide assortment of modern-looking people from late Pleistocene deposits in sundry parts of the Old World.

Lartet turned his materials over to Pierre Broca for description and analysis, and Broca found that there was little to distinguish the Cro-Magnon populace from *Homo sapiens*. Cro-Magnon adult males were tall and sturdy. They stood between 5 feet 6 inches and 6 feet in height; their forearms and shins were relatively elongated; and their skulls were massive and long in relation to breadth. At the same time, the face is broad and very short. This gives the entire cranium a disharmonic appearance, which is found in some members of *Homo sapiens*.

Cro-Magnon skulls have robust mandibles, but these are equipped with projecting chins and are perfectly modern in conformation. Foreheads are high and well-developed; eye orbits are long and narrow; brow ridges are moderate; and the nasal bones are narrow but humanly elevated. The brain case is large, and cranial capacities run to 1600 cubic centimeters or more (see Fig. 6–9).

The main trait that makes one hesitate to classify Cro-Magnon with *Homo sapiens* is an occasional bowing of the thighbones, much less marked than in *Homo neandertalensis*, that might possibly have interfered with perfectly upright posture. Apart from this doubtful feature, it is a tossup whether one calls Cro-Magnon the last of *Homo modernus* or the first of *Homo sapiens*.

CONCLUSION

This chapter makes an effort to picture some of the steps in the process by which living human beings came to be so widely separated from such other Primates as are exemplified by the existing apes. For this purpose a review was made of many of the extinct forms of hominids that had preceded *Homo sapiens* on earth. No attempt was made to provide exhaustive summaries of every single specimen that has been discovered,

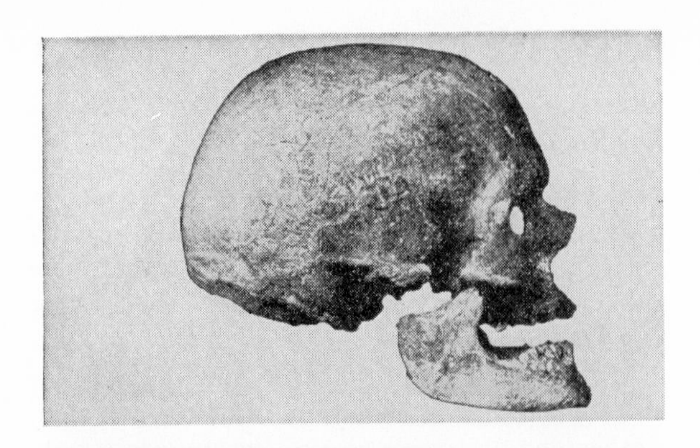

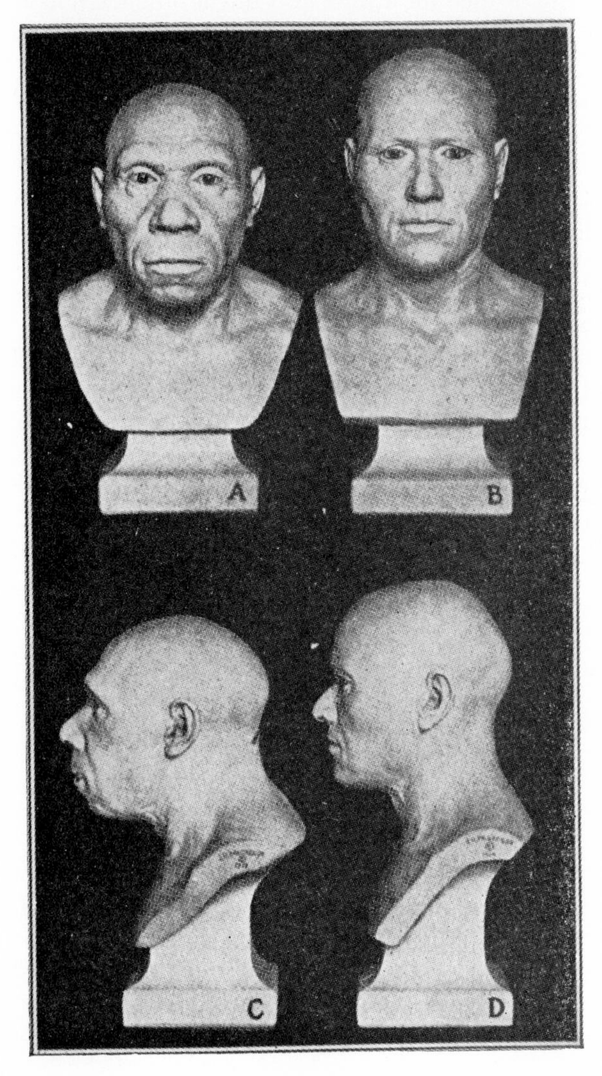

FIG. 6-9. Cro-Magnon hominids. Above: The skull of the "Old Man," one of the original discoveries at Cro-Magnon. About one fifth of its natural size. It is basically like that of *Homo sapiens.* (Courtesy of H. V. Vallois and the Musée de l'Homme.) Left: Restoration of Cro-Magnon and Neandertal men after McGregor). Cro-Magnon's head is higher, his neck is longer, his head and jaws are less out-thrust, his brow ridges are more delicate, and his chin is well developed. In short, he is a modern human in all respects.

and little was said of the heated controversies that usually sprang up whenever a new find was announced. Enough material has been presented, though, to indicate the vastness of the topic, and to furnish a rough and tentative outline of the evolutionary events that immediately preceded the emergence of modern man.

In the days when only a few forms of extinct men were known it used to be considered proper to put each form at the tip of a different branch leading from the trunk of an evolutionary tree. Nowadays, so large an assemblage has been discovered, and there are so many intergrades that combine, let us say, Neandertal and sapiens-looking features, that a treelike diagram in which each branch tip is separate from every other is plainly inadequate. Therefore, no such diagram is included in this chapter.

If, for the moment, we disregard the confusing welter of particular details and concentrate only on the broad sweep of events, a fairly clear picture emerges. Many millions of years ago, in Miocene times, there existed a good number of simians. Some of them specialized into the living apes, and others moved away to become man. Assuming that the interpretation of Oreopithecus is correct, the break between apes and man may already have been under way in the Pliocene.

Very early in the next geological phase, at the start of the Pleistocene about one million years ago, the separation is no longer a matter of speculation and had gone far enough to produce the Australopithecinae. Then, between early and mid-Pleistocene times, roughly from 600,000 to 500,000 B.P., the manlike forms had the appearance of *Homo erectus.* This presumed species may be looked upon as formative man. It was anatomically distinct from *Homo sapiens,* but was much closer to the species than were any of the apes of the time. Somewhat later, with a climax between 100,000 and 40,000 B.P., diversified forms of *Homo neandertalensis* dominated the scene. All of the Neandertaloids may be regarded as old-style men and women who were surely human and less bestial than is sometimes supposed, but whose bodies showed enough simianlike or else highly specialized traits to set them apart from *Homo sapiens.* Then, in the closing phases of the Pleistocene, perhaps around 35,000 B.P., *Homo modernus,* in the form of Cro-Magnon man, arrived in number. He was so greatly diversified that, according to the opinions of some, he ought to be subdivided into several types, some of which may have been ancestral to the varieties that now prevail. On the other hand, G. M. Mourant, one of our leading specialists in physical anthropology, is impressed with the unity of the late Pleistocene forms of man.

With all due respect to Mourant, who had only dry bones, mainly skulls, to guide him, it is entirely likely that *Homo modernus,* in late

Pleistocene times, was at least as diversified as is living mankind. Of course, no one knows exactly how to interpret Cro-Magnon diversification. After all, anthropologists who deal with hominids from the remote past are forced to rely on chance finds of individuals or small clusters of remains from a given spot. They have no way of determining how typical, normal, or abnormal their material may be, and that is why they can seldom tell whether the distinctions that they observe are merely individual peculiarities or features that are common to a large group.

It will be noted that a gap of 5000 years is suggested between the end of the Neandertal climax and the arrival in force of modern kinds of men. This is based on the fact that Neandertal and *Homo modernus* remains are never found side by side. An opinion has even been expressed that only one kind of hominid ever existed at a time. Still, it has been shown that some varieties of *Homo sapiens* exhibit typical Neandertaloid features. How did they get them? In the past such resemblances were attributed to interbreeding. A more recent hypothesis states that modern types of man may always have had some of the same characteristics that are found in *Homo neandertalensis* and that these characteristics could have been received directly from their ancestors without the necessity of postulating interbreeding. In the same connection it is no longer considered certain that *Homo sapiens* had ever passed through a distinct Neandertal stage.

There is not much, other than time, to separate *Homo modernus* from *Homo sapiens*. As to the sequence of events, surely, even the most conservative of anthropologists will have to agree that by the time the Recent (Holocene) epoch replaced the Pleistocene, somewhere about 12,000 B.P., *Homo sapiens* was the only species of man to be on hand.

Where did man originate? Formerly, it was believed that the "Garden of Eden" must have been in Asia. In support of theories of Asiatic origin, anthropologists were wont to point out that Asia has yielded the bones of fossil apes, possesses two kinds of living apes, and was once the homeland of *Homo erectus,* forms of *Homo neandertalensis,* and several varieties of *Homo modernus,* prior to the coming of *Homo sapiens.* Only Africa, among the remaining continents, can challenge Asia's claim. Here are found extinct and living manlike apes, as well as the Australopithecinae, some of which may have had connections with *Homo erectus.* In addition, there are several reputedly Neandertaloid specimens and an assortment of forms that may be classed with *Homo modernus,* to say nothing of *Homo sapiens.* No final verdict can be reached, but since no other continent reveals signs of so great a series of steps in the evolution of modern man, the cradle of mankind must tentatively be placed either in Asia or, as Darwin believed, in Africa. Many modern scholars also favor Africa.

Selected References

Boule, Marcellin, and Vallois, Henri V., *Fossil Men,* rev. ed., New York, 1957.

Howell, F. Clark, "The Evolutionary Significance of Variation and the Varieties of 'Neanderthal' Man," *The Quarterly Review of Biology,* Vol. 32, 1957, pp. 330–47.

———, "The Place of Neanderthal Man in Human Evolution," *American Journal of Physical Anthropology,* Vol. 9, 1957, pp. 379–416.

Keith, Sir Arthur, *New Discoveries Relating to the Antiquity of Man,* London and New York, 1931.

———, *The Antiquity of Man,* London, 1929.

Kroeber, Alfred L., *Anthropology,* rev. ed., New York, 1948, Chap. 3.

Lasker, Gabriel W., *The Evolution of Man,* New York, 1961, Chaps. 10–12.

Mayr, Ernst, "Taxonomic Categories in Fossil Hominids," *Cold Spring Harbor Symposium in Quantitative Biology,* Vol. 15, 1950, pp. 109 ff.

McCown, Theodore D., and Keith, Sir Arthur, *The Stone Age of Mount Carmel,* Vol. 2, London, 1939.

Straus, William L., Jr., "The Riddle of Man's Ancestry," *The Quarterly Review of Biology,* Vol. 24, 1949, pp. 200–23.

van Koenigswald, G. H. R., *Meeting Prehistoric Man,* New York, 1956.

Washburn, Sherwood L., "Tools and Human Evolution," *Scientific American,* Vol. 203, No. 1, 1960, pp. 3–15.

Weidenreich, Franz, *Apes, Giants, and Man,* Chicago, 1946.

———, "The Skull of Sinanthropus pekinensis," *Palaeontologia Sinica,* new series D, No. 10, 1943, pp. 1–484.

———, and von Koenigswald, G. H. R., "Morphology of Solo Man," *Anthropological Papers of the American Museum of Natural History,* Vol. 43, 1951, pp. 205–90.

The Varieties of Homo Sapiens

CHAPTER 7

When the physical or biological anthropologist, who deals with living subjects, takes over from the paleoanthropologist, who studies extinct forms of man, he is at once confronted with problems of numbers and variation. The world's population has reached a total of three billion, and no two persons, with the possible exception of identical twins, are exactly alike. In these circumstances the physical anthropologist faces a grave dilemma. Should he concentrate on similarities or variations among single individuals, or should he lump people into fairly large categories and then examine the resemblances and differences between the groups? Traditionally, physical anthropologists have chosen to work with big divisions of mankind.

Many years ago, when next to nothing was known of human genetics, subdivisions of *Homo sapiens* were established on the basis of external, anatomical landmarks that could be objectively measured or observed. Large numbers of people who showed similar traits or combinations of traits were grouped together and were assumed to have biogenetically inherited their similarities from common ancestors. Such practices and interpretations, it was believed, conformed to those of zoological taxonomists.

There then arose the question of what to call the different groups. Most anthropologists came to use the term "race" for any subdivision of *Homo sapiens,* often with qualifying adjectives such as primary and secondary, or geographical and local. But this usage can be very confusing, particularly when a writer leaves out the qualifying adjective.

Even a superficial examination of the variations among human groups makes apparent two orders of magnitude. Major distinctions set apart from one another the widely recognized divisions of *Caucasoid, Mongoloid,*[1] *Negroid,* and *Australoid*; and lesser differences separate the clusters of individuals contained inside each of these big units. When we recall that both the major and minor sets of distinctions apply to members of a single species, it follows that any subdivisions that are made must refer to something less than a species.

The suggestion has been put forth, and will, in the interests of clarity, be followed in this textbook, to call the greater units by the term *stock,* with the implication that each stock corresponds to a subspecies.[2] Then, the smaller groups contained within each stock may be called *races,* with the implication that each race comprises a subsubspecies.[3] It is a matter of record that all biological taxonomists find it harder and harder to make clear-cut categories when they deal with groupings that are ever smaller than a species. Anthropologists have exactly the same trouble. That is why there is practically no dissent from the notion that all living persons make up a single species, and there is relatively little disagreement about stocks; but when it comes to races there are wide differences of opinion.

There is a powerful trend on the part of some physical anthropologists nowadays to discard both the term and the concept of race in dealing with *Homo sapiens.* They stress the fact that all of living mankind belongs to one species, and instead of emphasizing different units, they prefer to arrange all the human varieties on one continuum or cline. Instead of dealing with *Homo sapiens* as broken up into stocks or races, they like to think of mankind as divided into numerous breeding populations, each with a different combination of gene frequencies.[4]

Let us return now to the physical variations observable among the divisions of living mankind. Only a tiny minority of scholars thinks that

[1] Some anthropologists treat the American Indians (*Amerinds*) as a distinct unit, equivalent to the stocks mentioned above, but others regard them as being variants or derivatives of Mongoloids. The author favors the latter view.

[2] Many writers on this subject regard all divisions of mankind as subspecies. Obviously, they do not recognize as valid the distinctions that are here made.

[3] The idea of separating stocks from races was proposed by W. M. Krogman in his essay entitled, "The Concept of Race," in Ralph Linton, ed., *The Science of Man in the World Crisis,* New York, 1945, pp. 46 ff. Krogman's suggestion has not gained universal acceptance, yet Kroeber speaks of "The Grand Divisions or Primary Stocks" of *Homo sapiens.* A. L. Kroeber, *Anthropology,* rev. ed., New York, 1948, p. 131.

[4] This view has been forcibly expressed by Frank B. Livingstone of the University of Michigan. If it does nothing else, his article shows a modern distaste for traditional (and vague) concepts of race. See, together with T. Dobzhansky's comment, and Livingstone's reply, F. B. Livingstone, "On the Non-Existence of Human Races," *Current Anthropology,* Vol. 3, No. 3, 1962, pp. 279–81.

people are different because each unit has made a different evolutionary descent from a different set of ancestors. Instead, it is widely believed that all the living varieties of man stem from a common ancestral background; and that the stocks and races had long ago acquired distinctive traits as they settled in variegated environments. As a starting point for such a hypothesis, let us assume that about 35,000 B.P. there appeared in the Eastern Hemisphere the first members of *Homo sapiens,* whose descendants gradually spread through the entire world. If we then assume, as Krogman has proposed, that these first modern humans carried in their reproductive cells assorted genes for skin color, hair form, nasal shape, etc., then we would have a genetic basis for the variations that exist among stocks and races.[5]

It is fairly well known that the earliest representatives of *Homo sapiens* lived in tiny clusters while gathering wild foods, hunting, or fishing.[6] It is, therefore, reasonable to postulate that as they moved about they could readily have become separated and even isolated from one another. Such factors provide the conditions for forming distinct physical varieties. Within each cut-off unit natural selection, or the need for adapting to the immediate environment, would have favored the preservation of some genes at the expense of others. Then, again, each of the cut-off units would, of necessity, have become a breeding community, with mates exchanging their genes back and forth. This would have countered the tendency toward continuous variation; and, in due time, a common *gene pool* must have been formed. Variability would also have been cut down through the agencies of sexual and sociocultural selection. On the other hand, any mutations or changes of genetic structure that might have arisen in one isolated group were unlikely to have arisen in another. In some such fashion, after many generations of geographical and biological separation, all of the units, despite their originally common genetic background, would have come to differ from each other both *genotypically* (in the actual nature of their genes), and *phenotypically* (in external appearance). Then, as means of communication and travel improved and increased, the once-isolated and varied breeding populations would have been brought in touch with each other, thus paving the way for the high degree of intermixture that is an outstanding phenomenon of our own day.

There is a big difference of approach to racial classification between

[5] W. M. Krogman, *loc. cit.* C. S. Coon, *The Origin of Races,* New York, 1962, pp. 4–5, disagrees with this assumption.

[6] S. M. Garn, *Human Races,* Springfield, Ill., 1961, p. 96, *et passim.* It has been estimated that in early Pleistocene times the entire human population was only ten million. M. Bates, *Man in Nature,* Englewood Cliffs, N.J., 1961, p. 55.

the physical anthropologists of the past and those of the present. Formerly, it was taken for granted that the features that typified a given subdivision of *Homo sapiens,* such as the blue eyes of the Nordic race, were the exclusive possession of that subdivision. Hence, whenever blue eyes showed up among peoples, even if they were remote from the homelands of Nordics, it was attributed, usually without substantiating proof, to one-time admixture with Nordics. Modern physical anthropologists disagree. They note that features like blue eyes may arise independently from a variety of causes. Accordingly, they will not accept intermixture as an explanation of trait resemblances, unless adequate supporting proof is brought forward. It should also be carefully noted that the belief "that the subdivisions of mankind had always possessed their characteristic features," implies something fixed and static, rather than dynamic and adaptive.

In the past, too, physical anthropologists were so sure that the subdivisions of mankind had always possessed their characteristic features that they often believed, consciously or subconsciously, in the former existence of "pure" races. At present such a notion is almost never encountered.

On this score, the late E. A. Hooton, who made a marked impact on early physical anthropology, once felt that the best racial markers were "nonadaptive" characteristics, because they were neutral in the struggle for survival, and were therefore likely to be handed on unchanged from generation to generation. Later, when Hooton came to realize that races develop through the natural selection of some of a variety of adaptations; and when it was shown that many traits were actually adaptive, although he had once thought that they were nonadaptive, Hooton changed his mind and admitted adaptive traits to be proper criteria of race.[7]

Finally, it used to be believed implicitly that there were certain folk who showed the features assigned to their race, while others did not. Such "typical" or "average" individuals were always hard to find. Yet, the belief persisted that some people were so representative of their race that, in extreme cases, one person might stand for an entire group. Contemporary physical anthropologists refuse to believe that any individual, no matter how "average" or "typical" he may be, can possibly be the equivalent of a whole subdivision of mankind.

Despite these criticisms, and others to be mentioned later, the racial classifications established by traditional workers are usually taken for granted and are still being used. It seems necessary, therefore, to provide

---

7 Hooton's "about face" is explained in E. A. Hooton, *Up from the Ape,* rev. ed., New York, 1946, p. 452.

an account of former procedures in race classification, and of some of the results that were obtained.

Traditional methods of stock and race classification

Absence of great and outstanding biological differences among the various subgroups of *Homo sapiens* has forced the classifiers of living man to deal with anatomical minutiae. On the whole, they go about their tasks by using a combination of three techniques: (1) wherever possible, on skeletal material or live bodies, they try to make careful measurements between specific points; (2) where this is impossible, as in dealing with color differences, they resort to detailed observations based on agreed-upon standards; and (3) for computing averages or for establishing proportions between one body part and another, they utilize a number of statistical devices.

Until the current generation of physical anthropologists began to work, the traditional techniques were universally employed and seldom questioned. It was firmly believed that they would yield an accurate knowledge of the nature, range, and meaning of the variations among mankind; throw light on the evolutionary processes that had produced man and divided him into stocks and races; afford a sound point of departure for studies of the relationship of race to health and disease, longevity, fertility, crime, alcoholic tolerance, or intelligence; and help to elucidate the biological consequences of such practices as inbreeding or race mixture. Not all of these goals have been achieved, despite the dedication of many traditional workers. However, since much anthropological writing utilizes their ideas and terminology, their work will be summarized in some detail.[8]

Measurements and Indexes

With the help of specially designed instruments and with precisely designated landmarks, it is possible to measure accurately several segments of the body—alive, dead, or skeletalized. A tall, calibrated, metal

[8] Much additional information, and many more bibliographic sources may be obtained by consulting E. A. Hooton, *op. cit.*, pp. 699–764; M. F. Ashley Montagu, *op. cit.*, pp. 440–524; E. P. Stibbe, *An Introduction to Physical Anthropology*, rev. ed., New York and London, 1938; and J. Comas, *Manual of Physical Anthropology*, rev. English ed., Springfield, Ill., 1960.

rod with a sliding bar attached (*anthropometer*) is used for determining a subject's total stature, the height of his head and neck, the length of his limbs, the width of his shoulders and hips, and similar items. A smaller implement of comparable construction (*sliding calipers*) is used for taking such measurements as the length and width of the nose. Still another tool, with arms that open outward (*spreading calipers*) is made to measure rounded or spherical parts, and is handy for getting the length and breadth of the head, or the width of the face (Fig. 7–1). A

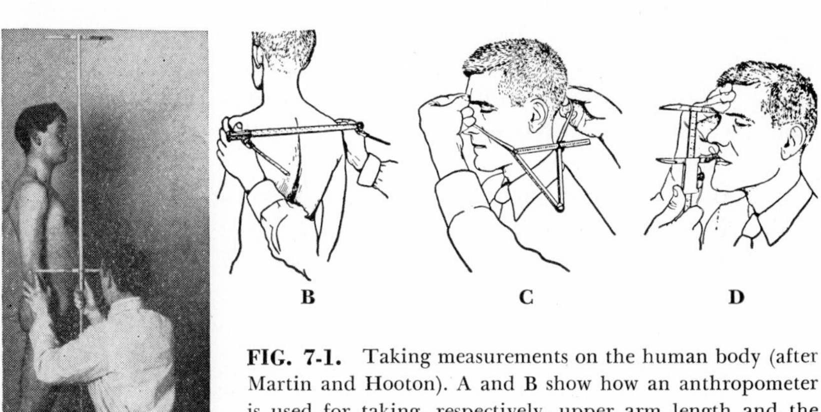

FIG. 7-1. Taking measurements on the human body (after Martin and Hooton). A and B show how an anthropometer is used for taking, respectively, upper arm length and the width of the shoulders. C illustrates how a spreading caliper measures the length of the head, and D pictures the measurement of upper face height with a sliding caliper. (From E. A. Hooton, *Up From the Ape,* rev. ed. New York, 1946. Courtesy of the author and The Macmillan Company.)

different tool is used for determining the height of a cranial vault. This dimension is usually measured from the ear openings, while a head or skull is in the Frankfort plane, that is, with the eye-ear line parallel to the ground. All the data obtained with these and other more highly specialized implements are recorded in the metric system in order to make possible comparisons with results secured by fellow scientists throughout the world. Figures obtained by trained investigators using standardized tools, methods, and landmarks, are likely to be accurate and to provide a sound basis for statistical comparisons and analyses.

Measurements may be allowed to stand by themselves, but it is a general practice to determine the proportions of one body segment to another. This is done by finding the ratio between measurements, and the result is called an *index*. One that was very widely utilized in traditional racial studies is the *cephalic index*. It expresses the ratio of the head's breadth to its length, and is conveniently calculated as a percentage by the use of a simple, mathematical formula: Breadth of head times 100 divided by length of head. If an individual's cephalic index is under 77, which is the same as saying that the breadth of the head is less than about 3/4 of the length, a person is considered to be *dolichocephalic* or longheaded. If the result is between 77 and 82, a person is classed as *mesocephalic* or medium-headed; and a figure of 82 or more is interpreted as *brachycephalic* or broadheaded.[9]

Another commonly used index expresses the proportion of nasal width relative to length. Again, a simple formula suffices: Nasal breadth times 100 divided by nasal length. A *nasal index* of less than 70 on a living subject is taken to indicate a narrow-nosed or *leptorrhine* condition; 70 to 85 is medium-nosed or *mesorrhine;* and over 85 means broadnosed or *platyrrhine.*

A third ratio that has been widely used is known as the *facial index.* It describes a person's facial length, given as a percentage of his facial width. A living individual whose index is below 85 is considered to be broad-faced (*euryprosopic*); he is medium-faced (*mesoprosopic*) if the proportion falls between 85 and 88; and long- or narrowed-faced (*leptoprosopic*) if the length is over 88 percent of the width.

Many other measurements and indexes are in use among professional physical anthropologists, and their calculations and interpretations are patterned along lines similar to the examples here given.

Observations

Accurate measurements between definite landmarks unquestionably provide the most satisfactory method of determining anatomical variations between groups of humans, but unfortunately there are bodily aspects that cannot be readily measured. These include skin, hair, and eye color; nasal prominences and profiles; face and jaw projections (prognathism); straight, wavy, curly, or frizzly hair forms (Fig. 7–2); lip thickness and eversion; ear shapes; and so on. It must not be overlooked that many observational features can, to a greater degree than points of measurement, be altered from their original or inherited appearance by tanning, bleaching, plastic surgery, or the ministrations of imaginative beauty-parlor operators. Anthropologists are aware of the difficulties involved in making accurate, unbiased, systematic, and standardized observations, but rather than abandon this technique altogether they pre-

[9] These figures apply to measurements on live subjects. With skulls, longheadedness is based on a percentage of 75 or less, and broadheadedness means anything over 80.

fer to use it with caution and in conjunction with data obtained by other means.

Sometimes, in an effort to achieve uniformity of results, physical anthropologists employ things like color charts, not much different from

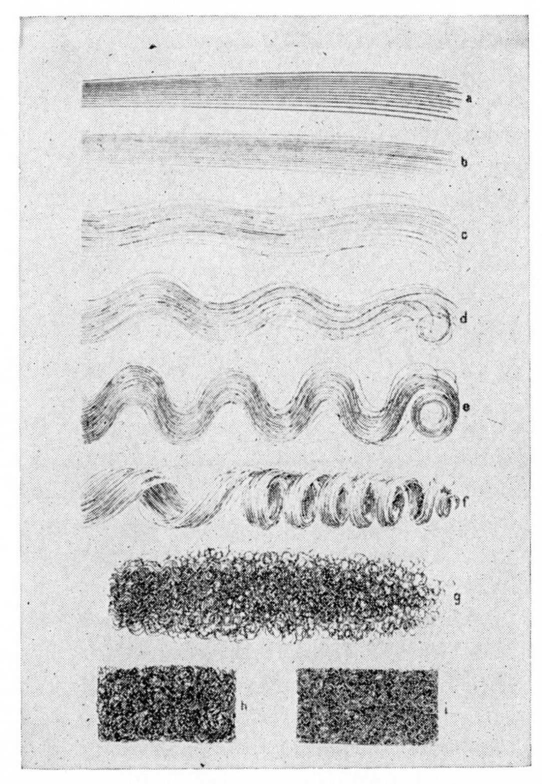

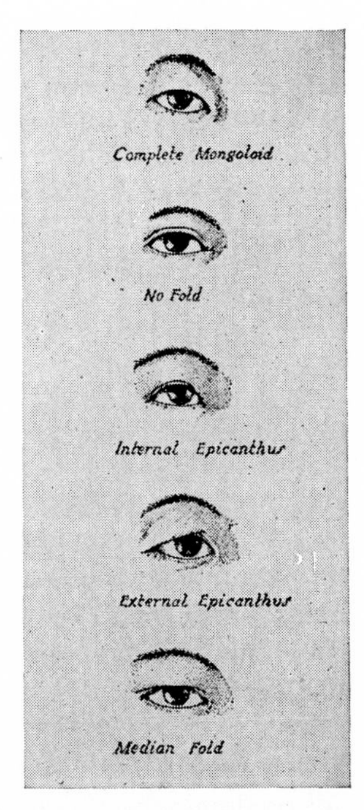

FIG. 7-2. Aids to observations. Left: Varieties of human head hair. Mongoloids have types *a* and *b,* and, occasionally, *c.* Caucasoids have some *c,* but are usually *d, e,* or *f.* Negroids generally have the spiral forms lettered *g, h,* and *i.* Right: Eye folds. Although eye folds are most characteristic of the Mongoloids, they may sometimes be noted in individuals of other stocks. (From E. A. Hooton, *Up From the Ape,* rev. ed. New York, 1946. Courtesy of the author and The Macmillan Company.)

those used for selecting paints or ladies' stockings. Even so, it is virtually impossible to make observational judgments with mathematical precision. And that, of course, is one of the most serious difficulties of all, for observations cannot readily be expressed in numbers and are not easy to elaborate statistically. Some mathematical formulas and coefficients have been worked out, and their use helps overcome one of the most serious drawbacks of this approach. In the long run, experienced observers get far more reliable and consistent results than laymen think possible, and observational data provide a highly valuable supplement to information secured by other techniques.

Placing man in the stocks and races

Without deviating too far from established taxonomic principles it is now possible to classify *Homo sapiens* into stocks and races by grouping into subdivisions those people who live in one area, function as an interbreeding unit, and have bodies that are similar in terms of measurements, proportions, and observations. Such old-fashioned classifications will have to do until more valid groupings of people are agreed upon. Only four of the best-known stocks will be described here. Their boundaries are by no means rigidly fixed, and alternative systems of classification are perfectly possible.

Out of the generalized ancestral hominids from whom all living humans are thought to be descended, the *White* or *Caucasoid* stock is believed to have been differentiated quite early. It is the least specialized and the most variable of the human subspecies.[10] Within this category may be found individuals with skin colors ranging from clear white through pink or ruddy to light brown or ripe olive. Hair color runs from platinum blond to red and dark brown; and eye color goes from pale gray-blue or green to various shades of brown. It is an interesting fact that far more people with lightly colored skins, eyes, and hair belong to this stock than to any other. Hair form on the head is usually wavy or lightly curled, and the face and body show considerable hairiness. Noses are predominantly high-bridged, with profiles that vary from straight to concave or convex. There is little facial protusion, lips are only moderately thick and slightly turned out (everted), and the chin is usually prominent and well-developed. Cephalic indexes fluctuate all the way from very dolichocephalic to extremely brachycephalic, and body builds are too variable to be classified, although pelves are proportionately broad in both sexes.

There are many races within the Caucasoid stock (see Fig. 7–3). They include the short and slender *Mediterraneans,* who are dolichocephalic brunets with delicate features, and who occupy all lands adjoining the Mediterranean; thickset *Alpines* from central Europe, who are broadheaded brunets with "blobby" noses; long-headed, lightly pig-

---

[10] Stock and race descriptions customarily take the adult male as a standard.

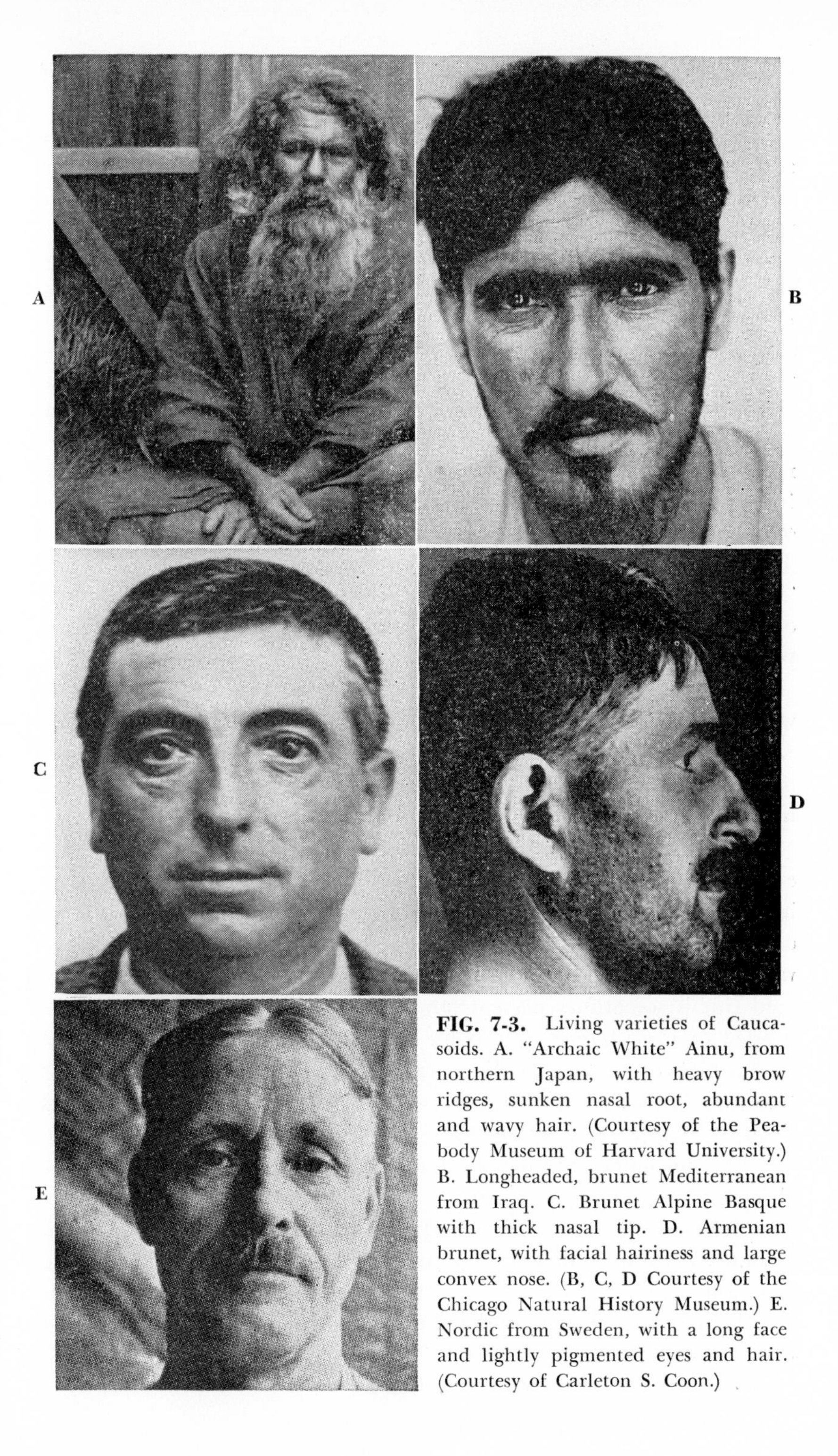

FIG. 7-3. Living varieties of Caucasoids. A. "Archaic White" Ainu, from northern Japan, with heavy brow ridges, sunken nasal root, abundant and wavy hair. (Courtesy of the Peabody Museum of Harvard University.) B. Longheaded, brunet Mediterranean from Iraq. C. Brunet Alpine Basque with thick nasal tip. D. Armenian brunet, with facial hairiness and large convex nose. (B, C, D Courtesy of the Chicago Natural History Museum.) E. Nordic from Sweden, with a long face and lightly pigmented eyes and hair. (Courtesy of Carleton S. Coon.)

mented *Nordics* of northern Europe, who have long faces and deep jaws; and *Armenoids* from the Balkans and the Near East who have sugar-loafed heads, brunet coloring, ample beards, and big, thick-tipped convex noses. In cartoons, Jews are often drawn with exaggerated Armenoid features. A related group, called *Dinarics,* is occasionally given separate racial status. A great deal of controversy exists over a Caucasoid race that is sometimes called *Archaic White.* Members of this group are generally short, stocky, and brunet. What sets them apart from other Caucasoids are the facts that they often have large and projecting brow ridges that overhang the nasal root and make it appear sunken or depressed; that they generally have large palates and teeth; and that the men have so much wavy head and facial hair, that they are often termed "hairy." In a few respects the so-called Archaic Whites resemble Pleistocene forms of man, and they show up early in the populations where they are found. That is why they are called archaic. They are best known among the "hairy" Ainu of northern Japan, but variants occur among the Veddahs of Ceylon, and among some of the aboriginal (for example, Dravidian) peoples of southern India.

In broad terms, the various races of the Caucasoid stock occupy western Asia (the Near East), north Africa, and the continent of Europe. As European colonization and immigration proceeded, they also spread to many parts of the world, including vast portions of the Western Hemisphere and the continent of Australia.

Another stock that is supposed to have been differentiated quite early in human history is the *Australoid.* These people have long, narrow heads, large brow ridges, receding foreheads, big teeth, and a marked degree of prognathism. They have a fair amount of beard and body hair, which is usually wavy and of a dark brown color. However, a reddish-gold tint is sometimes present, and youngsters, especially, may be red-headed or even blond. Skin color runs from milk-chocolate to deeper shades of brown, and the eyes are generally dark or medium brown. Noses are broad, with depressed nasal roots and thick tips; and faces are generally euryprosopic or broad.

As the name implies, most members of this stock make up the aboriginal population of Australia. A few closely related races, however, once lived in Tasmania, and similar people exist among the native inhabitants of New Guinea. It used to be thought that Australoids resulted from a mixture of ancient Caucasoids with some kinds of Negroids, but such beliefs are no longer widely held. Australoid origins are just as obscure as are those of other stocks.

A third subspecies comprises the *Negroid* or *Black* stock. Its members are characterized by dark brown to black skins and eye colors, and by black head hair that tends to loop into tight or intertwined spirals. Beard and body hair is generally black, but less abundant than in the Caucasoid stock. Most Negroids are dolichocephalic, with considerable prognathism, broad, low noses, thick, greatly everted lips, and somewhat receding chins. Body sizes and proportions vary, but the pelves are relatively narrow, calf muscles may be poorly developed, and the arch of the

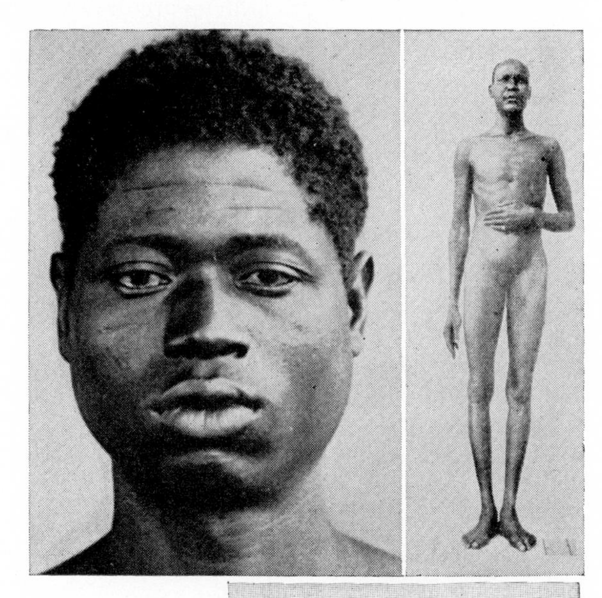

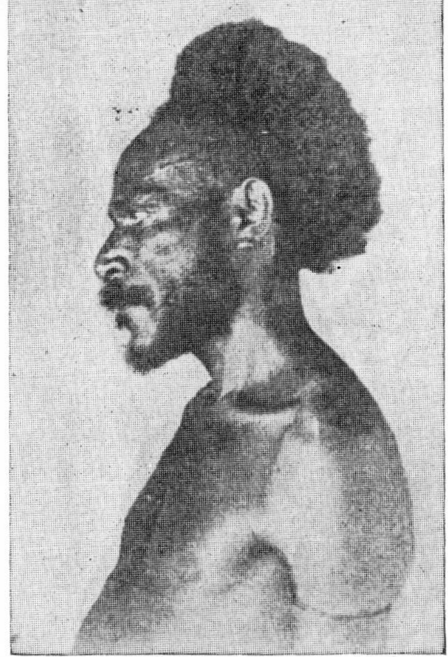

FIG. 7-4. Three racial varieties of the Negroid stock. Above, left: Forest Negro from Dahomey in western Africa. He exhibits the "typical" features of his race and stock. His skin is dark; his nose is broad and low-bridged; his head hair is spirally; and his lips are thick and everted. Above, right: Nilotic Negro from eastern Africa, who belongs to the Dinka tribe. He is tall and thin, and his Negroid features appear to be so "diluted" as to suggest the possibility of an ancient admixture with Caucasoids. Right: Oceanic Negro from the Papuan district of New Guinea. His nasal configuration, head hair, and other features differ markedly from the corresponding features of African Negroes. (Courtesy of the Chicago Natural History Museum.)

foot is often low. Infants are occasionally born with purplish Mongoloid spots that usually disappear by adolescence.

There are a number of Negroid races or varieties (Fig. 7–4). Most typical of the stock, but somewhat more barrel-chested, broad-shouldered, and muscular than most of their fellows, are the *Forest Negroes,* who live in west central Africa, between the Atlantic coast and the Congo basin. Many Negroes in the United States are Forest Negroes, and a high proportion of American Negro athletes are drawn from this race.

Nilotic Negroes comprise another important segment of the Negroid stock. They are widely distributed throughout east Africa, and are well represented in the basin of the Nile. As a rule, they are tall and slender, with long, thin legs, and comparatively short trunks. Quite often, they are less prognathous, and have narrower noses, and thinner, less everted lips than Forest Negroes.

Besides their distribution in Africa, Negroid people comprise the aboriginal inhabitants of numerous islands in the South Pacific, particularly in Melanesia, which runs from New Guinea to Fiji. On the whole, they are called *Oceanic Negroes.* No one knows what connections they may anciently have had with African Negroes. Oceanic Negroes are dark-skinned and heavily pigmented, but in several respects they may be quite different from African Negroids. One variety of Oceanic Negroes, the *Papuans* of New Guinea, is very distinctive. Papuans have high mops of frizzly head hair, frequently accompanied by thick-tipped, convex noses that are strangely reminiscent of Armenoids. Then, too, Oceanic Negroids are often less prognathous, and have thinner and less everted lips than African Negroids.

Although all stocks of *Homo sapiens* have shorter and taller varieties, it is only among Negroid people that large types and *Pygmies* are customarily distinguished, even when they live in close proximity (see Fig. 7–5). Pygmies consist of populations whose normal adult males seldom reach 5 feet in height. Negroid Pygmies are found in such parts of Africa as the Ituri forest; in parts of southern Asia, chiefly in the interior of the Malay peninsula; on the Nicobar and Andaman islands in the Bay of Bengal; and in several parts of Oceania, especially in New Guinea and in the Philippines. Several kinds of Pygmies have been noted, and it was once customary to call the African types Negrilloes, and the Oceanic-Asiatic varieties Negritoes. It is no longer conventional to make a terminological distinction, and Negrito may be used for any Negroid Pygmy.

One interesting but puzzling group in Africa, that is believed to have affiliations with African Pygmies, may be called by the combined term *Bushman-Hottentot.* There are several important cultural differences between Bushman and Hottentot, but both live in the vicinity of the Kalahari Desert, and racially they are much alike.

In shortness of stature and in the possession of peppercorn hair they resemble African Pygmies, but each sex has a minor peculiarity of

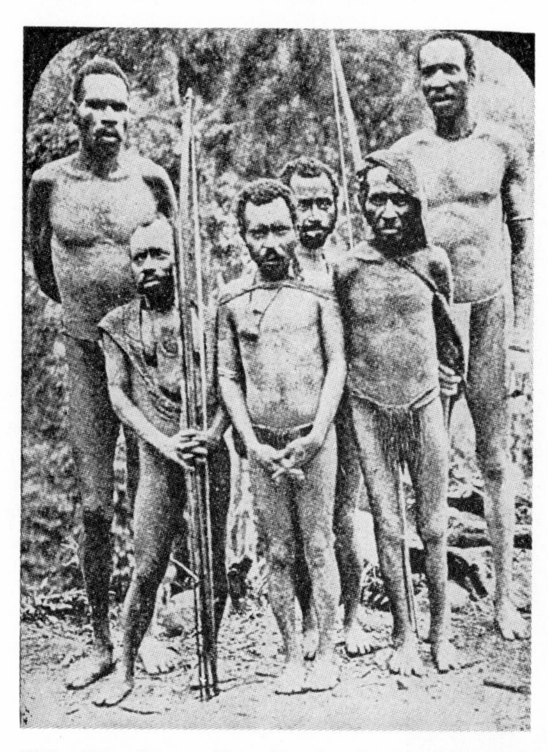

FIG. 7-5. Pygmy Negroids. In the Negroid stock there are sometimes found entire groups of very short (Pygmy) people, who may be known as Negritoes. Occasionally, as these natives of New Guinea indicate, Pygmies and normal-sized Negroids may live side by side. (Courtesy of the Museum of Anthropology, the University of Michigan.)

the genital organs. In men, the penis tends to be partially erect at all times; and in women an extra tissue (apron) is generally found over the vagina. Females, too, are especially addicted to the condition known as *steatopygia* (see Fig. 7–6). In this condition a vast deposit of fat accumulates on the thighs, and especially on the buttocks. Exactly what steatopygia signifies is unknown, although some believe that the huge buttocks may serve as a food reservoir.

Even more puzzling for physical anthropologists to understand is the presence among Bushman-Hottentots of high cheekbones, extra folds of skin over the eyelids, and a yellowish tinge in the skin. As these traits are common among Mongoloids, it was once thought that they had resulted from Mongoloid admixture. Such "explanations" are no longer

FIG. 7-6. A case of steatopygia. This Bushman-Hottentot woman exhibits a marked case of steatopygia. Similar accumulations of deposits of fat on the thighs and buttocks are common among women of her race. (Courtesy of the Chicago Natural History Museum.)

considered adequate, for no Mongoloids are known to have lived in this part of Africa.

Although convincing proof is lacking, and there are ample grounds for skepticism, some writers claim that the *Mongoloid* or *Yellow* stock was the last subspecies of *Homo sapiens* to make its appearance. On the whole, members of the Mongoloid division may be described as broad-headed, broad-faced, and broad-shouldered. Skin colors generally show a yellowish tint, but may vary from lemon-colored to reddish-brown. Eyes are dark brown as a rule. Head hair is long, coarse of texture, straight, and black. On face and body, Mongoloids are distinctively devoid of hair (*glabrous*). Several special characteristics are found in the facial area. The eyes seem to be slanted, and have narrow openings; the lids are heavy, with extra folds of skin (*Mongoloid* or *epicanthic folds*) stretched across the upper lids from the eyebrows to the lashes and from the outer corners to the nose. Nasal bridges tend to be of medium breadth but rather low; and cheekbones are prominent and padded with fat. They jut out from back to front as well as from side to side. Prognathism, chin, and lip development are all average, but the incisor teeth frequently have an unusual concavity, on the inner sides, that gives them a "shovel-shaped" appearance. Stature is variable, but not uncommonly a little short of the male average for all mankind (about 5½ feet), and the body build is most often compact and sturdy. In this stock, too, infants are sometimes born with Mongoloid spots (purplish areas) that generally fade out by adolescence.

What appear to be *Classic Mongoloid* races (Fig. 7–7, left, top), exhibiting the basic characteristics of their stock, are widely distributed throughout east Asia (the Far East). Although they occur in many tribes and nations, most Classic Mongoloids are to be found in a vast belt ranging eastward from Tibet and Mongolia, across much of southern Siberia and China, and on into Manchuria, Korea, and Japan. Strictly speaking, no single term has been applied to them, but since they seem to be so typical of their stock they may be described as races of Classic Mongoloids.

Variations exist both north and south. In northern Siberia, among such tribes as the Koryak and the Chukchee, and to a lesser extent among some of the Eskimo groups in polar Asia and northern Canada, there is to be found a type that is sometimes called *Arctic Mongoloid* (see Fig. 7–7, right). Arctic Mongoloids are to be distinguished from Classic Mongoloids because they are less broadheaded, and have higher roofed, and sometimes centrally peaked heads, less obvious Mongoloid folds, browner skins, and noses that are narrower and have more elevation.

On the southeast Asiatic mainland, and on a number of adjacent islands, roughly from Sumatra up to New Guinea, but generally south of the main range of Classic Mongoloids, live a great many diversified people who are sometimes lumped into an *Indonesian-Malay* race. It is hard to give one description for so many variegated folk, but they are commonly held to be the results of crosses between Mongoloids and Negroids, with, perhaps, an admixture of Mediterranean Caucasoid. Many Indonesian-Malays look like short, dark Mongoloids, but some have too much wavy hair, or lips that are too thick and everted, or faces that have too much prognathism, to be taken for Mongoloids. Much about these people is unknown to science, and the same is true of the

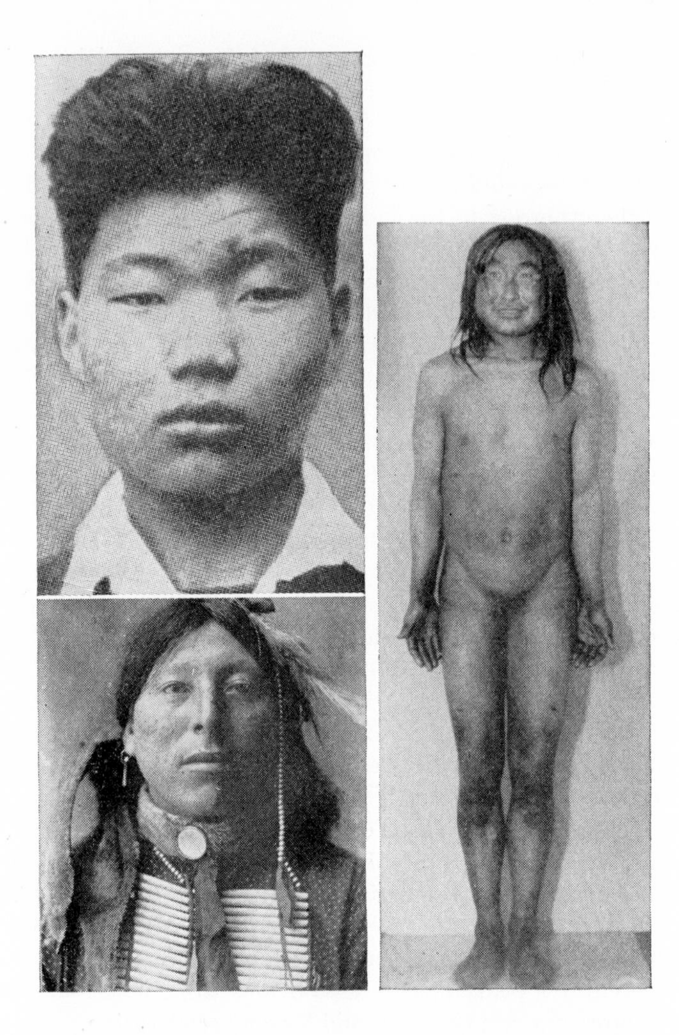

FIG. 7-7. Some Mongoloid racial types. Left, top: An east Asiatic (Classic) Mongoloid. He is a speaker of the Tungus language, which is widespread in northeastern Asia. He exhibits all the diagnostic features of his stock and race, including full Mongoloid (epicanthic) eyefolds. (From C. S. Coon, S. M. Garn, and J. B. Birdsell, *Races,* Springfield, Ill., 1950. Courtesy of Charles C Thomas, Publisher.) Left, bottom: A Sioux-speaking American Indian (Amerind), with Mongoloid head hair and cheekbones, but non-Mongoloid nose and eyes. (Courtesy of the Chicago Natural History Museum.) Right: An American Eskimo, showing his nonhairy (glabrous) body. (Courtesy of the Peabody Museum of Harvard University.)

Polynesians who live on more easterly islands in the south Pacific. In matters of biology the Polynesians present many unsolved characteristics.[11]

Somewhat better known, but still imperfectly understood, is the *American Indian* (*Amerind*) group (Fig. 7–7, left, bottom). Although several biologically different kinds of American Indians can be readily recognized, lack of detailed information makes it necessary to describe them as a single but variable race of Mongoloids. Unlike their presumed Classic relatives, they have somewhat reddish-brown skins, faces that are often both very wide and very long, mesorrhine noses that are frequently high-bridged and convex, facial skin that becomes greatly wrinkled in old age, and brown eyes that do not always show a Mongoloid fold. It is their straight, coarse, black head hair, high cheek bones, and relatively glabrous bodies that lead some race classifiers to call them Mongoloids in racial terms; but in the opinion of others they deserve separate ranking as a subspecies or stock.

Some bald facts about race

No matter how crude some of the traditional techniques of physical anthropology are now regarded to be, earlier workers in the field did make some valuable contributions to a scientific understanding of racial differences. From the outset, they showed a marked determination to avoid preconceived notions and to deal with human variations with the same objective detachment that zoologists exhibit when classifying other animals. Some of their pronouncements on race are still valid and worth repeating.

All anthropologists are united in the belief that stock and race distinctions are biogenetic, resulting from geographic isolation and the interplay of environmental, evolutionary, and reproductive forces. Accordingly, differences of race or stock cannot possibly be expressed in terms of nongenetically heritable, nonbiological, or nonsomatic traits. Anthropology does not recognize such so-called "races" as Aryan, Latin, or Semitic, which are best regarded as linguistic groups; Mohammedan, Hindu, or Jewish, which most commonly refer to followers of particular religions; and Italian or British, which have primarily national or political significance. Students of man must never allow themselves to

[11] Much information about the present state of Polynesian studies may be found in D. S. Marshall, "The Settlement of Polynesia," *Scientific American*, Vol. 195, No. 2, 1956, pp. 58–72.

forget the fundamental distinction between inborn, biogenetically determined, lifelong, racial characteristics that one receives involuntarily at his conception and cultural attributes that all individuals must acquire through postnatal education. After all, a member of any stock or race may be taught to speak any language whatsoever; may learn to worship any god; may, without altering his inherited biology, live in any part of the world, and may acquire citizenship in many a different country.

The anatomical features of individuals are always genetically predetermined at conception, but racial boundaries are not rigidly fixed, and some physical traits are constantly in the process of being modified or changed. In fact, races are sometimes thought to be embryonic species, or units that are going through a process of change which may ultimately convert them to a new subdivision.[12] More than one study has shown that any given race of human beings possesses so much *plasticity* that its members are likely to become at least phenotypically different from each other if some of them grow up in dissimilar environments. Wherever migration is involved, this amounts to saying that the offspring of migrating members of a race who grow up in a new geographical locality will vary considerably from the children of stay-at-home members of the same race.[13] By itself, however, plasticity is probably limited by one's inherited genes and therefore does not seem sufficient to cause an individual to differ from the stock of his parents. We do not know of a single case whereby, through plasticity alone, a full-blooded child has turned into a stock division that differs from his father's and mother's.

No race or stock, taken in the aggregate, can be judged to be more highly evolved than any other. Biologically speaking, a race could be called superior if it proved to have more strength, vitality, longevity, disease resistance, or fertility. After many years of research, anthropologists have reached the conclusion that in these terms there are neither superior nor inferior stocks and races. In all basic anatomical details, all of living mankind is alike. At the same time, there are indications of some lesser biological differences. Some Mongoloids appear to have a lower metabolic rate than Caucasoids of corresponding sex,

---

[12] An elaboration of this concept, based on recent theories of human genetics, is to be found in S. Garn, "Race and Evolution," *American Anthropologist,* Vol. 59, 1957, pp. 218–24, especially p. 219.

[13] This demonstration was first made over 50 years ago by the very traditional anthropologist, Franz Boas, in *Changes in Bodily Form of Descendants of Immigrants,* Washington, D.C., 1911. It was then verified by later workers and was given a new statement by H. L. Shapiro, *Migration and Environment,* New York, 1939. Also, see G. W. Lasker, "Migration and Physical Differentiation," *American Journal of Physical Anthropology,* Vol. 4, 1946, pp. 273–300.

age, and size; Negroids are the most susceptible to sickle-cell anemia; and in the United States cancer strikes an exceptionally high percentage of Caucasoids. So far the data on this topic are too meager to permit the formulation of general laws, but comparative pathology is one of the most interesting fields of research involving physical variations among differing groups of men.

Neither race nor stock mixture produces harmful biological consequences and, contrary to opinions that prevail in some quarters, they may occasionally bring about beneficial results through the agency of *heterosis,* or *hybrid vigor.* On this topic anthropologists speak with assurance because members of the profession have studied the offspring of a great many interstock matings in all parts of the world.[14] Nowhere have they found signs of physical deterioration resulting from intermixture. Even the descendants of such varied parents as Dutch (Caucasoid) men and Hottentot (Negroid) women turned out to be vigorous, fertile, and long-lived.[15] Popular prejudices often create difficult social and cultural situations for hybrid individuals or groups, but in strictly biological terms, race mixture produces no harmful results.

Less is known about the consequences of inbreeding, but the few investigations that have been made by unprejudiced observers have led to the tentative conclusion that it is not invariably dangerous. In terms of conception, gestation, and childbirth there are no differences. As far as can now be determined, inbreeding does little more than intensify the usual procedures of heredity, because the parents have more than the usual number of genes in common. Therefore, if inbreeding occurs in a group with a good genetic background, it should do no harm, but if it takes place among people with many deficient genes, it may lead to biological disaster.

These findings have been directly opposed in our day to the exaggerated claims of unscientific speakers and writers on racial topics. The term *racist* has come into current usage to denote those who harangue about race and racial differences, without reference to observed and known facts. It is to the credit of physical anthropology that it has provided effective material to counteract the extravagant statements uttered by unabashed racists.[16]

---

[14] See, for example, L. C. Dunn, *Eugenics in Race and State,* Baltimore, 1923, pp. 109–24.

[15] Consult the famous study of E. Fischer, *Die Rehobother Bastards,* Jena, 1912. "Bastards" is inaccurate, as the subjects were born of legally married parents. Its very use may connote a degree of cultural prejudice.

[16] The problem of racism has recently been discussed in J. Comas, " 'Scientific' Racism Again," *Current Anthropology,* Vol. 2, No. 4, 1961, pp. 303–40, and in M. Nash, "Race and the Ideology of Race," *ibid.*

To date, no convincing proof has been brought forward to show that the races of mankind differ in the *potentialities* of their mental equipment. Assuredly, vast differences of intellectual *performance* can be demonstrated, but when it comes to measuring potential the going gets harder and harder. The reason that anthropologists are more concerned with comparative ratings of mental potential rather than performance is because no one knows to what extent the latter is based on cultural conditioning instead of on biogenetic inheritance. Varying scores on intelligence tests between American Negroids and Caucasoids, for example, have been shown to relate so directly to cultural factors such as the amount and quality of education and social or economic status, that it is hard to tell whether the tests measure inborn, racial differences of mental capacity or differences of training and background. Until sound techniques are devised for evaluating intellectual ability without reference to cultural influences, it can only be maintained that no distinctions of basic mentality are known to exist among the races of man.

Inasmuch as human beings live bioculturally rather than biologically, it follows that wherever race mixture takes place a degree of cultural mingling is also likely to occur. By no means is this to be regarded as detrimental. We, in the United States, are proud of the high level of culture that we have attained, but we tend to overlook the fact that our way of life is the product of a great deal of borrowing and mixture. Only too often do we forget, for instance, that Semitic-speaking peoples from Asia and Africa were the first to develop such basic features of American culture as the Christian religion, the Phoenician alphabet, and Arabic numerals.

There is no need to belabor the point. It is enough if we remember the hybrid nature of our way of life[17] and remain aware of the great enrichment that may result from the mingling of cultural traditions that often results when race mixture takes place.

Selected References

Boas, Franz, "Changes in Bodily Form of Descendants of Immigrants," *61st Congress, second session, Senate Document,* No. 208, Washington, D. C., 1911.

Comas, Juan, *Manual of Physical Anthropology,* rev. English ed., Springfield, Ill., 1960.

[17] Ralph Linton's "One Hundred Per Cent American," *American Mercury,* Vol. 40, New York, 1937, pp. 427–29, provides an amusing but factual treatment of this topic.

Coon, C. S., *The Origin of Races,* New York, 1962.
———, *The Races of Europe,* New York, 1939.
———, Stanley M. Garn, and Birdsell, Joseph B., *Races,* Springfield, Ill., 1950.
Count, Earl W., ed., *This Is Race,* New York, 1950.
Garn, Stanley M., *Human Races,* Springfield, Ill., 1961.
———, ed., *Readings on Race,* Springfield, Ill., 1959.
Hooton, Earnest A., *Up from the Ape,* rev. ed., New York, 1946.
Krogman, Wilton M., "The Concept of Race," *The Science of Man in the World Crisis,* R. Linton, ed., New York, 1944, pp. 38–62.
Shapiro, Harry L., and Hulse, Frederick, *Migration and Environment,* New York, 1940.
Stewart, T. Dale, ed., *Hrdlička's Practical Anthropometry,* rev. ed., Philadelphia, 1947.
Stibbe, E. P., *An Introduction to Physical Anthropology,* rev. ed., New York and London, 1938.
Vallois, Henri V., "Race," in A. L. Kroeber, ed., *Anthropology Today,* Chicago, 1953, pp. 145–62.
Washburn, Sherwood L., "Thinking about Race," *Smithsonian Report,* Washington, D. C., 1946, pp. 363–78.

Some Recent Developments in Physical Anthropology

CHAPTER 8

NEW OUTLOOKS AND METHODS

On the basis of data collected by Erminie Voegelin in 1949 and 1950, Georg K. Neumann ascertained that out of 604 teachers of anthropology in American schools no more than 65 were offering work in physical anthropology, and of these only 27 were themselves primarily physical anthropologists. This little band, grown somewhat and supplemented by a few specialists who do not teach, plus a limited number of colleagues abroad,[1] makes up for its small size by the vigor with which it attacks problems and the boldness with which it searches out and pursues new lines of investigation. Among the members of the group there is to be detected a feeling of impatience with the methods and accomplishments of the more traditional scholars. The leaders of the new movements are seldom unwilling to acknowledge their debts and links to the past, but they prefer to think of themselves as representing a brand-new stage in the evolution of their profession.

As was the case formerly, the chief objective of physical anthropology remains the study of the evolutionary processes that brought man on the scene and produced his many variations. But there is a profound change in regard to which of the differences are selected for study, the techniques by which their extent and distribution are to be determined, and the ways in which they should be classified, analyzed, compared and interpreted. Although it is still conceded that an accurate sorting of man-

[1] In 1951 the American Association of Physical Anthropologists had a total of 245 members, by no means all of whom were full-time professionals.

kind into races is a desirable achievement, it is argued stoutly that classification should not be an end in itself. The new group charges that there was a time, not so very long ago, when the traditionalists thought that by means of adequate classification they would learn how *Homo sapiens* had evolved, and how the species had become separated into stocks and races. When this hope was disappointed, so it is charged, the older workers did not seek new methods of investigation but tried only to refine their customary techniques by making them more and more painstaking and elaborate. All this was love's labor lost, in the modern point of view, and classification as such is felt to be valueless as a problem-solving device.

A primary cause of failure, it is being said, was undue reliance on measurements and observations made exclusively on the final appearance of body parts in adult males. No search was made for the genes that give rise to mature anatomical features; women and children were just about omitted from consideration; and no account was taken of age changes, or of environmental or cultural influences. Hence, the older school could never hope to learn how body parts developed and became adapted to the environment; what they were like at various stages of growth; what influences sex factors exerted; or what may have been the effects of mating customs.

Dissatisfaction has also been expressed because so many observations and measurements were taken on surfaces of bones or their nearest equivalents in the flesh. It is true that this custom persisted in part because of historical accident or mere repetition of established procedures; but it is equally true that efforts to understand evolution require comparison of living populations with dead or extinct hominids whose remains consist only of teeth and bones. Furthermore, museums and laboratories can maintain collections of skeletal fragments for study much more readily than they can house large numbers of whole bodies. Just the same, it must be admitted that measurements of gross, external features, such as head length and head breadth, are incapable of throwing light on the formative processes by which long or broad heads come into being. Accordingly, it is not always possible to refute the charge that the old custom of measuring was deteriorating into a kind of ritual procedure that led to the compilation of vast amounts of data of dubious worth.

Even statistics, the new voices proclaim, were inadequately handled in the past. Most of the time they did little more than to restate already ascertained data in mathematical terms, as when an observable judgment such as "light brown" was written as a number. Quite often, too, statistics were used mainly for the purpose of deriving mathematical averages that might or might not have been truly typical of a given group. Thus, if a unit of people had 100 men who stood 6 feet high, and another 100 who were 5 feet tall, the average male stature would be correctly given as 5½ feet, yet not a single man out of 200 would actually have stood at the average height.

As to indexes, it does not take much appreciation of mathematics to become suspicious of the threefold pattern into which they consistently fall. Putting three billion individuals into so small a number of categories invariably would lump together many different kinds of people. Modern physical anthropologists are also correct when they point out that the most widely used indexes were arbitrarily established long ago, and that they have no reference at all to known biological processes. A great many new mathematical procedures have been developed of late, and their use holds forth the promise of furnishing clues to analysis and interpretation that no one had previously suspected and that could have come to light in no other way.

Also occupying a prominent place in the current bill of complaints is the failure of orthodox physical anthropologists to have developed theories of human origins or variations that might have led the way to greater insights or new techniques. There was too much speculation and not enough formulation of hypotheses that could be experimentally confirmed or disproved. Worst of all was the relative inflexibility of former approaches. Professor Washburn stated the case effectively when he wrote: "The methods of observation, measurement, and comparison were essentially the same, whether the object of the study was the description of evolution, races, growth, criminals, constitutional types, or army personnel."[2]

Above all, the modern student of man's body is deeply concerned with process. He does not ask an investigator simply to describe what features people possess, and to indicate what is their size, range, and proportion. He is much more interested in trying to understand the process that brought man's characteristic traits into being, and in trying to determine what effects these traits may have on human activities. This shift of emphasis calls for a major reorientation from a fixed or static approach to one that deals with changes or dynamics. This is, perhaps, the greatest single difference of viewpoint between traditional and contemporary physical anthropology. Such a viewpoint fits in very

[2] S. L. Washburn, "The New Physical Anthropology," *Transactions of the New York Academy of Sciences,* new series II, Vol. 13, No. 7, May, 1951, p. 298.

neatly with those studies of organismal changes through time that are the concern of all students of organic evolution.

Thanks to the increase of scientific knowledge, development of new techniques, interest in different sets of problems, and the creation of fresh points of view, it is not surprising that physical anthropologists are no longer willing to follow blindly in the footsteps of the pioneers of their profession. With very few exceptions, they are less interested in refining and perfecting the old procedures than they are in striking out boldly along new paths.

IN THE BEGINNING WAS THE GENE[3]

As the science of genetics developed, many physical anthropologists sought to apply its findings to their work. *Genes,* ran the argument, are the very stuff of heredity, variation, and evolution, and to study man's genes is much more fundamental than to investigate their ultimate expression in human anatomy. Genes are much less adaptive and less subject than external features to environmental influences, they are strictly biological in character, they are transmitted only through sexual reproduction, and they remain practically unaltered during an individual's entire lifetime. So, in some quarters, the genotype rather than the phenotype was proclaimed to be the object of research in physical anthropology. There can be no quarrel with a modest statement along these lines, but human genetics is so complicated a subject that only a little has been accomplished in the primary business of identifying particular genes.

No one discusses genetics without making reference to the work of Gregor Mendel (1822–1884), and to the pioneering essay that he published in 1865.[4] Before Mendel it was believed, as phrases like "blood relatives" still indicate, that hereditary factors were transmitted and blended by blood. Mendel was the first to show that this was not true. He also demonstrated that external appearances could be deceptive, for

[3] A summary study of genes may be found in N. H. Horowitz, "The Gene," *Scientific American,* Vol. 195, No. 4, 1956, pp. 78–90. For further, more up-to-date material consult S. Benzer, "The Fine Structure of the Gene," *Scientific American,* Vol. 206, No. 1, 1962, pp. 70–84.

[4] Mendel's original paper has been translated from German to English by William Bateson. Under the title of "Experiments on Plant Hybridization," it may be found in the appendix to E. W. Sinnot, L. C. Dunn, and T. Dobzhansky, *Principles of Genetics,* rev. ed., New York, 1950.

hybrid parents might have one out of four descendants who failed to resemble them.

It was Mendel who first proved that in all cases of bisexual reproduction an offspring, at its conception, gets one set of trait determinants from the father and a parallel set of determinants from the mother.[5] Each ultimate feature, however, is based only on either the father's or mother's determinants, but the unused determinant does not disappear. Instead, it is passed on, unused by one's self, to one's progeny, and it may thus play a part in the formation of a later descendant's external appearance. It has also been shown that a child-to-be's characteristics never result from the totality of either parent's determinants, but that some features (or parts of features) are determined by the contents of the father's sperm cell, whereas others arise from the mother's egg cell.

Modern genetics started in 1900, and is based on the notion that the principles of heredity, first noted and described by Mendel, unfailingly operate with mathematical precision on all living things. This is just as true of men as it is of any other organism. Much of what has just been said will now be restated and elaborated in the terminology of genetics.

Every child that results from bisexual mating begins as a combination or zygote of a male and a female gamete (sex cell). Within its cells a fetus has 23 pairs of chromosomes,[6] one of each pair contributed by its father and the other by its mother. All corresponding spots or *loci* on each chromosome are thought to be occupied by equivalent submicroscopic genes. It is either the particular portion of a chromosome, or the gene that is supposed to be located there, that determines all or part of one or more of an offspring's inherited external traits. Those genes or gene loci that find expression are called dominant (D), and those alternates that fail to be expressed are known as recessives (R or r). If the corresponding genes on each of a child's chromosomes are alike it is *homozygous,* if they differ it is *heterozygous.* In terms of dominants and recessives, four combinations are possible. Parental genes or gene loci may be DD, DR, RD, or RR. Since dominants always mask recessives in heterozygotes, an average of three out of four offspring will show the dominant characteristic, thus yielding the Mendelian ratio of 3:1 (see Fig. 8–1). If, however, as is usually done by geneticists, the two heter-

---

[5] Conception takes place in higher mammals when a male's ripened sperm enters a female's mature egg. Cellular division into 2, 4, 8, 16, etc., then begins. Early in this process, the embryo's future reproductive or germ cells are separated from its bodily or somatic cells.

[6] It used to be thought that every human cell had a complement of 24 pairs of chromosomes. Recent studies suggest that the number should be reduced to 23.

ozygotes are counted together, then we get a ratio of 1:2:1—that is, one pure dominant, two heterozygotes, and one pure recessive. The masked, recessive genes, however, are passed on to all the progeny of two heterozygous parents, and may thus come to light in some of the descendants. The equal transmission of dominant and recessive genes is an important part of the *Hardy-Weinberg law.*

Many different things may cause progeny to differ from parents. Among them may be the normal workings of heredity, mutations that

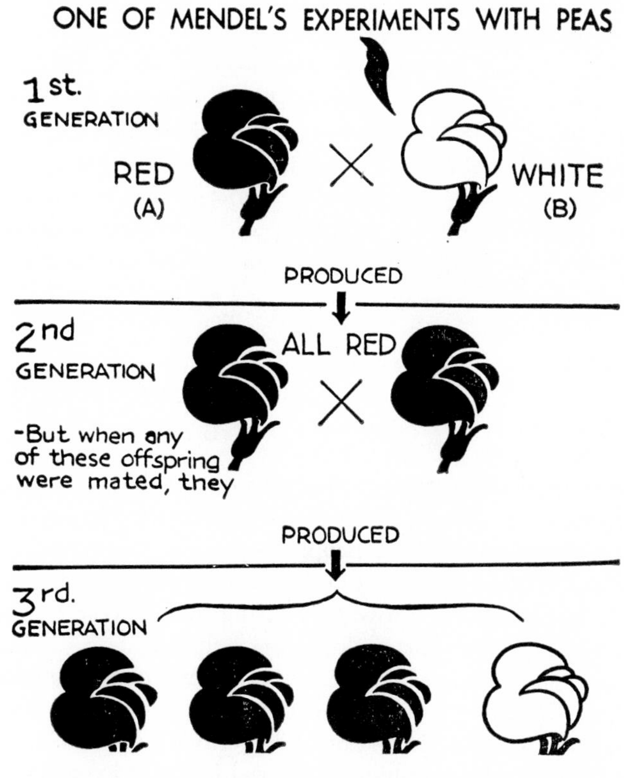

FIG. 8-1. The Mendelian ratio. If a dominant, red pea is crossed with a recessive, white pea, they will produce reds in the second generation. Actually these offspring are heterozygotes (DR) but they appear red phenotypically, because the dominant masks the recessive. If the two heterozygotes are crossed, the third generation will show the Mendelian ratio of 3 (red): 1 (white). Since two of the reds are DR, the ratio can be written as 1 (DD); 2 (DR); 1 (RR). (Courtesy of the Museum of Anthropology, The University of Michigan.)

produce new or altered genes,[7] diseases, breaks in chromosomes, reversal of position in chromosomes, the crossing over of part of one chromosome to join the other of a pair, or the introduction of different genes through race mixture. Furthermore, it commonly happens that at the same *locus* on a chromosome there may be as many as an average of four alternative or even contrasting genes. These are known as *alleles*; and one offspring may show a trait determined by one allele, whereas his sibling may exhibit a contrasting feature brought about by the influence of a different allele.

In terms of genetics it is hard to imagine how much variation may exist in the progeny of the same parents. If two progenitors differ in only ten of their genes, we get 2^{10} or 1024 possible combinations for their offspring to inherit. If the two parents should differ in twenty genes, we would have 2^{20} or 1,048,576 possible combinations resulting. Since each human being is thought to have no less than 20,000 genes or distinct gene loci,[8] the number of differing combinations open to children is fantastic. No wonder one can say with assurance, always remembering that identical twins may be exceptions, that no two individuals are exactly alike.

GENES, BLOOD GROUPS, AND DISEASE

So far the genes that determine certain aspects of blood are among the best known and the most clearly understood. It was long ago noted that the blood streams of different people contained different ingredients, some of which could be harmoniously mingled while others could not. This was dramatically demonstrated during World War I, when some transfusions proved fatal instead of being helpful.

Research showed that blood has many components, some of which, the *antigens,* lie on the surface of the red corpuscles, while others, known as *antibodies,* float in the blood's plasma or serum. Antigens and antibodies have to be harmonious. Otherwise, the red corpuscles clump together, or agglutinate, and can no longer circulate properly. This ex-

7 Most mutations, we must not forget, are lethal. Since increased doses of radiation are known to increase mutation rates, many biologists are afraid that the radioactivity resulting from nuclear explosions may have harmful genetic effects.

8 James N. Spuhler, in "On the number of genes in man," *Science,* Vol. 108, 1948, pp. 279–80, has estimated that the gene loci in a human being are of the order of 20,000 to 42,000. Physical anthropologists believe that the bulk of gene loci are the same throughout *Homo sapiens,* and that all noted stock and race differences arise from the variations in only a small number of assumed genes.

plains why transfusions of blood containing the wrong antibodies sometimes produce fatal results.

The first elements to have been identified in blood are the basis of the A-B-O system. This system rests on the fact that the red corpuscles contain antigens known as A, B, AB; or else fail to contain any of them, as in the case of O. To ensure that his circulatory system functions properly, an individual with A antigens must have plasma with anti-B antibodies that keep out B. Similarly, one who has B antigens, must have anti-A antibodies; and a person with AB antigens cannot have either antibody. Conversely, anyone who is O and lacks both kinds of antigens must have plasma with both anti-A and anti-B antibodies.

Subsequent studies have shown that the original classification of blood in terms of the A-B-O system may have been too gross, for it appears that there are at least several different kinds of A. Just what this implies has not yet been established.

Another well-known set of genetic factors results in the Rh series of blood groups. There are several varieties of Rh, written as Rh^o, Rh^z, etc. The most spectacular cases arise when a woman gives birth to a *blue baby*. This comes about, it has been established, when a woman who is Rh-negative mates with an Rh-positive man. If she should become pregnant with an Rh-positive child, her system would automatically begin to protect itself by producing anti-Rh-positive substances. Should she become pregnant for a second time with an Rh-positive child, her blood stream might come to contain enough anti-Rh-positive elements to make her second baby turn blue from lack of oxygen. Only an ample transfer of suitable blood can save such a child from death.

Today a large number of blood group systems, based on different biochemical ingredients, have been identified. For various reasons they are known as Kell, MNS–U, P, Duffy, Lewis, Kidd, Lutheran, Diego, Vel, and Sutter. Most of them differ from the A-B-O classification because they are not known to have naturally occurring antibodies. Nor do they seem to be capable of causing very tragic consequences in the event of wrong transfusions. One's place within each of the named blood classifications is separately inherited. It is unlikely, therefore, that any two children will inherit exactly the same type of blood according to every one of the known systems.

Sometimes blood-group substances are secreted or carried in such other liquids as semen, saliva, or cervical fluid. One startling consequence of the study of these secretions has been in connection with infertility. There is a strong likelihood that if a woman's cervical fluid contains secretions that are antagonistic to those in her husband's semen, she will either be unable to conceive, or else will abort a baby before the period of pregnancy is ended.[9]

Another genetically determined trait is concerned with a person's ability to taste low concentrations, in solution, of phenyl-thio-carbamide (PTC). "T" represents the gene that makes taste possible, and "t" stands for the nontasting gene. It is believed that inheritance of these genes follows the regular pattern of biological transmission through sexual reproduction. Variations have been noted among individuals, and also when one subdivision of *Homo sapiens* has been compared with another. For instance, nearly every Amerind has "T," but about 43 percent of European Caucasoids have "t."

One of the most promising leads for the study of genetic transmission arises from the occurrence of diseases or abnormalities that run in family lines. So far, specific, dominant genes are thought to be responsible for a number of peculiarities in regard to fingers and toes. These include multiple digits (polydactyly), webbing between fingers and toes (syndactyly), and exceedingly short digits (brachydactyly). Recessive genes, too, can produce disorders. This seems to be true of albinism, dwarfism, some varieties of color blindness, and hemophilia, in which blood fails to clot, with the result that a victim can bleed to death from even a minor wound.

Cases are also known where a heterozygous (DR or RD) inheritance has a selective advantage over a homozygous (DD or RR) condition. This has been most strikingly demonstrated with regard to *sickle-cell anemia* and malaria. There is one recessive gene that causes red cells to assume a sickle shape and to bring on anemia. If a child inherits this gene from both parents he is homozygous (RR), is bound to suffer from sickle-cell anemia, and is not likely to live to reproduce. On the other hand, a child born to normal parents may also be homozygous (DD). He will not have sickle-cell anemia, but he may fall victim to malaria. Best off, under these conditions, is a heterozygote (DR or RD). He does not suffer from sickle-cell anemia, since he carries the responsible gene as a recessive, and he is better able than a homozygote to withstand the ravages of malaria.[10]

---

[9] For a report on these possibilities, see S. J. Behrman, J. Buettner-Janusch, R. Heglar, H. Gershowitz, and W. L. Tew, "ABO(H) Blood Incompatibility as a Cause of Infertility: A New Concept," *American Journal of Obstetrics and Gynecology,* Vol. 79, 1960, pp. 847–55.

[10] This hypothesis was first advanced in A. C. Allison, "Protection afforded by sickle-cell trait against sub-tertian malarial infection," *British Medical Journal,* Vol. 1, 1954, pp. 290–94; and has been verified by several other investigators. He has lately re-explained his position in A. C. Allison, "Sickle Cells and Evolution," *Scientific American,* Vol. 195, No. 2, 1956, pp. 87–94.

Some diseases seem to be restricted to one region of the world, or else to be extraordinarily common in some particular subdivision of mankind. This is true of sickling and of *thalassemia,* or Cooley's disease, which acts something like sickle-cell anemia, but which is most often found in those Mediterranean districts where malaria is widespread. Another well-known disease of this kind is *favism.* Favism is a genetically controlled ailment that produces an allergic response leading to anemia, whenever a sufferer eats or is exposed to the broad bean, *Vicia fava.* The distribution of favism is limited to people of Mediterranean origin.

When it was first noted that some human genes predominate in particular regions or are found primarily among the members of one subdivision of mankind, it was thought that the study of genetics might throw much light on racial movements and might even lead to a more adequate classification of the varieties of *Homo sapiens.* Unfortunately, these hopes for a new and improved classification of mankind have never materialized.

One of the most uncompromising critics of old-style racial classification, William C. Boyd, has written the most comprehensive work yet published on human genetics as a basis for classifying mankind.[11] He worked with the genes that have been identified as affecting the blood groups. After studying the percentages in which these genes occur in human populations throughout the world, Boyd drew up a tentative scheme of six racial groups. There is a hypothetical Early European category, now represented, Boyd believes, by the Basques of France and Spain; a European (Caucasoid) group; an African (Negroid) class; an Asiatic (Mongoloid) group; an American Indian division; and an Australoid classification. Boyd readily admits that his six divisions correspond fairly well to the traditional scheme of stocks and races. Oddly enough, he interprets this to mean only that his own system is probably soundly based. He uses the older catalog, but he gives it no credit. An unbiased observer cannot escape the conclusion that the two approaches supplement rather than contradict each other.

Since the publication of Boyd's work, a large number of blood-group studies have been made on human beings all over the globe. Many interesting facts have emerged. O blood is commonest throughout the world; Amerinds have no B; and A may fluctuate in Amerinds from

---

For an interesting study of this condition in Africa as part of a large culture complex including agriculture, forest clearance, and other factors, see F. B. Livingstone, "Anthropological Implications of Sickle-Cell Gene Distribution in West Africa," *American Anthropologist,* Vol. 60, 1958, pp. 535–62.

[11] W. C. Boyd, *Genetics and the Races of Man,* Boston, 1950.

under 5 percent in some groups to over 75 percent in others. So far there is no consensus regarding what these facts mean, but there is a hope that they will some day indicate the genetic connection between various strains of men, and that they will throw light on ancient movements and migrations.

One of the earliest criticisms of the use of blood groups in the study of *Homo sapiens* was based on the limitation that samples could be obtained only from live subjects or recent corpses. Blood groups were thus considered of little use in evolutionary studies concerned with remote ancestors of modern man. Now, the Boyds and at least two other ingenious investigators, P. B. Candela and W. S. Laughlin, have shown that while it is impossible to get blood out of a stone it is possible to get blood groups out of mummies and old bones.[12] Thus has the exciting prospect been revealed to the scientific world of finding out the blood groups of ancient kinds of men. It is hoped that extensions of the new techniques will enable physical anthropologists to discover the blood groups of all extinct hominids, which will make it possible for them with greater certainty than ever before to establish the links that bind ancestral forms of man to living stocks and races.

POPULATION STUDIES—THE PHENOTYPE MAKES A COMEBACK

Many students of man's physical composition have begun to examine what are known as *breeding isolates* or *populations*. It is entirely realistic, they feel, to study units of people who customarily trade their

[12] P. B. Candela, "Blood-group reactions in ancient human skeletons," *American Journal of Physical Anthropology,* Vol. 21, 1936, pp. 429–32; and W. S. Laughlin, "Preliminary tests for presence of blood-group substance in Tepexpan Man," in H. de Terra, *et al.,* "Tepexpan Man," *Viking Fund Publication,* No. 11, New York, 1949, Appendix F.

The techniques used in the pioneering studies are not now regarded as always accurate. Moreover, it has been shown that blood-group material sometimes occurs in the ground. Therefore, a long-buried bone may absorb blood-group substances from the earth. New techniques are being developed that take such factors into account. On this point see F. P. Thieme, C. M. Otten, and H. E. Sutton, "A Blood Typing of Human Skull Fragments from the Pleistocene," *American Journal of Physical Anthropology,* Vol. 14, 1956, pp. 437–43.

Paleoserology is the subdiscipline that studies ancient blood. For an interesting article and an important bibliography, consult M. Smith, "Blood Groups of the Ancient Dead," *Science,* Vol. 131, 1960, pp. 699–702.

genes back and forth at marriage. They define a population as an interbreeding community with a common gene pool, and they maintain that populations differ from one another either in actual gene content or else in their combinations of *gene frequencies.*

Population studies are most satisfactory when they are conducted on isolated groups. Members of an isolated population, as was discussed on page 128, within the course of time come to be different from other groups through the combined agency of several forces. Inasmuch as these are the same forces that bring about evolutionary changes, it is believed that sound population studies ought to shed light on evolutionary processes.

Although anthropologists who study human populations are greatly influenced by genetics and try to use genetic approaches, it did not take them long to discover that in practice they were often dealing not with genes but with resemblances and differences in external features. In the words of Frederick P. Thieme, one of the most vigorous of the current students of population, "The problem for these studies is, in the last analysis, to examine and obtain knowledge about the interrelationship between genetic and environmental factors in shaping the phenotype. The phenotype is largely our unit of study. This is the individual."[13]

Shape-producing forces

Another approach that takes full cognizance of new developments in genetics and general biology, without being enslaved by them, is best exemplified by the work of Sherwood L. Washburn. Long in revolt against the static aspects of traditional physical anthropology, he has turned from efforts at race classification to attempts at understanding the dynamic processes that result in differences of body shapes, and to the relationships between biological forms and functions. Not satisfied to speculate about these matters, nor to deal with groups of so large a size that precise analysis is impossible, Washburn prefers to ask the kinds of questions that give promise of being answered by laboratory experiments. To cite one instance, many writers on vertebrate anatomy had speculated about the possible connection between the size of the eyeball and the dimensions of the socket that contained it. In 1943 S. R.

---

[13] F. P. Thieme, "Problems and Methods of Population Surveys," *Cold Spring Harbor Symposia on Quantitative Biology,* Vol. XV, 1951, p. 25. See also D. F. Roberts and G. A. Harrison, *Natural Selection in Human Populations,* New York, 1959.

Detwiler and Washburn sought a reply through experimentation.[14] They removed the natural eyes from embryonic specimens of the amphibian *Amblystoma punctatum,* a salamander, and transplanted extremely large eyes from a related species. As the embryos grew, they developed abnormally large orbits that encroached on surrounding portions of the olfactory and optic regions. This demonstrated that the pressure of growth exerted by a very large eyeball directly influences the form of adjoining areas of the face and head.

Another effort to understand the forces that shape the body led Washburn to remove temporal muscles from one side only of the heads of day-old rats. Several months later it was found that the associated skull parts on the operated side were much less well-developed than on the corresponding normal side. Such experiments have established the likelihood that bones do not independently assume their characteristic sizes and shapes. What, then, is one actually measuring when he measures a skull—external bones or the end products of dynamic stresses caused by various fleshy parts and muscles?

Washburn, now at the University of California, is presently engaged in changing the pelvic alignments of monkeys. He is trying to determine the exact relationships between pelvic position and means of locomotion. Simply stated, he is trying to find out whether a monkey would walk upright if its pelvis were placed in an upright position.

Of late, Washburn has advocated use of the *split-line* technique, which makes possible separate analysis of different portions of a single anatomical structure—such as the skull (Fig. 8–2).[15] On a larger scale he has cited evidence that suggests the possibility that the total body of man is actually a combination of three distinct regions, each of which may have developed at a totally different rate of speed (Fig. 8–3). In this new concept of asymmetrical evolution, Washburn considers it likely that the upper body segment, consisting of the entire chest area and the forelimbs, was the first to attain its current pattern; that the bipedal complex, centering about the pelvis and lower limbs, was the next to be evolved to its present form; and that the skull, with its attendant face and brain, was the last to reach modern proportions. In none of the three regions are important evolutionary changes known to have arisen since the emergence of the Cro-Magnons.

---

[14] S. L. Washburn and S. R. Detwiler, "An Experiment Bearing on the Problems of Physical Anthropology," *American Journal of Physical Anthropology,* Vol. 1, 1943, pp. 171–90.

[15] See, for example, N. C. Tappen, "A functional analysis of the facial skeleton with split-line technique," *American Journal of Physical Anthropology,* Vol. 11, 1953, pp. 503–32.

A number of investigators are engaged in trying to discover what processes or forces are responsible for differences in fat deposits and distribution,[16] weight and stature, coloring matter or pigment, heat and energy production (basal metabolism), and resistance of various parts of the body to very cold temperatures. Sometimes the differences seem to be ingrained in various subdivisions of *Homo sapiens*; sometimes they are attributed to variations in nutrition, or caloric intake;

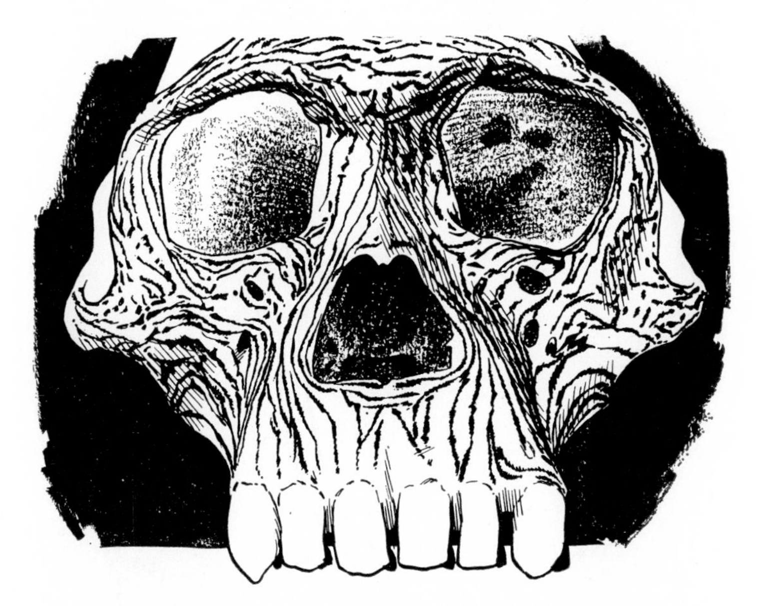

FIG. 8-2. Split-line technique. By inserting dye at appropriate places, it is possible to see and study each of the basic segments that make up a complex bony structure. (Courtesy of the Museum of Anthropology, the University of Michigan.)

and sometimes they are related to such environmental factors as humidity or temperature.

An early work along these lines deals with problems of stock and race formation.[17] The authors are entirely aware of physical anthropology's past errors, and they cleverly try to steer around them. They state their thesis boldly: "Human beings differ in their physiological reactions to their different environments and consequently differ in

16 An up-to-date study of this kind is J. Brožek, "Body Composition," *Science,* Vol. 134, 1961, pp. 920–30.

17 C. S. Coon, S. M. Garn, and J. B. Birdsell, *Races: A Study of the Problems of Race Formation in Man,* Springfield, Ill., 1950.

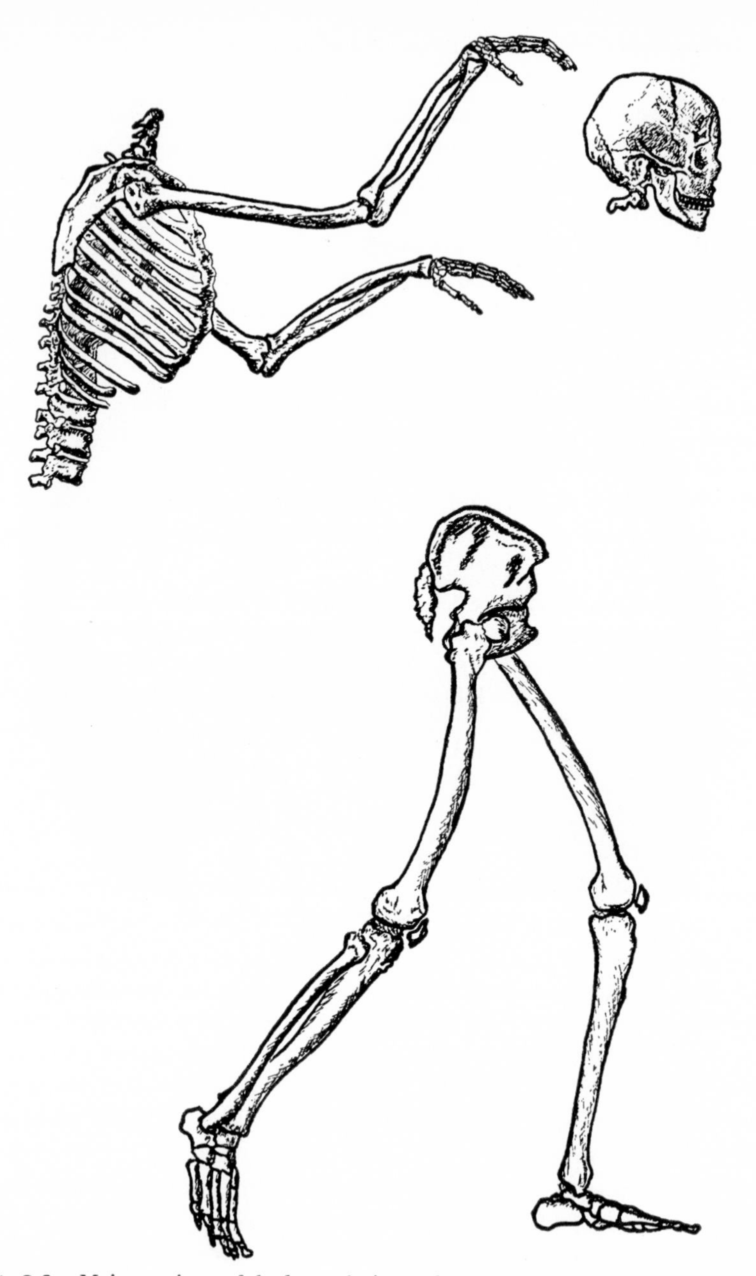

FIG. 8-3. Major regions of body evolution (after Washburn). Each of the three areas indicated appears to have had an independent evolution. In point of time, the thorax, shoulders, arms, and hands are thought to have been the first to have attained modern form. They were probably followed by pelvis, legs, and feet. The head and brain are considered to be the last to have fully evolved. Some think that the development of man's large brain may even have been stimulated by a prior use of tools. (From S. L. Washburn, "The New Physical Anthropology," *Transactions*, New York Academy of Sciences, May, 1951. Courtesy of the author and the editor.)

appearance as much as do the members of any other animal species."[18]

They then proceed with an original and provocative effort to explain how race differences may have been brought about by adaptations to differing environmental and cultural conditions. The short stature of some Mongoloid groups is attributed to a diet of polished rice; meat eaters in mid-latitudes grow large, heavy, and muscular; life at high altitudes pays a premium to those with spacious lungs and big chests; desert dwellers thrive best if they are tall and lean; and inhabitants of the Arctic are most likely to survive if they are short and thickset. Peppercorn hair is advantageous in hot zones because it permits sweat from the scalp to evaporate; cold weather has engineered the Mongoloid face with large pads of fat resting on extended cheekbones, and a flat nose designed to provide maximum heat for air passing to the lungs; and absence of pigment is associated with life in cool, damp, and cloudy areas.

Approaches of this sort are similar to methods followed by zoologists who study the relationships of nonhuman animals to their environments (*ecology*). Some of their hypotheses have been expressed as rules. Thus, *Gloger's rule* states that birds and mammals living in warm and humid regions will be darker in color than their relatives who reside in cool and dry climates. *Bergman's rule* says that in related species smaller sizes will be found among those in the warmer portions of a species' range; and *Allen's rule* claims that protruding body parts, such as tails, ears, bills, and limbs will be shorter in a colder climate than they are among species members who live in hot climates. Many of these zoological findings are being applied to man.[19] In fact, there is a marked tendency among present-day anthropologists to define races and racial variations in terms of geographical distributions, or by adaptations to differing geographical regions that provide differing environments.

Various kinds of attacks on problems of body formation and racial differences have been made in a large number of studies devoted to growth. One of the leaders in this aspect of physical anthropology is Wilton M. Krogman, who has published a valuable, comprehensive syllabus that gives references to numerous works covering the entire field.[20] In addition, J. M. Tanner has prepared a guide to growth studies, which lists all the important research centers of some fifteen years ago, and describes the particular problems they were trying to

[18] *Ibid.*, p. 4.

[19] Some anthropologists find that these rules make good points of departure, even though certain zoologists regard them as outmoded.

[20] W. M. Krogman, "The Physical Growth of the Child," *Yearbook of Physical Anthropology*, New York, 1949, pp. 280–99.

solve.[21] Another prominent leader in this field is Stanley M. Garn, who directs the physical growth department of the Fels Research Institute, connected with Antioch College in Ohio.[22]

Examining the Constitution

For many centuries observers of mankind, both laymen and specialists, have taken for granted a correlation between body build and temperament or behavior. Expressions such as "jolly, fat man" or Shakespeare's description of the lean and hungry-looking Cassius who "thinks too much" have not always been dismissed as mere folklore or poetic license.

By all odds the most ambitious studies conducted along these lines have been those of William H. Sheldon and his associates. Their first efforts were directed toward the establishment of well-defined body or constitutional types, and then they tried to relate them to particular kinds of temperaments and other aspects of behavior. Not satisfied with the standard measurements taken by physical anthropologists, Sheldon devised a technique known as *somatotyping.* Its essence rested on his conviction that each human being develops in greater or lesser degree from a combination of three basic components: *endomorphy, mesomorphy,* and *ectomorphy.* Endomorphy means a comparative predominance of soft and rounded body parts, particularly in the region of the stomach or digestive tract; mesomorphy stands for a relatively great development of muscle and bone; and ectomorphy implies a tall, thin body, with much skin surface and little depth or volume behind it, coupled with a sensitive nervous system and a big brain.

By means of measurements and observations, ideally taken with specially designed tools on carefully standardized photographs in the nude, Sheldon rates five sectors of each individual's body in terms of the three components. His scale runs from 1 to 7, so that an extremely endomorphic person averages 7-1-1; extreme mesomorphs average 1-7-1; and extreme ectomorphs average 1-1-7 (Fig. 8–4). A person who exhibited absolutely no extremes of body build would earn an average

[21] J. M. Tanner, "A Guide to American Growth Studies," *Yearbook of Physical Anthropology,* New York, 1947, pp. 28–33.

[22] An extremely valuable work on this topic is S. M. Garn, and Z. Shamit, *Methods for Research in Human Growth,* Springfield, Ill., 1958. This book contains a fine recent bibliography. Readers who are interested in human growth should also consult J. M. Tanner, ed., *Human Growth,* London, 1961.

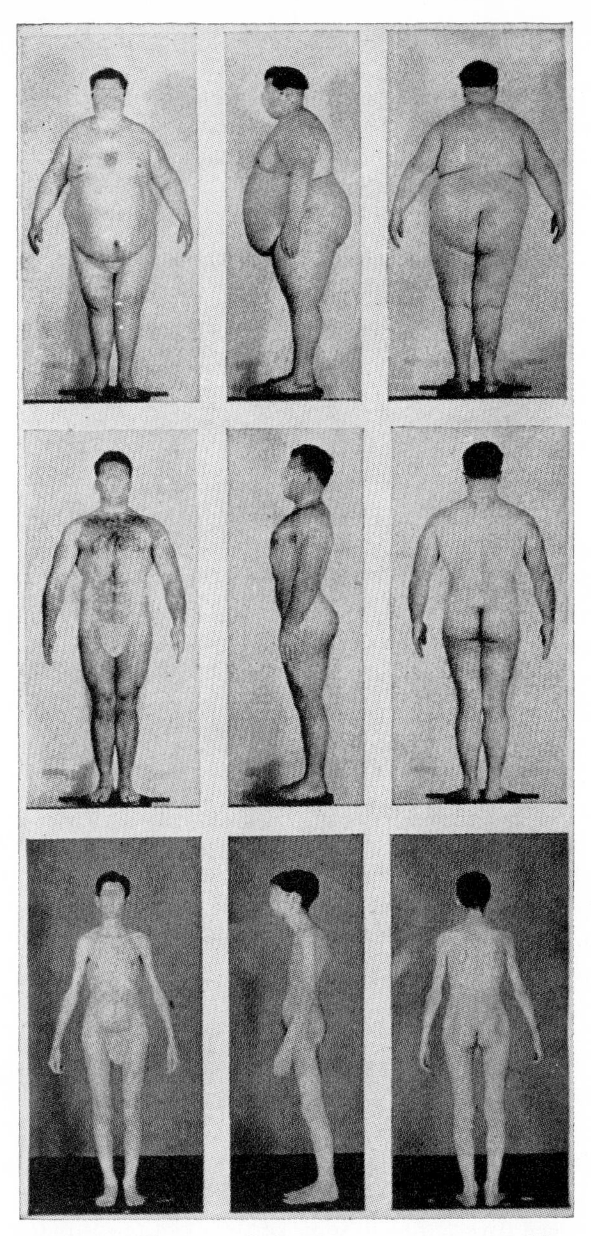

FIG. 8-4. Extreme varieties of human somatotypes (after Sheldon). At the top is an extreme endomorph (7-1-1), who is likely to be viscerotonic in temperament. The center shows an extreme mesomorph (1-7-1), with whom a somatotonic disposition is usually associated. The bottom pictures an extreme ectomorph (1-1-7), whose temperament is often cerebrotonic. (From W. H. Sheldon, *et al.*, *The Varieties of Human Physique,* New York, 1940. Courtesy of the author and Harper & Row, Publishers.)

rating of 4-4-4. Other subjects would vary from 1 to 7 in each of the three components.[23]

Hardly had Sheldon's account of somatotyping appeared than physical anthropologists divided into two camps. Some felt that he had broken new ground which promised to produce a rich scientific harvest, but others maintained that he was a visionary employing an unsound and biased, subjective approach. Unperturbed by the caustic comments of many of his colleagues, Sheldon went on to relate his constitutional types to forms of temperament or behavior. Again he rated his subjects on a seven-point scale for each of three components. Extroverts, who enjoyed comfortable living, good food, and pleasant companionship were called *viscerotonic* and were found to predominate among endomorphs; those who liked vigorous exercise and other forms of strenuous muscular activity were labeled *somatotonic* and linked with mesomorphs; while introverts who were shy and studious were described as *cerebrotonic* and associated with ectomorphic body build.[24]

Among the outstanding weaknesses of Sheldon's approach has been his insistence that under all conditions a somatotype remains the same throughout a person's life. When a research worker demonstrated that starvation actually changes a person's somatotype, Sheldon brushed off the criticism with the implication that the investigator was incompetent.

Whatever the final evaluation of Sheldon's work turns out to be, he has already exerted a profound influence on many students of man and his behavior. Very likely, the most lasting results will be achieved by those who, stimulated by Sheldon, are revising and modifying his techniques, rather than by the few disciples who are adhering rigidly to his concepts and methods.[25]

Physical anthropology expands

The habits of careful measurement and observation of human bodies that were the principal stock in trade of physical anthropologists have lately been diverted from some of their old pursuits to a surprising number of new and practical applications. Between 1937 and 1939, pre-

---

[23] Sheldon's techniques and findings are given in W. H. Sheldon, S. S. Stevens, and W. B. Tucker, *The Varieties of Human Physique,* New York, 1940.

[24] W. H. Sheldon and S. S. Stevens, *The Varieties of Temperament,* New York, 1942.

[25] E. E. Hunt, Jr., "Human Constitution: An Appraisal," *American Journal of Physical Anthropology,* Vol. 10, 1952, especially pp. 65–72.

cise measurements were obtained on 147,000 American boys and girls from 4 to 17 years of age in order to establish more accurate standards in the making and distribution of children's clothing. Pressure for the study came especially from mail-order companies whose customers, lacking opportunities for preliminary fittings, found that former label sizes were consistently misleading. To be effective, the standard techniques of anthropometry had to be altered to fit the conditions of the particular project under consideration. Apparently, so much success was achieved that the decade of the 1940's saw many more measurements being taken on women and children, and applied to practical use in the manufacture, labeling, and sale of countless garments.[26]

While this was going on, engineers were also seeking anthropometric information that would permit the making of machinery best suited for handling by a large percentage of potential operators. One specific program, undertaken in 1945 at the Naval Medical Research Institute, sought to determine how far a man could reach in various directions from a fixed, sitting position. Some of the results were put to use in the location of instruments when designing military aircraft, but the basic information has also proved of value in civil aeronautics.[27]

Both in the United States and Great Britain many problems during World War II were turned over for solution to teams that included personnel trained in physical anthropology. Among other things these teams dealt with questions connected with sizing and fitting wearing apparel, handling of weapons, vehicle guidance, personal equipment such as gas or oxygen masks, and seating devices. Again the results obtained were deemed so valuable that civilian agencies continued to seek similar information after the war. Hooton gained no small amount of fame from a comfortable chair he designed to suit the sitting contours of riders in railroad cars.

In all the years since World War II, the United States Air Force has continued to maintain an Anthropometric Unit at Wright Field, on which H. T. E. Hertzberg serves as anthropometrist. His team has made many contributions that are valuable not only to the armed forces, but also to the general populace.

Physical anthropology sometimes plays a highly important part in

---

[26] For a review of these studies, consult R. W. Newman, "Applied Anthropometry," in A. L. Kroeber, ed., *Anthropology Today,* Chicago, 1953, pp. 741–49.

[27] For further details about this project and some of those mentioned in the remainder of this section, see "Symposium on Applied Physical Anthropology," *American Journal of Physical Anthropology,* Vol. 6, 1948, pp. 313–80.

legal medicine.[28] That is why W. M. Krogman, and later, T. D. Stewart and Marshall T. Newman, physical anthropologists on the staff of the National Museum in Washington, have often been asked by the Federal Bureau of Investigation to help identify skeletal materials found under suspicious circumstances. They have become expert at sorting human from other animal bones, and in estimating age, stature, and sex. Race is so frequently dependent on perishable features for making judgments, that it is hard to determine from skeletal fragments. Even here, though, physical anthropologists sometimes make startlingly accurate analyses. Similar identifications of the remains of unknown war dead have been made by Harry L. Shapiro of the American Museum of Natural History in New York, and Charles E. Snow of Kentucky University. It is estimated that over 80 percent of 1500 unknown war dead are being definitely identified.

Far from having remained an obscure, academic, and impractical field of endeavor, physical anthropology has turned out to have wide usefulness in many ways. Apart from the projects already mentioned it has been applied to numerous programs of dental and medical research.[29] Whenever necessary, revisions of old-fashioned procedures have been unhesitatingly made, and have often proved to be of great value. In a review of this branch of the science of man it is not surprising to discover that many questions concerning the biology of human beings remain unanswered, but it is little short of amazing that so much has been accomplished by so few in the short space of several decades.

Selected References

Boyd, William C., *Genetics and the Races of Man,* Boston, 1950.

Coon, Carleton S., "Climate and Race," *Climatic Change,* H. Shapley, ed., Cambridge, Mass., 1954, pp. 13–34.

Dobzhansky, Theodosius, *Genetics and the Origin of Species,* rev. ed., New York, 1951.

Draper, George, *Disease and the Man,* London, 1930.

———, Dupertuis, Wesley C., and Caughey, J. L., Jr., *Human Constitution in Clinical Medicine,* New York and London, 1944.

Fisher, R. A., *The Genetical Theory of Natural Selection,* London, 1930.

[28] Many important details are given in T. D. Stewart, "Evaluation of Evidence from the Skeleton," *Legal Medicine,* St. Louis, 1954, pp. 407–50.

[29] A summary of this essential topic may be found in W. M. Krogman, "The Role of Physical Anthropology in Dental and Medical Research," *American Journal of Physical Anthropology,* Vol. 9, 1951, pp. 211–18.

Laughlin, William S., "Aspects of Current Physical Anthropology," *Southwestern Journal of Anthropology,* Vol. 16, 1960, pp. 75–92.

———, "Preliminary Tests for Presence of Blood-group Substance in Tepexpan Man," in H. de Terra *et al.,* "Tepexpan Man," *Viking Fund Publication No. 11;* New York, 1949, Appendix F.

Mourant, A. E., *The Distribution of the Human Blood Groups,* Oxford, 1954.

Sheldon, William H., *et al., The Varieties of Human Physique,* New York, 1940.

———, *The Varieties of Human Temperament,* New York, 1942.

Spuhler, James N., "On the Number of Genes in Man," *Science,* Vol. 108, 1948, pp. 279–80.

Symposium on Applied Physical Anthropology, *American Journal of Physical Anthropology,* Vol. 6, 1948.

Thieme, Frederick P., "The Population as a Unit of Study," *American Anthropologist,* Vol. 54, 1952, pp. 504–09.

Waddington, C. H., *New Patterns in Genetics and Development,* New York, 1962.

Washburn, Sherwood L., "The Strategy of Physical Anthropology," in A. L. Kroeber, ed., *Anthropology Today,* Chicago, 1953, pp. 714–27.

The Biological Foundations of Culture

CHAPTER 9

The human animal

By the time the first truly hominid forms had made their appearance, their organs for meeting the requirements of the biological imperatives, and thus for sustaining life, were of considerable antiquity and time-tested utility. Except for matters of degree there were almost no differences, when they began to diverge, between the ways in which human and other Primate bodies breathed, chewed and swallowed food, digested, excreted waste matter, reproduced, or used their sense organs. It seems safe to postulate that the biological conduct of the very earliest hominids was not significantly different from that of their Primate contemporaries. Yet the later stages of man's behavior stand out in sharp contrast because of his dependence on nonbiogenetic mechanisms. Herein lies a problem that is worthy of the most careful consideration, for it involves the basic question of how human beings, only, came to fashion with a generally Primate form of biology a whole system of extrabiological patterns of action.

There is no evidence to show that man's body and culture started to evolve together, at exactly the same points of time. It is far more probable that the body had started to move toward a *Homo sapiens* condition long before the beginnings of cultural development. Presumably, this means that at some distant time there must have been cultureless prehominids. In the absence of culture, how did these creatures live?

Of course scientists know absolutely nothing of what such presumed potential hominids really did, but it may be instructive to try to imagine how they lived. As a guess, it may be supposed that their lives were adjusted to meet the needs, exclusively, of the biological world. Involuntarily, their lungs took in oxygen, their hearts pumped blood, and their body temperatures normally remained at a constantly high level. Whenever they exerted themselves, they breathed harder than usual and felt tired; when they were cold, their teeth chattered and their bodies shivered; when they were hot, they sweated; and whenever they grew sufficiently weary, they rested or slept. When their stomachs contracted, they felt hunger pangs and sought to put food into their mouths, where it was moistened and chewed, then swallowed into the digestive tract. When there was pressure on the bladder, they urinated; and when their bowels were full, they defecated.

Male bodies were organized to form sperm cells in the testes and female bodies to produce egg cells in the ovaries. From time to time their genital organs were stimulated and they engaged in copulation. If fertilization followed, the female's menstrual periods were suspended and an embryo formed within her body, where it was nourished through a gestation of about nine months by means of a placental arrangement. After giving birth to her child, the female discharged the placental mechanism from her body as the afterbirth, suckled the baby, and aided it in many ways until it reached a stage where it could shift for itself. As years passed the bodies of males and females became subject to some fatal accident or disease, or else grew old and deteriorated. Then death came to terminate the biological aspects of their behavior, and the corpses decomposed in response to fixed laws of chemistry and physics.

This is essentially the behavior of any placental, or eutherian, mammal, even when it applies to incipient hominids. Within the limits mentioned, every mechanism for action is biogenetically inherited and developed, and every response is somatically directed and controlled. Had man continued to live in such fashion, his way of life would have been virtually indistinguishable from that of other large Primates.

But man didn't continue to live in this fashion. What he did was to use some of his biogenetically inherited parts and functions as foundations for the building of culture. It would certainly be unwarranted to maintain that every single thing a nonhuman animal does is entirely biological, nor can it be argued that Homo merely superimposed culture on top of his somatic equipment. Most anthropologists think, instead, that culture grew out of the biology of hominids. In any event, it is certain that no infrahuman animal has ever reared and maintained anything like man's clear-cut and complex cultural system.

All living things, in order to survive, must make successful adaptations to their environments. Every kind of animal, with the sole exception of *Homo sapiens,* makes its adaptations through biology. It is only man who occasionally makes adaptations through his culture. From this viewpoint one can regard culture as an adaptive mechanism. Surely, however, this mechanism must have been imperfect at the outset and must have gained in efficiency as it evolved through time.

Before culture had attained much efficiency, man had no way of making palatable foods that were unfit to eat in their natural state; if he wished to get to a distant spot in a hurry, he had no recourse but to run or be carried by others; if he wanted to shatter something, he had to depend primarily on his muscular strength; if his eyes began to fail, he had to become reconciled to dim vision or blindness; and if a woman could not be delivered normally of a baby, she was practically doomed to die in childbirth. Today, each of these matters can be handled differently. Cooking and other methods of preparing food make many things fit to eat that were previously unsuited for human consumption; people who are in a hurry to get to distant places employ all kinds of vehicles, instead of running or being carried by other humans; many power-driven contrivances or explosives are used for shattering hard substances; corrective glasses give excellent vision to people whose eyesight is biologically poor; and modern obstetricians, with the aid of instruments and surgery, regularly deliver women who would otherwise die.

Certain anthropologists have tried to fit the development of culture directly into the biological record of human evolution. According to them, some hominid genes are better suited for culture than others. Natural selection as man evolved, they argue, favored the genes that were more suitable for culture, and thus established them in modern man's ancestors. Once they had become established, the argument continues, they served to facilitate the acquisition, development, and transmission of culture. At the moment, there is no proof for this bit of speculation.

It has also been pointed out by some scholars that various facets of hominid conduct such as aggression, are found only among vertebrates. Others read a great deal of significance into man's unique dietary habits. Among the Primates, Homo stands out as the greatest of the carnivores. He consumes great quantities of meat protein, and is the most persistent big game hunter and killer of his order. This yields him a great many calories at a time, but it also calls for a more extensive territorial range than vegetarians require, and a far greater degree of cooperation and social control. It is a matter of record that such food sharing as exists among nonhuman creatures is found only among flesh eaters (carnivores), and no animal save man so regularly provides for others by sharing its food. This is, indeed, a distinctive trait of human behavior, and there are those who would trace all economic and political institutions back to man's habits of food sharing.[1] Several anthropologists feel that mutual aid may thus turn out to have biological survival value.

It is also true that no Primate save man eats regularly scheduled meals. At the very least, such a custom calls for the advance preparation of food. Among humans, eating must always be delayed while a meal is being prepared; but among nonhuman Primates, food is generally consumed on the spot.

A few anthropologists trace some cultural practices back to certain features of the biology of human infancy. They stress the facts that simian babies mature more rapidly and achieve total independence much sooner.[2] By contrast, human infants must remain dependent on their mothers or other adults for long stretches of time.[3] Protracted periods of helpless dependence on others cannot fail, every one will agree, to influence the later behavior of all human beings.

Enough has been said to explain the anthropological conviction that man's culture grew out of and is closely geared to his biology. So far, however, nothing has been said of the particular, and sometimes unique, physical features that appear to have made hominid culture possible. These will be treated in the next sections.

WALKING—NO HANDS

The vast majority of man's anatomical distinctions seem to be concentrated in three of his body areas. They are the lower limbs, the forelimbs,

[1] For a stimulating discussion of food sharing as a human characteristic, see M. D. Sahlins, "The Social Life of Monkeys, Apes and Primitive Man," *The Evolution of Man's Capacity for Culture,* J. N. Spuhler, ed., Detroit, 1959, pp. 54–73, especially p. 66. See also H. W. Nissen and M. P. Crawford, "A preliminary study of food-sharing behavior in young chimpanzees," *Journal of Comparative Psychology,* Vol. 22, 1936, pp. 383–419.

[2] S. L. Washburn and V. Avis, "Evolution of Human Behavior," in A. Roe and G. G. Simpson, eds., *Behavior and Evolution,* New Haven, Conn., 1958, pp. 421–36.

[3] Harry F. Harlow, director of the Primate laboratory at the University of Wisconsin, is conducting a series of fascinating studies on the influences of "mothers" on rhesus monkey infants. His experiments revolve about two artificial mothers, one of whom gives milk but no comfort, while the other gives comfort but no milk. The reactions of the baby monkeys are analyzed and compared with the behavior of naturally reared babies. An excellent preliminary account of these experiments is given in H. F. Harlow, "Basic Social Capacity of Primates," in J. N. Spuhler, ed., *The Evolution of Man's Capacity for Culture,* Detroit, 1959, pp. 40–53, especially p. 52.

An outstanding series of articles along the lines discussed in this chapter appears in "Social Life of Early Man," S. L. Washburn, ed., *Viking Fund Publications in Anthropology,* No. 31, New York, 1961. These articles should be consulted by all who are interested in this topic.

and the head. Each of these somatic sets of features helped to provide a biological foundation for man's development of culture.

Homo sapiens is the only Primate that habitually walks on the ground in a bipedal or *orthograde* (upright) posture. On the one hand, this may be connected with the development of his lower-limb structures, which seem to have become stabilized to the point where they could, unassisted, hold the body upright and move it about; and on the other hand, these structures came to do their job so well that other portions of the body were left free and could be devoted to other functions. This feature, which applies chiefly to the upper limbs, is conventionally described as the *emancipation of the forelimbs,* and is of great importance in the formation of culture. Primates who go about in a four-legged or quadrupedal stance, and even those which may be considered partially bipedal, have muscle systems that bind the front or upper limbs, wholly or in part, to the support or movement of the body. Consequently, their forelimbs are not completely emancipated and cannot be freely used for nonpostural or nonlocomotor activities. On this score *Homo sapiens* differs markedly from all other Primates.

Once the forelimbs are completely freed they can be used for exploring the environment, embracing lovers or children, feeding, grooming, and manipulating objects, particularly tools. It does not always require large brains to utilize some implements. Monkeys use stones to crack nuts or to break mussel shells; wild chimpanzees have been observed to use twigs for getting honey; and microcephalic idiots handle some external objects properly. This suggests that the use of tools came *before* the expansion of man's brain. It has even been said that the development of suitable anatomical mechanisms, in advance of the habitual use of tools, may be an example of biological preadaptation.

All infrahuman Primates have so little skill and accuracy in making or wielding nonsomatic devices that they regularly rely on body parts, such as teeth or nails. Only hominids consistently depend on manufactured objects and even go so far as to carry them along for use at some future time and place. Moreover, no Primate except man has sufficient bipedal stability to enable him to stand up and use his fists, thread a needle while standing, or wield such implements as axes, daggers, and clubs.

The importance of vision

As has probably been anticipated, man's use of tools does not exist by itself, set apart, as it were, from all other attributes. Obviously, it is connected with other aspects of human body structure. Many of these aspects are directly geared to the special nature of man's vision. Increased reliance on the sense of sight is a noteworthy feature of biological evolution as we trace its story from fish to man. A world-famous neurophysiologist, Ralph W. Gerard, has estimated that approximately two thirds of all the nerve fibers that enter the human central nervous system come from the eyes.[4] Any one of us, faced with the choice of losing either the sense of smell or the sense of sight, would unhesitatingly sacrifice the sense of smell.

Going a step further, we know that *stereoscopic* vision is just as important to human beings as is the accurate and rapid perception of simple light waves. Without the proper anatomical arrangement that makes possible overlapping or stereoscopic vision there would be little sense of depth, and without a sense of depth we could not tell a thin twig from a thick branch; it would be foolhardy ever to try to pass another automobile on the road; and motion-picture producers could save themselves the boundless costs of trying to perfect 3-D and similar devices for achieving the third dimension of depth.

Close coordination of hand and eye is a prerequisite for any human activity that involves the use of artifacts. Even so simple a matter as writing one's name becomes difficult if one tries to do it with his eyes shut. Baseball coaches and golf instructors constantly remind players who are using bats or clubs to keep their eyes on the ball. Similarly, no one of us, if we had any say in the matter, would accept the offer of a free operation at the hands of the most skilled of surgeons if we knew that he planned to operate while blindfolded.

Another important tie between the sense of sight and other body parts is involved in reaction speed, that is, in the length of time that it takes for a message from the eyes to reach the brain, and for the brain to interpret the message and to send suitable instructions to the appropriate muscles that are to carry out a necessary task. Many people are prone to disregard reaction time and to think that sight and body behavior occur almost simultaneously. Not so with pilots of jet-propelled aircraft. As the speeds of their planes have increased, they have come to realize more and more how slow and imperfect are their own bodily mechanisms. No longer are they content to read instrument panels, to translate what they see, and to figure out what to do.[5] What they want is a luminous screen that will show them at a glance the actual terrain

[4] R. W. Gerard, "Units and Concepts of Biology," *Science,* Vol. 125, 1957, p. 429.

[5] It has been estimated that the nerve impulses involved in reaction speeds travel at various rates up to 330 feet per second. This amounts to approximately 225 miles an hour, which is about three times slower than a commercial jet plane travels.

toward and over which they are flying. And to further their sense of security, they would like this visual aid combined with a computer that would make all necessary calculations for them in only a few thousandths of a second.[6]

Using your head

It takes but a fraction of a moment to realize that every hominid tool or artifact has to be made by a human being. Such things are so important to all members of *Homo sapiens* that anthropologists devote much effort to the understanding of how, when, where, and why they came into use; their methods of manufacture; and the ways in which they are utilized.

All clues once more lead back to Primate anatomy. Bipedal posture on the ground and the attendant emancipation of the forelimbs, together with the special construction of the front limbs, an amazingly large brain, and acute, stereoscopic vision, suffice to delineate the minimum potential for tool usage; but it remained for a special kind of brain power to put that potential to work. A number of species of animals, far below the level of man in the evolutionary sequence, are known to use bits of wood, stone, grass, earth, or other materials for a variety of purposes. In all such cases, there is clear evidence that extrasomatic devices are being employed as supplements to biologically inherited mechanisms. But as long as these things are used in their natural condition, it does not seem correct to class them as manufactured tools, even when they are combined into such complicated structures as nests.

To further the argument that extrasomatic items could have been in use before the appearance of hominids on earth, we have only to point to certain animals that, under experimental conditions, not only use tools but even show a limited capacity for making them.[7] Credit for at

[6] More details may be found in *Time,* October 22, 1956, p. 65.

[7] Some of the best studies of ape behavior are reported in the publications of the Yerkes' laboratories at Orange Park, Fla.

Other good articles on Primates are J. E. Frisch, "Research on primate behavior in Japan," *American Anthropologist,* Vol. 61, 1959, pp. 584–96; K. Imanishi, "Social Organization of Subhuman Primates in their Natural Habitat," *Current Anthropology,* Vol. 1, 1960, pp. 393–407; and P. E. Simonds, "The Japan Monkey Center," *Current Anthropology,* Vol. 3, No. 3, 1962, pp. 303–05. Also, see the appropriate articles in S. L. Washburn, ed., "Social Life of Early Man," *Viking Fund Publications in Anthropology,* No. 31, 1961.

There is at present a great deal of interest in the brains and intelligence of porpoises. Some exciting experiments and observations have been made by W. N. Kellogg, of Florida State University, John Lilly, of the Communications Research least a small amount of manufacturing skill cannot be withheld from chimpanzees, for example, which can bend flexible straws to make a stiff, unyielding brush; fit two short sticks together to make a long one (Fig. 9–1); and can sometimes go so far as to chew on a thick stick until it is slim enough to penetrate a slender socket.

According to what we now know about the behavior of various beasts, then, it is evident that some tool-using, and possibly toolmaking

FIG. 9-1. Chimpanzee making a tool. Some credit for a degree of manufacturing skill cannot be withheld from a chimpanzee that can fit two sticks together to make an elongated implement with which to secure food. (From B. W. Köhler, *The Mentality of Apes,* 2d ed. New York, 1925. Courtesy of Harcourt, Brace & World, Inc.)

ability is an ancient feature of life in the animal kingdom and was characteristic of man's ancestors. Not very long after the appearance of hominids, at the very latest by the time level of *Sinanthropus pekinensis,* clear and irrefutable signs indicate that men were no longer living exclusively in the biophysicochemical world, but had entered into the realm of culture. The most conclusive proof rests on the occurrence of systematically manufactured stone tools that were found directly asso-

Institute in the Virgin Islands, and by other reputable investigators. They report that in some mental activities, including communication with sounds, porpoises may equal or exceed human beings. For a good article on these matters, see R. J. Andrew, "Evolution of Intelligence and Vocal Mimicking," *Science,* Vol. 137, 1962, pp. 585–89. Nevertheless, since porpoises have never developed culture, they need not concern us here.

ciated with skeletal remains.[8] Regularly manufactured tools, it need hardly be emphasized, are not a part of any animal's biogenetic inheritance. They have to be fashioned with the help of a body, but they carry on an independent, extrabodily existence. We may speak of inheriting a kit of tools, but we realize full well that the manner of transmission is quite different from inheritance through sexual reproduction. By following all the implications of toolmaking, it is possible to learn a great deal about how man came to use his inherited biological equipment for nonbiological purposes and in nonsomatically determined ways.

To make a tool requires the mental capacity to plan ahead freely without biological predetermination, to look unrestrictedly into the future, and to deal with imaginary situations in the sense that all future events are imaginary before they have come to pass. Anthropologists have learned not to confuse the two different levels at which planning ahead may be found. One kind is biogenetically controlled, as when squirrels store nuts before the coming of winter, or when birds migrate from north to south and back again. The other kind is cultural, and is neither biologically inherited nor a fixed response to environmental clues. The essential difference between these two levels of planning ahead is the matter of freedom of action. Biological planning ahead leaves almost no room for individual choice but is imposed, with only a little flexibility, on all the members of a given species. But cultural planning ahead permits each individual to act within a wide range of possibilities and sets few limitations on how one may decide to meet a future contingency. Squirrels of a particular species must store nuts at certain times, in certain ways. Men, by contrast, may store any or no kinds of nuts, may decide to hoard instead potatoes or cans of soup, or may prefer to put money into the bank, or to go on relief when winter comes.

If it be granted that infrahuman animals, particularly chimpanzees among the living apes, sometimes use and even manufacture tools, then it must be admitted that they too have at least a restricted ability to look ahead. This capacity has been proved in a series of revealing and sometimes amusing experiments. A vending machine, appropriately called a *Chimp-O-Mat,* was constructed in such fashion that by inserting a token comparable to a poker chip a raisin could be "bought." Experimenters showed the animals to be tested how to do a bit of work, operating a weight-lifting lever or pulling a sliding tray, by means of which

---

[8] It is now becoming likely that hominid tool usage should be attributed to some of the Australopithecinae, who lived approximately a million years ago.

a food token was earned. This was inserted into the Chimp-O-Mat and a raisin "purchased," and eaten.[9] Chimpanzees promptly caught the idea and were soon busily working for tokens and buying raisins (Fig. 9–2). Sometimes the Chimp-O-Mat was deliberately rendered out of order, but the apes continued to look ahead and to work for tokens, with somewhat diminished eagerness, in anticipation of going on a buying spree when the machine resumed operation. Tests yielding roughly comparable results have been carried out with a wide assortment of animals, not necessarily Primates.

By comparison with other creatures, man uses his ability to plan

FIG. 9-2. An ape looks ahead. This picture shows a chimpanzee using the Chimp-O-Mat. It is buying a raisin with a special token for which it has worked. This demonstrates that it does have the capacity to look to the future. The apes in this experiment also showed how thoroughly they had grasped the man-assigned value of a token, by refusing to accept counterfeits. (Courtesy of H. W. Nissen and J. B. Wolfe. "Effectiveness of Token-rewards for Chimpanzees," *Comparative Psychological Monographs,* Vol. 12, 1936.)

ahead so much more frequently and freely that it forms one of the most essential traits that separates him from the rest of the animal kingdom. Yet, there is a convention among ourselves that we cannot guess about the future, and all of us are familiar with remarks like, "No one knows what the future will bring," or "It's ridiculous to try to predict the future." Of course, there are many vast and important areas in which prediction is futile, as in trying to guess who will be the President of the United States in 1990. Just the same, in spite of the wealth of proverbs and popular sayings to the contrary, human beings constantly indulge in predictions.

Every day, and at practically every moment of the day, huge num-

[9] The short account given here is based on a combination of two reports, which may be found in J. B. Wolfe, "Effectiveness of Token-rewards for Chimpanzees," *Comparative Psychological Monographs,* Vol. 12, No. 5, 1936; and J. T. Cowles, "Food-tokens as Incentives for Learning by Chimpanzees," *Ibid.,* Vol. 14, No. 5, 1937.

bers of men and women are constantly predicting, and to a great extent accurately predicting, many important future events. Countless school children select their colleges and professions years in advance; lovers decide to marry "when John gets out of the Army"; youngsters repeatedly make dates for "after school"; wives ask husbands each morning to bring something or other "on the way home from the office"; people make travel or hotel reservations months ahead; college football schedules are made out for so many years in advance that most of the anticipated players of future years have not yet entered high school; and invitations to great affairs go out long before they are supposed to take place. Obviously death, sickness, accident or some other unforeseen contingency may upset one's prediction; yet, for all that, human beings persistently and to a large extent successfully base their lives on the premise that their plans for the future will be carried out.

It is time now to see how man's aptitude for planning and looking ahead applies to the making of tools. If one decides to manufacture even the simplest of implements, say a homemade toothpick of wood, he must plan for the future in several ways. He must know where he can get the necessary raw material and where he can secure the needed tools. More important still, he must have clearly in mind, before he begins manufacturing, the size and shape of the finished object that he wants to make. Unless he has in mind an advance blueprint of the completed object, he is unlikely to turn out even so elementary an implement as a simple, wooden toothpick.

Once he had developed the capacity to think ahead in ways that were not biogenetically predetermined or somatically controlled, man was able to escape biophysicochemical limitations and to begin fashioning culture. Yet, he could not entirely divorce himself from biology, for if he refused to obey its imperatives, as by failing to breathe while manufacturing tools, he would surely die. Furthermore, to show how these things work together, even if a man had the necessary materials and the clearest of mental pictures of something he wanted to make, and even if he obeyed biological imperatives, he would still require strong and flexible fingers, hands, wrists, and arms, accurate muscular controls, and keen hand-eye coordination in order to be a successful manufacturer. Cultural behavior must always utilize body parts, and that is why human toolmaking is always a biocultural activity.

Words and symbols

Man's capacity to deal with future or imaginary situations calls for a kind of mentality that is, as far as is known, unique among animals.

Because of this special ability the test of reality among human beings is no longer restricted to physical, chemical, sensory, or any biological standards.[10] This is what Emily Dickinson meant when she wrote her famous lines:

> "I never saw a moor
> I never saw the sea
> Yet know I how the heather looks
> And what a wave must be."

Man can and does deal with nonexistent or imaginary things with just about as much assurance as he does with tangible objects. Mermaids are not supposed to be real, but human beings can count them, paint or carve them, and write stories or poems about them. Let us try the experiment of reading the following couplets:

A

> There were ten mermaids, sporting in the brine;
> One swam away, and then there were nine.

B

> There were ten sea bass, sporting in the brine;
> One swam away, and then there were nine.

Admittedly, sea bass are real and mermaids are not, but we do not understand couplet B any better than we do couplet A. As a matter of fact, many of us could probably give a better description of a mermaid than we could of a sea bass.

It is also easy to give any normal human being verbal instructions that will enable him to go to some place where he has never before been and to take up an object which he has never before seen. I can readily tell a person who has never been to my house how to enter my study and remove the only black mask that hangs on the wall, but I cannot with speech alone similarly instruct any other animal.

One of man's most extraordinary mental accomplishments is his capacity for dealing with *abstractions.* By no test of biophysicochemical or sensory reality can one establish the existence of such abstract ideas as "pride," "civic duty," "loyalty," or "thoughtfulness"; yet, human beings have no trouble in grasping these intangibles, and even in measuring or comparing them, as when we say that one person has more or less pride than another. With the emergence of the mental ability to

---

[10] The birthday of the Queen of England furnishes an excellent example of man's ability to disregard reality. Elizabeth II was born on April 21, 1926, but her birthday is officially celebrated on June 10. This may be much more convenient for her subjects, but it has nothing to do with the actual day on which she was born.

deal with abstractions, the way is opened for the development of higher mathematics, philosophy, poetry, religion, ethics, and similar fields.

Abstract ideas achieve a kind of reality, as a rule, only when they have been expressed in words. Accordingly, the human capacity for dealing with abstractions cannot be separated from the use of language. In essence, a spoken word is a sound or combination of sounds to which a group of persons (a society) has assigned a particular meaning. Take the sound "C" as commonly uttered in the English-speaking world. By itself it has absolutely no meaning, as any skeptic can discover if he will travel about the world saying, "C," "C," "C." Nor has this sound any specific meaning even to speakers of English. When used in one context the sound "C," spelled "see," means "look"; but if spelled and used another way the same sound, "sea," means "a body of salt water." "C" can just as well stand for the third letter of the alphabet, a note of our musical scale, an athletic award won at Colgate or Cornell, or a familiar form of address for a girl named Celia. How can the same sound "C" mean so many different things in English, to say nothing of meaning "yes" in Spanish or Italian, and "if" in French? Paradoxical as it may seem, the reason why "C" can mean all these things, plus whatever else human beings may choose to have it mean, is that in and of itself it has absolutely no meaning. Since it is entirely without meaning it does not restrict any society from assigning to it as many different meanings as it wishes. Even when this has been done with as much variety as in the English use of "C," no one of the assigned meanings becomes permanently attached to the sound. We can still, if we like, change the meanings at will. In making up a code we can make "C" stand for an oboe or a windmill.

To deny that other animals are able to use *true speech* is not to deny that they can utter *meaningful sounds*. Birds, chickens, fish, dogs, cats, Primates, and many other creatures produce sounds that convey definite meanings, but on analysis it turns out that their sound-making ability is genetically inherited in its manner of production as well as in its content. Somatic controls impose rigid limitations on all infrahuman communication. There is apparently neither variety nor flexibility. Sea gulls who endangered jet pilots, or who robbed fishermen of their catch, were invariably frightened off by a recording of a sea gull cry that meant something like "Fly away." The sea gull response to these sounds was invariable, fixed, and unchanging. This is quite different from man's capacity for flexibility and for changing the meanings of sounds whenever he so desires.

Among all species below man the sounds used are usually limited to the expression of subjective states like fear, hunger, joy, or sexual desire. There is no capacity for dealing with abstractions or sheer speculations, and not even the most ardent of animal fanciers really expects a parrot to discuss philosophy. Moreover, nonhuman creatures apparently cannot make sounds that apply to precise details. Even if one knows from the whine of a pet dog that it has been hurt, one realizes that the beast cannot utter detailed information about who injured it, when, or under what circumstances. To make meaningful sounds is a common aspect of animal behavior, but to use true speech is an exclusively human ability.

The mental power to assign one or more meanings to something which has no meaning of its own is the basis of *symbolic behavior.* A standard dictionary definition of a *symbol* reads in part, "That which suggests something else . . . especially a visible sign of something invisible, as an idea, a quality. . . ."[11] A symbol does not necessarily have to be a sound. In fact, it is universally agreed that the invention of a mark for *zero* is one of the highest mental achievements ever made by man because it expresses the very essence of symbolism by providing something that stands for absolutely nothing. So extraordinary is this idea that anthropologists believe it has been separately hit upon only three times in the known history of the world's cultures. Only the Babylonians, Mayans, and Hindus are thought to have introduced symbols for zero into their mathematical systems as *independent inventions.* Wherever else zero figures occur they are considered to be borrowings from one of the three just-mentioned sources.

Anything at all can be endowed with symbolic meanings or values, and the meanings cannot be perceived except by members of the society who have been taught to know them. In purely physicochemical terms, two pieces of wood in the shape of a cross are nothing but two pieces of wood and will be so regarded by true pagans. But to believing Christians the symbolic meaning of a wooden cross is very real and of far greater significance than the chemical or physical properties of wood.

Ability to symbolize depends on a kind of mentality for which the term *algebraic* has been proposed.[12] This idea can easily be grasped if we think of the commonest statement used in algebra, "Let *x* equal." Whenever we use this expression the symbol *x* has no meaning of its own, but in problem after problem it can be assigned any meaning within the limits of human imagination. The symbol *x* can just as well

---

[11] *Webster's Collegiate Dictionary,* abridged, 5th ed., Springfield, Mass., 1948, p. 1010.

[12] W. Köhler, *The Mentality of Apes,* rev. ed., New York, 1925, p. 11, speaks of experiments with apes that call for "a complicated geometry of movement." L. A. White has carried the concept a step further and describes human mentality as "algebraic."

equal 8 railroad cars, or half an orange, or 37 women, or 14 pairs of green shoes, or 3 unicorns. Here again we find that no matter how many meanings are assigned to *x*, the symbol itself remains without fixed meaning and so stands ever ready to have any of its assigned meanings changed at the will of those who manipulate it.

Because the entire range of culture leans so heavily on the use of language and other forms of symbolization, scientists are eager to know if nonhuman animals have similar capacities, perhaps in a less developed form. Experimenters have worked with a host of creatures to see whether or not they were able to symbolize.[13] Claims of all sorts, some clearly extravagant and others hard to deny, have been made for beasts that seem to deal successfully with symbols. Seeing-eye dogs that stop at a red traffic light, apes that remember which of several identical doors was briefly lighted up as an indication that it led to food, mice that repeatedly run a difficult maze, numerous animals that "speak," and rats that learn to distinguish the symbol "A," leading to a reward, from the symbol "B," that leads to punishment, are only a few that have been cited. Yet all the uncertainties that have been raised by these cases can be swept away if we limit ourselves to two factors.

In the first place, in every experiment of this kind so far devised, the symbolic value—such as a red light meaning stop, or "A" signifying food, and "B" standing for punishment—has been thought up by a human being.[14] There is no record of any other animal that has *invented* a symbolic meaning and arbitrarily assigned it to a particular sound,

---

[13] So much experimentation with animals has been going on of late that it is hard to make a flat statement about symbolization. This ability may prove to be less exclusively human than was once thought. Nevertheless, there does seem to be a mental border, with all of mankind safely across and the rest of the animal kingdom usually on the other side.

[14] The reader must again be reminded that words may have a variety of different meanings assigned to them. Thus, a recent investigator has claimed that infrahuman Primates could symbolize because they could remember, after a lapse of time, which of several identical doors had been lighted up as a signal that it led to food. As the "capacity to symbolize" is used in this book, it is not equivalent to an act of memory. Moreover, it was not a lower animal but a human experimenter who first determined that a lighted door should be a sign of food. To this writer it seems clear that the truly symbolic behavior was carried out by a representative of *Homo sapiens* and not by some lesser Primate.

Yet, it would be wrong to think that all problems connected with symbolization and communication have been solved. In recent years, for example, some member or members of a species of birds in England, learned to open and sip from milk bottles. As the evidence of complaints to police shows, knowledge of this new trait soon spread in ever-widening circles. The question is: Was information spread by some symbolic means or just by direct observation and imitation?

mark, color, or object. It is one thing to *recognize* a man-established symbolic meaning, which many animals can learn to do, but it is quite another matter to make up a symbolic value, which man alone can do. In the second place, all human beings, even small children, can learn to switch symbolic meanings about. If "B" stands for punishment today it can just as well stand for reward tomorrow. To fool an enemy, perhaps, we might decide to stop traffic on green and proceed on red. There would probably be some confusion, especially at first, but it would not be too difficult for people to learn the new system. The situation is very different with nonhuman animals. Once they have learned to associate "B" with punishment, it is no easy matter to retrain them to link "B" with reward.

Beginners in anthropology sometimes find it hard to understand the truly vital roles of symbolization and speech in the formation and continuation of culture. Luckily, their doubts can be resolved because every now and then persons more devoted to science than comfort have taken into their homes baby apes, treated them with the same care lavished on human infants, and tested them in every conceivable way. They have found their little charges capable of learning much that human children are expected to know and do before they begin to speak. Sometimes small Primates prove to be on a par with their sapiens fellows, occasionally they exceed them, and once in a while they fail to equal them. Now and then an over-indulgent "parent" is carried away by enthusiasm and claims to have taught an ape to speak, but careful investigation always reveals that the utterances are limited to a word or so, that they are not always clear to an unbiased observer, and that they are frequently used out of context as well as in their proper place.

A painstakingly thorough experiment of this general sort was reported about thirty years ago by W. N. Kellogg and his wife, both psychologists, then at Indiana University.[15] They took into their home and for nine months reared with their small son, Donald, a baby female chimpanzee named Gua (Fig. 9–3). They very carefully gave identical treatment to the ape and their own infant, and both youngsters were subjected to various tests. Among other things, Gua learned to wear clothes, sit in a high chair, eat with a spoon, and respond to a number of spoken commands. Ape and child ran neck and neck on most tests

---

[15] W. N. and L. A. Kellogg, *The Ape and the Child,* New York, 1933. W. N. Kellogg has lately been studying porpoises.

A later account of a chimpanzee living with humans may be found in C. Hayes, *The Ape in Our House,* New York, 1957. For a fuller analysis of the whole subject, see K. J. and C. Hayes, "The Cultural Capacity of Chimpanzees," in A. Gavan, arranger, *The Non-Human Primates and Human Evolution,* Detroit, 1955.

throughout the experiment's duration, but at the end of nine months Donald began to speak and to forge ahead rapidly, while Gua was unable to make further progress. Thereupon the Kelloggs returned her to a cage.

FIG. 9-3. The ape and the child. Donald Kellogg is shown walking with Gua, who is dressed in human style. Although the young chimpanzee learned a great deal at the Kellogg home, she was unable, lacking true, symbolic speech, to share her knowledge with anyone else. (From W. N. and L. A. Kellogg, *The Ape and the Child.* New York, 1933. Courtesy McGraw-Hill Book Company, Inc.)

Although most of the psychological data published in 1933 are out of date, a few positive conclusions may be drawn that cannot be challenged today. The Kelloggs never claimed that Gua had learned to speak, and therein lies the key to the building or absence of culture. Lacking the ability to speak, Gua was utterly incapable of communicating to other apes a single item of her experiences in Bloomington, Indiana. She had no means of handing on any of her special knowledge either to her own generation of chimpanzees or to any offspring that she might have borne. Whatever she had learned had, inevitably, to die with her. Had she been enabled to reconstruct the physical setting of the Kellogg home, she might conceivably have acted out some of her activities there and evoked imitation. Had this been the case, which is, of course, entirely fantastic, she might have transmitted part of her

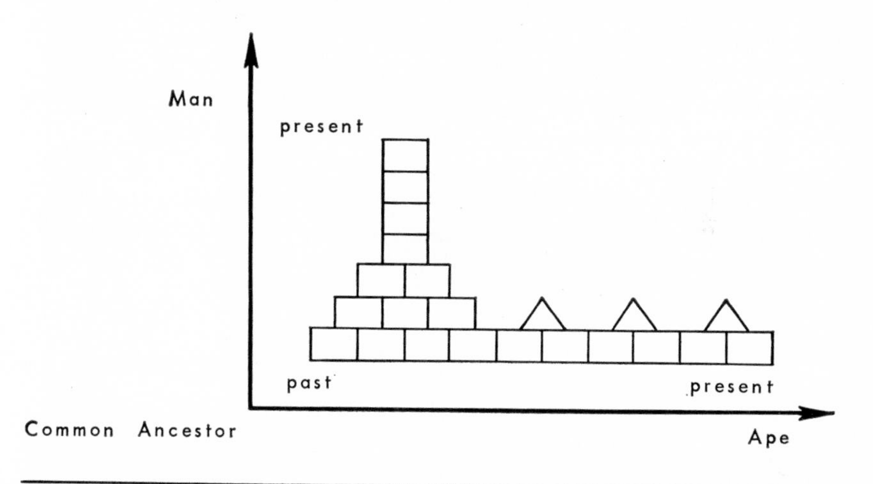

FIG. 9-4. Ape and human knowledge. When an individual ape learns something, represented by the triangular peaks, it has virtually no means of communicating what it learned to other members of its species. Hence, the species makes no appreciable increase in knowledge from past to present. On the other hand, man, with the help of speech, has been able to preserve bits of information and to communicate individual experiences to others. Accordingly, his stockpile of knowledge has, through time, increased tremendously.

knowledge to other Primates, but this is a difficult and limited way of passing on information. It is the use of language that frees man from the need of acquiring knowledge either through direct sensory observation or by some form of imitation, and permits him to learn from the experiences of others. Human educability is far greater than that of the rest of the animal kingdom, and a much higher percentage of the totality of man's activities is postnatally learned behavior.

To bring the main issue into sharp focus, one has only to imagine Gua's situation in reverse. If a human being had lived for nine months among apes, the chances are that he would bore his listeners to tears with petty details. Through the use of speech he could reconstruct every aspect of his unusual experience, and with the aid of translations anything that he had learned or experienced could, theoretically, be made a part of human knowledge throughout the world. His words could be carried even to people who never saw or heard him in person, and who had never seen an ape. Sharing experiences with others, contributing to the sum total of human knowledge, and transmitting ideas and information to succeeding generations are things that normal human beings can easily do; but so long as they lack the ability to invent symbolic values and to assign some of them to sounds (speech), no other animals are capable of doing likewise. Whatever a nonhuman creature learns is almost certain to perish with it unless it can be biogenetically transmitted; whatever man learns can be spread about and handed on indefinitely and nonbiologically.

The chances are nil that culture could have originated without speech, and it is equally certain that without speech there could have been none of the adding on or stockpiling of knowledge that lies at the very base of culture growth (Fig. 9–4).

The biological basis for algebraic mentality

Only one feature of the hominid body gives promise at this time of holding the key to man's exceptional mentality, and that is his highly developed brain. Relative to the size and weight of the average body, *Homo sapiens* has by far the largest brain of any Primate.[16] Correspondingly, the species has the greatest cerebral cortex of any related group. It is perhaps possible that the combination of gross size, intricate convolutions, and multitudinous cells, coupled with a rich blood supply and, perhaps, other physical traits, may some day yield a clue to man's most distinctive mental characteristic. Among other things, it has been shown that ape brains tend to be low and broad, the front hemisphere (cerebrum) does not completely cover the cerebellum at the rear, and the simian regions devoted to motor controls are poorly equipped to regulate the manifold and intricate tongue movements that are required for human speech. Much the same may be said of the parts concerned with the association areas involved in such activities as planning ahead and memory. Because of the great importance of specific, structural details, no one dares to speak with assurance about the relationship of

[16] Whales and elephants have bigger brains than humans, but a normal man's brain is about 2 percent of his body weight, a higher percentage than is usually found in other animals.

gross brain size alone to symbolic behavior, but certain tentative suggestions may be advanced.

If it is true, as there is reason to believe, that man alone has an algebraic mentality, then it may not be improper to point out that the average European man has a cranial capacity of 1450 cubic centimeters, which is two and one half to three times that of a large gorilla. Running from the living apes through the man-apes and extinct hominids to *Homo sapiens,* there appears to be a continuum that spans the gap between the ape and human brain sizes. Algebraic mentality is thought to have made its appearance somewhere along the line, but no one knows exactly where. Because it is obviously impossible to observe the mental workings of extinct animals, behavioral scientists are forced to make comparisons between living humans and living apes, and that may explain why differences in brain quantity stand out as so great and all-important.

Although increases of size do not invariably result in changes of quality, there are instances where differences of quantity lead to a critical point or threshold beyond which a qualitative difference may be noted. An informal experiment, recently performed, may help to clarify the concept of critical thresholds. A young man was asked to tear piles of sheets from a ream of lightweight paper. He had little difficulty until the pile of sheets reached 120. If we take the number 20 as a unit, it made little difference in the ranges 20 to 40, 40 to 60, 60 to 80, 80 to 100, or 100 to 120; but the same unit from 120 to 140 made a critical threshold beyond which the subject's ability to tear a pile of papers could not go.

Another significant case of this kind is that of water temperature. When ordinary water at sea level is chilled below 32 degrees Fahrenheit, it becomes a solid, ice, and remains a solid no matter how much colder it gets. Between 32 and 212 degrees Fahrenheit there is a wide range without critical points, in this regard, within which water retains the properties of a fluid. But 212 marks another threshold, above which hot water becomes converted from a liquid to a gas—steam. Solids, fluids, and gases certainly have different properties and different ways of acting and reacting. Yet, in the case just cited, they are all composed of water, with varying quantities of heat added or subtracted.

By analogy with other things, it is possible that cranial capacities may also have critical thresholds. It may be stated tentatively that a healthy Primate brain that is normally smaller than 800 cubic centimeters stands for a mentality that is incapable of true symbolization; a size between 800 and 900 cubic centimeters may represent a border zone about which nothing definite is known; and any normal Primate brain well above 900 cubic centimeters probably has the full potential for using symbolic speech and other features of algebraic mentality (Fig. 9–5). Once this threshold has been crossed, additional cubic centimeters of cranial capacity do not seem to affect the quality of mental behavior. No tests have ever demonstrated that a normal Primate brain of around 900 cubic centimeters is any less efficient in dealing with symbols than one of 1600 cubic centimeters or more.

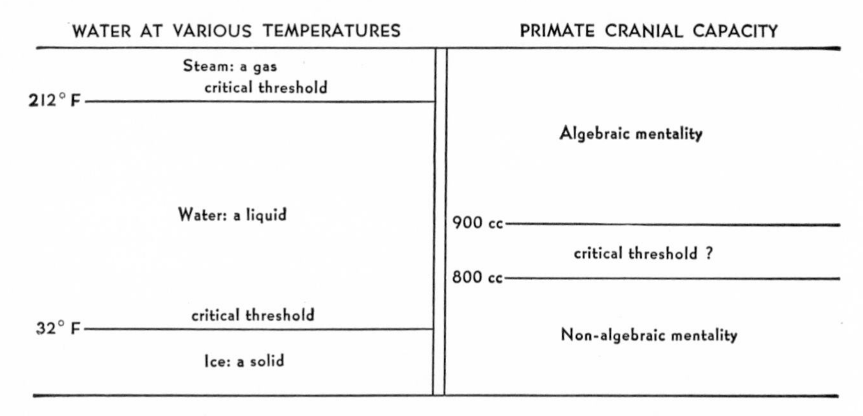

FIG. 9-5. A suggested analogy between water temperature and cranial capacity. Under certain conditions quantity may affect quality. The cranial capacity of healthy Primates may turn out to have a critical threshold between 800 and 900 cubic centimeters, at which symbolic behavior may be impossible. However, it is certainly possible when the cranial capacity exceeds 900 cubic centimeters. If this should prove to be true, it would explain the origin of algebraic mentality.

The figures of 800 cubic centimeters, below which algebraic mentality is dubious or impossible, and 900 cubic centimeters, above which it is more than likely to be present, have not been capriciously chosen. In the case of the Australopithecines, whose ability to speak is very much subject to debate, cranial capacities are variable, but average far below 800. As to human infants, not enough studies have yet been made, but cranial capacities seem to average around 600 cubic centimeters in the first 12 months, and to jump to about 950 cubic centimeters at 2 years[17]—that is, at about the same time that speech may be assumed to have begun.[18]

[17] F. A. Mettler, *Culture and the Structural Evolution of the Neural System,* New York, 1956, p. 3, table 2.

[18] The problems of setting critical thresholds of brain size with respect to speech are exceedingly complex. Many questions are unanswerable at present. No one knows whether the critical threshold here postulated was crossed once or several times in the course of evolution.

Selected References

Carpenter, C. R., "Characteristics of social behavior in non-human Primates," *Transactions of the New York Academy of Science,* Vol. 4, 1942, pp. 248–58.

Hayes, Catherine, *The Ape in Our House,* New York, 1957.

Kellogg, W. N., and L. A., *The Ape and the Child,* New York, 1933.

Köhler, Wolfgang, *The Mentality of Apes,* rev. ed., New York, 1925.

Kroeber, Alfred L., "Subhuman Cultural Beginnings," *Quarterly Review of Biology,* Vol. 3, 1928, pp. 325–42.

Mettler, F. A., *Culture and the Structural Evolution of the Neural System,* New York, 1956.

Spuhler, James N., ed., *The Evolution of Man's Capacity for Culture,* Detroit, 1959.

———, "Somatic Paths to Culture," in J. N. Spuhler, ed., *The Evolution of Man's Capacity for Culture,* Detroit, 1959, pp. 1–13.

von Bonin, G., "Toward an anthropology of the brain," *Annals of the New York Academy of Science,* Vol. 63, 1955, pp. 505–09.

Washburn, Sherwood L., ed., "Social Life of Early Man," *Viking Fund Publications in Anthropology,* No. 31, 1961.

White, Leslie A., "The Mentality of Primates," *Scientific Monthly,* Vol. 34, 1932, pp. 69–72.

———, "The Origin and Nature of Speech," in W. S. Knickerbocker, ed., *Twentieth Century English,* New York, 1940, pp. 93–103.

———, "The Symbol: the origin and basis of human behavior," *Journal of the Philosophy of Science,* Vol. 7, 1940, pp. 451–63.

Zuckerman, Solly, *The Social Life of Monkeys and Apes,* London, 1932.

PART TWO

The March of Culture

The Archeological Approach to Culture

CHAPTER 10

THE STUDY OF ARCHEOLOGY

Archeology is primarily a study of man's culture rather than of his body, although it sometimes deals with skeletal remains that have to be analyzed. With the study of cultures that are usually non-literate and always extinct as his objectives, the archeologist is generally deprived by the very nature of his work of any opportunity for gaining information by questioning live persons.

The archeologist, like his colleagues in other branches of anthropology, is interested in all hominids; and he, too, is concerned with resemblances and differences. Through his techniques he seeks to shed light on such problems as the origins and early stages of culture, universally repeated cultural norms, or the astonishing cultural diversities that are to be found throughout the world. Since he is dedicated to an investigation of the past, often the remote past, the materials with which he deals are strictly limited by an inexorable rule. They must be capable of resisting the forces of decomposition and disintegration over long periods of time. Only under the most exceptional of circumstances does the archeologist have the advantage of studying extinct people with the help of soft body parts; and rarely does he get a glimpse of an ancient culture except in terms of objects made of stone, bone, baked clay, metal, or some other durable substance. And, of course, he must be prepared to find that even the objects that he does discover are broken or damaged or are only fragments of things that were originally much larger.

To add to his woes, the archeologist is committed to try to reconstruct from the physical objects that come into his hands something of the nonmaterial aspects of the culture that they represent—its system of symbolic values, its ideas of right and wrong, its social regulations, or the forms of its religion. Without the help of the language that was spoken when the culture was flourishing, the archeologist is seldom in a position to make dogmatic statements about the intangible features of an extinct way of life. Yet, it would be a serious error to think that he is completely shut off from this feature of human activity. Surely, no one will deny that when an archeologist comes across a large stock of weapons and many skeletons showing wounds he is justified in deducing a battle or something else of a military nature. And if he finds the remains of a large and well-laid-out city, he is certainly correct to infer that the inhabitants must have had some system of planning. Likewise, a richly endowed grave inevitably leads one to surmise that the deceased probably was highly regarded in his lifetime. There are also times when the customs of living primitives, if proper cautions are taken, provide a basis for archeological inferences (see Fig. 10–1). Such would be the case if ethnologists had observed some people in the act of using implements whose manner of handling had puzzled archeologists. In other cases, use might be made of the frequent association noted in living societies between herding groups and descent through males (*patrilineality*); or the commonly encountered tie between farming and descent through females (*matrilineality*). Instead of being content, therefore, to limit themselves to descriptions and analyses of imperishable, physical objects, archeologists everywhere have labored to develop subtle techniques for reading into their materials interpretations and meanings that may penetrate into the intangible and nonmaterial spheres. Even so, there is much that cannot be recovered by any known method and there is always the danger of grave error, but archeologists are well aware of the pitfalls and try hard to avoid them.

Most of the material that makes up the subject matter of archeology consists of artifacts, which may here be defined as objects fashioned by man in accordance with a preconceived plan; even though some natural things are now and then utilized by human beings. Most often, artifacts are found at sites that have been abandoned by their former occupants for so long that they have become covered with layers of dust, loose dirt, or solid earth. Consequently, a standard part of a field archeologist's equipment consists of implements suitable for digging.

Places chosen for large-scale study are not picked at random. Sometimes they are selected after careful ground or air reconnaissance in an area whose surface exhibits signs of former habitations, walls, monuments, tombstones, or burial places. Sometimes a place is discovered by a farmer whose plow turns up ancient bones or tools; and sometimes old histories provide clues to the location of buried settlements. It is only when he has reason to think that a spot is likely to yield worthy material

FIG. 10-1. Archeology and ethnology. Left: A famous painting, made on a cave wall in France during the Upper Pleistocene. From the name of the cave it is known as the Sorcerer or Shaman of Trois Frères. It shows a masculine figure wearing horns, a tail, and what looks like an animal-skin disguise. Archeologists have traditionally postulated that he is either performing a hunting ritual or trying to cure a patient. (Courtesy of the Peabody Museum, Harvard University.) Right: A Luiseño hunter. This ethnologically recent photograph shows a disguised deer hunter, who closely resembles the figure at left. This raises the possibility that the famous "Shaman" or "Sorcerer" was really a hunter. (Courtesy of *Masterkey*.)

that an archeologist undertakes a major job of excavation. Modern Italy provides a fine example of the care and ingenuity with which a digging site may be selected. Frequently, old habitations or tombs are first spotted from the air, after which they are examined through specially devised periscopes. Only when they reveal promising material is archeological excavation undertaken.

A professional archeologist is seldom interested in a single specimen or in recognizably individual peculiarities of manufacture or adornment. His major concern is with numbers of objects that can be grouped into types or classes. These can be established on many grounds. Sometimes, objects are grouped together on the basis of the raw material, such as shell, stone, metal, bone, clay, etc., from which they were made; sometimes, as with daggers or axes, on the basis of the principal function they are assumed to have performed; sometimes, as in the case of dart points or arrowheads, by shape, style of manufacture, or size; and sometimes on the basis of color or decoration. Often classification is made by means of a combination of several factors. Such typing frequently reveals *patterns* of workmanship, and occasionally helps to indicate relationships between one type and another.

Archeologists are always on the alert for any shred of evidence that might indicate what activities had once prevailed. Religious structures and burial places provide them with many clues; and they avidly study habitations and their contents, as well as settlement patterns. These may range from isolated rock shelters or caves to dwelling units, such as multistoried pueblos, and even large towns or cities. Shell mounds are examined from time to time, and refuse heaps are carefully studied because they often contain discarded objects and yield other valuable evidence of former ways of life. Never does an archeologist hesitate to "get dirty" in his quest of material from which information can be wrung.

Objects and objectives

Although they both devote themselves to digging up ancient objects, there is a vast distinction between an archeologist and a pothunter or mere treasure seeker. Entirely unlike the latter, the archeologist digs carefully and systematically, taking great pains not to damage anything that lies in the ground. He never works surreptitiously, but is always careful to secure the permission of the person who owns the ground he intends to explore. In addition, the archeologist is interested in every object that comes to light, no matter how unesthetic, commonplace, or fragmentary it may be; and he keeps such careful records and takes so many photographs that when an excavation is finished, it is possible to tell precisely where everything dug up was originally located. Locational facts are exceedingly important because they may provide clues to the time order in which different things appear, and they may indicate when changes first arise. Also, as will promptly be realized, frequently repeated associations of objects found together are likely to be meaningful rather than accidental.

Above all, the archeologist studies and restudies his material, and he is duty bound to make it available to others in the form of published reports. His principal aims are to gain an understanding of all that transpired at the particular site under investigation, and, at the same time, to help unravel the tangled skein of all of mankind's cultural development. Obviously, it is impossible for archeologists to probe under the surface of the entire world, and no single place or region can possibly be expected to reveal all the phases of man's total cultural evolution. It is also a truism that no two spots need necessarily show identical courses of adjustment and progress. How, then, is the whole march of culture to be revealed?

The only way known has been the skill and willingness of some scholars to fit together, into one consecutive story, the information contained in a huge quantity of detailed, local reports. In this way a synthesis of man's cultural attainments can be made, and there is now available a tentative record of the order in which hominids moved from early to later phases of culture. Many archeologists have worked along these lines, but the late V. Gordon Childe made some of the most outstanding contributions.[1]

Techniques[2]

When a suitable site has been located and all necessary arrangements have been made with its owner, an archeologist does not immediately plunge his shovel into the earth. Instead, he closely examines the terrain and, often with the help of paleontologists, paleobotanists, geologists, and other scientists, tries to figure out what the nature of the place was in former times, where its sources of water may have been, what the climate was like, what plants and animals lived in the area, what fuels

---

[1] Those who are particularly interested in this topic would do well to read V. G. Childe, *The Danube in Prehistory,* Oxford, 1929, and *New Light on the Most Ancient East,* New York, 1934. A great deal of important material may also be found in V. G. Childe, *What Happened in History,* rev. ed., London, 1943; and in V. G. Childe, *Man Makes Himself,* London, 1936. See, too, J. G. D. Clark, *Prehistoric Europe,* London, 1952.

[2] Although his manual was first prepared for student use at the University of California, there is a great deal of professional material on archeological methodology, in R. F. Heizer, *A Guide to Archaeological Field Methods,* Palo Alto, Calif., rev. ed., 1958. Readers are also advised to see the appendix, J. H. Rowe, "Archaeology as a Career." For more information on archeological techniques, consult C. C. Meighan, *The Archaeologist's Note Book,* San Francisco, 1961.

and raw materials were available, how close it was to an old road or trade route, what factors attracted man to the spot, and what changes in the external environment may have killed him off or driven him away.

A surface reconnaisance is usually followed by the drawing of a map of the place to be dug. The map should show among other things, the location of the site, its extent and form, and the contours and surface features in the vicinity.

When, at last, it is time to start digging, the archeologist does not tunnel straight down, unless he is deliberately making a test pit that may yield a synopsis of the things that are likely to be encountered underground. If conditions permit, archeologists often mark a site into regular squares or rectangles and excavate a fixed distance downward at a time. Ordinarily this calls for the preparation of a *grid* (Fig. 10–2). Where there are no signs of disturbance a grid extended horizontally from a fixed or *datum point* may serve to indicate horizontal distribu-

FIG. 10-2. Use of grid. Above: An early stage in the use of the grid technique. In this case the grid is fashioned of string. Its use makes it possible to indicate where all excavated objects had been located. Opposite, above: Results of grid use. View of a site that has been cleared according to a grid arrangement. (From K. M. Kenyon, *Beginning in Archaeology,* London, 1952. Courtesy of the author, Phoenix House publishers, and the Society of Antiquaries.) Opposite, below: A stage during the digging of a Folsom complex at the Lindenmeier site, Colorado. Careful excavation of a fixed area, a few inches at a time, has produced a steplike effect.

tion; and its use downward from a fixed spot may provide both vertical distributions and a clue to time depth or age. The distance downward that each stage is dug customarily depends on internal conditions, such as marked changes in the layers of earth, the occurrence of walls, fireplaces, or other structures, or noteworthy differences in the kinds of objects found. There are times, though, when the depth of excavation stages is arbitrarily set so that accurate records can be kept of the vertical and horizontal positions of everything that is uncovered. When the results of a "dig" are published, they should be comparable point for point with the results of any similar excavation. Delicate tools are used as necessary to minimize the disturbance of buried objects, all loose dirt from each excavated section is screened through a fine wire mesh to make sure that nothing has been overlooked, and everything that may be of cultural significance is photographed *in situ,* preserved and stored, no matter how small or damaged it may be. Plant remains, animal bones, human skeletal parts, and other materials may be sent to specialists whose analyses will help the archeologist to piece together the full story of the extinct culture under study.

MARKING TIME[3]

Every archeologist is keenly responsive to whatever cultural variations have taken place at various points of time while his site was occupied by living people. In this way every "dig" is a study of culture change. Accordingly, archeologists are always on the alert for something such as pottery, that is quick to reflect many kinds of changes. These sensitive artifacts help him to make an adequate reconstruction of the culture history of the place he is investigating. It is in conjunction with this vital aspect of his work that the previously described techniques of excavation must now be considered. The practice of digging down from the surface by carefully fixed stages may be said to be dictated by an interest in *stratigraphy.* Under ideal natural conditions, where there has been

[3] A great deal of basic material on this topic is to be found in R. F. Heizer and S. F. Cook, eds., "The Application of Quantitative Methods in Archaeology," *Viking Fund Publications in Anthropology,* No. 28, 1960. Also, consult M. J. Aitken, *Physics and Archaeology,* New York, 1961. I am indebted to C. S. Chard, of the University of Wisconsin, for this reference.

FIG. 10-3. (opposite). Stratigraphy in archeology. Where there has been no disturbance, the artifacts in the lowest stratum of a site are the oldest; and those in the top stratum are the youngest. This is the way that stratigraphy sometimes provides a clue to chronology. The excavation here pictured shows a "dig" in Syria. (Courtesy of the Museum of Anthropology, the University of Michigan.)

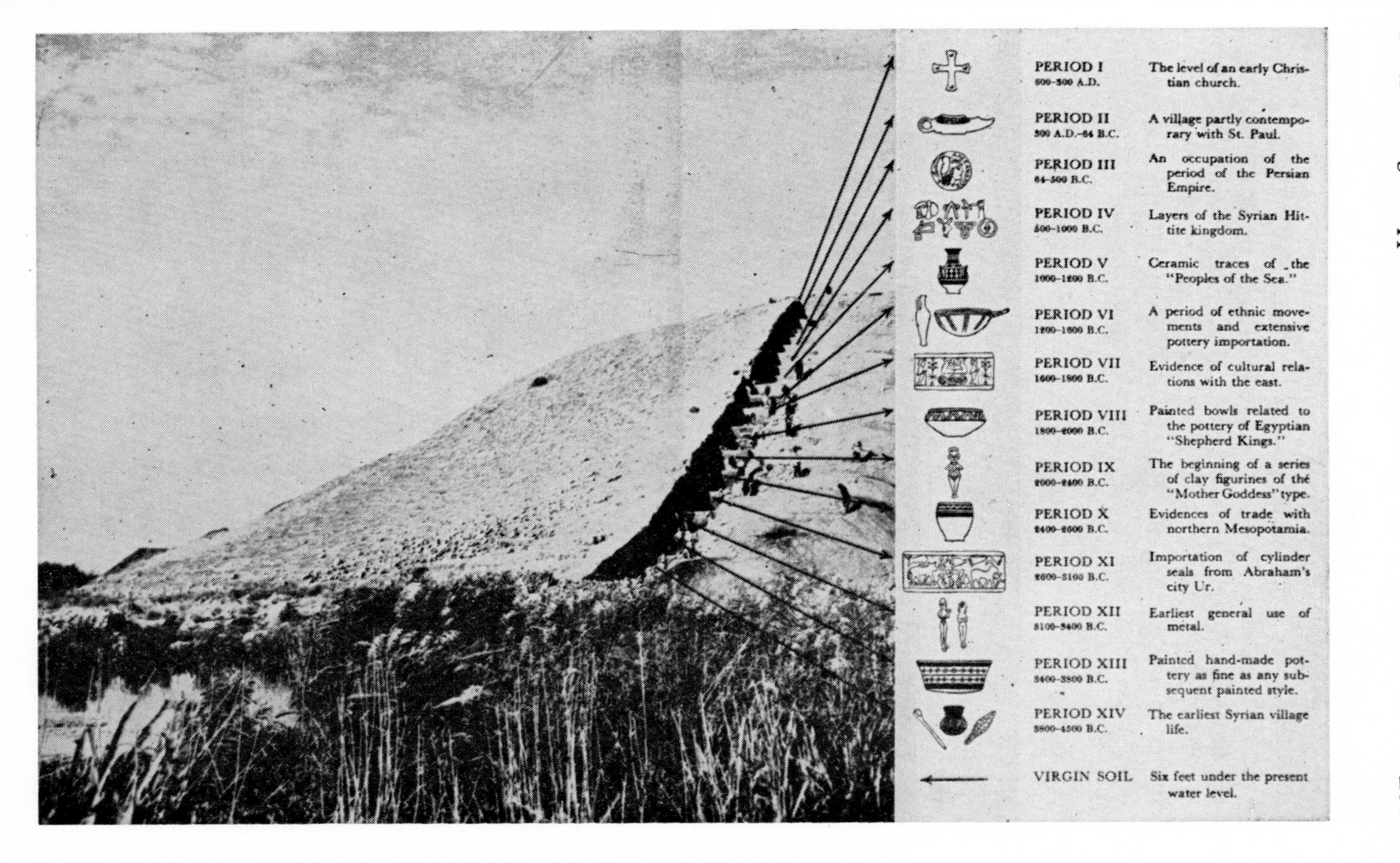
PERIOD I
The level of an early Christian church.
PERIOD II
300 A.D.–64 B.C.
A village partly contemporary with St. Paul.
PERIOD III
64–500 B.C.
An occupation of the period of the Persian Empire.
PERIOD IV
500–1000 B.C.
Layers of the Syrian Hittite kingdom.
PERIOD V
1000–1200 B.C.
Ceramic traces of the "Peoples of the Sea."
PERIOD VI
1200–1600 B.C.
A period of ethnic movements and extensive pottery importation.
PERIOD VII
1600–1800 B.C.
Evidence of cultural relations with the east.
PERIOD VIII
1800–2000 B.C.
Painted bowls related to the pottery of Egyptian "Shepherd Kings."
PERIOD IX
2000–2400 B.C.
The beginning of a series of clay figurines of the "Mother Goddess" type.
PERIOD X
2400–2600 B.C.
Evidences of trade with northern Mesopotamia.
PERIOD XI
2600–3100 B.C.
Importation of cylinder seals from Abraham's city Ur.
PERIOD XII
3100–3400 B.C.
Earliest general use of metal.
PERIOD XIII
3400–3800 B.C.
Painted hand-made pottery as fine as any subsequent painted style.
PERIOD XIV
3800–4500 B.C.
The earliest Syrian village life.
VIRGIN SOIL
Six feet under the present water level.

no disturbance, layers of soil accumulate one above the other, and study of the order in which they were deposited is known as stratigraphy. In archeology, stratigraphy often provides the most ready key to chronology, for objects found in the deepest undisturbed levels are the oldest, and those found in the topmost strata are the most recent (Fig. 10–3). Unfortunately, disturbances caused by flooding, animal intrusion, volcanic eruption, or some other means are all too common, and the archeologist must learn not to rely uncritically on stratigraphic evidence when it comes to dating his material.

For a while it was thought that an object might reveal its age by the acquisition of a discoloration or *patina*. Now it is known that patinas develop at unequal speeds due to a variety of causes. Contemporary archeologists do not, as a rule, regard *patination* as a reliable index of age.[4]

If excavated specimens are of great antiquity, a geologist may establish their approximate dates by studying the soil in which they were located; if bones of extinct animals are found associated with artifacts a paleontologist may provide a clue to their age and the living conditions to which they were accustomed; and if cultural objects are discovered in conjunction with ancient plants or pollen a paleobotanist may ascertain how old they are as well as the circumstances under which the plants grew or were grown. At the opposite extreme, if artifacts are of recent age they may be dated by comparison with historically known materials. Between these extremes the archeologist is often hard put to establish accurate dates and time sequences, but even so he still has several resources at his command. By consulting field reports of other excavations he is sometimes able to *cross date* objects of uncertain age by close comparison with similar things found in places where dates have already been ascertained. Should this approach fail, the archeologist may try to derive chronological information from comparative studies based either on spatial distribution *(diffusion)* or on stylistic changes (*typology*).

Artifacts made at one spot are likely to spread or diffuse to other areas. Archeologists sometimes plot on a map the reported frequencies with which identical objects have been found throughout a wide stretch of territory. If it develops that there is a very heavy concentration in one place and less frequent occurrence elsewhere, it may be argued that the artifact in question originated where it is most

[4] An elaborate study of patination, in this context, is to be found in V. J. Hurst and A. R. Kelly, "Patination of Cultural Flints," *Science,* Vol. 134, 1961, pp. 251–56. See also A. J. H. Goodwin, "Chemical Alteration (Patination) of Stone," in R. F. Heizer and S. F. Cook, eds., *op. cit.,* pp. 300 ff.

common and diffused to other regions through such agencies as simple borrowing, trade, migration, or war. If this assumption is correct, it follows that the object is oldest in the place where it originated. Such reasoning is far from infallible, partly because the margins of a zone of distribution are sometimes more conservative than the center, and novices are warned that professional archeologists do not rely unduly on the indirect evidence of diffusion for setting up comparative timetables.

As for typology, it may be said to depend on the possibility of working out a time sequence during which variations took place in the style of a particular artifact. Once in a while it can be shown that some forms of manufacture or decoration are older than others. A homely example might be made of the shifts from horse-drawn carriages to old-fashioned automobile bodies, thence to modern streamlined cars. Or else, one might trace the development of automobile tires from very thin to balloon to tubeless blowout-proof types. In circumstances where typological sequences have been established for archeological materials, a study of stylistic changes may throw light on comparative dates. However, no reputable archeologist employs one technique to the exclusion of the others. Wherever possible he uses a variety of approaches and he feels safest when the results of several methods of analysis point to the same conclusion.

It is usually easier to establish *relative* than *absolute dates.* Put very simply, this means that it is easier to tell if an artifact is older or younger than something else, than it is to tell an object's exact age. In one form, relative dating is known as *sequence dating.* In other cases observed changes of style or technique are put into a serial order to provide a basis for *seriation,* which may here be described as another means of relative dating.

Occasionally, a chronological device makes possible absolute dating under special circumstances or in a particular region. Throughout the southwestern United States, especially, archeologists make use of *dendrochronology.* This is a system based on the observed fact that where rainfall is highly irregular the trees produce different kinds of annual rings. When there is much moisture in a given year the rings that are laid down are thick and resemble wide bands, but when there is drought the rings are thin and appear close together. Dendrochronology was developed about thirty-five years ago by A. E. Douglass, an astronomer from the University of Arizona. By cutting down successively older trees, Douglass was able to plot the annual order in which narrow or wide bands occurred. Since certain species of trees in a given locality showed the same pattern, he found it possible to build up a master plot which went back in time until it overlapped tree-ring specimens found in prehistoric places. Today, when an archeologist in the Southwest secures a bit of wood or even a piece of charcoal from a site, its tree-ring pattern is diagramed and moved along the master chart until the two plots coincide exactly. By this means, the earliest and latest rings on the specimen can be absolutely dated, and the last ring will give the year in which the tree was cut down (Fig. 10–4). Douglass' master plot at present runs from our own day back to about the start of the Christian era.[5]

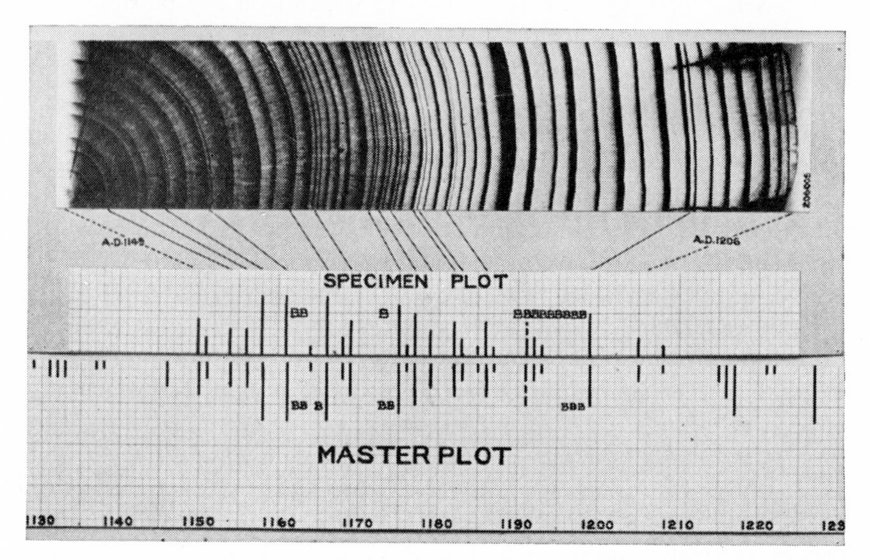

FIG. 10-4. Absolute dating by dendrochronology. A tree-ring specimen is plotted on graph paper, and matched with the master plot compiled by Douglass. In this fashion, the first and last years registered on the specimen are dated with reasonable accuracy.

Dating by radiocarbon—which can be applied to any part of the world, and is, therefore, better for comparative purposes—is presently replacing dendrochronology.

The *carbon-14* (radiocarbon) method is the most widely employed absolute time-measuring device in current use. It is based on the circumstance that all living things maintain a fixed equilibrium of substances containing C-14, a radioactive form of carbon. As soon as death comes, there is no replacement of C-14 and the organism's atoms begin to break up at the fixed rate of 15.6 disintegrations per minute per gram of

[5] F. E. Zeuner, "Advances in Chronological Research," in R. F. Heizer and S. F. Cook, eds., *op. cit.*, pp. 340–41 discusses the dendrochronological technique in Europe and pp. 354–55 give an excellent bibliography.

carbon. After 5568 $\pm$ 30 years, the carbon-14 atoms reach their half-life,[6] following which their disintegrations are slowed down to half speed, 7.8 per minute per gram. By determining the exact amount of C-14 left in each gram of organic substance, as well as the progress of its disintegration, scientists can calculate the date at which the material ceased to live. This technique was devised by W. F. Libby, now a professor of chemistry at UCLA, and several colleagues.[7] While the method is unquestionably sound, the conclusions are sometimes uncertain because of the influence of substances surrounding a specimen. Greater accuracy will certainly be achieved as more experience is gained, but at its best the technique will be of restricted value in archeology, because it requires fairly large quantities of organic things that perished no earlier than about 30,000 years ago. Beyond that time span, which marks the clearly identifiable range of carbon-14 disintegration, the scheme fails to work satisfactorily.

However, new techniques are being devised by physical scientists that hold forth the promise of pushing absolute dates still further back. One of these calls for the enrichment by isotopes of material datable by radiocarbon. When this is done it may be possible to fix dates for 70,000 years.[8] Another method is known as *thermoluminescence.* It is based on the premise that objects of stone or earth, such as some projectile points and all kinds of pottery, that have once been in contact with fire, give off a glow curve if reheated under controlled, laboratory conditions. The amount of glow is in proportion to the total dose of radiation that the object has received since it was last heated, and the total radiation is thought to be proportional to the rate of dosage multiplied by time. So far, thermoluminescence has been most successful in dating lava flows and ceramic materials. The method has not yet been perfected, but if it should become so, it would provide archeologists with

---

[6] The National Bureau of Standards claims that the half life of C-14 is 5760 years.

[7] For this achievement Libby was awarded a Nobel prize in 1961. He has recently published an authoritative review of his method, adapted from his Nobel address. See W. F. Libby, "Radiocarbon Dating," *Science,* Vol. 133, 1961, pp. 621–29.

Several institutions and American universities, including Chicago, Columbia, Michigan, and Yale, have radiocarbon laboratories. For two series of dates pertaining to archeological materials, consult H. R. Crane, "University of Michigan Radiocarbon Dates I," *Science,* Vol. 124, 1956, pp. 664–72; and Crane, H. R., and Griffin, J. B., "University of Michigan Radiocarbon Dates II," *Science,* Vol. 127, 1958, pp. 1098–1105. Crane, who is in charge of radiocarbon dating at The University of Michigan, is a professor of physics.

[8] Details are given in A. Haring and H. E. deVries, "Radiocarbon Dating Up to 70,000 Years by Isotopic Enrichment," *Science,* Vol. 128, 1958, pp. 472–73.

a means of estimating the dates of certain objects that may be as much as 500,000 years old.[9]

There is even a hope that dates can be established for some things that are as much as a million years old. For this accomplishment archeologists are awaiting the perfection of a method tentatively known as the *potassium-argon technique.* It rests on the fact that all living things absorb potassium-40, a radioactive substance that is converted to argon-40 at the rate of 50 percent in 1.25 billion years. When death occurs, no more potassium-40 is taken in, so that the proportion of potassium-40 to argon-40 becomes a measure of the time that has elapsed since an organism died. Because it is known that adjacent material may contaminate a specimen, this technique is hard to apply and has not been perfected.[10]

All of these scientific developments make archeologists optimistic that a time will come when it will be possible to secure absolute dates that range over the entire period since culture began. One can only hope that such optimism proves to be well-founded.

THE MARCH OF CULTURE BEGINS

On the basis of many comparative studies, it seems reasonable to assume that hominids, whenever and wherever they came into being, were anatomically quite similar to the big Primates and could probably do whatever big Primates could do, with the exception of a few activities directly associated with life in trees. Also, even at the outset the earliest men had much bigger brains than the large simians. It may be assumed, therefore, that the first men could have matched or exceeded any of their animal relatives mentally. Among other things this means that,

[9] Thermoluminescence as a dating technique is being developed at UCLA's Institute of Geophysics, under the direction of George C. Kennedy a geologist. Although the method has not yet been perfected, preliminary accounts have been published in *Archaeology,* Vol. 13, No. 2, 1960, pp. 147–48; and in G. C. Kennedy, *The Application of Thermoluminescence to Problems in Archaeology,* Berkeley, Calif., 1959.

[10] The potassium-argon method has not yet reached the stage of being definitively announced in print, but a preliminary account has been published in an Italian periodical, *Quaternia,* Rome, Vol. 4, 1957, pp. 13–17. It is in the process of development by the seismologist, J. F. Evernden and his colleagues at the University of California, and was used for dating Leakey's Zinjanthropus discovery at 1,750,000 years ago.

Complete information on archeological dating may be found in R. F. Heizer and S. F. Cook, "The Application of Quantitative Methods in Archaeology," *Viking Fund Publications in Anthropology,* No. 28, 1960.

like the apes, they were capable of making and using some tools, and of planning ahead. It follows that the first men were at least on the threshold of culture.

Initially, man's extrasomatic devices were crude, limited in scope, and generally inefficient. They had so little effectiveness within themselves that their efficiency depended directly on the muscular power of their users. If we may be permitted to use mathematical terms in an imprecise way, it is as though efficiency in the use of tools originally consisted of 99 percent of biology and 1 percent of culture. Gradually, this proportion came to be reversed, so that efficiency today depends on only 1 percent of biology and 99 percent of culture. It is interesting to note in passing that, with the exceptions of sports and recreations, we tend to assign low value to anything that requires great biological or muscular exertion.

Because archeologists cannot, as a rule, recover nondurable objects of great antiquity, we may never know what implements the earliest hominids used or fashioned from perishable materials such as wood or bone. Fortunately, durable artifacts of stone were developed very early. *Pebble tools*—that is, tools made by fracturing pebbles to produce a sharp, cutting edge—have even been associated with those curious creatures, the African man-apes. Pebble tools may have come into use during the Villafranchian phase of the early Pleistocene, about one million years ago.[11] After a slow beginning, hominids proceeded to improve their implements and to increase their range of cultural equipment. Thus, *Homo erectus,* in the person of *Sinanthropus pekinensis,* had advanced, culturally, to a point where he knew how to manufacture quartz tools. This indicates that by 500,000 B.P., culture was already an accepted feature of human life; and from that time on, mankind has never, while alive, reverted to a purely biological or physicochemical existence.

As has been stated, archeologists have long been interested in working out the successive stages of the whole march of culture. In the accomplishment of this goal it was found that when dealing with early phases the most common substances for manufacturing tools and weapons could serve as measuring rods. Putting aside the possibility of an osteodontkeratic industry,[12] what is known as "the doctrine of the three

---

[11] It now seems likely that this date may have to be pushed back to something earlier than one million years ago. See p. 84, f.n. 13.

[12] It is altogether possible that at the start of human culture tools were devised from such organic and perishable materials as sinews, tendons, hides, hair, and teeth, or else of gourd, wood, antler, horn, or bone. Breuil at Chou Kou Tien, and Dart at Makapansgat, South Africa, came across such substances under conditions that sug-

ages," (stone, copper-bronze, and iron), was first publicized, though not originated, by Christian J. Thomsen, curator of the Danish National Museum in Copenhagen from 1816 to 1865. Archeologists are thoroughly agreed that Thomsen's scheme is far too elementary and oversimplified to describe the whole march of culture, but within its limits it has never been proved false. Man, especially in the Old World, did proceed from a reliance on stone to the use of copper-bronze and iron in that order.

Throughout the mid-nineteenth century, Thomsen's little scheme was vehemently attacked and as stoutly defended. It never was destroyed, but it was literally broken up. As archeological specimens came to be accumulated in prodigious quantities, the artifacts of stone were recognized to have been made by so many differing techniques that it was meaningless to lump them together as products of a single age of stone. French and British archeologists early insisted on a need for separating the *Old Stone Age (Paleolithic)* from the *New Stone Age (Neolithic)*, and this distinction gained currency in 1865 when it was adopted by Sir John Lubbock, later Lord Avebury, in his book, *Prehistoric Times*. Soon after, between 1867 and 1883, the famed French archeologist, Gabriel de Mortillet, proposed a further separation of the Paleolithic into five periods, and the names he assigned to these phases, though most applicable to cultural sequences in France, have come to be widely used to designate similar cultural stages in many parts of the world. Refinements have been made in each of the three ages, as well as in all of de Mortillet's stages, and problems of terminology, classification, sequence, absolute chronology, distribution, and interpretation are being actively debated at present.[13]

All of these scientific concerns are directed ultimately toward a single goal—to provide an accurate and fully detailed account of man-

gested the possibility that their use may have come before stone. Dart goes so far as to name the presumably prestone culture osteodontkeratic. It has even been proposed that unbroken long bones may have served as clubs; splintered bones for piercing; flat bones as shovels; and hard bones as anvils. Those who accept this hypothesis may go so far as to argue that such putative bone tools might actually have been fabricated according to consciously preconceived plans.

Further details along these lines are found in H. Breuil, "Bone and Antler Industry of the Chou Kou Tien *Sinanthropus* Site," *Paleontologica Sinica,* 1939; R. A. Dart, "The Osteodontkeratic Culture of Australopithecus prometheus," *Memoir 10, Transvaal Museum,* 1957; and R. A. Dart, *Adventures with the Missing Link,* New York, 1959, p. 137, *et passim.*

[13] An up-to-date treatment of many of these topics is to be found in H. L. Movius, Jr., "Radiocarbon Dates and Upper Paleolithic Archaeology in Central and Western Europe," *Current Anthropology,* Vol. 1, 1960, pp. 355–91, and in a series of comments and addenda entitled, "More on Upper Paleolithic Archaeology," *Current Anthropology,* Vol. 2, 1961, pp. 427–54.

kind's cultural development from the start. Since man is known to have originated in the Old World, the beginnings of culture must be sought there. Moreover, because hominids branched off from a Primate stem, efforts are being made to discover the source of cultural behavior by observation of the most highly evolved of nonhuman Primates. That explains why so many experiments are being conducted on living great apes. Anthropologists seldom feel qualified to perform these experiments, but they eagerly await the findings of those who are trained for this work.

Selected References

Aitken, M. J., *Physics and Archaeology,* New York, 1961.

Atkinson, R. J. C., *Field Archaeology,* rev. ed., London, 1953.

Barker, H., "Radiocarbon Dating; Its Scope and Limitations," *Antiquity,* Vol. 32, 1958, pp. 253–63.

Bibby, Geoffrey, *The Testimony of the Spade,* New York, 1956.

Brainered, George W., "The Place of Chronological Ordering in Archaeological Analysis," *American Antiquity,* Vol. 16, 1951, pp. 301–13.

Childe, V. Gordon, *Piecing Together the Past,* London, 1956.

Clark, J. Grahame D., "Archeological Theories and Interpretation: Old World," in A. L. Kroeber, ed., *Anthropology Today,* Chicago, 1953, pp. 343–60.

Daniel, Glyn E., *The Three Ages,* Cambridge, England, 1943.

Douglass, A. E., "The Secret of the Southwest Solved by the Talkative Tree-rings," *National Geographic Magazine,* Vol. 54, 1929, pp. 737–70.

Griffin, James B., "The Study of Early Cultures," in Harry L. Shapiro, ed., *Man, Culture, and Society,* New York, 1956, pp. 22–48.

———, ed., "Essays on Archaeological Methods," *Anthropological Papers, Museum of Anthropology, University of Michigan,* Ann Arbor, Mich., 1951.

Heizer, Robert F., *A Guide to Archaeological Field Methods,* rev. ed., Palo Alto, Calif., 1958.

———, and Cook, Sherburne F., "The Application of Quantitative Methods in Archaeology," *Viking Fund Publications in Anthropology,* No. 28, 1960.

Libby, Willard F., *Radiocarbon Dating,* Chicago, 1952.

———, "Radiocarbon Dating," *Science,* Vol. 133, 1961, pp. 621–29.

Pyddoke, E., *Stratification for the Archaeologist,* London, 1961.

Willey, Gordon R., and Phillips, P., *Method and Theory in American Archaeology,* Chicago, 1958.

Lower and Middle Paleolithic Culture in the Old World

CHAPTER 11

It is customary to trace the early phases of the universal march of culture by describing the sequence of events in western Europe according to the framework of periods named by de Mortillet, most of which, although greatly modified, still serve as convenient points of reference. Western Europe is used, not because it saw the start of culture, nor because it led the way at all times, but simply because its early archeological record has been more intensively studied and is better known than that of any comparable region of the world.

At the time that culture was beginning our planet was entering on the Pleistocene epoch of the Cenozoic era. During the Pleistocene, the earth's more northerly latitudes, including Europe, Asia, and North America, were subjected to great movements of ice. Immense fields of packed snow and ice, as much as a thousand feet or more thick, crept out of the polar regions or down the slopes of high mountains. The glaciers never touched each other to the extent of becoming contiguous and leaving no unglaciated corridors. At no time, too, did hominids and other animals find it impossible to live on the edges of the glaciers. Never did the huge glacial fields fail to withdraw after a considerable lapse of time. Their comings and goings have been carefully studied around the Alps, where it was found that glaciers came and went at least four times. The glacial advances, bringing long, long stretches of bitterly cold weather each time, were named in chronological and alphabetical order, *Günz, Mindel, Riss,* and *Würm.* In between the ice flows came *interglacial periods,*[1] with warm weather that permitted plants

[1] American archeologists, in particular, often call a protracted period of ice and cold weather a *stadial* advance. Long-lasting warm spells are then known as *interstadials.*

and animals that thrive in heat to flourish. Although modern experts find the scheme of only four glacial and three interglacial periods much too simple, and recognize a great many additional fluctuations back and forth, the old schedule of major events still serves as the basis for a timetable of Pleistocene cultural events.

The recognizable march of culture seems to have started outside of Europe with crudely made pebble tools, such as those found in Africa. Not much can be said of their makers, nor can their time be established by Europe's glacial fluctuations. Africa had periods of heavy rain (*pluvial periods*) while much of Europe had glaciers; and rains

FIG. 11-1. Survival of an eolithic usage. An Australian aborigine, using a sharp, unworked stone for cutting into a tree. (Courtesy of C. P. Mountford.)

leave far fewer identifiable traces. Some attempts have been made to correlate Africa's pluvial periods with European glacial movements, but the results so far are entirely tentative.[2]

As to the progress of culture in western Europe, it is hard to know where to begin. Usually, it is assumed that hominids entered Europe during one of the warm interglacial periods. Unfortunately, no one knows for certain which it was, but it may well have been at the start of the interstadial between the Mindel and Riss advances, or *Interglacial II*. Whenever it was that he reached Europe, man seems not to have brought along pebble tools. In fact, some scholars believe man started

[2] The Günz glacial advance has been equated with Africa's Kageran pluvial period; Mindel with Kamasian; Riss with Kanjeran; and Würm with Gamblian.

European culture from scratch. They believe that hominids used natural stones as implements before they learned to manufacture stone tools. The supposedly utilized stones are called *eoliths* ("dawn stones"—that is, stones used at the dawn of culture). Eoliths are usually impossible to distinguish from unused, natural stones, but supporters of the *eolithic theory* insist that any hominid use of a lithic object causes markings that are entirely different from natural ones.[3] Modern archeologists tend to laugh such claims out of court. Almost no one today maintains that he can unfailingly recognize man-used, but not necessarily man-made, implements. Just the same, a number of students firmly believe that if all the circumstances of discovery are known, bits of utilized but unworked stone can be identified (Fig. 11–1).

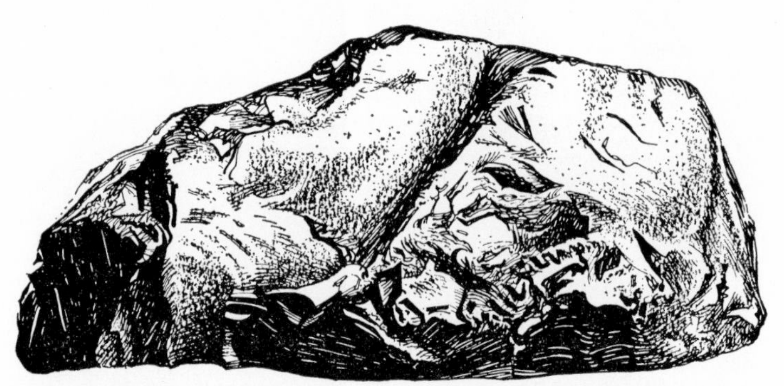

FIG. 11-2. A rostro-carinate (after Sir Ray Lankaster). This is the type specimen of a keeled flint. It was found in the Crag in England. (Adapted from M. Boule and H. V. Vallois, *Fossil Men,* rev. ed., New York, 1957.)

omit

Between the presumed tools that are doubtfully associated with hominid use and objects of unquestioned human make, come a variety of stones that are known as *rostro-carinates.* They are beak-shaped lumps of flint from which small bits have somehow been removed. When attention was drawn to their uneven shapes, proponents replied that perfection in turning out regularly formed instruments was hardly to be expected of the earliest of workmen.[4]

[3] For a discussion of this topic, see A. S. Barnes, "The difference between natural and human flaking in prehistoric flint implements," *American Anthropologist,* Vol. 41, 1939, pp. 99–112.

[4] Along the shores of East Anglia, where Reid Moir and Sir Ray Lankaster made many discoveries of rostro-carinates, there is a series of marine deposits called *the Crag.* All supposed tools that occur below the Crag are generally spoken of as *pre-Crag.*

old stone age = paleolithic

Comments on the Old Stone Age

Stones treated in accordance with definite patterns of workmanship are usually identifiable as implements, and those that lie in the lowest undisturbed layers of a stratified site are presumed to be the most ancient. Hence, the phrase *Lower Paleolithic* refers to the oldest level of the *Old Stone Age; Middle Paleolithic* to an intermediate stage; and *Upper Paleolithic* to the latest. Similar terms are used for subdividing the Pleistocene age.

For the earliest of his recognizable tools, man seems to have used as raw material fine-grained, cryptocrystalline stones, such as flint and other varieties of quartz, basalt, diorite, and volcanic glass or obsidian. These have the advantages of being hard but brittle and, if skillfully hit with a piece of rock (*hammerstone*) or a billet of wood, or if they are struck against an anvil, they can be broken into even segments that have very sharp edges. When stones of these kinds are deliberately worked into tools, they develop definite markings that experts have learned to recognize. The first widely employed technique of manufacture, which prevailed all through the Old Stone Age, comprised two steps. First, with the form of the finished product already in mind, a workman selected a suitable chunk of stone as a nodule or core. Then, the core was trimmed by the removal of fairly large flakes or smallish chips either by striking them off (*percussion*), or else, in somewhat later times, by pressing them off (*pressure flaking*). Two different kinds of instruments could be produced by these procedures. If the removal of lesser bits was continued until the original nodule had itself been worked into a desired shape, it turned out to be a *core tool*; but if fairly large flakes were detached and themselves made to serve as implements, they became *flake tools* (Fig. 11–3D). Both styles of artifacts were widely made in Paleolithic times.

To shape flint, or similar stones, blows were struck on a flat spot on the core, which is known as a *striking platform*. When a carefully directed blow hit the striking platform, a flake having a smooth inner surface was detached. Below the point of contact there ordinarily forms a convex swelling, or *bulb of percussion*, together with a number of conchoidal ripple marks (see Fig. 11–3B). Professional archeologists are troubled by many variations and fine points of stoneworking methods, but seldom do they lack the skill to differentiate a truly man-manufactured tool from a random bit of stone.

Nevertheless, when claims of authenticity were advanced for the first-recognized products of human craftsmanship, a storm of controversy

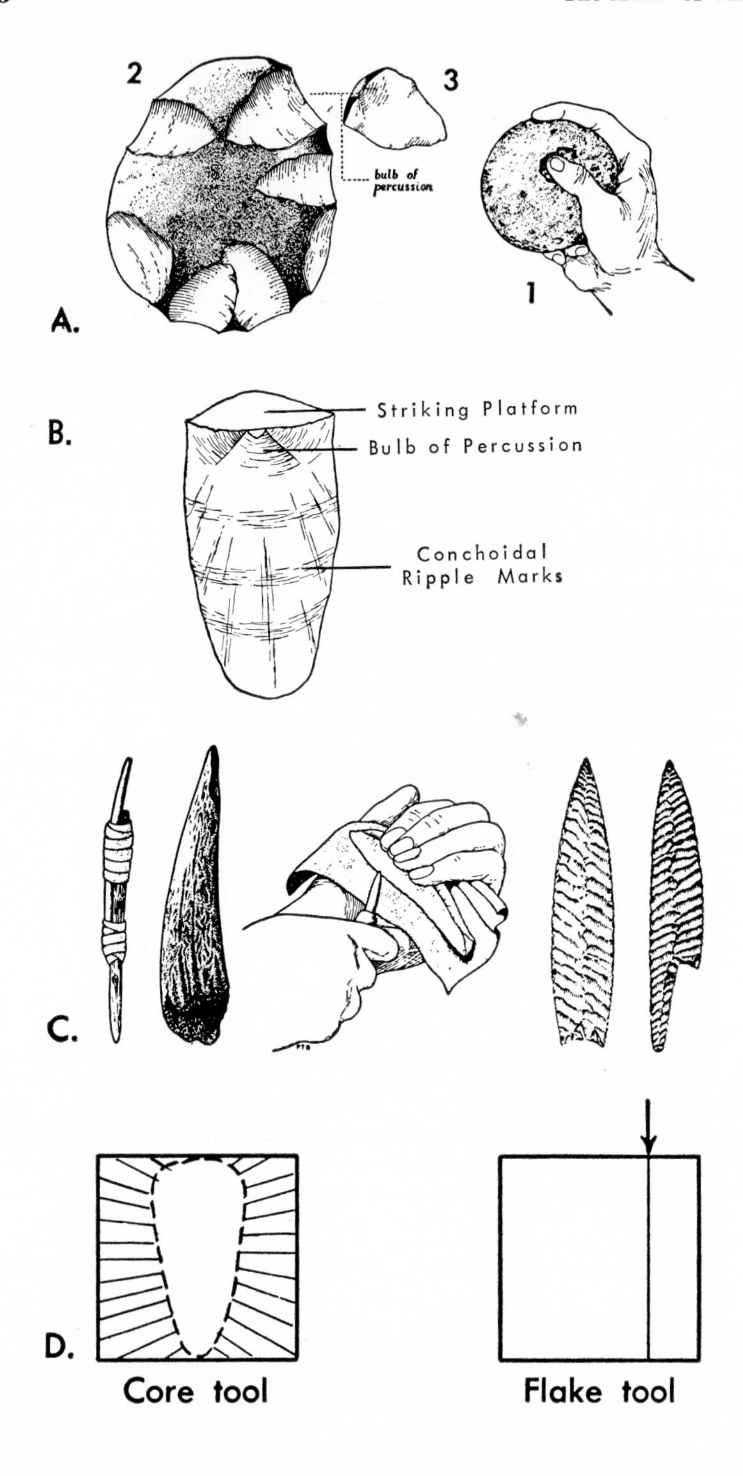

2
3
bulb of percussion
1
A.
B.
Striking Platform
Bulb of Percussion
Conchoidal Ripple Marks
C.
D.
Core tool
Flake tool

arose. Apart from doubts raised by technical questions, much reluctance was based on religious grounds. The oldest implements assigned to man were found with the remains of extinct animals in deposits of soil that vastly antedated the traditional time of human creation. Few western Europeans over a century ago were ready to accept evidence of such great antiquity for man. Regardless of the stubbornness and amused contempt of his contemporaries, an amateur archeologist named Jacques Boucher de Crèvecoeur de Perthes, a French customs official, went right on collecting regularly chipped flint objects from old gravel deposits of the river Somme. He began to astonish the world with his findings in 1837, and when some of his worst critics searched ancient gravel beds in the hope of refuting him, they found to their amazement that they were actually discovering additional evidence in support of his viewpoint. The tide of critical opinion changed completely in 1859, the very year when publication of Darwin's theory of evolution gave a modern turn to studies of the biology of man. A small commission of eminent British scientists visited Boucher de Perthes in 1859, scrupulously examined his collections, and proclaimed that he had discovered indisputably man-made stone tools of great age in the Somme River gravels. From the day it was so announced in 1859, this conclusion has never been seriously challenged in scholarly circles.

Broadly speaking, the term Lower Paleolithic may be applied to the way of life practiced by early man well into the third interglacial. Very little is known of the kinds of hominids then alive, but there are suggestions to indicate that they were pre- or non-Neandertaloids, possibly like the creatures represented by the Heidelberg jaw. There is also doubt as to the exact time involved, but in very approximate figures the major part of the Lower Paleolithic may be dated between 500,000 and 120,000 B.P. Even in the matter of cultural accomplishments there

---

FIG. 11-3. Paleolithic stoneworking techniques. A. The three basic elements of the percussion method. (1) A hammerstone, held in the hand. (2) An original core from which flakes have been struck off. (3) A detached flake. B. A worked core of flint. A workman first prepared a striking platform. He then struck it sharply, producing a bulb of percussion and conchoidal ripple marks. C. Pressure flaking. Two tools widely employed in pressure flaking are shown at the left. Solutrian tools, from the period when this technique reached its height in western Europe, are pictured at the right. D. How core and flake tools were made. Manufacture of either kind of tool began with an advance blueprint in the mind of the worker. For a core tool he removed unwanted chips, indicated by the unbroken lines, until the original core was reduced to the desired form, indicated by the broken lines. A flake tool (*right*) began with the removal of one segment of a core. The segment was then chipped into a flake tool. (A. and C. after N. C. Nelson. From F. Boas, ed., *General Anthropology*, Boston, 1938. Courtesy of D. C. Heath and Co.)

is not much that can be said with conviction, since only a few stone tools have survived. These precious bits of evidence have been intensively examined by archeologists, who agree that they should be grouped into two classifications, based upon whether they were manufactured from an original core or fashioned from flakes. A number of archeologists hold the opinion that core tools are southerly and the work of people in the *Homo modernus* category, whereas flake implements are more northerly and the product of classical Neandertaloids. Such opinions are far from universal, but nearly everyone agrees on the likelihood that both core and flake traditions originated outside of Europe.

Lower Paleolithic industries in western Europe

Throughout western Europe, Lower Paleolithic core tools are most commonly made into big, clumsy, roughly pear-shaped objects, about 10 inches long, and with two working sides. Apparently they were meant to be used while clenched in the fist. They are, therefore, designated as hand axes, fist axes, or *coups de poing*, even though it is fairly clear that they were not axes in the modern sense. The earliest varieties are known

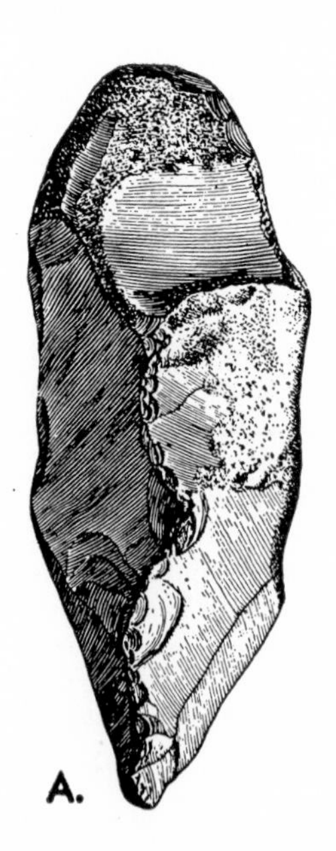

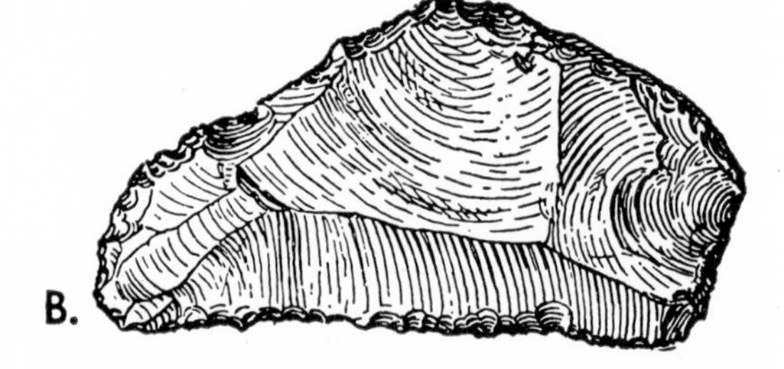

FIG. 11-4. Commonly made stone tools of the Lower Paleolithic. A. Typical fist ax of Abbevillian (Chellian) style. It is a crudely made, bifacial tool, fashioned by percussion chipping on both surfaces or faces. B. A percussion-made flint knife or side scraper. The rounded border fits into the palm of the hand. (From George G. MacCurdy, *Human Origins,* New York, 1926. Courtesy of Appleton-Century-Crofts, Inc.)

as *Abbevillian* (formerly, they were called *Chellian*), and the later ones are termed *Acheulian.* Characteristic of the Abbevillian industry are unsymmetrical fist axes with heavy butts at one end and rounded or pointed tips at the other (Fig. 11–4). The sides are wavy and not always even. These rough hand axes may first have been blocked out by striking one piece of flint against another. Finer chips may then have been struck off with a hammerstone.

Acheulian hand axes are smaller and far more symmetrical, oval or almond in shape, trimmed to a thin edge along the whole circumference, and with a center of gravity near the middle (Fig. 11–5).

Abbevillian and Acheulian fist axes were made by the removal of many flakes from each side of an original nodule; thus, both types are known as bifacial. Practically all of the flakes knocked off were wasted, but it is possible that some of the larger ones were themselves used as tools, particularly in the Acheulian phase. Often the flake tools that are the incidental results of core workmanship have one sharp edge and are called *side scrapers*; and broad, heavy scrapers are sometimes termed *cleavers.* As an indication of some of the refinements that have taken place in Lower Paleolithic studies, numerous archeologists now distinguish as many as seven Acheulian substages.

Archeologists who specialize in the Lower Paleolithic differentiate flake utensils that were merely by-products of core techniques from tools that were deliberately planned to be made of skillfully detached flakes. Best known of the earliest flake industries are the *Clactonian* and *Levalloisian.* Although their relative dates are far from precisely fixed, it is customary to regard Clactonian as somewhat prior, overlapping with the earlier stages of Abbevillian-Acheulian, and Levalloisian as associated with later phases. Purposely produced Clactonian flakes are often thick and squat, and do not seem to have been designed for use as fist

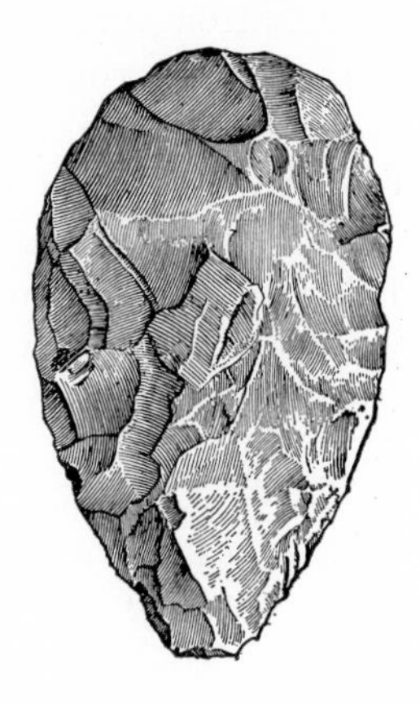

FIG. 11-5. An Acheulian fist ax. This is a typical flint implement of the period. It is chipped on both faces by percussion. It is much evener and more finely made than the fist axes of earlier times. Some think that the drive for symmetry goes further than efficiency requires, and may therefore be an early instance of man's esthetic drive.

axes.[5] From their appearance, it is judged that they were made by striking a natural rather than an especially prefashioned core against a heavy stone that served as an anvil. When necessary, the working edge of a flake was secondarily sharpened by the removal of tiny chips. Most Clactonian tools probably served as choppers, knives, or scrapers, and a fair percentage of the latter are concave, giving the impression that they may have been used to shave down lengths of wood that were to be fashioned into clubs or spears (Fig. 11–6). Specialists separate the early, rather bulbous Clacton implements from later varieties that were better chipped and more refined.

At least by the close of the second Interglacial period in western Europe, during the Acheulian culture phase, some workmen were using the Levalloisian technique of flake production. This called for very careful preliminary shaping of a core in such a manner that when the work was finished, flakes ready for immediate use as tools could be detached with single blows. Prefashioned Levalloisian cores were made by hammerstones, with one face flat and the other convex. Because the cores had a fancied resemblance to the backs of turtles, they came to be called *tortoise cores*. Customarily, they had irregular or faceted striking platforms. The more carefully the cores were prepared in advance, the more suitable for prompt service were the struck-off flakes. The Levalloisian method thus forcibly brings home the truth of the statement that tool manufacture calls for an advance pattern in the mind of the workman. As the new style became perfected Levalloisian craftsmen became capable of trimming tortoise cores in various ways to furnish a basis for producing flakes that were long, thin, and symmetrical, and either pointed, triangular, oval, or rectangular. Whatever their shapes, all Levalloisian flakes are smooth and unworked on the inner side. Even though some of them resemble flat fist axes, they can always be distinguished from similar core tools because they are never trimmed on both sides and are, consequently, never bifacial. When Levallois cores were properly handled, they were reduced to nothingness or else were discarded when no more flakes could be struck off.

As a whole, the Acheulian covers the longest time span of all the Paleolithic stages and is subdivided into various levels or horizons. It was in association with the Middle Acheulian that the Swanscombe remains (pp. 118–19) were discovered. The final period of the Acheulian

---

[5] The Clactonian industry is best known from England. Comparable flake implements from France are sometimes called *Tayacian*. They are frequently smaller and lighter than their Clactonian equivalents. Both styles were made from unprepared cores.

is often known as *La Micoque. Micoquian* hand axes, which characterize this horizon, are elongated and narrowly triangular in form. They are ordinarily well-made, with straight, finely chipped edges. In western Europe, tools of the La Micoque style bring the Acheulian to a close.

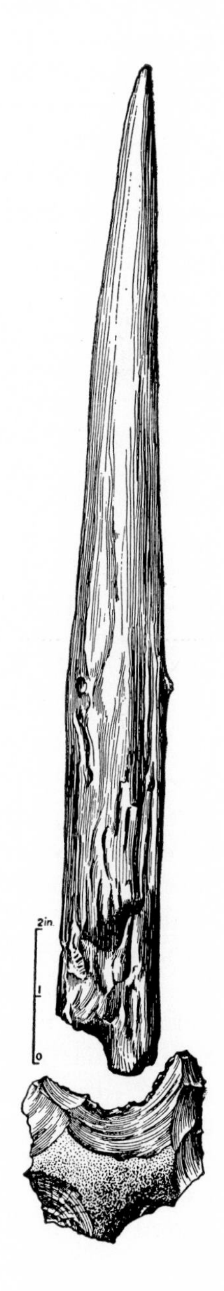

FIG. 11-6. A Clactonian stone tool (after Oakley). The wooden shaft suggests that the concave lithic implement may have been used as a spoke shave. (Courtesy of the British Museum of Natural History.)

THE LOWER PALEOLITHIC ELSEWHERE IN THE OLD WORLD

Not many years ago it was believed that the divisions and sequences established for the Lower Paleolithic of western Europe were typical of the entire Old World. This theory is no longer held to be true. Discoveries in Africa and Asia have made it clear that in several details the western European scheme is valid locally but not universally. Some would have it that procedures begun elsewhere occasionally came to a head in western Europe. Core tools generally are much alike wherever they may be found, but flake tools are apt to show great variations. On the African continent, finds of Lower Paleolithic implements have been made, some of which are very much restricted in distribution and are not at all like western European instruments. There are, however,

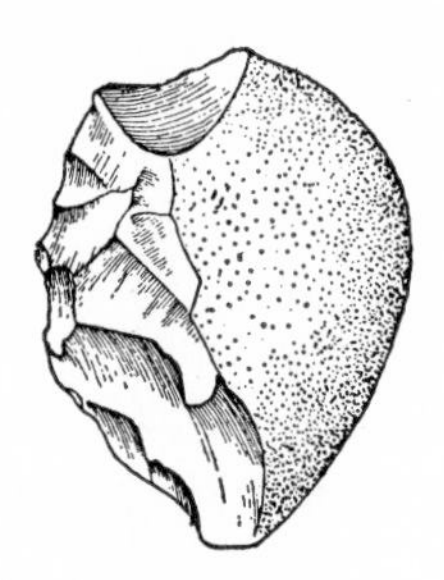

FIG. 11-7. An eastern Asiatic chopping tool. Flakes have been struck from one side of a pebble to make a chopper. (From Kenneth P. Oakley, *Man, the Tool-Maker,* rev. ed., London, 1950. Courtesy of the British Museum of Natural History.)

other varieties from these two vast areas that are virtually identical. The suggestion has been offered that one or more African techniques were later adopted in western Europe, but it is difficult to establish beyond reasonable doubt the priority of the material from Africa. The crude pebble tools that are very ancient in Africa are usually called *Kafuan,* and there is a belief that they may have evolved into *Oldowan.*

Possibly distinct from the Lower Paleolithic industries of western Europe are a number of toolmaking traditions from eastern and southeastern Asia. There are some early chopping tools, with only a single cutting edge, usually made from pebbles (Fig. 11–7) that may prove to be related to African types; but in northwestern India, Burma, Java, and China there is neither an Abbevillian-Acheulian core industry, nor a recognizably Levalloisian style of flake manufacture. Instead, the commonest early tools have been described by Harvard's Hallam L. Movius,

Jr., as choppers, chopping tools, and hand adzes.[6] Some of the choppers are like large, crude, core-made scrapers, but others are manufactured from flakes and bear some resemblance to the Clactonian of western Europe. None of the east Asiatic implements is extensively chipped on both surfaces, and none has the appearance of a bifacial, core-made fist ax.

Movius has also made a first-hand study of the stone tools that were found together with the bones of *Sinanthropus pekinensis* at Chou Kou Tien. He has named that industry *Choukoutienian* and has assigned it to the chopper, chopping tool, hand adze complex of east Asia, and not to any of the Lower Paleolithic cultures of western Europe.

A SUMMARY OF LIFE IN LOWER PALEOLITHIC TIMES[7]

Any effort to present a fully rounded picture of Lower Paleolithic life is predoomed to failure because of the meager evidence available. That men of those days lived while the climate was warm is strongly suggested by the occurrence of Abbevillian-Acheulian implements, particularly, in soils containing remains of heat-adjusted species of elephant, rhinoceros, lion, and hippopotamus. Such associations reinforce the interpretation of a warm spell based on discoveries of Lower Paleolithic tools along the banks of, or in the beds of ancient streams. Throughout western Europe Paleolithic people seem to have camped outdoors, probably close by their sources of water and game, but at Chou Kou Tien they are known to have lived in caves.

Details are lacking for most of the Old World. Men and women probably wandered in small bands along the banks of streams, fishing,

[6] For further details consult H. L. Movius, Jr., "Early Man and Pleistocene Stratigraphy in Southern and Eastern Asia," *Papers of the Peabody Museum of American Archaeology and Ethnology,* Cambridge, Mass., Vol. 19, No. 3, 1944.

A good synopsis and bibliography by the same author may be found in A. L. Kroeber, ed., *Anthropology Today,* Chicago, 1953, pp. 163–92. Some of his conclusions are tentative and the distinctiveness of Far Eastern chopping tools is being questioned. For example, it is sometimes held that Far Eastern chopping tools may have developed out of pebble tools, such as those occurring in Africa. There is also a possibility that choppers may prove to have affinities with western European implements.

Chopping tools have been found in Siberia and throughout central Asia. They are not always early, and they may turn out to be better indices of cultural development than indicators of time.

[7] For further details on many of the topics treated in this section, and for information on several additional subjects, see the appropriate essays in S. L. Washburn, ed., "Social Life of Early Man," *Viking Fund Publications in Anthropology,* No. 31, 1961.

hunting, and gathering edible plants, seeds, fruits, nuts, roots, and berries. They were at best collectors or gatherers of food provided by nature; they were not food producers. Nothing certain is known of their social organization, although it is thought to have been primarily biogenetically controlled, as in the case of large simians. The populace probably had a degree of social cooperation, for some of the beasts they killed could have been slain only by numbers of hunters working together.

Little that is definite is known of whatever system of familial descent may have prevailed. There are indirect signs of algebraic mentality because of the size of cranial vaults and the ability these folk demonstrated for planning ahead while making tools. Similarly, their capacity for speech cannot be directly proved, but secondary evidence makes it likely that they could talk, because by no other known means could cooperation have been achieved, or could traditions and styles of manufacturing have been so readily maintained, taught, and spread over wide stretches of territory.

Archeologists believe that Lower Paleolithic people customarily lived in temporary camps. If habitations were put up, they must have been too flimsy and impermanent to have survived or to have left identifiable traces on the ground. One can only surmise what use may have been made of perishable materials for building or other purposes. There is much less need for speculation when it comes to the functions of Lower Paleolithic artifacts of stone. Taking the entire range of artifacts into account, there were sturdy fist axes for killing game; sharp knives for cutting up slain beasts or severing branches; scrapers capable of working wood or hides; and pointed implements suitable for stabbing or digging operations. Well-made fist axes may, indeed, have served as all-purpose tools; but the great number of knives, scrapers, points, cleavers, and choppers suggest that there was at least a modest preference for specialized implements, based on the concept of a particular kind of tool for a specific purpose. In general, the Lower Paleolithic seems to have begun with a few simple kinds of tools, each useful for a variety of purposes, and to have moved in the direction of increasingly varied, complicated, and specialized implements.

When everything that is known about the Lower Paleolithic is considered, it is immediately apparent that culture started slowly and remained relatively unchanged in the course of hundreds of thousands of years. True, archeologists know of many variations in the early lithic industries, but all of the manufacturing methods are but modifications of a single approach—the shaping of tools by knocking or pressing smaller fragments from a larger piece of stone. Dependence on one method, most commonly a percussion technique, delimited man's use of the natural resources around him to fine-grained varieties of stone, capable of segmenting evenly instead of crumbling to bits when struck or pressed hard. No matter what the cause may have been, it is an undeniable fact that early man used very few of the raw materials provided by nature.

Some workmen were without question more skillful than others, but any normal individual could—within just a matter of minutes—speedily turn out a reasonable facsimile of a satisfactory tool. The quantity of rather poorly made implements is so great that it is fantastic to think of Lower Paleolithic societies as having specialized workmen who devoted themselves, on a full-time basis, to the making of stone products. Every man his own craftsman is much more likely to have been the rule.

Although it is the present contention that core-made bifacial implements and unifacial flake tools have always existed side by side, the preparation of core instruments diminishes with time and disappears long before the Paleolithic has run its full course. It is interesting to guess at the meaning of this trend. If we apply modern economic ideas to the situation, the termination of core workmanship may be explained on two counts. Making core tools is more costly because it requires bigger blocks of raw material to start with, and nearly all of the struck-off chips are wasted. Furthermore, core tools take longer to produce because they must be worked on both surfaces. Flake tools, especially of the well-developed Levalloisian style, waste very little raw material, are worked only on one side, and are rapidly produced by single blows after a satisfactory tortoise core has been prepared. There can be little question that flake techniques displaced core methods of production because they were more economical in terms of raw materials and time. This dual trend, barely discernible in the Lower Paleolithic, becomes increasingly apparent as we approach our own era.

As far as anyone knows, all of the Lower Paleolithic implements were meant to be used by hand. Differences of effective use depended less on the skill with which a utensil was made than on the muscular power and strength of the user. A weak little man holding an excellent fist ax could not hope to stand up to a big brute of a fellow armed with a third-rate fist ax. How different from today, when it is possible for a dainty female with a small revolver in her hand to kill a husky 200-pound man. Along similar lines, no Lower Paleolithic tool could be hurled for any great distance, the amount of space covered being dependent once more on the power of the thrower. Judged by what we know of it, Lower Paleolithic culture was only in a very limited degree capable of serving man as a substitute for, or as an adjunct to, biology. Hominids for several hundred millenniums were not a great deal better off in this regard than were other Primates of their size and strength. It may be hard to believe that the Lower Paleolithic, alone, is thought to have lasted for 75 percent of the total time of hominid prehistory. No imaginary observer who might somehow have been enabled to watch how slowly man was building his culture throughout the many centuries of the Lower Paleolithic would have been willing to bet that it would ever amount to much.

MIDDLE PALEOLITHIC CULTURE AND CLASSIC NEANDERTAL MAN

The picture of hominid life, which is so hazy and dim for the Lower Paleolithic, comes into a much clearer and sharper focus in the Middle Paleolithic. Although the origins of *Mousterian* culture are still undetermined, it is believed to have flourished in western Europe from approximately 120,000 to about 40,000 B.P. It is better known because it is closer to our own time and because its remains are found in caves where materials are likely to accumulate, be kept together, and preserved. Its products are so often directly associated with Neandertal skeletons that it is hard to escape the conclusion that in western Europe, at least, traditional Mousterian culture was the way of life of Classic Neandertal man.[8]

In western Europe the transition, without the implication of a sharp break, from Lower to Middle Paleolithic must be considered in relation to a severe change of climatic conditions. Toward the end of the Lower Paleolithic, the weather got drier and shifted from warm to cool to cold. Southern species of animals disappeared, in the course of time, and were replaced by similar types that were biologically adapted to cold conditions. The continued lowering of temperature is connected with the advance of the Würm glaciation. Some of the earlier people may have changed their cultures to fit the oncoming Ice Age, but most of them probably died out or moved southward, possibly taking with them the core-biface tradition. Beyond speculations of this sort, nothing is known of the fate of Lower Paleolithic man.

[8] Apart from some sites in western Europe, Mousterian culture appears in a variety of forms and is not inevitably associated with Classic Neandertal man. Some details of the numerous and varying aspects attributed to Mousterian culture are pointed out in F. Bordes, "Mousterian Cultures in France," *Science,* Vol. 134, 1961, pp. 803–10. A number of writers would even limit the term "Mousterian" to its Würm phase. Others refuse to regard the Mousterian as a distinctive, Middle Paleolithic, stage of human culture. What is here labeled Mousterian is sometimes called Mousterian of Acheulian tradition, and is broadly comparable to what is sometimes called Levalloiso-Mousterian.

Mousterian culture is divided into subsections, and cannot always be directly traced to earlier ways of life in western Europe. It continued to be based on hunting, fishing and gathering, and its practitioners never learned to become food producers. Unrestricted wandering out-of-doors and camping in the open along the banks of streams grew impossible as the weather became increasingly severe, and Neandertal man is known to have had to resort to caves. Judged by the location of his cultural left-overs, he preferred to live near the threshold of a cave where there was more light and fresh air than in the dank interior. So abundant are the remains of hearths and charred substances that fire must commonly have been used for light, heat, and the preparation of food. Life in heated caves affords testimony of Neandertal man's ability to sustain himself during the frigid Würm period by making cultural rather than biological adjustments. Without the help of cultural equipment and, in all likelihood, a measure of social cooperation, Middle Paleolithic man would have been unable to hunt down such enormous Ice Age beasts as the mammoth and woolly rhinoceros. He sometimes used their large bones for chopping blocks or anvils, but bone, ivory, and similar materials were not widely used, and most of his implements continued to be fashioned from fine-grained stones. What use was made of skins, furs, or hides is not certain, but it seems reasonable to guess that some pelts were worn for clothing. Scraps of shells and tiny bones indicate that fish and shellfish were eaten, but there is little to tell how they were obtained, nor is anything known about the extent to which vegetable products were gathered and utilized.

Classic Neandertal man's stone work is based on Paleolithic percussion methods. Resemblances or relationships have been noted to core-made, Acheulian bifacial fist axes, as well as to Clactonian and Levalloisian flake implements. Specialists agree that many Mousterian flakes were struck from a discoidal core, and not from a typically Levalloisian tortoise core. Apart from technical details, the great majority of Middle Paleolithic tools are made from flakes that resemble Levalloisian, and terms like Levalloiso-Mousterian are common. In addition, a small, bifacial fist ax, almost triangular in form, is fairly widespread and is the only core-made implement regularly used by Neandertal man. For the rest, his stone tools consist chiefly of D-shaped side scrapers and small, triangular points (Fig. 11–8). Also found on occasion are rounded objects of flint, whose purpose is undetermined. They may have been intended for hurling one at a time, and it is sometimes thought that they may have been attached in small sets to leather thongs. Instruments of such types, called *bolas,* are known to have been used by

FIG. 11-8. Specimens of Mousterian culture. Top, left: Back and front sides of a Mousterian point. There is a pronounced bulb of percussion, and the chipping on one face only suggests a connection with the Levallois technique. Top, right: Reverse and front views of a Mousterian scraper. Bottom: An imaginary scene of Mousterian life. Many of the details were supplied by the artist, but Neandertal man is known to have lived at the mouths of caves, and the manner in which a Mousterian point is hafted to a spear shaft is indicated by archeological evidence.

various living tribes to entangle small game, but it is going too far to assume that Middle Paleolithic men similarly employed balls of stone.

A nice problem arises when one tries to consider the possible use of the commonly found small, triangular, Mousterian points. If they were meant to be held in the hand, even of a very strong man, they could have had but doubtful efficiency. Indeed, none of the Middle Paleolithic tools, held in hand, seems to have been capable of striking a deadly blow on a mammoth. To have been effective, a Mousterian point must have been attached to a long handle to form a spear. Neandertal man was thus confronted with a difficult problem of *hafting,* because a spear is worthless if it has a tip that is not securely attached to the shaft. In this instance, the difficulty was increased by the fact that Mousterian points are straight across at the base and therefore hard to affix to anything like a pole. The problem was very likely solved by notching the upper end of the shaft and wedging the stone point into the cleft. There is also a possibility that extra firmness was achieved by binding the notched portion, after the stone tip had been wedged in, tightly around the outside with strips of leather.

If it be granted that Neandertal man successfully met the challenge of a difficult problem of hafting, it follows that he had devised a new kind of weapon that combined at least two different kinds of materials and incorporated the principle of leverage.[9] Thus, for the first time, hominids were able to add a significant amount of extrabodily mechanical power to biologically inherited strength. One can picture a relatively weak man with a good, long spear, holding at a distance and jabbing to death a stronger man armed with a splendid fist ax that can be effective only at close range. Spears would give similar advantages to Neandertal hunters of big game. In such situations cultural efficiency is being used in place of biological force, or, to express the central idea in colloquial terms, brain is being substituted for brawn.[10] This is another important trend that is hardly noticeable in the Middle Paleolithic but becomes more and more noteworthy as we approach modern times.

Once the usefulness of leverage, as applied to handles, became recognized, it was never dropped from human culture. Modern tools make such a widespread use of handles that we rarely bother to analyze their utility. And yet we know full well that it is comparatively easy to dig a hole with a long-handled shovel, whereas the same task would be exceedingly difficult if we had to use only the blade of a shovel, with no handle at all.

There is one more feature that sets Mousterian culture apart from the Lower Paleolithic. Some Classical Neandertal skeletons have been found deposited in graves that were deliberately dug into the floors of caves. The most amazing of such discoveries was made at La Chapelle-aux-Saints, where a corpse had been laid out in a carefully excavated trench and left surrounded by typical Mousterian implements. To appreciate the meaning of this find it is necessary to know that analogous customs still prevail in a great many primitive societies. Everywhere the habit of putting objects into graves is explained in the same way—they are for the use of the dead in the other world. By analogy, we may infer that Neandertal man had a belief in an afterlife. Thanks to what can legitimately be deduced from study of some of his burial practices, we

[9] There is evidence that Lower Paleolithic man had already made use of a one-piece wooden spear, with a fire-hardened tip.

[10] Charles O. Frake has also pointed out that man is unique because he carves his ecological niches with cultural tools rather than with biological specializations. See Paul T. Baker, *et al.*, "Ecology and Anthropology," *American Anthropologist*, Vol. 64, No. 1, Part 1, 1962, p. 53.

get our first hint of Middle Paleolithic man's religious concepts, and no further proof of Classic Neandertal man's algebraic mentality is needed.

Selected References

Bordes, Francois, "Mousterian Cultures in France," *Science,* Vol. 134, 1961, pp. 803–10.

———, and Bourgon, M., "Le complexe Mousterian: Mousteriens, Levalloisen, et Tayacien," *Anthropologie,* Vol. 55, 1951, pp. 1–23.

Burkitt, Miles C., *The Old Stone Age,* Cambridge, England, 1933.

———, *Prehistory,* Cambridge, England, 1925.

Clark, J. Desmond, "Early Man in Africa," *Scientific American,* Vol. 199, No. 1, 1958, pp. 76–83.

Hawkes, Jacquetta, and Wooley, Sir Leonard, *Prehistory and the Beginnings of Civilization,* New York, 1963.

Hibben, Frank C., *Prehistoric Man in Europe,* Norman, Okla., 1958.

Kelley, H., "Acheulian Flake Tools," *Proceedings of the Prehistoric Society,* Vol. 3, 1937, pp. 15–28.

MacCurdy, George G., *Human Origins,* New York, 1924.

McBurney, C. B. M., "The Geographical Study of the Older Paleolithic Stages in Europe," *Proceedings of the Prehistoric Society,* Vol. 16, 1950, pp. 163–83.

———, *The Stone Age of Northern Africa* (Penguin), London, 1960.

Menghin, Oswald, *Weltgeschichte der Steinzeit,* Vienna, 1931.

Upper Paleolithic and Mesolithic Cultures in Western Europe

CHAPTER 12

No scholar can tell how long Classic Neandertal Man and Mousterian cultures, in all their varieties, persisted after 40,000 B.P., but their survival thereafter in western Europe was probably of short duration. They seem to have been crowded out by a succession of important changes that were taking place in nearly every sphere. These were of such significance as to warrant distinguishing the new era, Upper Paleolithic, from the Mousterian that had preceded it. Among the innovations, heavy emphasis must fall on radically different styles of workmanship, as well as the replacement of Classic Neandertal men by Cro-Magnon types. A wide cultural and physical gap is thus indicated between Middle and Upper Paleolithic; and if it is correct to associate the former way of life with Classic Neandertal man, broadly speaking, it is equally appropriate to link the latter with *Homo modernus* and *Homo sapiens.*

Wintry blasts greeted Cro-Magnon man when he first appeared in western Europe. The Würm glaciation had not yet ended, although it might have been wavering. By common agreement, Upper Paleolithic culture is thought to have begun no later than the closing phases of the Würm and to have remained in effect until the end of the Pleistocene some 12,000 years B.P. Thereafter, the Holocene (Recent) period started and modern climatic conditions were established. No single climate prevailed all through the late stages of the Pleistocene, but extended cold spells alternated with long stretches of warmth. One must realize that under such conditions Upper Paleolithic life must have varied from time to time and place to place. For purposes of simplification, three major stages of culture are conventionally recognized: *Aurignacian, Solutrian,* and *Magdalenian.* Each phase differs from the others in several respects and each may be variously subdivided, but all possess some major characteristics in common. Upper Paleolithic tools of stone were still customarily made of fine-grained varieties by percussion or pressure methods. Hunting, fishing, and gathering pursuits continued to form the basis of economic life, and there is no indication of food production, animal domestication, or pottery manufacture. For the first time, there are signs of identifiable dwellings. They were oval or elongated, semisubterranean pit houses, but they do not seem to have been congregated into large settlements. Whatever cultural innovations were introduced to western Europe do not seem to have grown out of the Mousterian, yet they did not go beyond the general pattern of the Old Stone Age. A faster tempo of change was inaugurated by *Homo sapiens,* but the magnitude of Upper Paleolithic man's achievements must be considered minor when compared to what was going to take place after the end of Pleistocene times.

It was once thought that the original bearers of Upper Paleolithic cultures had penetrated western Europe from the east, possibly from some point in Asia; and a few manifestations used to be attributed to north Africa. Conservative archeologists of today feel that the entire Upper Paleolithic is much too diversified to have come from a single source, and they prefer to treat separately each of the many regional forms that has so far been recognized. Beyond that, very little can be said on the subject of origins. Local patterns are being carefully studied in respect to their own evolutions, but no over-all synthesis is yet available.

Aurignacian achievements

With the opening of western Europe's Upper Paleolithic era, the "contest" between core and flake tools was resolved in favor of the latter, but the kind of flake utilized differs from anything widely used before. Essentially, it is parallel-sided, 2 or 3 inches in length, at least twice as long as it is wide, thin, and very sharp along the cutting edges. In this form it is known as a blade (Fig. 12–1) and comprises the basis for the most common run, especially of Aurignacian and Magdalenian lithic implements. Most of the blades appear to have been detached from a carefully prepared prismatic core by a blow on an accurately placed pick, the point of which rested on a nodule of stone. So well were cores preworked —even better than with the Levallois technique—that many blades were used exactly as struck off, although some had their working edges secondarily retouched.

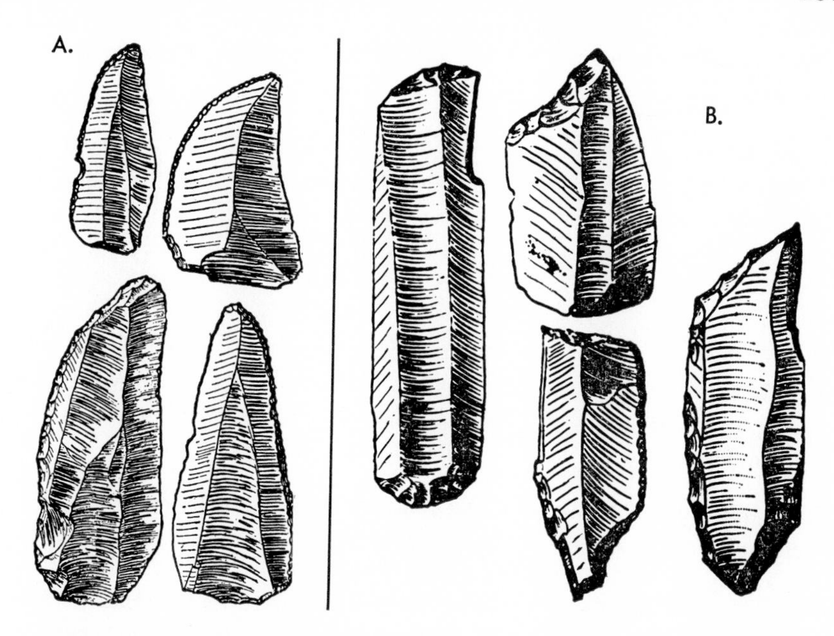

FIG. 12-1. Some Upper Paleolithic stone-blade tools. A. Aurignacian types. B. Magdalenian specimens. Note the similarity of workmanship. Aurignacian and Magdalenian implements commonly have a vertical channel on one surface and are unworked on the other. (From George G. MacCurdy, *Human Origins,* New York, 1926. Courtesy of Appleton-Century-Crofts, Inc.)

The late Abbé Henri Breuil, one of the foremost authorities on the Upper Paleolithic, particularly of France, has suggested dividing the Aurignacian into three major stages on the basis of tool variations; Dorothy Garrod proposes a fourfold division; Denis Peyrony thinks that there were two distinct traditions, Aurignacian that worked in bone and *Périgordian* which used stone, each of which went through five phases; and H. L. Movius feels that Périgordian was a distinct stage that preceded the Aurignacian at the very beginning of the Upper Paleolithic.[1] These differing schemes of classification indicate how difficult it is to treat the Périgordian-Aurignacian as a single period of culture. Nevertheless, authorities agree reasonably well that the earliest Aurignacian lithic industry was the *Châtelperronian,* which featured the manufacture of flint blades with one edge straight and very sharp and the other

[1] References to the works in which the authors here cited suggested various schemes of classification may be found in H. L. Movius, Jr., "Old World Prehistory: Paleolithic," in A. L. Kroeber, ed., *Anthropology Today,* Chicago, 1953, pp. 191–92; and in H. L. Movius, Jr., "The Old Stone Age," in H. L. Shapiro, ed., *Man, Culture, and Society,* New York, 1956, pp. 49–93.

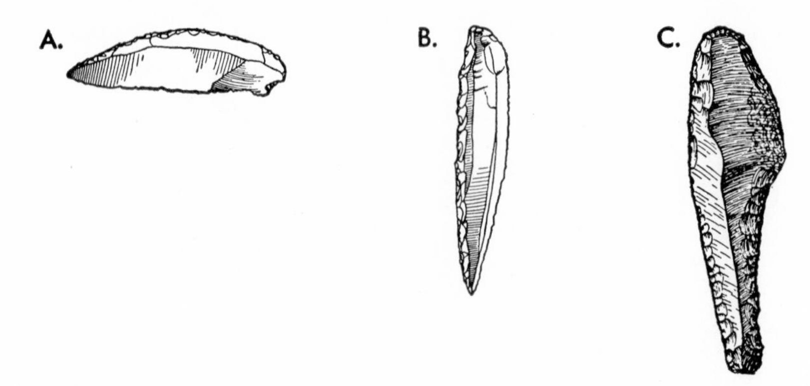

FIG. 12-2. More specimens of Upper Paleolithic industries. A. Châtelperronian blade knife. B. Gravettian knife. C. Font Robert point.

deliberately blunted and curved to provide a good grip (Fig. 12–2A). These instruments made very serviceable knives.

Following the Châtelperronian came the bulk of Aurignacian stonework. Among the most useful blade tools were *end scrapers*, with the sharp working surface at one end rather than along the side, giving more leverage to the user; *drills* and *gravers*, worked to a sharp point for purposes of boring holes or making fine incisions; *shoulder points*, with long, backward-projecting tangs, presumably meant for insertion into an arrow or javelin shaft; a variety of knives; and *burins*, with beveled cutting edges that functioned in the manner of chisels.[2] Burins represent one of the cleverest innovations of the Upper Paleolithic. They were so made that a user could guide the cutting edge with his index finger, thus enabling him to achieve precise effects. Burins and several other stone tools were ingeniously made to cut wood across the grain and also to permit a wider employment than ever before of bone, antler, horn, ivory, and shell. In this way they made possible an increased use of natural resources. Quite often the use of the new materials called for boring or drilling operations that required some utilization of *rotary motion*. It is true that no widespread application of this principle was made in Upper Paleolithic times, but it is important to note that rotary motion was being modestly employed.

Not only do the various stages of Aurignacian work in stone reveal some of the new features introduced by Upper Paleolithic craftsmen,[3] but there is ample evidence that man has added to his earlier employ-

2 For illustrations showing most of these forms and suggesting modern parallels, see R. J. Braidwood, *Prehistoric Men*, Chicago, 1948, pp. 62–65.

3 Students are reminded that archeologists cannot always tell apart two related kinds of stone tools, unless they know all the circumstances of their discovery.

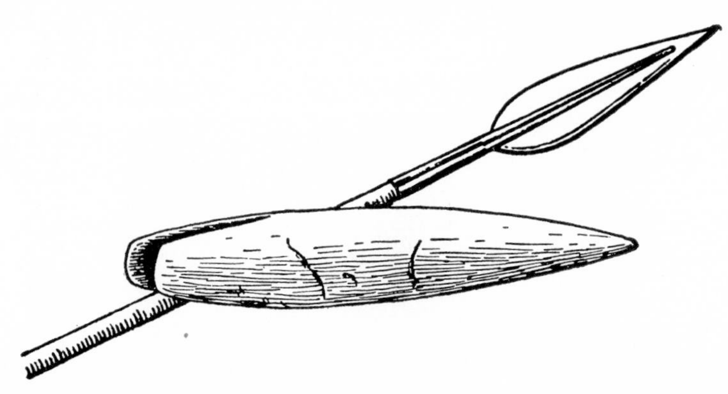

FIG. 12-3. Aurignacian bone point. It is split at the base, presumably to accommodate a shaft. The manner in which it might have served as a spear tip is suggested in the accompanying drawing. (From Robert J. Braidwood, *Prehistoric Man*, Chicago, 1948. Courtesy of the author.)

ment of raw materials a much more widespread use of bone. Soon after the early Châtelperronian phase there occur in Aurignacian deposits a great number of bone points, split at the base as if to admit a shaft in order to make a hafted spear or a javelin (Fig. 12–3). Other kinds of bone points are so common throughout the Aurignacian that Peyrony, let us recall, feels the entire period can be arranged into five parts on the basis of changes in bonework.

An odd Aurignacian object, generally made of horn or antler, is sometimes called a *baton de commandement*. As their function was not known they were thought to be staffs of authority and were supposed to have been carried, like swagger sticks, by those in positions of responsibility or command. *Batons de commandement* are no longer regarded as status or rank symbols. Instead, they are believed to have functioned more prosaically as devices for straightening the shafts of darts or spears.

Among the most important Aurignacian innovations is the *spear-thrower* or *javelin-thrower*, customarily fashioned of antler or horn. Its appearance is deceptively simple, much like a stick with a raised hook at one end. When it is to be used, a spear or javelin is laid flat against the throwing device, with the butt end pressing against the raised hook. This has the effect of increasing the stretch of the user's arm by the length of the spear-thrower, and gives him more mechanical power than his own body possesses (see Fig. 12–4). In America, spear-throwers are often called by the Aztec word, *atlatl*. To become adept in the use of a spear-thrower requires considerable practice. This calls for the mental ability to look ahead to a future reward while one is undergoing the comparative drudgery of perfecting a skill.

FIG. 12-4. Use of a spear-thrower. Native of New Guinea hurling a fish-spear with a spear-thrower. The use of this implement has the same mechanical effect as lengthening the arm by the length of the spear-thrower. (From H. T. Hogbin, *Peoples of the Southwest Pacific,* New York, 1945. Courtesy of the Asia Press, Inc.)

In addition to the coming of Cro-Magnon men, the development of lithic blade industries and new kinds of tools, the utilization of additional raw materials, and the gain of mechanical efficiency provided by the use of spear-throwers, the Aurignacian marks a departure from the Mousterian by its flair for ornamentation and other expressions of the fine arts. These range all the way from lines that look like mere doodles through engravings and sculptures to exceedingly realistic paintings of animals. Customarily, objects that can readily be carried about are classified as home or portable art, whereas items such as wall paintings are classified as mural or immovable art.

Taken in its entirety, the catalog is long and cannot possibly be covered here, but one item demands special mention. Figure 12–5A shows a "necklace" made of a combination of fish spinal bones, perforated canine teeth of stags, and the drilled shells of gastropods. They are arranged into regular units, each one consisting of two sets of four vertebrae, three shells, and a tooth. The same grouping is duplicated over and over, thus showing that even at this early stage of art the concept existed of using fixed units made up of divergent parts and regularly or rhythmically arranged. It is hard to believe that in fashioning such a necklace, crude and unesthetic though it is by present standards, some unknown Aurignacian artist had hit upon the basic principle of repetition coupled with variety that makes up the essence of so much modern art from

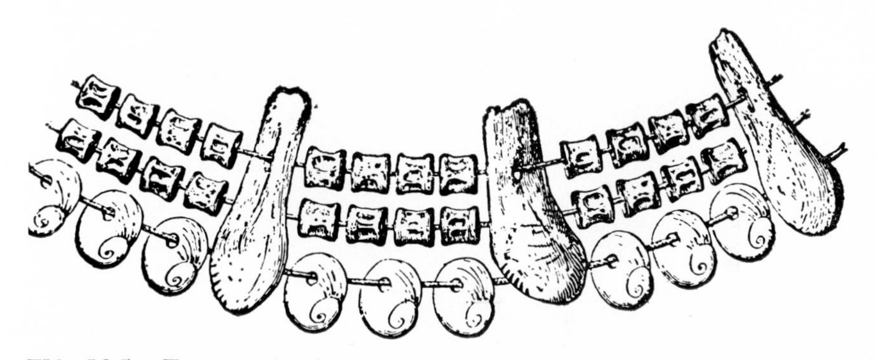

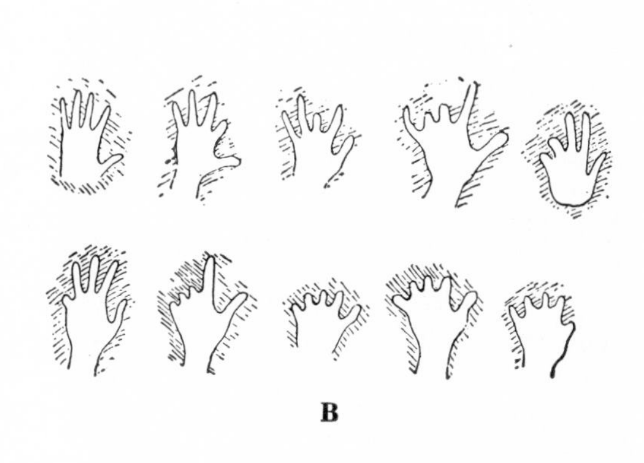

FIG. 12-5. Two examples of Aurignacian symbolic behavior. A. An Aurignacian necklace (after Vernau and MacCurdy). Three units are discernible, each of which consists of four fish vertebrae, three gastropod shells, and one canine tooth of a stag. These units are rhythmically repeated at fixed intervals, showing an appreciation of the esthetic principle, "repetition coupled with diversity." B. Hand imprints (after MacCurdy, following Cartailhac and Breuil). Such mutilated hands are common in various primitive societies, where fingers are offered as sacrifices. The preponderance of left hands furthers the notion that fingers were deliberately cut off with the right hand. It should be remembered, however, that leprosy sometimes causes similar mutilations. (Courtesy Peabody Museum, Harvard University.)

FIG. 12-6. Upper Paleolithic "Venuses." Top, left: Female figurine, carved in ivory, known as the "Venus of Lespugue." There may have been no effort to gain realism. (Courtesy of the American Museum of Natural History.) Top, right: The famous "Venus of Willendorf." This little statue was found in Austria. It was carved in limestone. (Courtesy of the American Museum of Natural History.) Bottom: Another Upper Paleolithic figure of a female, carved in low relief in a block of limestone. It was found at Laussel, in the province of Dordogne, France. This sculpture shows a woman holding a bison horn. It conforms to the Aurignacian tendency to portray details of sex, but to neglect facial features, hands, and feet. (Courtesy of the Peabody Museum, Harvard University.)

poetry and music to architecture. Moreover, the art work reveals that some Upper Paleolithic people were keen and astute observers of nature.

Archeologists have also been intrigued by outlines or impressions of mutilated human hands (Fig. 12–5B) made on cave walls in Aurignacian times. Their meaning can only be guessed, but hands with one or more finger joints missing immediately bring to mind a well-known primitive custom. Several American Indian tribes regularly expected their men to lop off finger joints as sacrifices while striving to communicate with their deities. It is tempting to consider the possibility that similar practices prevailed during the Upper Paleolithic.

Widely known, too, are several stone carvings and statuettes of large-breasted women (Fig. 12–6). They are called, somewhat inappropriately, "Venuses." Many a scholar has tried to guess at their meaning, and the most frequently heard explanations refer them vaguely to a "mother goddess," or to a "fertility cult." Such interpretations cannot be dismissed, but all that can be said with absolute certainty is that Aurignacian man, like his predecessors and successors, was interested in sex and reproduction.

Far and away the most exciting examples of Aurignacian art are the paintings recently discovered on the walls of Lascaux cave, near Les Eyzies, Dordogne, France. A variety of large mammals is depicted, often in motion, such as plodding oxen or running horses (Fig. 12–7). Every observer has been amazed at these splendid and vigorous paintings, some of which are monotone and some in multiple colors.[4] There is much to admire in these pictures, even by the most rigorous of modern standards, but their original significance is not known.

However inadequate our surmises about its meaning may be, Aurignacian art shows an interest in the nonmaterial and extrabiological. A further indication along these lines is found in Upper Paleolithic burial practices. They are more elaborate than the ones noted in the account of the Mousterian. A number of deliberate burials have been found, each with some feature to suggest a concern with the fate of the deceased after death. This may be expressed by daubing skeletal remains with red, perhaps to suggest blood, or by leaving implements and ornaments in the grave. The high development of fine arts and the burial customs combine to show that *Homo sapiens* was making considerable use of algebraic mentality during the Aurignacian phases of cultural evolution.

---

[4] There are several fine studies of the Lascaux paintings. Among them are F. Windels, *The Lascaux Cave Paintings,* New York, 1950, and G. Bataille, *Lascaux or the Birth of Art,* New York, 1955. Also, see H. Breuil, *Four Hundred Centuries of Cave Art,* New York, 1950.

FIG. 12-7. An Aurignacian cave painting. This running horse is depicted in the Lascaux cave. (From F. Windels, *Lascaux Cave Paintings*. New York, 1950. Courtesy of The Viking Press, Inc.)

THE SOLUTRIAN INTERLUDE

Either as a result of the spread of new ideas from places outside of Europe, or by virtue of an actual influx of different kinds of people, there next developed in western Europe a distinct culture complex termed *Solutrian*. One possible source of origin leads to Hungary and another points to north Africa by way of Spain. Wherever it may have originated and however it may have been carried to western Europe, the manifestations of Solutrian culture usually succeed the Aurignacian. At this time the extremely frigid weather of the Würm glaciation had somewhat subsided, and the Solutrians lived under cold but open steppe conditions. Pitifully little is known of the total range of their lives, but they are thought to have been hunters who slew and ate quantities of wild horse (*Equus przewalskii*), as well as reindeer and other animals of that day. At the original station of Solutré, there is a vast deposit of earth mixed with partially burned remnants of game, among which bones of wild horses are especially conspicuous. Above this heap were found items of Solutrian style.

Accompanying the remains of Solutrian folk are numbers of Upper Paleolithic blade tools, but their really distinctive implements, fancifully called *laurel- or willow-leafed,* stand entirely apart.[5] They are sometimes made from flakes or blades, retouched on one or both surfaces by pressure. So skillful were the craftsmen that by dint of precisely controlled pressure-chipping they produced symmetrical, low, flat, ripple-like ridges across the entire face of an implement and reduced it to remarkable thinness and delicacy (Fig. 12–8). All Solutrian tools of stone are likely to be pointed, but they may be as small as an inch or as large as a foot or more. They may also be divided into those that are pointed at both extremes and those that culminate at one end in a tang, presum-

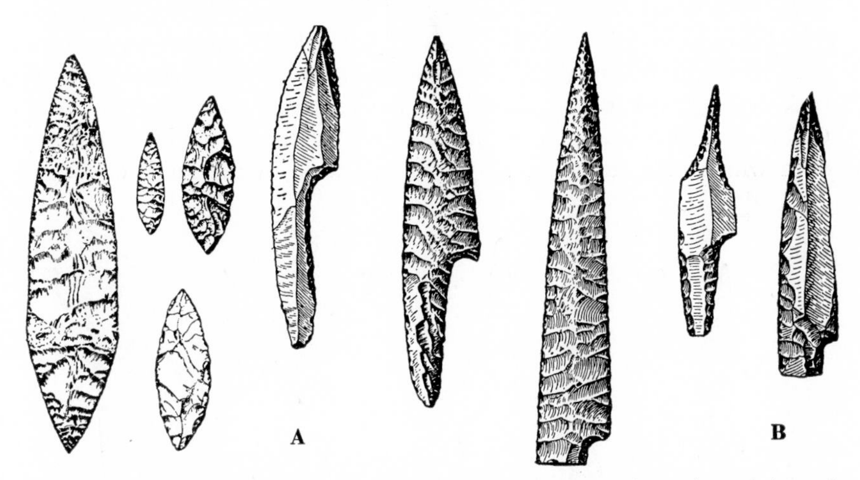

FIG. 12-8. Solutrian tools from the Upper Paleolithic. A. Flint points of the style known as laurel leaf. B. Willow leaf points. The notched shoulders are thought to have facilitated hafting. Solutrian lithic implements show the highest peak of Old Stone Age workmanship. The ripple effect is achieved by precisely controlled pressure-flaking. (Courtesy of Peabody Museum, Harvard University.)

ably for greater ease in hafting. Because they were made with such skill, precision, delicacy, and symmetry, the pressure-flaked stone implements of the Solutrian period reach the greatest heights of Upper Paleolithic workmanship. They were as functional as they were beautiful, and their varied shapes and sizes indicate that they could have served all the purposes of the average tool kit of their day. The lithic materials were supplemented by a few tools and ornaments of bone, horn, and ivory.

The duration in time and the geographic range of Solutrian culture are both restricted. Cro-Magnon men were its carriers, but its appearance and disappearance in western Europe are equally mysterious.

[5] A distinction that, unfortunately, does not apply in all cases, is occasionally made between laurel- and willow-leafed implements. Most laurel leafs are chipped on both faces, whereas willow leafs may have one worked and one unworked side.

In general, Solutrian remains are later than Aurignacian, but they soon give way to Magdalenian.

Magdalenian closes out the Upper Paleolithic

Magdalenian culture, last of western Europe's Upper Paleolithic series, falls in the terminal phase of the Pleistocene. The recession of glacial conditions under which Solutrian man had been lucky enough to live, was followed by the coming of another Ice Age brought about by a late advance of the Würm glacier. Homes were again made in caves or within rock shelters, and animals that live in the cold were once more abundant. On scientific evidence, it can be demonstrated that summers alternated with winters and that the Magdalenians were in the habit of leaving

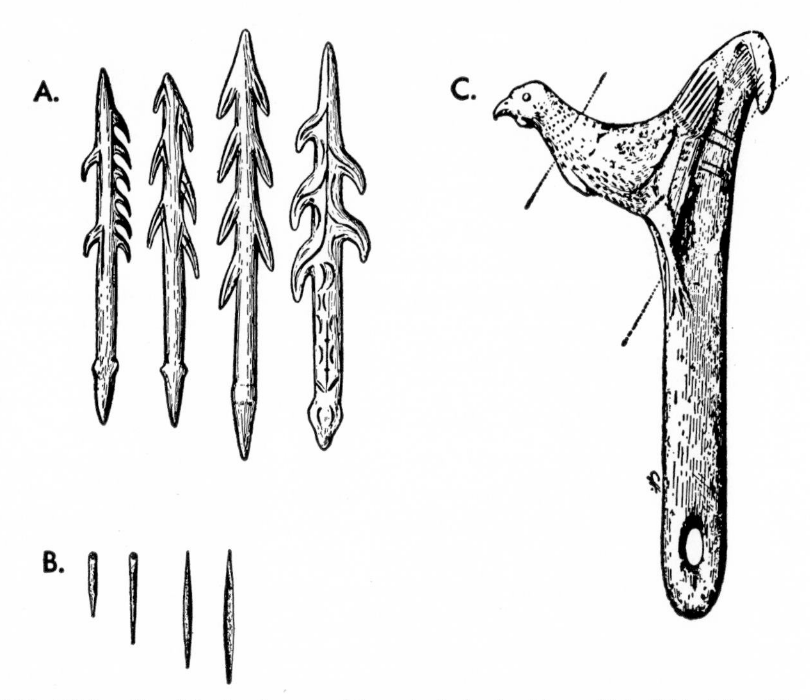

FIG. 12-9. Magdalenian bone and horn tools in the Upper Paleolithic (after MacCurdy, following Breuil). A. Several harpoons with double barbs, made of reindeer horn. B. Needles, with circular eyes, and awls of bone. C. An ornamental horn spear-thrower, from the Magdalenian stage of the Upper Paleolithic. The portions outside the dotted lines were reconstructed by Abbé Breuil. (Courtesy of Peabody Museum, Harvard University.)

their winter residences to hunt reindeer at summer grazing grounds. It can also be shown that arctic grouse and hares were occasionally caught, and there is ample proof of fishing for pike, trout, and salmon.[6]

No longer found as Magdalenian culture progresses are the exquisitely made Solutrian stone tools, and back on the scene come blade artifacts that are reminiscent of various Aurignacian styles. But whatever loss of stoneworking skill may be charged to Magdalenian craftsmen is more than compensated for by an advance and expansion in handling bone, antler, ivory, and horn. Javelin points of horn show progressive evolution, and Abbé Breuil has proposed a classification of Magdalenian subdivisions based on variations of plain and barbed harpoons made of reindeer horn. Needles, buttons, awls, and fishhooks of bone are common, and the use of horn spear-throwers, some of which are elaborately ornamented, becomes widespread (Fig. 12–9).

Occurring sporadically in deposits of earlier culture but gaining prominence in the Magdalenian are tiny stone implements, suitably called *microliths,* that require mere bits of raw material. Many microliths are so small that they fail to cover an average man's fingernail, but each is carefully made and gives clear proof of human workmanship. Ordinarily, microliths are sharp-pointed and suggest that they might have been inserted to form barbs for larger objects. There is also proof that they were sometimes hafted in rows to provide a saw-tooth effect, or worked into wooden shafts to make stone-tipped darts. Archeologists formerly denied knowledge of bows and arrows to Upper Paleolithic people, but it is now fairly generally conceded that such weapons were in use during Magdalenian times.[7]

If one accepts this opinion, an exceedingly important forward step in cultural development must be acknowledged (Fig. 12–10). Adequate use of a bow and arrow implies a further application of algebraic mentality, for no one can become a skillful archer without a great deal of practice. This means that Magdalenian man, even more than any of his predecessors, must have been willing to work long and hard without immediate compensation in order to gain worthwhile but delayed rewards at some time in the future. Now, a comparatively weak individual who had taken the trouble to become a crack shot could triumph over a much stronger person who had never practiced, or who was armed only with older types of weapons. Nor should it be overlooked that a good bowman can discharge deadly arrows while protected by rocks or trees. The mechanical proficiency of a bow is much greater than that of a

[6] For further details, see J. G. D. Clark, *Prehistoric Europe,* New York, 1952, pp. 26–27, *et passim.*

[7] *Ibid.,* pp. 30–31.

FIG. 12-10. "It's a nice trick but it has no significance." (From *Herblock's Special for Today,* New York, 1958. Courtesy of the author and Simon and Schuster, Inc.)

spear-thrower. So it is that *Homo sapiens* was coming to rely increasingly on the effectiveness of his tools, and was meeting many of life's crises by resorting to postnatally learned culture rather than by relying on inherited biology. Yet, use of the bow is possible only to a Primate of human form. An archer must be able to stand firmly on his hind legs; and he must have at least a powerful shoulder girdle with a sturdy clavicle; strong but flexible wrists and fingers; prehensile hands; opposable thumbs; rotating forearms; good vision; and keen coordination of hand and eye (Fig. 12–11).

Magdalenian interest in the nonbiologic is attested by the care taken with burials. Graves are more regularly and frequently dug than ever before, there is much use of red ocher, and bodies are often ornamented with shell necklaces or accompanied by numerous tools. Only

FIG. 12-11. Youthful archers. Pygmy Negro boys learning to shoot bows and arrows. Primate anatomy and close coordination of hand and eye are needed to permit straight shooting. Above all, much preliminary practice is required to achieve skillful use. No one undertakes practice without the foresight to anticipate future rewards. Bows are the first cultural implements to have a great deal of power in themselves. (Courtesy of the American Museum of Natural History.)

the most unreasonable of skeptics would try to deny that the Magdalenians had some concept of religion, at least to the extent of belief in an afterlife.

Until the discovery of the Lascaux paintings, it was thought certain that Magdalenian artists were far and away the best of the Upper Paleolithic. Even now the claim is by no means unwarranted. There are countless ornaments, carvings, engravings, sculptures, clay figures, and paintings from this era, a good percentage of which are of breath-taking excellence. Many techniques, styles, subjects, and color schemes were employed, but the highest critical acclaim is generally reserved for polychrome paintings cleverly shaded to give an illusion of depth or solidity. Two of the very finest examples are reindeer figures at *Font-de-Gaume* near Les Eyzies, France, and the bison depicted on the roof of the world-famous *Altamira* cave, near Santander in Spain (Fig. 12–12, Top).

Archeologists are seldom content to discuss Magdalenian art in purely esthetic terms. The mere fact that some of the very best specimens are found in dim recesses of inaccessible caverns that were never used as habitations makes it improbable that such works were produced only to be admired by the general public. Once more one is tempted to have recourse to analogy with known primitive customs. Many peoples believe that ritual acts of slaying representations of animals will lead, on the principle of *mimetic* or *imitation magic,* to great success on an actual hunt. Religious interpretations of this kind are supported, in part, by Magdalenian portrayals of wounded animals, or realistically drawn beasts with crudely figured hearts shown outside the body. Also found is a tendency to paint one creature right over another. Such a custom, too, plays a part in some primitive religions. Once a spot has acquired a sacred character it is not likely to be readily changed, and wherever such a belief prevails it is not surprising to find paintings superimposed on one another. There is always a possibility that archeological interpretations based on analogy with existing primitive procedures may be wrong, but there is scarcely a writer who touches on the subject of Magdalenian art without suggesting that there may be religious implications.

With the end of the Pleistocene in western Europe, modern climatic conditions begin. Some there are who like to speculate on the post-Pleistocene fate of the Magdalenians. They argue that as the glaciers withdrew for the last time, Magdalenian hunters followed their usual game northward, where they became or mingled with the Eskimo. Unfortunately, there is too little evidence to permit uncritical acceptance of so plausible a bit of speculation.

Whoever takes the trouble to study the details of man's cultural achievements throughout the many centuries of the Old Stone Age can-

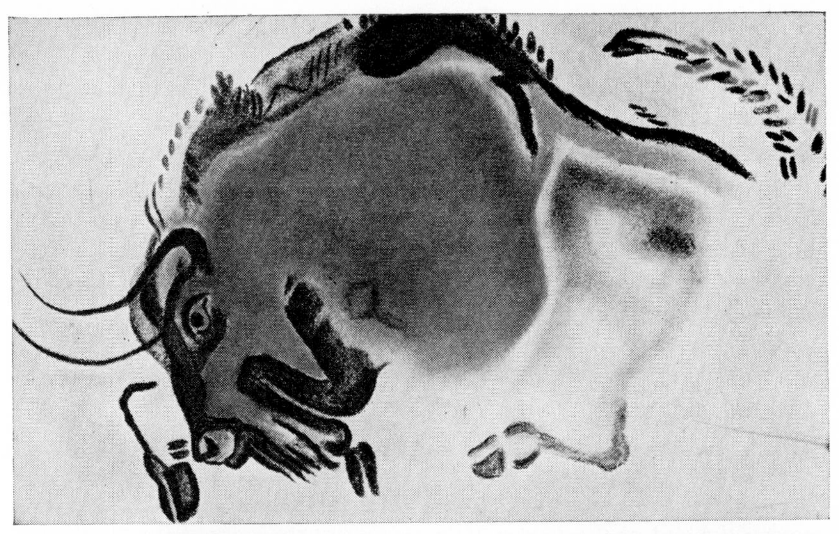

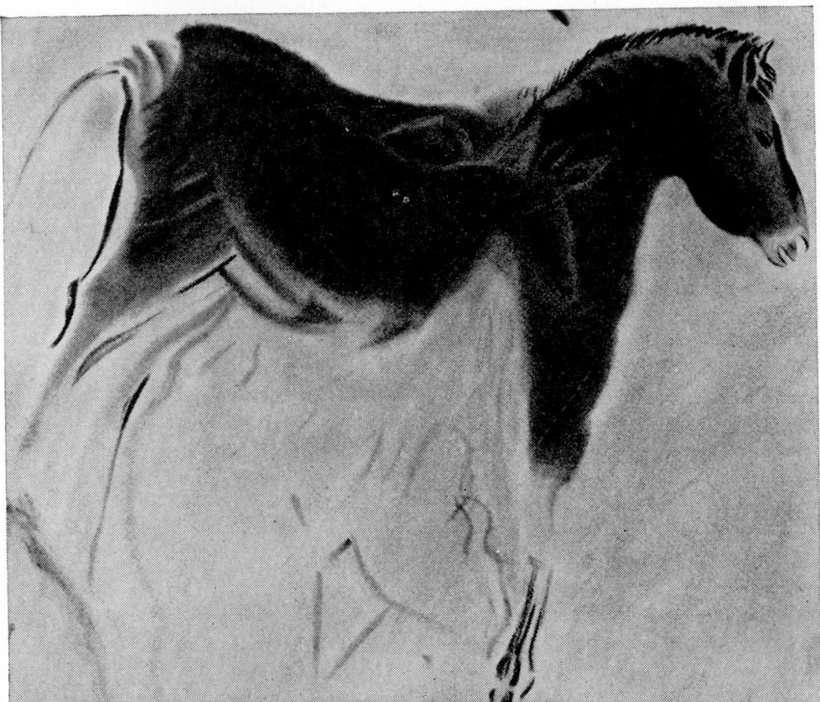

FIG. 12-12. Magdalenian examples of Upper Paleolithic cave painting. Top: A charging bison from the cave at Altamira, Spain. In contrast to the splendidly executed outer form of the animal, the heart is crudely depicted by the diamond-shaped design. (Courtesy of the American Museum of Natural History.) Bottom: Horse and hind from Altamira. The larger figure of a horse is drawn on the same spot, and directly over, the picture of a hind, possibly because of a religious belief that this particular spot was sacred. (Courtesy of the Peabody Museum, Harvard University.)

not escape the feeling that considerable progress was being made. At first, in the earlier phases of the Lower Paleolithic, there is an impression of a fumbling and slow beginning. Even in the Mousterian, it can be maintained, the pace of cultural accomplishment was far from swift; but in the Upper Paleolithic, the march of culture accelerates rapidly. Thus, when one examines the developments of the entire Old Stone Age, it becomes indisputably clear that from beginning to end cultural evolution was taking place.

Introduction to the Mesolithic of Western Europe

Between the end of the Upper Paleolithic and the start of the Neolithic (roughly from 12,000 to 8,000 B.P.), there is a spread of about four millenniums during which man's cultural progress is but slightly understood. Until the turn of the present century, this phase, currently known as the *Mesolithic* or *Middle Stone Age,* was rather contemptuously dismissed as a Dark Age. Part of the low regard was attributable to ignorance of what man had then accomplished, and part of it was based on the patent fact that some of the highest attainments of the Upper Paleolithic were lost. No stone work in the Mesolithic reaches the perfection of Solutrian pressure-flaking; some of the javelins are flat, unsymmetrical and poorly made; and there is no continuation of the splendid artistic creations of the Aurignacian and Magdalenian periods.

In all fairness to the human beings of Mesolithic times in western Europe, it must be recognized that they were living in an era of drastic environmental changes. The huge glaciers of the Pleistocene were shrinking as they moved northward, leaving enormous fields of melting ice that ultimately raised water levels throughout the region. When much of the water finally drained into the sea, the land was relieved of its heavy burden and began to rise and to establish new shorelines. These fluctuations of land and water extents and levels, and the establishment of new equilibriums between them, were greatly influenced by the mounting temperatures that continued in force even after they had initiated the melting of glaciers.[8] Aided by the heat and moisture, forests and grasslands sprang up, and animals adjusted to Ice Age weather became ex-

[8] Melting glaciers sometimes deposit in lakes twin soil layers or *varves* annually. During warm weather, a band of sand or silt forms and is overlaid the next winter by clay. The number of varves in a glacial lake bed thus gives a clue to its age. This method of dating has been well developed in Scandinavia.

tinct or migrated far to the north. In place of woolly mammoth, reindeer, musk ox, and arctic hare, came the brown bear, wild pig, elk, beaver, red deer, wild horse, and bison. At first the new fauna showed adaptations to tundra and steppe conditions, but herd-roaming, forest types gained in prominence as the Mesolithic grew older. All this called for numerous adjustments on the part of all living things. However, once again, it was only *Homo sapiens* who continued to meet the challenges of drastic environmental changes by adjusting his culture instead of his biology.

Certainly, over a long span of time during which there took place so many alterations of climate, fauna, and flora, no one form of culture could have been universally appropriate. For the Mesolithic, much more than for the Upper Paleolithic, it is necessary to deal with local or regional patterns instead of with one generalized way of life. People who hunted game in forests must inevitably have differed from coastal folk who caught fish and gathered shellfish; and what was suitable for northern Denmark might have been unfit for southern France. Understandably enough, archeologists differentiate a good many particular Mesolithic cultures, but we shall deal only with a few samples.

Efforts have been made to derive some of the Mesolithic cultures from specific Upper Paleolithic manifestations, but many of them are farfetched. Satisfactorily proved connections may some day be demonstrated because it is unlikely that all Upper Paleolithic cultures and their carriers vanished completely as soon as the Pleistocene closed. Even though their tracks cannot be followed, there must have been Upper Paleolithic survivors who persisted into the Mesolithic. In fact, a number of anthropologists look upon the entire Mesolithic as no more than a continuation of the Upper Paleolithic under different climatic conditions.

The subsistence patterns of Mesolithic culture, on the whole, did not advance from hunting, fishing, and the gathering of natural food. Nevertheless, efforts at greater efficiency did take place in this sphere of human activity. One of the outstanding specialists in Mesolithic archeology has expressed the opinion that, with the exception of one or two places only, use of the bow made possible the killing of more game.[9] Similarly, Mesolithic people wrought many changes making for better utility on implements that might have been carried over from Upper Paleolithic times. In addition, a few basic innovations were devised. These may not be extensive, but they suffice to show that universal cul-

[9] J. G. D. Clark, *op. cit.*, p. 35. This volume contains much valuable information about Upper Paleolithic and Mesolithic economy.

ture was making a degree of progress during the Mesolithic, and was neither stagnant nor degenerate.

Mesolithic cultures in southwestern Europe

Credit for finding the first overlap of Upper Paleolithic and Mesolithic cultures goes to E. Piette, who began in 1887 to excavate a northern French site called Mas d'Azil. Above five soil layers containing Magdalenian objects he found a sixth holding new types of artifacts, which he called *Azilian.* They included small, flat, crudely barbed harpoons of stag horn, perforated near the base; an assortment of microlithic tools made from blades of flint; and about 200 smooth, water-worn pebbles, painted with red ocher in a miscellaneous variety of linear and geometric designs (Fig. 12–13).

From the start it was plain that Azilian culture was later in time than Magdalenian, but not so well advanced in material ability or artistic skill. Much conjecture was stimulated by the painted pebbles, which

FIG. 12-13. Azilian Mesolithic artifacts. Shown are irregularly shaped, perforated harpoon heads of stag horn (after MacCurdy); and some examples of painted pebbles (after Hoernes). (Courtesy of the Peabody Museum, Harvard University.)

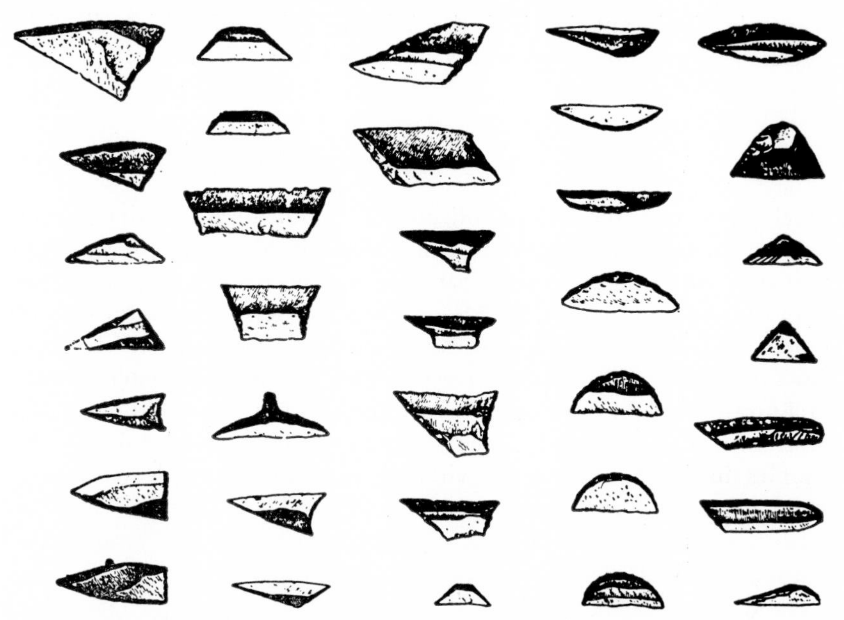

FIG. 12-14. Tardenoisian Mesolithic microliths (after de Mortillet). Tardenoisian culture made wide use of microliths in a great profusion of geometric shapes. (From George G. MacCurdy, *Human Origins*, New York, 1926. Courtesy of Appleton-Century-Crofts, Inc.)

promptly became hall marks of Azilian culture. Strenuous but unsuccessful efforts were made to interpret the designs as forming a crude alphabet and the pebbles themselves as religious tokens or an unknown kind of currency. Speculations of this kind are out of keeping in these days, and the puzzle of the painted pebbles remains unsolved.

Very little has survived of other aspects of Azilian culture, yet discovery of its typical remains throughout southern France and far to the east proves it to have been quite widespread and probably long-lived.

At several stations in southwestern Europe Azilian culture blends with *Tardenoisian* (Fig. 12–14), which is outstanding for its extensive use of microliths made in various geometric forms, such as crescents, triangles, semicircles, and rhomboids. There is not much to distinguish Tardenoisian from Azilian, except that the former has no painted pebbles and makes greater use of trapezoid and chisel-ended microliths.[10]

[10] In some parts of Spain, along the Bay of Biscay, a Mesolithic culture called *Asturian* may overlie Azilian. It is featured by vast shell mounds and the occurrence of rough stone tools.

Another Mesolithic culture, *Campignian,* occurs in Belgium. It is characterized by a chipped stone implement that is known as a *Campignian pick.* Other

It may be significant that both the Azilians and Tardenoisians lived in treeless regions and lacked sturdy woodworking tools.

Ax wielders of the north

Much more is known of Mesolithic life in northwestern than southwestern Europe. Although there is a probability that some Upper Paleolithic people from Spain or France moved northward in post-Pleistocene times, the Scandinavian Mesolithic seems less of an outgrowth of Upper Paleolithic culture than the Azilian or Tardenoisian. Changing environmental conditions are so well marked in the northwestern sectors of Europe that they provide archeologists with a good dating system. Most intimately adjusted to the changing times were several ax-using peoples in Denmark and the vicinity, whose main implements were hefty enough to cope with growing forests. The first phase of their

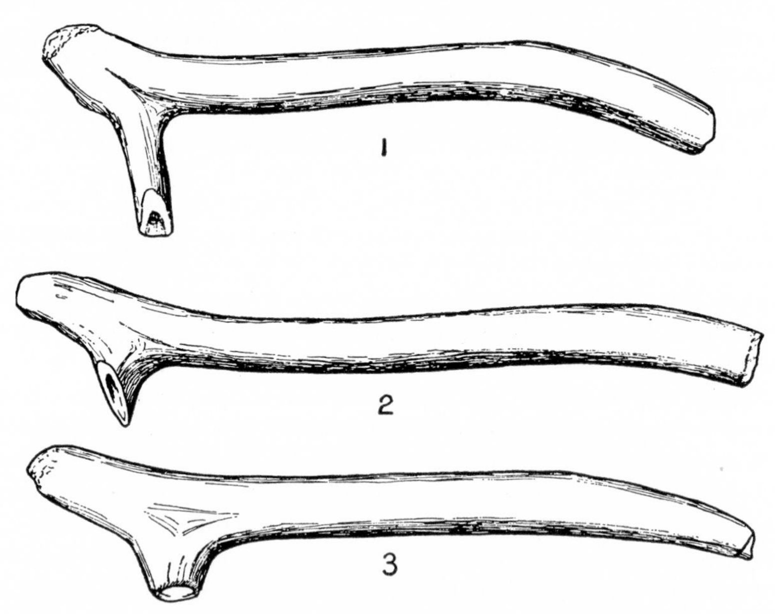

FIG. 12-15. Three forms of Lyngby axes. All are made from reindeer antlers. Number 1 is in the shape of an ax; 2 is an adze; and 3 is a haft. (From J. G. D. Clark, *The Mesolithic Settlement of Northern Europe,* Cambridge, England, 1936. Courtesy of the author and the Cambridge University Press.)

implements comprise a mixture of what may be Tardenoisian and Ertebølle tools (see p. 254). Its bearers did not, however, build up shell mounds, nor did they work in bone. On the other hand, they did make Ertebølle-like pottery.

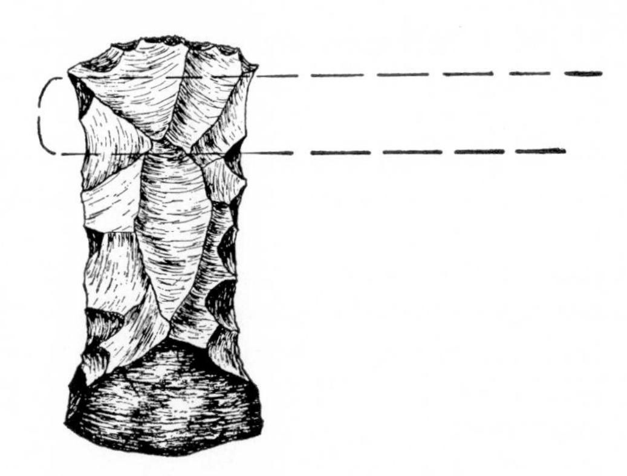

FIG. 12-16. A Mesolithic ax. Although it is core-made and shaped, primarily, by percussion, its cutting edge has been beveled by grinding or polishing. It was not meant to be held in the hand when in use. The sketch suggests a manner of hafting that makes it resemble a modern ax.

culture is called *Lyngby,* and is distinguished by the employment of reindeer antlers. Axes were manufactured by cutting brow tines obliquely; adzes were similarly made; and hafts were fashioned to accommodate a stone axhead (Fig. 12–15).

Some aspects of Lyngby culture were probably incorporated into the succeeding *Maglemose* phase, which has left more ample remains. People following the Maglemose way of life hunted elk, red deer, and wild pig; caught many pike and other fish from inland waters; did a considerable amount of fowling; and collected edible plants and shellfish. They made stone tools that vary from microliths in many shapes to heavy core-built axes (roughly rectangular, and not to be confused with generally pear-shaped Lower Paleolithic fist axes; see Fig. 12–16), adzes, picks, and chisels, or *tranchets.* A number of experts believe that the Maglemose type of ax was a fresh invention rather than an outgrowth of any previous tool. They also point out that the Mesolithic ax development may have originated from something like the old rostro-carinates (p. 214). Maglemose people also made harpoons and barbless fishhooks of antler and bone, as well as assorted items of wood. Among the most interesting of the wooden remains are a number of large paddle rudders that point to a knowledge of water transport, most likely in the form of dug-out canoes.

No doubt Maglemose folk had the resources to deal with forest life and some think it was in connection with the hunting of forest animals that they achieved their greatest cultural triumph, domestication of the dog. There is a question as to whether they originated the idea or borrowed it from outsiders, but this marks the first instance in our outline of cultural progress where man was beginning to use another animal for practical purposes other than food or as a source of raw materials.

It is important not to confuse domestication with simple taming. A completely domesticated animal must not only be so tame that it will not attack people or run away, but it should also be dependent on man for protection and at least for some of its food, as opposed to foraging on its own. It should also be capable of breeding under conditions of captivity. If a beast has been thoroughly domesticated, so many of its genes will be discarded, or else deliberately selected for reproduction, that paleontologists can tell, even thousands of years later, a domesticated creature from its wild relatives. It has been established that dogs were the first beasts to have been brought under domestication by man. Their ancestors were wolves. There is no way of telling by what steps the dog's domestication was brought about, nor are the uses to which the animal was put at all clear.[11] Even so, domestication represents such an important concept that its presence stands out as a Mesolithic contribution to the march of culture.

According to several experts, some of the Maglemose hunters apparently settled permanently at the seashore, supporting themselves by catching fish and gathering shellfish. Their culture at this stage is called *Ertebølle*[12] and is often, but not in every instance, marked by huge mounds of debris known as *kitchen middens.* The largest of these may be as much as 100 yards long, 50 feet wide, and 5 feet deep. Kitchen middens consist of discarded shells, bits of food, bones, earth, lost or rejected tools, and other odds and ends densely packed together and sometimes containing skeletal remains. Those who lived at the seashore long enough for large heaps of debris to accumulate were probably permanent residents, for the kitchen middens contain enough fire hearths to suggest that the inhabitants stuck it out even during inclement seasons. This evidence shows that permanent settlements can be made without agriculture. Material remains of Ertebølle culture run closely parallel to those of the Maglemose, except for the addition of a chisel of stone (*petit tranchet*), so small that it must have been hafted, as well as bone combs, bracelets, and pottery vessels. The invention of pottery is an exceedingly important attainment, but Ertebølle is so recent a phase of Mesolithic culture, dated around 5000 B.C., that nearly

[11] The theory has been advanced, by analogy with known areas where livestock are kept for social or religious purposes, that animal domestication may not have started as a practical measure. This is an interesting hypothesis. For a strong argument along these lines, see Erich Isaac, "On the Domestication of Cattle," *Science,* Vol. 137, No. 3525, 1962, pp. 195–204.

[12] Some scholars refer to all of the Mesolithic cultures of northwestern Europe as Maglemosean. According to them, Maglemosean may be subdivided into Lyngby, Maglemose, and Ertebølle.

FIG. 12-17. Mesolithic pottery from Ertebølle. It is crudely made. Impressed designs may be found on the rims, and the bases are customarily conical. Current opinion holds that some objects of burned clay (pottery) were known to mankind long before the start of the Neolithic age. (Courtesy of the Danish National Museum.)

everyone doubts that the concept was original. The probability is great that it had come from some area where at that time Neolithic culture was already well advanced. A description of pottery-making and its implications will, therefore, be reserved until the New Stone Age is discussed. Borrowed or not, Ertebølle pottery manufacturing was not greatly skilled. Vessels were formed of black clay, mixed with coarse grit, that took on a gray-brown color when fired. They were so poorly made that they often cracked open. Only oval saucers and wide-mouthed jars with conical, pointed bases seem to have been made, and the most common style of decoration was limited to a series of fingernail impressions along the rim (Fig. 12–17).[13]

After the forests and coasts of northern Europe had been settled by Maglemose and Ertebølle ax wielders, respectively, there came into the area bands of microlith users. Perforce, they took what land remained unoccupied, most of which was sandy soil. On this they built small settlements consisting of reed houses plastered with mud, sometimes with subterranean foundations. Their culture lacks the distinctive implements of bone, stone, or antler that characterize much of the Mesolithic, and they were unable to make pottery. They seem to have had a shadowy Tardenoisian culture and are thought to have offered but little opposition to the Neolithic invaders who were soon to displace them.

During most of the Mesolithic, the British Isles are believed to have been connected by land bridges with the European mainland. This would have made it easy for peoples and cultures to have penetrated what are now islands. Implements that resemble Azilian, Tardenoisian, and Maglemosean have been found in various parts of Great Britain. Some changes in the customs of the immigrants doubtless came about in the new environment, and, on all sides, a considerable amount of interplay and intermixture seems to have taken place.

Whether one chooses to treat the Mesolithic as a distinct stage or as a continuation of the Upper Paleolithic, it certainly was not an era of cultural stagnation.

Selected References

Bataille, Georges, *Lascaux, or the Birth of Art,* New York, 1955.
Braidwood, Robert J., *Prehistoric Men,* Chicago, 1948.

[13] The presence of pottery no matter where it originated, in a pre-Neolithic context, conclusively demonstrates that pottery and Neolithic culture do not always go hand in hand. Such a demonstration has been repeatedly made, especially in the New World.

Breuil, Henri, *Four Hundred Centuries of Cave Art,* New York, 1950.
Burkitt, Miles C., *Our Early Ancestors,* Cambridge, England, 1926.
Childe, V. Gordon, *Prehistoric Communities of the British Isles,* Edinburgh, 1949.
Clark, J. Grahame D., *The Mesolithic Settlement of Northern Europe,* Cambridge, England, 1936.
Cook, S. F., "A Reconsideration of Shellmounds with Respect to Population and Nutrition," *American Antiquity,* Vol. 12, 1946, pp. 51–53.
Garrod, Dorothy A. E., "The Upper Palaeolithic in the Light of Recent Discovery," *Proceedings of the Prehistoric Society,* Vol. 4, 1938, pp. 1–26.
———, *Prehistoric Europe,* New York, 1952.
Movius, Hallam L., Jr., "Radiocarbon Dates and Upper Paleolithic Archaeology in Central and Western Europe," *Current Anthropology,* Vol. 1, 1960, pp. 355–91.
Obermaier, Hugo, *Fossil Man in Spain,* New Haven, 1924.
Peyrony, Denis, "Le Perigordien, l'Aurignacien, et le Solutreen en Eurasie . . . ," *Bulletin de la Société préhistorique de France,* Vol. 45, 1948, pp. 305–28.
Windels, Fernand, *The Lascaux Cave Paintings,* New York, 1950.

The New Stone Age Takes a Giant Stride

CHAPTER 13

By the end of the Mesolithic, *Homo sapiens* had gone through a long and diversified cultural apprenticeship. Throughout the hundreds of millenniums of the Old and Middle Stone Ages the species had devised a great profusion of tools made in a variety of ways from wood, fine-grained stones, ivory, horn, antler, bone, and other materials that could be handled while they were cold or hot, but without preliminary melting. Members of *Homo sapiens* had made homes in caves, under rock shelters, in the open, in forested regions and on seacoasts. Fire was everywhere utilized and ingenious methods of obtaining food from nature had been developed. It is fairly certain that religious practices had begun, and fine arts occasionally reached amazing heights. Before the conclusion of the Mesolithic, the potential power of the human body had been greatly increased through the agency of such extra-corporeal things as bows and arrows, sturdily hafted tools, boats or canoes, and, probably, the domesticated dog. Also, during the Middle Stone Age of northwestern Europe, the making of pottery introduced a new industry and led to an expanding utilization of natural resources.

Despite the record of their achievements, Old and Middle Stone Age cultures advanced at a relatively slow pace, and cannot help but appear remote and drab to those living in the second half of the twentieth century A.D. This picture, as we shall soon see, changes with dramatic suddenness when man enters the *New Stone Age*.

Actually, a number of societies have lived on into recent times with patterns of culture that were no further advanced than the Neolithic. To cite only two instances, the American Indians were, with only two or three outstanding exceptions, culturally Neolithic or less in 1492

A.D.; and the Australian aborigines had doubtfully attained that level before they were brought into steady contact with Europeans in the nineteenth century.

The survival of ancient forms of culture in some parts of the world long after they had become outmoded elsewhere poses an interesting question about the situation 8000 years ago. Surely, there were many Mesolithic and even continuing Paleolithic communities that persisted in their old customs because of their isolation or because they lacked the desire or means to take up the new fashions. Viewed in universal terms, a previously negligible situation appears to have taken on increasing significance in the Neolithic. For the first time in human history there must have been numerous groups of hunters and food collectors or gatherers in the northern regions who looked with envy on prosperous agriculturalists in their vicinity, particularly in late fall or winter when game was scarce and natural botanical products were unavailable. These are seasons of the year when farmers and keepers of livestock are likely, except under the most wretched of conditions, to have food on hand. A marked distinction was probably felt at such times between "have" and "have not" societies, and it seems reasonable to believe that large-scale raids or wars, as distinguished from sporadic assaults or occasional murders, had their beginning in Neolithic times. By way of proof it may be noted that in the mature New Stone Age, settlements fortified by ditches and ramparts are commonplace.

The uneven distribution of Neolithic advances raises a cardinal point of theory. In tracing the march of culture, we are dealing not with universal stages through which all communities must have passed, but rather with a synthesis that puts into an orderly, chronological sequence the culturally high levels reached here and there by various people. No one race, tribe, nation, society, or corner of the globe showed the way at all times. Instead, numerous groups of humans made basic contributions at different times and places. Around 8000 B.P. many spots now regarded as "backward" were exerting vigorous cultural leadership and, conversely, such a "forward" area as western Europe was then far behind the times.

In this regard, it must be remembered that the only reason western European data were hitherto emphasized is that the sequence of man's earliest efforts to develop culture has been most intensively studied on that continent. When it comes to describing Neolithic progress, however, it becomes necessary to shift the scene. Not Europe but the *Eastern Mediterrean Zone* best reveals the manner in which *Homo sapiens* made his way into the New Stone Age. This zone extends from Egypt's Nile

River in northeastern Africa to the valleys of the Euphrates and Tigris rivers of western Asia. In general terms, the Eastern Mediterranean Zone incorporates what is often called "The Fertile Crescent." This is the region, so far as archeologists know, where Neolithic culture was born and from which it was diffused to many other parts of the Old World. That it did not spring into existence full-blown is readily acknowledged, but its immediate ancestry is still in dispute.

The treatment of the Neolithic Age's contributions to culture, one item at a time, should not mislead one into thinking that every step was made entirely by itself. Culture is cumulative, and developments often go together. Thus, the manufacture of pottery would have been impossible without an earlier control of fire. It would be most unwise to regard the New Stone Age as having made a large number of separate, unrelated advances.

STONEWORK CHANGES AND NEOLITHIC TRADE

Because Neolithic has become a time-sanctioned term for the new ways of life that started about 8000 B.P., it is appropriate to begin its study with a description of stone usages. Even during the antecedent Mesolithic of northwestern Europe, attempts had been made to handle stone in ways that were unknown to Paleolithic man. Large blocks were sometimes roughly shaped by percussion flaking, after which grooves might be pecked in them by repeated blows with a hard, sharp boulder. The pecked-out channels could then be used for hafting. Less often, trenches were cut into one stone by sawing back and forth in the same spot with a tougher one. Most frequent and valuable of the new methods, though, was a process of rubbing a bit of stone repeatedly over an abrasive substance such as sandstone, rough fibers, or plain sand. This technique, commonly known as grinding or polishing, produces a tool that has a smooth, highly burnished surface (Fig. 13–1). Grinding is sometimes applied to an entire implement, and sometimes only to a cutting edge.

While cases are known for the Mesolithic where rubbing techniques were used in shaping tools of wood, bone, and sometimes stone, it is not until the Neolithic that grinding or polishing customarily replaces the older percussion and pressure methods of dealing with stone. Widespread use of the new process is of deep significance because it greatly increased man's ability to use hitherto valueless raw materials. No longer was it necessary to seek out flint, quartz, or other fine-grained

FIG. 13-1. Lithic techniques of the New Stone Age. A. Club head or hammer. B. Ax head. C. Bannerstone. The *a* surfaces are natural; *b* surfaces are pecked; and *c* surfaces are rubbed or polished. (A, B, C, from F. Boas, ed., *General Anthropology*. Boston, 1938. Courtesy of D. C. Heath and Co.) D. An Australian aborigine grinding a Neolithic implement. (From B. Spencer and F. S. Gillen, *The Arunta*. New York and London, 1927. Courtesy of The Macmillan Company.)

stones. Almost any kind of stone, regardless of grain or internal composition, can be ground into a tool. Even granites which crumble when subjected to percussion or pressure flaking can be rubbed into a desired shape. Polishing has the further advantage of producing sturdier working edges than the older methods, which turned out implements that often split or cracked after hard use. When a pressure- or percussion-made tool is damaged it is seldom worth repairing and is likely to be discarded and replaced, but the working edge of a polished stone instrument can be resharpened or repaired by rerubbing, much on the same principle used in the repair of a metal tool on a grindstone. In the long run, therefore, Neolithic implements turned out to be more lasting and economical than their parallels from the earlier ages. They enabled man to cut down forests and to shape timbers efficiently, and they may

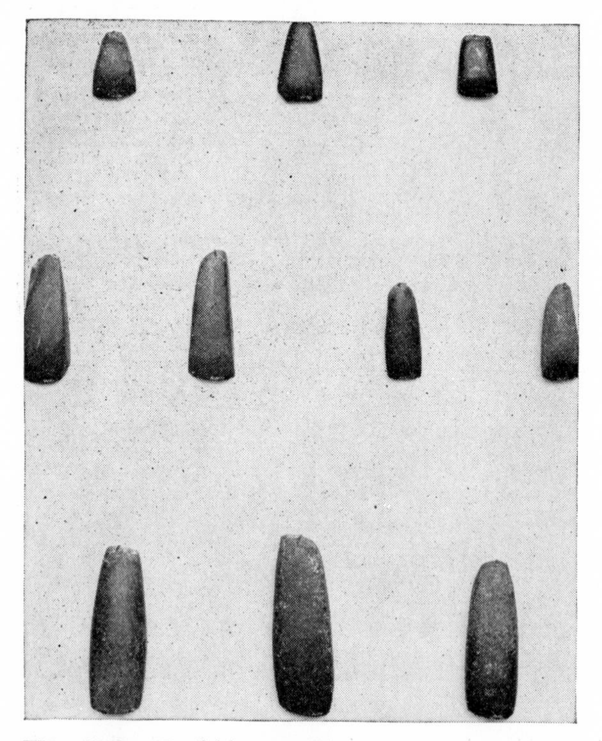

FIG. 13-2. Neolithic celts. They represent a very common type of lithic tool, widely used in the New Stone Age. They are rubbed smooth (ground or polished), and many of them have beveled edges. They were always used with handles, in the manner of adzes or axes. (Courtesy of the Chicago Natural History Museum.)

well deserve credit for providing the means of establishing carpentry as a more important craft than ever before.

With increased reliance on techniques of grinding, the old distinction between flake and core tools grew increasingly meaningless. The Neolithic process wastes so little raw material that it makes little difference whether a craftsman starts with a core or a flake. Nor did the use of polishing methods initially affect the forms or sizes of lithic objects that had already gained wide favor. Chiefly the same kinds of utensils continued to be made, but in the course of time Neolithic workmen came to show a preference for what is called a *celt*. This implement was commonly about 3 inches across, flared at the base, and around 6 inches long. A glance at a typical celt (Fig. 13–2) will show that, when suitably hafted, it is the prototype of our familiar hatchet or ax blade. Ever-increasing abandonment of tools designed to be held in the bare hand or fist is a very revealing feature of the Neolithic. The mechanical advantages of handles had become so thoroughly recognized that the principle of hafting was accepted as a matter of course.

Despite the almost undifferentiated use of stones made possible by Neolithic workmanship, there was a differing value put on various kinds of lithic materials. It is probable that mining for particular varieties of stone went on earlier, but not until the New Stone Age is there evidence of large-scale mining activity, with such devices as sunken shafts and connecting galleries. One of the best known centers of flint quarrying was located at *Grand Pressigny*, France. Here there was a prodigious deposit of high-grade flint, resembling amber or beeswax in color. Grand Pressigny flint is so distinctive and so readily identified that its distribution is easy to follow. Examples of Grand Pressigny flint, mined in France, have been found as far off as Italy, Switzerland, and Belgium, and it was doubtless a prized article of Neolithic commerce.

Hard as it may be for us to imagine, a number of materials were carried over great distances during the New Stone Age. We know little of the ways in which extensive traveling was done, but objects of amber have been found, far removed from their sources.[1] Seashells, too, occur at a distance from any sea; obsidian or volcanic glass shows up far from any volcano. Semiprecious stones, such as turquoise and lapis lazuli, were also widely spread. It appears that Neolithic man was capable of traveling more frequently and extensively than early students thought possible.

---

[1] Efforts have been made to discover ancient routes by plotting the places where objects, far from their sources, have been found. For a good example of this technique, see J. M. deNavarro, "Prehistoric Route between Northern Europe and Italy, Defined by the Amber Trade," *The Geographic Journal*, Vol. 46, 1925.

From mud to spode

Neolithic man learned to increase his material resources not only by contriving a means of utilizing coarse-grained stones, but also by coming to understand how to convert some kinds of wet clay, which as sticky mud had hitherto been nothing but a nuisance, into fine dishes and outlets for artistic expression. Invention of pottery-making must be ranked as one of man's greatest cultural triumphs. No better appreciation of the value of mental foresight can be had than if one tries to imagine the first person who saw in his mind's eye the possibility of turning clay into the kinds of ceramic vessels that have culminated in the Lenox, Wedgwood, and Spode products of our day. To become a successful potter is no easy matter; and ever so many anonymous craftsmen must have made contributions that helped carry the art to perfection. V. Gordon Childe regards pot-making as the beginning of science and perhaps man's first conscious utilization of a chemical change.[2]

Many of the basic complexities of this skill come to light even in a brief account of some of the steps involved. To begin with, a suitable deposit of clay containing silicate of aluminum must be located. The clay must then be mixed with water to form a paste that is plastic but not too sticky; then it must be seasoned and kneaded until it is perfectly uniform inside and out. To the clay paste must be added a small percentage of *temper,* which is any coarse gritty substance, such as chopped-up bits of straw, grains of sand, fragments of crushed shell, or minutely crumbled pieces of stone. At a later stage, while a vessel is being fired, steam or other gaseous by-products escape through tiny outlets provided by the temper and so prevent the clay body from cracking. A potter must make a neat calculation of the exact amount of tempering matter to add in order to get the desired effect without making the finished vessel too coarse. After the clay, water, and temper have been well worked together, the difficult task of shaping the pot begins. Early Neolithic workers were inclined to mold small objects like cups by hand, somewhat in the fashion of sculpture. Larger vessels were customarily made by coiling, a process whereby a potter first rolls out "ropes" or coils of clay, and then fits one above the other until the shape wanted has been achieved (Fig. 13–3). The coil junctures may be allowed to show or they may be obliterated by squeezing and rubbing. A preliminary outdoor drying follows, after which the pot must be fired. At a temperature of about 1100 degrees Fahrenheit, the clay loses its plasticity and bakes into a hard, waterproof, solid material that will, until smashed, retain its form in any environment.

[2] V. G. Childe, *Man Makes Himself,* London, 1936, p. 101.

A B

FIG. 13-3. Coiling pottery. A. A Pueblo Indian woman affixing a "rope" or coil of clay to the base of a pot. B. The potter is rolling a new coil, which she will add to those already in place to build up her pot. Several coils have already been put in position. Their junctures may later be smoothed out and obliterated, or exaggerated to give a decorative effect. (Courtesy of the Museum of Anthropology, the University of Michigan.)

This synopsis really tells only a small part of the full story. Omitted are the problems of handles, legs, or covers, the entire question of baking arrangements (*kilns*), including ways of achieving and controlling firing temperatures, and much information concerning decorations. Early forms of decoration were simple, ordinarily consisting of impressions made on the prefired vessel while the clay was still soft and plastic. Little cuts could be made with a fingernail, bits could be pinched or pulled out with the fingers, lines might be scratched with a stick or comb, and designs could be formed by pressing rope, a roughened or a cloth-wrapped paddle, or a carved stamp against the yielding body. Any impression made by these methods would become hardened and permanently fixed during the process of firing. Later, presumably, designs were quite commonly painted on pottery, often with the help of a preliminary *slip*. A slip is a very fine clay wash, sometimes tinted, that is evenly applied over a pot before it is baked. It serves the double purpose of helping to obliterate surface irregularities and, when dry, of providing a smooth background for painting (see Fig. 13–4).

A long time elapsed before pottery-making reached a high degree of perfection, but pottery's usefulness for storage and the cooking and serving of food, as well as its artistic potential, were recognized early. Although the serviceability of pottery vessels as containers was extremely important, the widespread use of cooking pots was of even greater con-

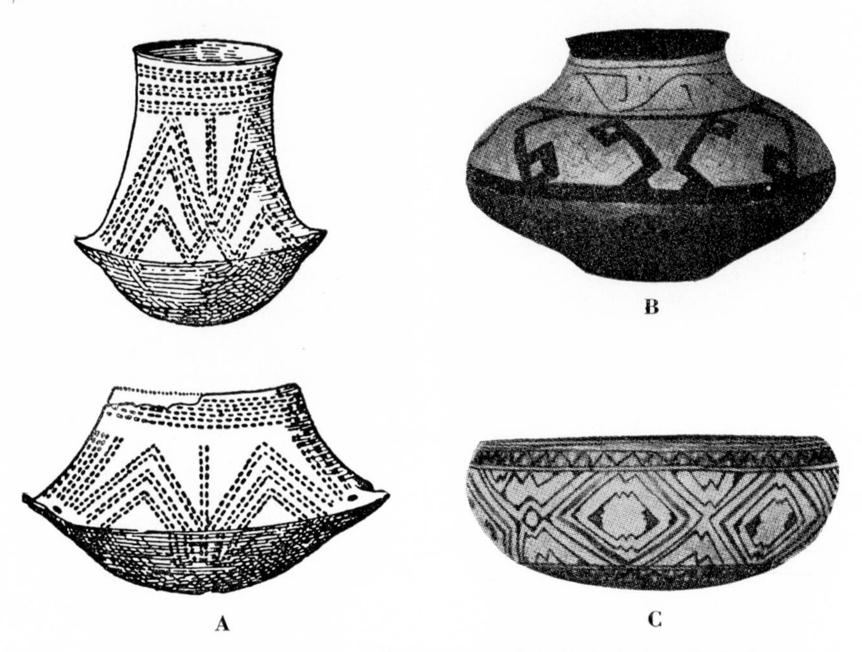

FIG. 13-4. Pottery decorations. A. One form of incised design. It is known as stroke ornamented ware. These specimens come from the Danube basin. (From V. G. Childe, *The Dawn of European Civilization,* London, 1936. Courtesy of Routledge & Kegan Paul, Ltd.) B. and C. Pottery vessels, with designs painted in black and red on a cream-colored ship. The pots are from the montaña region of Ecuador and Peru. (From J. H. Steward, ed., *Handbook of South American Indians,* Vol. 3, Washington, 1948. Courtesy of the editor and the Bureau of American Ethnology.)

sequence. Prior to the Neolithic the preparation of food for human consumption was done either by direct exposure to fire, as in the broiling of meat, or by use of the principle of the fireless cooker. That is to say, superheated stones could have been dropped into bark or leather vessels in order to cook a number of different foods; but with pottery it became easy to cook even more efficiently in vessels that could be set right on the fire. Then, again, the use of pottery dishes also made it possible to introduce entirely new ways of serving meals.

Broken fragments, known as *potsherds,* are conspicuous in most Neolithic remains. This provides a totally different kind of value that has become attached to ceramics. Although objects of pottery are notoriously fragile and easily broken, the resulting *sherds* are practically indestructible. They do not decompose in the ground, they are unattractive to hungry animals, they are worthless to their owners, and valueless to treasure seekers or grave robbers. Consequently, bits of broken pots are left behind when a settlement is abandoned and they remain in place for untold centuries. Modern archeologists are eternally grateful to the unknown discoverer of the potter's craft. They find potsherds so variable in form, composition, temper, manner of manufacture, decoration, firing range, and color, that they use them as indicators of cultural stability or change. In addition, highly specialized techniques of ceramic analysis make possible such scientifically accurate determinations of clays, coloring substances, tempering materials, and firing methods that archeologists can often tell where a given kind of pottery originated. Thanks to this information they are provided with a clue to the study of migration, trade, and cultural diffusion; and in some cases pottery styles furnish an excellent basis for time determination and cross-dating.

Although it is true that archeologists usually find pottery remains in conjunction with Neolithic settlements, this is not an invariable connection. At Jericho, for example, there are some New Stone Age communities without any pottery at all. Still, it must be acknowledged that, with the exception of a few Mesolithic occurrences, pottery-making seems to have been a Neolithic attainment.

Spinning and Weaving

Another important innovation of the New Stone Age was *textile* production. It combined manual dexterity with the capacity to look ahead and imagine. The essentials of *weaving* that were established in Neolithic days have continued to serve mankind throughout the ages. Whenever and wherever cloth is to be made, a suitable thread must first be spun. This is usually accomplished by twisting fibers together and connecting them into a long skein with the help of a spindle. A spindle is a simple contrivance, which need be no more than a slender, rounded stick capable of being twirled, to which yarn may be attached. Quite often, the spindle stick is set into a heavier circular disk or *spindle whorl,* which acts as a flywheel to help regulate the twirling action

(Fig. 13–5). Here again we find evidence of some understanding of rotary motion. After a thread has been spun, little more is needed than a frame or *loom* with at least one bar in horizontal position. To this are tied at regular intervals fixed threads that hang vertically downward and are known as the *warp*. Cloth is then woven by introducing a movable element (*woof* or *weft*), which is passed horizontally over or under one or more warp strands at a time. In many places a *heddle* is used to permit the simultaneous raising or lowering of all the warp strings that play a part in a given operation, and the weft may be tied to a *shuttle* to speed up its horizontal movements (see Fig. 13–6). Even the most complicated, automatic, power-driven looms of our era operate on an elaboration of the original plan that was figured out by some unknown Neolithic genius.

Designs can be produced by the pattern or order in which warp and weft elements cross each other, or by coloring some of the strings. There are also styles of *negative dyeing*. Sometimes, as in *tie dyeing*, some fibers are so fastened that they cannot be colored, and in the pro-

FIG. 13-5. A spindle in action. An elderly Navaho woman is spinning thread from a heap of wool. The circular disk on the stick of her spindle is a spindle whorl. The woman's loom, with a partly woven rug on it, stands behind her. (Courtesy of the Museum of Anthropology, the University of Michigan.)

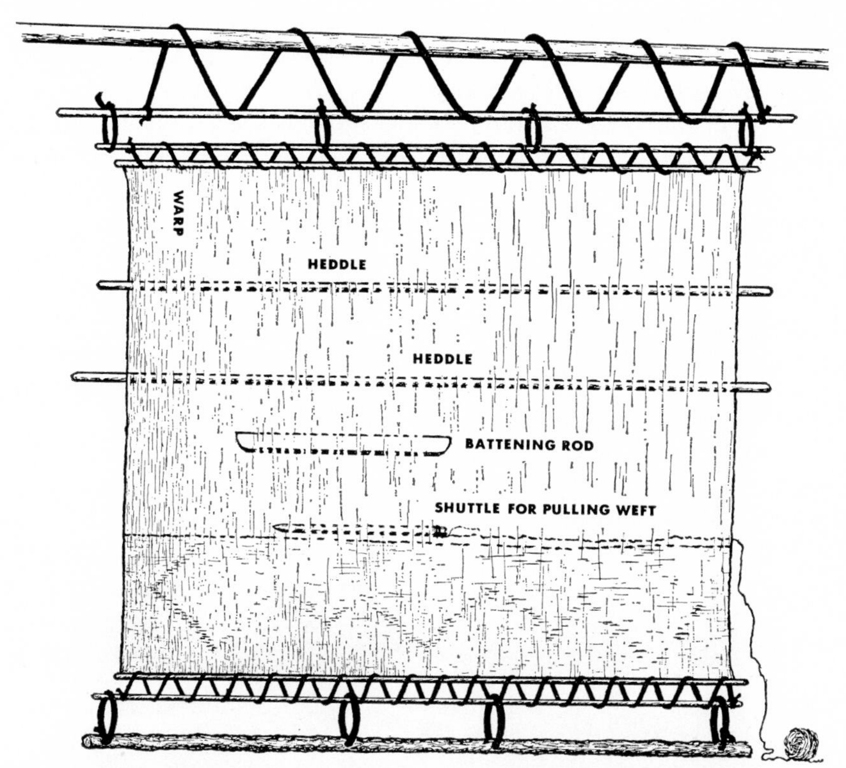

FIG. 13-6. A primitive loom. Weaving by hand requires warp threads that are tied in place and hang vertically downward. They are crossed at right angles, over and under, by weft elements that move horizontally. One heddle raises the required warp strings as the weft goes from right to left, and the other heddle raises the required warp threads as the weft goes in the opposite direction. The weft is usually attached to a shuttle to speed its movements, and a battening rod is used to pack each weft thread firmly into place.

duction of *batik* the areas that are to be left undyed are covered with wax.

Much basketry is produced along the same principles as cloth weaving. When *twined* or woven objects are to be made, stiff vegetal fibers are fixed in position, without need for a loom, to serve as the warp, and similar elements are passed over and under them in the manner of a weft (Fig. 13–7). Another basketry technique is more like sewing than weaving. This is the *coiling* method, in accord with which a worker prepares rings of fibers and then stitches them in position, one ring above another (Fig. 13–8). It is also possible to produce baskets, mats, or flat plaques by braiding or by *twilling*. When objects are twilled, similar materials are crisscrossed or interlaced, usually at right angles. When a flat weft is passed over and under alternate flat warp elements, the automatic result is *checkerwork* (Fig. 13–9). These are but a few of the most widely used techniques, and specimens of all these processes are known from Neolithic remains. Many people throughout the years

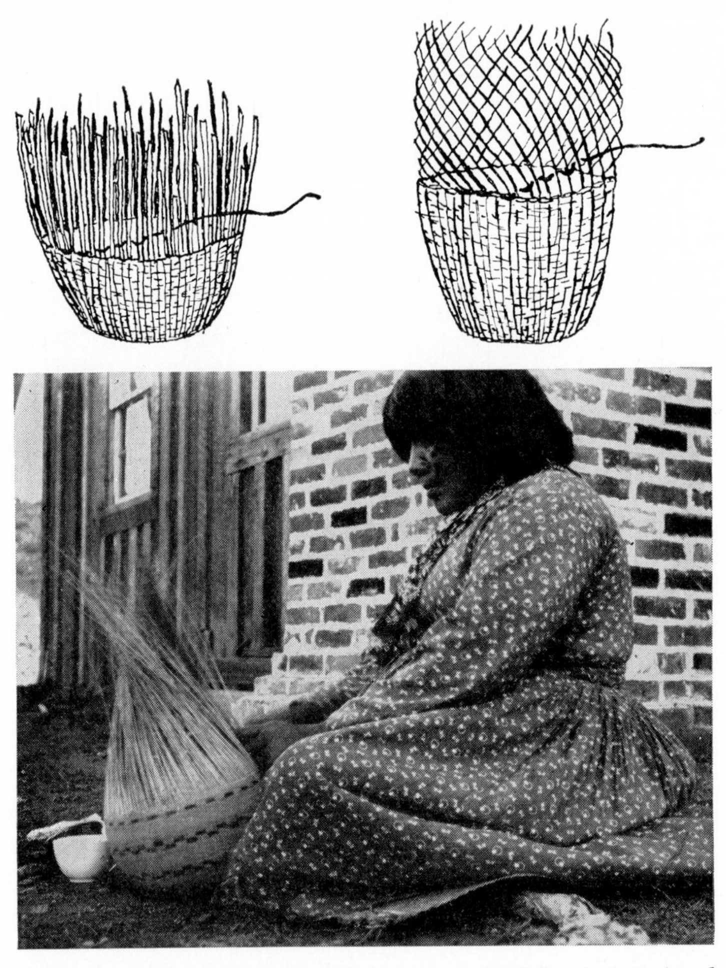

FIG. 13-7. Twined basketry. Variant ways of twining baskets, based on the principle of having weft elements crossing fixed warp elements, are illustrated. The woman shown below is a Pomo Indian, whose tribe is famous for its excellent basketry. (*Top, left and right,* after G. Weltfish, *The Origins of Art,* Indianapolis and New York, 1953. Courtesy of the author. *Below,* Courtesy of the Smithsonian Institution, Bureau of American Ethnology.)

FIG. 13-8. Coiled basketry. Left: This sketch shows the manner in which rings of fibres are bound together to produce coiled basketry. (Courtesy of G. Weltfish.) Right: A Yemenite woman fashioning a coiled plaque. The large basket beside her has also been made by coiling.

since the New Stone Age have become skillful makers of baskets. None, however, has exceeded the mastery achieved by the *Pomo Indians* of California, whose descendants live north of San Francisco. In addition to being beautiful, Pomo baskets were so tightly made that they were often waterproof.

The concept of the wheel

Long before the Neolithic reached a close the principle of the *wheel,* which converts straight-line to rotary power, or vice versa, was discovered. Its quality of eliminating friction was early recognized as suited for improving means of transportation, but use of the wheel was preceded by drags, sledges, or rollers (Fig. 13–10). How long the clumsier devices persisted is unknown, but the chances are slim that wheels

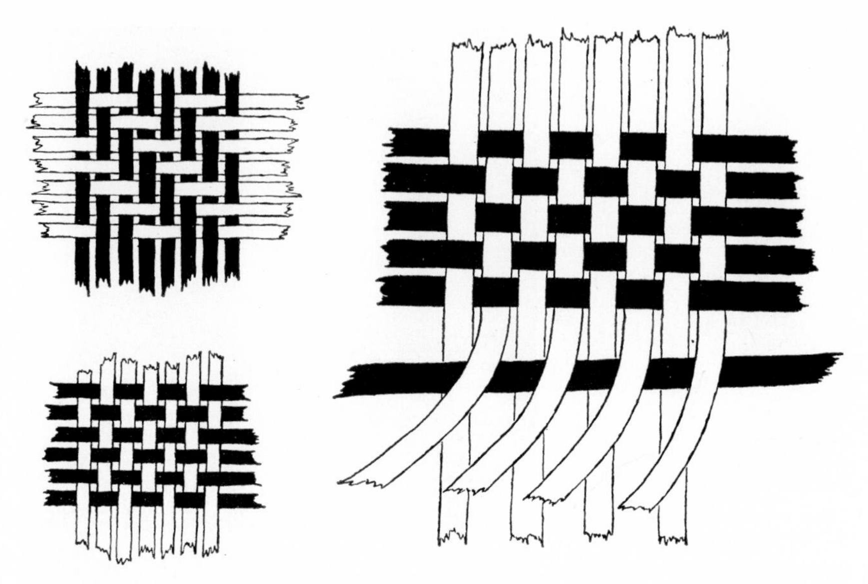

FIG. 13-9. Twilling techniques (after Weltfish, by permission). Twilling is a very common technique. It usually employs flat warps and wefts that are criss-crossed at right angles.

played a great part in transport throughout the Neolithic. When wheels first came to be attached to vehicles they were very crude (Fig. 13–11), and it was only after a long while that they evolved into the standard arrangement of hubs, spokes, and rims. In spite of its slow development, discovery of the basic concept of the wheel must rank as a major accomplishment.

Wheeled vehicles, of course, can carry heavier loads at greater speeds than any of the older forms of transport. To achieve their maximum efficiency, however, they require a host of related developments, such as good roads, and nonhuman sources of pulling power. Furthermore, as journeys got longer and longer, there was a need for places of shelter and rest. Inns and innkeepers thus came into being.

Wheels proved to be useful not just in matters of transport, but also in connection with the crafts of pottery and spinning. There is little evidence of the employment of a potter's wheel in the New Stone Age, but round spindle whorls occur in such profusion that they testify to the wide use of circular disks.

To appreciate the full and ultimate significance of the wheel one must consider its importance to modern industry. Not only are wheels placed on all sorts of vehicles from perambulators to airplanes, but

FIG. 13-10. An early means of transportation. A dog-drawn travois. Bundles were tied on the frame close to the animal. Although this picture shows a Blackfoot Indian travois, comparable devices may well have been used elsewhere prior to the full development of wheeled vehicles. (Courtesy of American Museum of Natural History.)

they are also of prime importance to the operation of contrivances as varied as watches, record players, and electric generators. Nor should it be overlooked that wheels are also useful in pulleys made for lifting heavy weights. The Neolithic inventor of the wheel could not have

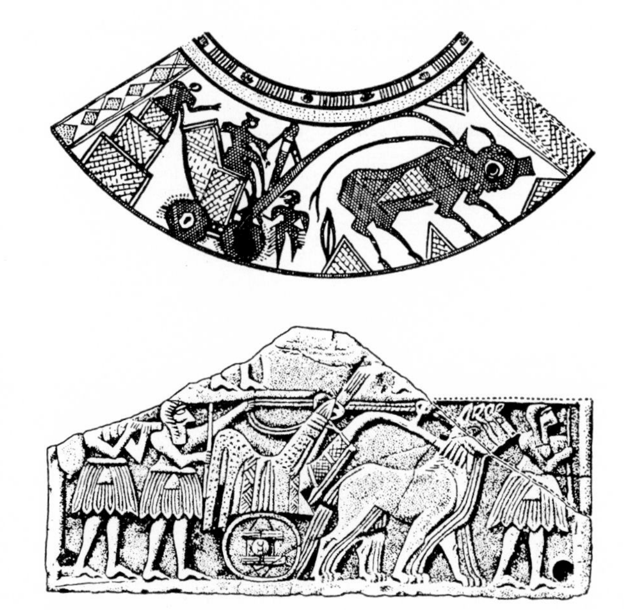

FIG. 13-11. Early wheeled vehicles. Ancient wheels, as depicted in the Near East. Top figure is from a scarlet pottery vase found in Susa in Iran; bottom figure is from a limestone relief discovered at Khafaje in Mesopotamia. Both are dated in the Copper-Bronze Age. (Courtesy the Prehistoric Society, England, and Oxford University Press.)

foreseen the consequences, but the idea of using rotary power has furnished one of the most valuable technological concepts of our day.[3]

Selected References

Amsden, Charles, "The Loom and its Prototypes," *American Anthropologist,* Vol. 34, 1932.

Barrett, S. A., "Pomo Indian Basketry," *University of California Publications in American Archaeology and Ethnology,* Vol. 7, 1908.

Bunzel, Ruth, *The Pueblo Potter,* New York, 1929.

Childe, V. Gordon, "The New Stone Age," in H. L. Shapiro, ed., *Man, Culture, and Society,* New York, 1956, pp. 94–110.

Fairservis, Walter A., Jr., *Wool through the Ages,* New York, 1955.

Holmes, William H., "Origin and Development of Form and Ornament in Ceramic Art," *Fourth Annual Report of the Bureau of American Ethnology,* Washington, D. C., 1886.

Mason, Otis T., "Aboriginal American Basketry," *Annual Report for 1902 of the Smithsonian Institution,* Washington, 1904.

O'Neale, Lila M., "Weaving," in J. H. Steward, ed., *Handbook of South American Indians,* Washington, D. C., 1949, Vol. 5, pp. 97–138.

Singer, Charles, *et al.*, eds., *A History of Technology,* Vol. 1, New York and London, 1954.

Walker, Charles R., ed., *Modern Technology and Civilization,* New York, 1961.

Willey, Gordon R., "Ceramics," in J. H. Steward, ed., *Handbook of South American Indians,* Washington, D. C., 1949, Vol. 5, pp. 139–204.

[3] Further development of this topic occurs in W. L. Bliss, "In the Wake of the Wheel," in *Modern Technology and Civilization,* C. R. Walker, ed., New York, 1961.

Additional Aspects of Neolithic Culture

CHAPTER 14

Early anthropologists, impressed by changed methods of handling stone, decided to call the cultural period that followed the Mesolithic the New Stone Age. Led by V. G. Childe, more recent students of man have come to regard this as a pity for it fails to mention what is now considered to be the central feature of the whole Neolithic period. There can be no denying the importance of new lithic techniques or of any of the other innovations treated in the preceding chapter, but far more significant was a shift from hunting, fishing, and the gathering or collecting of foods produced by nature to the humanly controlled production of foodstuffs based on the domestication of plants (*horticulture-agriculture*), and the *domestication* and *breeding* of several kinds of large mammals. These economic and environmental changes brought in their train a host of attendant features, all of which combined to help lay the foundations of modern life as we know it. Such a significant turning point was not reached instantaneously. Far from having been a rapid switchover, it seems to have come about after an extended period of close observation and careful experimentation. This was probably true both for the Old and New Worlds.

Some archeologists, notably Braidwood and Willey, believe that man's food quest went through a series of phases, particularly in regard to plants. In the beginning there was a rather indiscriminate *gathering stage,* followed by a more directed *collecting stage,* during which proto-agricultural implements, such as grinding stones, may have appeared. Then comes a stage of *incipient cultivation,* after which *true agriculture* may begin. From the collecting stage onward, whenever there is a sufficient supply of food, people may congregate into villages. No longer is it correct to assume, as Maglemose culture in the Mesolithic shows, that permanent settlements can arise only when the domestication of plants is practiced.

For all that, it was farming that made the biggest difference between Mesolithic and Neolithic patterns of culture, and farming could never have been started were it not for man's ability to plan ahead and to have confidence in his predictions for the future. Long before he can expect any benefit from his efforts, a farmer must be willing to expend time and labor in clearing a bit of land, breaking ground, planting seeds, and removing weeds. Only those who are farsighted enough to work hard in the hope of gaining future compensation can ever become successful farmers. Although the rewards may be long delayed they are, except in unusually bad years, likely to be very generous when harvest time finally comes.

Habits of farming brought about basic changes in man's relationships with his physical environment. Open land that was only of incidental worth to hunters became fundamentally valuable to farmers.[1] Then, again, while earlier folk made only trivial changes in the natural landscape, agriculturalists tended to change completely certain portions of the land that they inhabited. In tracing the growth of culture, it would not be impossible to measure development in terms of land values and landscape changes.

Man's control of his food supply took place quite gradually, probably through a series of preliminary steps. Each of these might have been trivial in itself, but their cumulative effect was tremendous. Thus, it is more likely that the custom of farming was evolutionary rather than revolutionary. A good number of wild plants and animals were potentially capable of being domesticated, but at the dawn of the Neolithic in the Eastern Mediterranean Zone *wheat* and *barley* were the first plants to be raised through human agency. They are known to have been present in the area in the form of natural, wild grasses; and farming seems to have begun when human beings learned to select for cultivation the seeds of those plants that were most productive and nutritious. Once the concept of domesticating and controlling the growth of wheat and barley came to be understood, it was extended to include other grains and cereals, such as *oats* and *rye*, and fruits, berries, and nuts. There is evidence for the early growing of such things as olives, figs, dates, apples, and grapes. Flax was grown first as a source of oil, and then for fibers that could be used in weaving linen cloth. Incidentally, the origins of

---

[1] Some anthropologists, noting that a great many corpses in the Neolithic are buried in contracted positions, think that the custom developed in an effort to conserve land.

cotton have not been satisfactorily worked out, but the use of cotton seems to be later than that of flax.

There is no reason to think that New Stone Age people gave up hunting, fishing, and gathering just as soon as they had acquired the arts of farming and keeping livestock. On the contrary, there is abundant archeological proof to show that the advantages of the new activities were added to the older ones. Hence Neolithic societies, unlike those with Paleolithic or Mesolithic cultures, grew less and less dependent for their welfare on the vagaries of nature. Food shortages and periods of want must have diminished when man became a successful food producer.

FARMING AND CHANGES OF CULTURE

As they developed in the Eastern Mediterranean Zone, Neolithic settlements came to differ radically from those communities remaining at the hunting, fishing, and collecting stages. Nor were the differences limited to changes in the material realm. Great advances in technology never fail to be accompanied by equally important shifts of social organization and religion. Farmers, particularly in the early stages of their reliance on agriculture, are not always unwilling to migrate, but surely no human being in his right senses will sow a crop and then voluntarily move away while someone else reaps the harvest. Soil exhaustion, lack of moisture, a heavy growth of weeds, or insect pests may induce cultivators to move, but assuredly their wanderings are negligible compared with those of the earlier Stone Age folk.

Anthropologists recognize several kinds of farming. One is classified as *slash-and-burn*, although it has various local names in different regions. As the term implies, this method calls for making clearings by cutting down trees and other natural vegetal growths. These are then burned and, in most cases, the ashes are used for fertilizer. Other techniques call for the laying out of regular fields. Whenever problems of water control become vital, terraces or irrigation systems may be built.[2]

In addition to being characterized by greater permanence, agricultural communities can support denser populations. Not until Neo-

---

[2] Karl Wittfogel believes that control of water, as well as the building of public hydraulic works, is inevitably tied up with particular kinds of societies. He expounds his theory in K. Wittfogel, *Oriental Despotism*, New Haven, 1957. For more material on this subject, see R. J. Braidwood and G. R. Willey, eds., "Courses toward Urban Life," *Viking Fund Publications in Anthropology*, No. 32, 1962.

lithic times do archeologists find signs of settlements sizable enough to be called towns or villages, with large and commodious houses and with correspondingly big refuse mounds to suggest long occupancy. People who live by hunting and gathering cannot possibly congregate into permanent groups of large size. The very magnitude and stability of Neolithic communities could not fail to have raised some serious social problems. Large numbers of people simply cannot live long in close proximity without a well-developed social organization. Even such matters as deciding where streets shall run or the setting aside of land for cemeteries call for a degree of social control. Elaborate and systematic rules for controlling the conduct of individuals toward each other invariably arise; these regulations must be made by some persons and enforced by others. Full-fledged ethical systems with correct and repetitive forms of behavior emerge, closed corporate communities arise, and political leadership becomes increasingly important, spreads over an ever larger territory, and controls more and more subjects. In other words, farming—and its attendant large, permanent settlements—leads to the emergence of a state.

Religion, too, underwent drastic changes in the Neolithic. There is little of a tangible nature to guide conjecture, but certain implications are fairly evident. People invariably seek aid and comfort from their deities, and it stands to reason that societies that depend on farming will not want the same sort of help that hunters and gatherers seek. As stated in the introduction, there is nothing startling in the statement that hunters are likely to worship gods of the chase, whereas farmers are more likely to worship agricultural deities. But such a statement, we know, also serves to reveal a direct connection between a society's subsistence pursuits and its religion. This is the sort of linkage that may often be readily detected in a primitive group, but which is generally much less clear in a complex society.

There is also a profound difference in the degree of *reliance* on supernatural or religious aid between these groups. When pre-Neolithic man was faced with a food shortage he could do little about it except pray for assistance. Neolithic man was not quite so limited as his predecessors. There were, of course, many things over which he had no control, but when threatened by a food shortage he might not only seek supernatural aid but he might, in addition, increase his own diligence. If, for example, the problem was drought, he might pray for rain, but he might also seek to improve the situation by building irrigation canals or deliberately hauling water from a distant source. No one pretends to know how often Neolithic man followed one course or the other, and no one knows which he found more satisfactory, but the fact remains that potentially the people of the New Stone Age were more the masters of their fate than were those who lived by Paleolithic or Mesolithic forms of culture.

Under favorable conditions a farmer can produce much more than his immediate family can consume. The excess creates a surplus which makes possible denser and larger population groups than any nonfarmers can form.[3] But this is not always a blessing, for epidemics and contagious diseases can thus spread more widely and affect more people than ever before.

Man's new ability to grow more than enough for his immediate needs created problems of storage of produce. Granaries and silos became necessary, and there was a call for moistureproof containers. Some anthropologists link the Neolithic production of pottery to the demand for storage and cooking vessels.

Creation of a surplus also means that a society can support craftsmen and specialists who develop skills that are not directly concerned with securing food. This comes about when farmers use some of their excess to acquire the goods made by specialists. Here, again, there must be a large population in order to create enough of a demand to support those who turn out nonfood products.

Without a surplus of food, too, it would be impossible for any society to maintain an army in the field for any length of time. This is why hunting societies, which do not regularly accumulate and store excess foodstuffs, cannot engage in long-sustained warfare.

One by-product of a successful war is the taking of captives who may become *slaves.* It is noteworthy that prior to the New Stone Age there is absolutely no indication of *slavery,* and when slavery does arise it is related to other aspects of Neolithic culture. Those who own slaves are always socially distinguished from those who do not. Moreover, slaves do not hold valuable farming land, and their owners may use slave strength and energy as they do those of domesticated beasts.

THE DOMESTICATION OF ANIMALS

Although it is usually conceded that the dog was domesticated by man during the Mesolithic, it was not until the New Stone Age that the concept of animal domestication received wide application. Many years ago

---

[3] One fairly high estimate states that agricultural communities can feed from 20 to 50 times as many people as can hunting societies. See L. C. Goodrich, *A Short History of the Chinese People,* rev. ed., New York, 1951, p. 4, footnote 1.

When use of the *plow* became widespread, late in the Neolithic, farming became increasingly productive and led to the formation of ever larger and denser settlements.

it was felt that there was a distinct stage, known as *pastoralism,* that came before agriculture, during which people lived, primarily, with large herds of domesticated animals. *Pastoral societies* still exist in the Near East and other parts of the world, but contemporary anthropologists do not regard pastoralism as a distinct and early stage in the march of culture. Present opinion holds the belief that the growing of plants and the rearing of animals took place at about the same time and were usually carried on together. This belief rests on the occurrence, throughout the Eastern Mediterranean Zone and elsewhere, of early Neolithic villages that practiced *mixed farming,* as it is sometimes called. In fact, if priorities have to be assigned, it is believed that agriculture may have come first since quantities of grown plants would have been necessary for the feeding of stabled beasts.

Students of animal domestication are impatient with older statements that were based on sheer conjecture. They prefer to rest their judgments on the identification of actual remains that come to light in the course of archeological excavations.[4] There is good reason to believe that after the dog the *goat* was the first mammal to be domesticated. There then followed *sheep, cattle,* and *pigs.* All other domesticated animals, whether birds, fowl, or mammals, came later. Donkeys were not early, and horses were domesticated either late in the Neolithic or in the succeeding age.

Before animal domestication could play its full part in human affairs, numerous objects like ropes, reins, harnesses, corrals, and barns had to be devised for controlling and sheltering various kinds of beasts. When it got into full swing, however, the keeping of livestock provided mankind with countless advantages. Meat and milk furnished valuable proteins; hides, furs, wool, horn, sinews, and other parts, yielded many raw materials for manufacturing; droppings served to fertilize fields; and large animals were trained to do much work for man, thus supplying him with immense amounts of extra energy and time for other pursuits. Nor was *Homo sapiens* always content to leave such precious resources to nature or to accident. Through the judicious choice of the creatures that he selected for slaughter, as well as through the careful regulation of breeding, Neolithic man improved his stock and developed those characteristics he deemed important. All in all, the domestication

[4] See, for example, C. A. Reed, "Animal Domestication in the Prehistoric Near East," *Science,* Vol. 130, 1959, pp. 1629–39. As it happens, most studies of animal domestication have been made by Germans, but Reed's article is here being followed. A somewhat different and much more detailed treatment of the whole subject of domestication may be found in F. C. Hibben, *Prehistoric Man in Europe,* Norman, Okla., 1958, pp. 108–13, and in E. Isaac, "On the Domestication of Cattle," *Science,* Vol. 137, No. 3525, 1962, pp. 195–204.

of animals provided him with a potential surplus, in addition to whatever he could get from his crops.

Neolithic communities are thought by Professor Childe to have been fairly self-sufficient, and as communities they probably were; but the same cannot be said of individuals. It is no great strain on the imagination to think of a Mesolithic or Paleolithic man who could carry out all the occupations demanded for a male by his culture, one who could manufacture his own tools, hunt, fish, make shelters, build fires, and the like. It is quite another matter to try to picture a Neolithic person who could by himself make all his own polished stone tools, build his house and outbuildings, breed and care for animals, manufacture pottery, weave cloth, and fashion baskets, all in addition to raising crops. Undoubtedly tasks were spread about through a division of labor between the sexes, between young and old, and among different groups of one's fellow villagers; but it is almost as certain that incipient classes of people with varying specialties and statuses were emerging. Archeologists have no way of measuring the extent to which new social forms accompanied the advanced technology of the New Stone Age, but it is certain that by 8000 B.P. the good old days of simple bodily behavior had, in Neolithic regions, been left far behind; and yet, the full complexities of modern life were just starting.

WHERE DID THE NEW STONE AGE BEGIN?

So fundamental to man's march of culture were the innovations of the Neolithic that strenuous efforts are being made to discover its origins. In a general way it has long been agreed that the New Stone Age probably started in the Eastern Mediterranean Zone, but now scholars are seeking the precise spot. For a time the *Natufian* culture of Palestine was regarded as the oldest of the Neolithic. Much of the evidence rested on the discovery of cylindrical pestles of stone and flint sickles that could have been used to harvest grain, but pottery was lacking and there were no sure signs of agriculture. Modern students feel that the Natufians were Mesolithic, and that their pestles and sickles were probably used for dealing with naturally occurring seeds or for harvesting wild plants.[5] Accordingly, such implements may have been pre- or proto-agricultural.

Within the Eastern Mediterranean Zone ancient Neolithic settle-

[5] See D. A. E. Garrod, "The Natufian Culture: the life and economy of a Mesolithic people in the Near East," *Proceedings of the British Academy,* Vol. 43, 1958, pp. 211–27.

ments have been found in Egypt and Mesopotamia (Iraq). Two Egyptian sites near the delta of the Nile have yielded signs of early Neolithic ways of life. *Fayum,* which has a radiocarbon date of about 6200 B.P., had cereal agriculture, domesticated goats, and possibly pigs and sheep. *Merimde,* also in northern Egypt, shows the remains of a village, with huts arranged in regular rows or streets over an area of more than six acres. The inhabitants of Merimde, as their remains show, did a considerable amount of hunting, fishing, fowling, and plant gathering. However, they seem also to have grown wheat and barley; and threshing floors, sickles, hoes, storage bins, and grinding stones for the milling of flour have all been found. In addition, pottery, woven cloth, and baskets are present.

Despite Neolithic antiquity in Egypt, western Asia presents a somewhat better claim to origins. Two different hypotheses are current. The British archeologists, Kathleen Kenyon and Sir Mortimer Wheeler, favor the *oasis theory,* and they cite evidence from *Jericho* in Palestine; whereas the American scholar, Robert Braidwood, supports the *hilly flanks theory,* and makes a strong case for *Jarmo,* in the Kurdish highlands of Mesopotamia.[6] Not only was Jarmo located in a region where there existed wild varieties of animals that were later domesticated, but its lowest levels are clearly pre-Neolithic, whereas its higher levels reveal such New Stone Age features as polished stone tools and domesticated strains of wheat and barley. The site of Jarmo covers nearly three acres, and it is hard to deny the claim that it may represent one of the actual places where man made the transition into the Neolithic.[7] Unfortunately, the radiocarbon dates for Jarmo are not clear, but a date of around 8000 B.P.—about when the New Stone Age is thought to have begun—seems to be indicated.

---

[6] For the "oasis" theory, see K. M. Kenyon, "Jericho and its Setting in Near Eastern Prehistory," *Antiquity,* Vol. 30, 1956, pp. 184–95, and for the "hilly flanks" theory, see R. J. Braidwood, "Jericho and its Setting in Near Eastern Prehistory," *Antiquity,* Vol. 31, 1957, pp. 73–80. See also R. J. and L. Braidwood, "Jarmo: A Village of Early Farmers in Iraq," *Antiquity,* Vol. 24, 1950, pp. 189–95, and K. M. Kenyon, "Reply to Professor Braidwood," *Antiquity,* Vol. 31, 1957, pp. 82–84. All four essays are conveniently reprinted in M. H. Fried, *Readings in Anthropology,* Vol. 1, New York, 1959, pp. 359–97.

Neither hypothesis has yet been established beyond a shadow of a doubt, but American anthropologists generally incline toward Braidwood's viewpoint.

[7] A good deal of important and stimulating material along these lines may be found in R. J. Braidwood, "The Near East and the Foundations for Civilization," *Condon Lectures,* Eugene, Ore., 1952. Also see R. J. Braidwood, "Near Eastern Prehistory," *Science,* Vol. 127, 1958, pp. 1419–30; as well as R. J. Braidwood and B. Howe, "Prehistoric Investigations in Iraqi Kurdistan," *Studies in Ancient Oriental Civilization,* Vol. 31, Chicago, 1960.

As for Jericho, here Kenyon found a stratified site located at an oasis, with mountains rising a few miles to the west. There was a non-pottery phase, featured by rectangular structures of unfired brick and a large amount of pink or creamy plaster. Later, there seems to have been a fully Neolithic occupation with pottery, grain, milling stones, and domesticated animals. Kenyon believes that, with the exception of pottery making, the first waves of Neolithic folk were culturally inferior to the people who had previously lived at Jericho.

Hassuna, in the upper valley of the Tigris in northern Mesopotamia, is another western Asiatic site that contains the remains of an early Neolithic village, made up of mud houses. The inhabitants of Hassuna were conversant with the usual run of New Stone Age materials, in addition to which they made painted pottery, fashioned little clay figurines of women, and practiced the custom of burying some of their dead in large pottery urns.

Within two or three millenniums after its start, Neolithic advances were being made in India, China, other parts of Asia, and at a few places in north Africa. Some of these practices may have spread from western Asia, but others apparently were independently achieved. India added the zebu (humped cattle) to the large mammals domesticated in the Eastern Mediterranean Zone, and places in southeastern Asia are credited with having brought under domestication the water buffalo and chickens. Later, other regions of Asia added to the list the horse, camel, and cat. To the record of important crops India contributed cotton, and either India or China was the first to grow rice. Not all of these additions are early, but they are thought to have become known before the Neolithic terminated. For the rest, Afro-Asiatic New Stone Age cultures differed only in detail from those already mentioned.

NEOLITHIC CULTURES IN EUROPE

Between the Eastern Mediterranean Zone and the heart of Europe the island of Crete, the Balkan Peninsula, and the valley of the Danube River furnish ready passageways. After the New Stone Age had become somewhat mature elsewhere, the Danube basin proved to be an attractive locality for settlement by some of the expanding populations of the Eastern Mediterranean Zone or the Balkans. This had not been the case earlier. At the very beginning of the Neolithic, the European climate was so warm and moist that forest growth made it hard for farmers to get a start. Later on, the Danubian corridor came to have areas of less timber and more *loess*. Loess is a fine, yellowish-brown soil, well suited for agriculture because it retains water, and it is often blown into a spot from places that are drying out. Along the Danube it is in the loess lands that archeologists find traces of early Neolithic settlements north of the Alps. Danubian farmers might well have come to depend on somewhat different plants and animals than had been domesticated in western Asia. Houses were made of wood and thatch, in the shape of long rectangles, and they were often large enough to have accommodated more than a single family at a time. How far central Europe lagged behind the Eastern Mediterranean Zone in those days is indicated by the fact that none of the Danubian sites is dated earlier than 5000 B.P., thus indicating a lag of about three thousand years.[8] Thereafter New Stone Age customs spread northward, usually following river valleys, until they ultimately reached Britain.

At about the same time other groups of Neolithic folk, sometimes referred to as "Westerners," were settling in and around parts of France, Belgium, Switzerland, and Italy. Although they were farmers, they relied heavily on large herds of domesticated cattle. Some of their equipment has given rise to a theory that they were offshoots of earlier north African centers, such as Merimde. In Europe they built rectangular houses of wood on platforms raised off the ground by stout posts (*pile dwellings*). In Switzerland and Italy, many of their homes, it was once thought, may have extended out into lakes, with wooden causeways or platforms leading to shore. Even the *Swiss Lake Dwellers,* however, who are sometimes believed to have lived over water,[9] maintained farms on land where they raised millet, lentils, poppies, oats, and apples, in addition to more than one variety of wheat, barley, and flax. Altogether, they made use of about 170 kinds of plants, most of them in their wild forms. Owing to the fortunate circumstance that the bulk of their remains was buried in mud, a good deal of perishable material was preserved that would probably have distintegrated if left in the open. Thus, in addition to pottery, specimens of their cloth and basketry have been recovered. The textile skill of the Swiss Lake Dwellers was great, extending even to the art of embroidery.

A different sort of late Neolithic culture has a distribution along

---

8 For details consult V. G. Childe, *The Danube in Prehistory,* Oxford, 1929.

9 A contemporary archeologist, Müller-Beck, working out of the Bern Historical Museum, claims that the so-called Swiss Lake Dwellers lived in pile dwellings on the shores of lakes. He regards as a fanciful myth the notion that they once dwelt on platforms erected over bodies of water.

A preliminary exposition of his views is given in H. Müller-Beck, "Prehistoric Swiss Lake Dwellers," *Scientific American,* Vol. 205, No. 6, 1961, pp. 138-47. No final verdict can be made in this matter until Müller-Beck's definitive report appears.

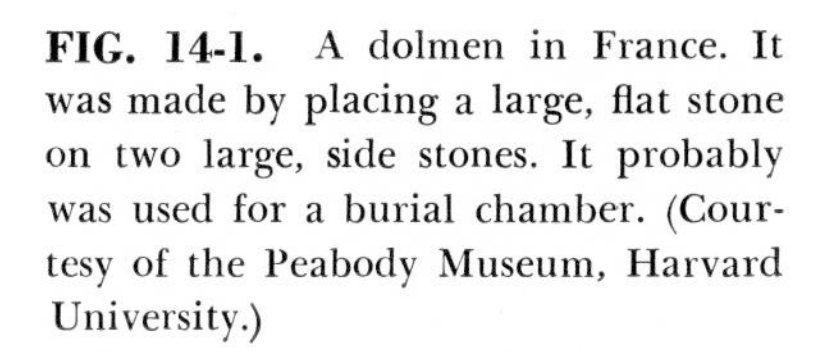

FIG. 14-1. A dolmen in France. It was made by placing a large, flat stone on two large, side stones. It probably was used for a burial chamber. (Courtesy of the Peabody Museum, Harvard University.)

the seacoasts and through much of northern Europe. Because it features constructions made of giant stones it is commonly spoken of as *Megalithic,* and some writers, on very poor evidence, would trace its source to Egypt. Quite a few of the structures contain burials and are commonly called *passage graves,* because a corridor leads to the place of interment. Other Megalithic chambers are made of vertical blocks of

FIG. 14-2. A remarkable alinement at Carnac, France. No one knows exactly why it was constructed. (Courtesy of the Peabody Museum, Harvard University.)

stone capped with a huge horizontal slab to form what is known as a *dolmen* (Fig. 14–1). Also pertaining to Megalithic culture are solitary upright columns, *menhirs*; pillars arranged in circles, *cromlechs*; or single slabs set in long rows, *alinements.* A very famous example of an alinement is to be found near Carnac, in northern France (Fig. 14–2).[10]

[10] For details consult G. G. MacCurdy, *op. cit.,* pp. 28–35, 109–29.

FIG. 14-3. Stonehenge. The circular portion is a cromlech, and the three-stoned arrangements are sometimes called "trilithons." Stonehenge is not an early Megalithic structure.

Nothing definite is known of the uses that the big, upended stones served, but a feeling persists that they were connected with burials or had religious significance. England's mysterious Stonehenge (Fig. 14–3) is often cited as an outstanding example of Megalithic construction. Stonehenge, however, is not of early Neolithic times, since it has been dated about 1840 B.C. Megalithic culture was formerly widespread, for its remains have been found at least in Corsica, Sardinia, Portugal, Spain, France, Scandinavia, England, and Ireland.

SUMMARY AND CONCLUSION TO THE NEOLITHIC

When man first started to develop culture he began to find ways of exploiting his physical environment for the production of things that might supplement or take the place of his inherited biology. Once started on this path he has never turned aside, and he has consistently given high value to his extrasomatic devices. By 8000 B.P. a series of interrelated inventions and discoveries had been made that contributed to the foundations on which our own culture has been built.

Despite its variations in different parts of the world, there is much that is uniform as well as solid and enduring in the totality of Neolithic man's accomplishments. The crops that he first brought under cultivation are still of prime importance; the animals that he succeeded in domesticating remain among the most valuable ever brought under human control; the techniques of pottery-making, basketry, and weaving that he worked out continue to form the basis of much modern industry; and wheels still play extremely important parts in our lives. Of the entire range of Neolithic man's cultural contributions, only his stone tools have become completely outmoded. It is no exaggeration to say that New Stone Age culture in the Eastern Mediterranean Zone so nearly resembled our own in many respects that even the most up-to-date of our farmers would require only a short space of time to adjust himself to the life of a well-developed New Stone Age community.

Several vital but unsolved problems of great theoretical significance vex the archeologists who specialize in the Neolithic. Since all of the New Stone Age developments do not appear at the same point of time, how many of the new traits must a site reveal in order to be classified as Neolithic? Is the occurrence of polished stone tools or true pottery enough? Does the presence of a single domesticated crop or animal suffice? If one of these features is not sufficient to warrant Neolithic classification, then how many are necessary? In what combination?

Other troublesome questions concern dates and origins. Above all, we should like to know if the New Stone Age traits were invented only once in a given spot and diffused elsewhere, or if they were independently originated in several places at different times. Exactly when and where was each feature first developed and how and by whom? By what agencies, specifically, were the new customs spread about? Does the Neolithic still exist, or has it come to an end? If so, when did it cease?

These questions are posed not to bewilder the reader, but to suggest some of the leads that remain to be explored by future investigators.

Selected References

Bishop, Carl W., "Origin and Early Diffusion of the Traction Plough," *Antiquity,* Vol. 10, 1936, pp. 261–81.

Braidwood, Robert J., "The Near East and the Foundations for Civilization," *Condon Lecture,* Eugene, Ore., 1952.

———, "The World's First Farming Villages," *Illustrated London News,* April 28, 1956, pp. 410–11.

Braidwood, Robert J., and Howe, Bruce, "Prehistoric Investigations in Iraqi Kurdistan," *Studies in Ancient Oriental Civilization,* Vol. 31, Chicago, 1960.

Caton-Thompson, G., and Gardner, E. W., *The Desert Fayum,* London, 1934.

Childe, V. Gordon, *New Light on the Most Ancient East,* London, 1934.

Coon, Carleton S., *Cave Explorations in Iran in 1949,* Philadelphia, 1951.

De Candolle, A., *Origin of Cultivated Plants,* rev. ed., New York, 1902.

Field, Henry, *Ancient and Modern Man in Southwestern Asia,* Coral Gables, Fla., 1956.

———, and Price, Kathleen, "Early Agriculture in Middle Asia," *Southwestern Journal of Anthropology,* Vol. 6, 1950.

Frankfort, Henri, *The Birth of Civilization in the Near East,* Bloomington, Ind., 1951.

Kenyon, Kathleen M., *Digging Up Jericho,* New York, 1957.

———, "Excavations at Jericho," *Journal of the Royal Anthropological Institute of Great Britain and Ireland,* Vol. 84, 1954, pp. 103–10.

Reed, Charles A., "Animal Domestication in the Prehistoric Near East," *Science,* Vol. 130, 1959, pp. 1629–39.

Sauer, Carl O., "Agricultural Origins and Dispersals," *American Geographical Society,* New York, 1952.

Metallurgy and its Cultural Consequences

CHAPTER 15

For all its near approach to modern patterns of living, the Neolithic failed to make the grade. If one central factor were to be singled out to account for the failure it would have to be ignorance of *metallurgy*. This is not the equivalent of ignorance of metal. A good number of Stone Age peoples used gold, silver, lead, and copper from time to time, but they dealt with them as solids, in a cold or slightly heated condition, as though they were unusual varieties of stone. Not until man discovered that metals undergo marked changes when liquefied by heat did he develop true metallurgy. Only then were previously unsuspected secrets unlocked for further exploration and exploitation.

There was no quick jump from the New Stone Age into an *Age of Metal*. Countless small steps were taken in various times and places, and it was the sum of these that brought mankind into a *Metal Age*. So extraordinary was knowledge of molten metals initially held to be that ordinary folk rarely took *metallurgists* for granted. Even today their craft is sometimes viewed with suspicion. It is not surprising, therefore, that when metallurgy began, its practitioners were frequently regarded as mysterious and in possession of supernatural secrets and powers. Consequently, metallurgists were commonly looked upon as gods or devils.

The first metal to have come under man's control in molten form was *copper*, and all signs point to the Eastern Mediterranean Zone as the place where the event occurred. A round figure of 4000 B.C. gives a good approximation of the time when the earliest Age of Metal began. There is marked disagreement among scholars as to whether copper was used in anything like a pure form long enough to warrant recognition of a *Copper Age* (*Chalcolithic* or *Eneolithic*), except in a few places such as the islands of Crete and Cypress. The *Cypriote dagger* is one of the best known copper implements. It is supposed to have been in use from Cypress to Hungary. Despite such evidence, most archeologists believe that copper so rarely occurs without admixture of other metals or minerals that metallurgists from the start were accustomed to using adulterated copper. Whether by accident or design, it was soon found that a combination of *copper* and *tin* made *bronze,* a more satisfactory substance because it is harder and melts at a lower temperature. Thereafter, bronze rapidly replaced pure copper as an important resource for manufacturing. By way of compromise we shall refer to the first Age of Metal as *Copper-Bronze.* It lasted from about 4000 B.C. to about 1500 B.C., when some metallurgists, again in the Eastern Mediterranean Zone, found out that *iron,* soon compounded to *steel,* had many advantages over bronze. Thereupon was inaugurated an *Iron Age,* which endured from around 1500 B.C. to the start of the Christian era. After the latter date it is no longer necessary to study the march of culture by means only of archeology, since written documents become abundantly available.

Before taking up the details of life in the Metal Ages it is necessary to repeat that human culture is additive and grows by the accretion of knowledge. Those societies that were among the earliest to learn the arts of metallurgy did not discard the many contributions of the preceding Stone Ages. The new stages of culture grew out of the earlier ones but did not break with them. Cold materials of long familiarity continued to be important; hunting, fowling, fishing, and food collection remained significant; pottery-making, basketry, and the weaving of cloth became increasingly widespread; and farming and stock breeding still formed the essence of the economy. Progress was made partly by the improvement of older devices like the wheel, partly by the expansion of such activities as crop raising and animal domestication, and partly by the introduction of entirely new practices.

As we trace the march of culture in the Metal Ages, we are again making a synthesis of high-water marks. No single society encompassed within itself all the innovations and improvements of the new era. Only a few groups in restricted portions of the Old World took the forward strides, and the bulk of mankind remained at Neolithic, Mesolithic, or Paleolithic levels. This is much like saying that only a few contemporary nations are learning to deal with atomic energy; or like making the simple observation that in any of our cities it may be possible to see moving about at the same time pedestrians, bicycles, automobiles, and airplanes, each representing a different phase of culture.

As was true in earlier stages, the attainment of previously unknown forms of material culture and the establishment of a new technology did not make up the sum total of Metal Age accomplishments. Far-reaching, though sometimes unrecognized changes of social and religious organization accompanied the introduction of metallurgy. In combination, all the fresh ideas, techniques, and customs paved the way for our present scheme of life, which is firmly grounded on Metal Age antecedents.

GOING THE NEOLITHIC ONE BETTER

Among the major Neolithic discoveries, it may be recalled, was the concept of the wheel. Yet, this concept received only little practical application until the start of the Copper-Bronze Age. Among other uses the wheel was then widely applied to the manufacture of pottery. A lump of prepared clay would be "thrown" on the center of a revolving disk, and, as it spun, the potter manipulated the clay until it took the shape he wanted. Not only did the new method greatly speed up the operation of pot formation, but the action of the wheel resulted in a vessel of greater thinness and symmetry than could be achieved free hand. A greater perfection of design was made possible by the same means. To produce a perfectly even, circular line that runs clear around a piece of pottery is next to impossible if the vessel must be turned by hand a little at a time. But one need only hold a stylus, comb, or brush steadily against a vessel while a potter's wheel makes a complete revolution, in order to achieve a perfect circle.

There is also an important sociological correlate of wheel-made pottery that is not based on biology, sheer mechanics, or technology. Throughout the primitive world the manufacture of handmade pottery is usually the task of women, but wherever the wheel is used pottery becomes, almost without exception, a masculine occupation (Fig. 15–1). The reason for this state of affairs is not satisfactorily known.

An even more significant application of wheels was developed in conjunction with vehicles. Ponderous two- and four-wheeled carts are known to have been long in use. Judged by clay models discovered in the ruins of Tepe Gawra, Syria,[1] the wheels appear to have been made of several heavy wooden sections, fastened with copper nails and held together with a rim of leather. The whole contrivance turned with the axle to which it was secured. Only gradually, after the Metal Ages were

[1] H. A. Speiser, *Excavations at Tepe Gawra,* Philadelphia, 1935.

FIG. 15-1. Pottery-making in India. A, B. A woman making pottery by hand. C. A male potter using a wheel. In most primitive societies, the sexual dichotomy of pottery-making is the same as it is in India. (Courtesy of Museum of Anthropology, University of Michigan.)

well under way, were light but strong wheels made with spokes and rims of metal. Even so, widespread use of wheeled vehicles could not have come about until strong animals had been trained to pull them.

It is a safe assumption that domesticated beasts had been employed to share some of man's labors in the preceding age. Nevertheless, no draft animals could have been put to work before the invention of suitable means of harnessing, and few signs of such trappings appear prior to the Metal Ages. Oxen were certainly among the first creatures set to the pulling of carts or wagons, but they must have proved too slow for many purposes. Asiatic asses and horses were subsequently found to be better suited and were commonly utilized thereafter. Horseback riding as a regular custom came late and may have followed driving by as much as a millennium.[2] There was a considerable amount of traveling back and forth, and European merchants occasionally buried *hoards* of tradegoods along the routes they took, presumably with a view to returning for them at a later time. Some of these hoards have been found and studied by archeologists, who thus learn much about the Copper-Bronze Age.

Use of strong animals for pulling was not invariably restricted to vehicles. Comparable utilization of their motive power had already taken place when plowing became widespread in the Eastern Mediterranean Zone. Again it had been necessary for suitable accessories to be devised first. Yokes were fashioned originally for oxen and later adapted to horses. Neolithic plows of wood must have preceded metal ones, but no specimens of premetallic plows have survived. As the custom of plowing made headway, another interesting sociological development took place. When small fields are worked with a hoe, as was generally the case in the New Stone Age and is still true in many primitive societies, the task ordinarily is left to women; but when large farms have to be plowed it becomes a masculine duty. In this case the greater muscular strength of men may be a deciding factor.

Plowing, in Copper-Bronze times, was much more extensively practiced than it had ever been before. Not only did it bring larger fields under cultivation, but it also led to the formation of larger communities and the potential accumulation of greater surpluses. For instance, whereas the early Neolithic settlements of Jarmo and Merimde

---

2 James F. Downs believes that oxen, onagers, other asses, and wild horses were ridden before domesticated horses and that the custom originated in Mesopotamia. He maintains that domesticated horses were not ridden until their size had been increased through selective breeding. For an exposition of his views, see J. F. Downs, "The Origin and Spread of Riding in the Near East and Central Asia," *American Anthropologist,* Vol. 63, 1961, pp. 1193–1203.

covered about three and six acres, respectively, the Bronze Age city of Ur in Mesopotamia covered over 110 acres.

Growth in settlement size inevitably means a larger number of inhabitants. In turn, an extension of social controls becomes necessary; and as political leadership covers more and more territory and more and more people, its power cannot help but grow. Then, when a leader's sphere of influence gets too extensive, he has no choice but to delegate some of his responsibilities to subordinates, thus leading to the formation of a bureaucracy and continuing the trend away from egalitarianism.

Likewise, as farming becomes increasingly extensive and important, all those who are believed to have influence with deities controlling weather and the production of crops also grow in power. At first, political and religious leaders tend to be combined and we have the institution of divine kingship, but the two spheres gradually diverge until we get a separation of "church" and "state."

These are only a few of the ways in which the people of the Copper-Bronze Age expanded notions and customs that began in the Neolithic. Improvements, changes and additions were made in every sphere of human existence. In respect to domestication, so many items were added to man's livestock and to the crops under his cultivation, that just about all the beasts and plants ever domesticated in the Old World before the discovery of America were known to Copper-Bronze Age farmers. There was also a new use made of grains, fruits, and cereals—that is, alcoholic beverages. It is perfectly possible that barley beer was made in the New Stone Age, but not before the Copper-Bronze period does proof exist that the drinking of beer and date and grape wines had become a fixed custom.[3]

THE MYSTERY AND MASTERY OF METALLURGY

Above and beyond their elaboration of Neolithic concepts, the Copper-Bronze Age folk opened new cultural outlets by learning to exploit a previously undeveloped natural resource. Let us begin with some of the advantages gained from man's mastery of molten copper. In liquid condition copper can be poured into a container, and upon cooling it becomes a solid in the shape of the container. The most exciting aspect of this simple fact is that the process is reversible, so that the same chunk

[3] For a discussion of this interesting subject, see R. J. Braidwood, *et al.*, "Did Man Once Live By Beer Alone?" *American Anthropologist*, Vol. 55, 1953.

of copper can repeatedly be transformed from solid to liquid to solid. Practically speaking, this means that man found out that he could rapidly change the shape of a solid copper object without wasting any of the precious raw material. Once the basic principle of reversibility had been grasped it became no trick at all to convert something originally in the shape of an X, by liquefying and recooling it, to the form of a Y; or something shaped like a Z to an A. This could not be done with wood, stone, bone, ivory, antler, horn, or any of the materials formerly in use.

Knowledge of this physicochemical reaction lies at the base of the technique of *casting* or *molding*, whereby a receptacle is first prepared in the desired shape and size from stone, pottery, or some other heat-resistant substance.[4] Then a sufficient quantity of molten copper is poured into the mold and allowed to cool and harden. If proper advance precautions have been taken to prevent sticking, it is then an easy matter to turn the solid product out of the mold and to give it any minor finishing touches that may be needed. Usually, no more is required than a bit of hammering or rubbing.

Casting made possible the first steps leading to mass production, for a well-made mold can be used repeatedly, and a number of molds can be filled and their contents allowed to harden almost simultaneously (Fig. 15–2). There are, furthermore, basic distinctions between the wealth required to own many molds, the skill and intelligence needed to design and prepare them, and what is necessary for filling and emptying them. Thus do we get a glimpse of an embryonic system that was destined to culminate in the modern distinctions between ownership, management, and labor; and between the skilled technicians who design machines, and the laborers who work on assembly lines. Here were other blows to sociocultural equality among men.

A different way of handling molten metal was well developed by 3000 B.C., but it was probably not known as early as simple casting. This is the ingenious *lost-wax* or *cire-perdue* process. With this method a wax model must first be made, correct in all the particulars wanted for the final product. Then the wax model is carefully covered with clay in which an entrance hole and outlet are provided. Next, the whole thing is subjected to firing, whereupon the wax melts and is lost, while the clay hardens to pottery. After that, the outlet is closed and liquid metal is poured into the space vacated by the wax. When cooling and hardening have been completed, the baked clay is broken open and the metallic

---

[4] Actually, the invention of molding was not so simple as it may seem. Much knowledge and many complicated preliminary steps were first necessary.

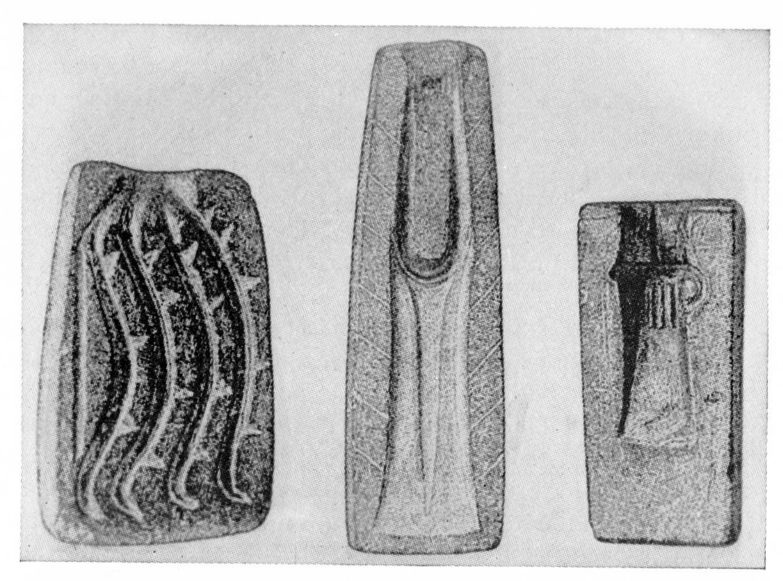

FIG. 15-2. Molds used for casting Bronze Age tools. Four saw blades at a time could be cast in the form at the left, thus making possible mass production. (Courtesy of Peabody Museum, Harvard University.)

object comes forth as an exact duplicate of the original wax model. Although the cire-perdue technique was much more complicated than casting, it was better for making rounded shapes or objects that would otherwise have had to be made in two parts and fitted together.

Awareness of the reversible nature of liquid and solid copper also makes possible a great saving of raw material. Cold objects can be fashioned only by striking, cutting, pressing or rubbing bits from a larger unit, and whatever comes off is generally wasted. But with metals like copper, any bits or scraps left over from the manufacturing process can be melted together and used afresh. There need be no wastage of chips, flakes, or shavings, no matter how small each particular fragment may be.

Another great advantage of copper is that it is *malleable* and can be pounded into sheets. True enough, certain kinds of bark can be similarly treated, but sheets of bark are woefully fragile when compared to sheets of metal. Again, copper, heated short of its melting point, can be forced through the hole of a die and drawn into *wire*. Some other materials, in this case strings and ropes of wool or vegetal fibers, were undoubtedly used in earlier days, but metallic wire is infinitely superior in strength and durability.

In addition, copper can be coiled into springs that may be held taut or released at will. Only very rarely can spring coils be made with

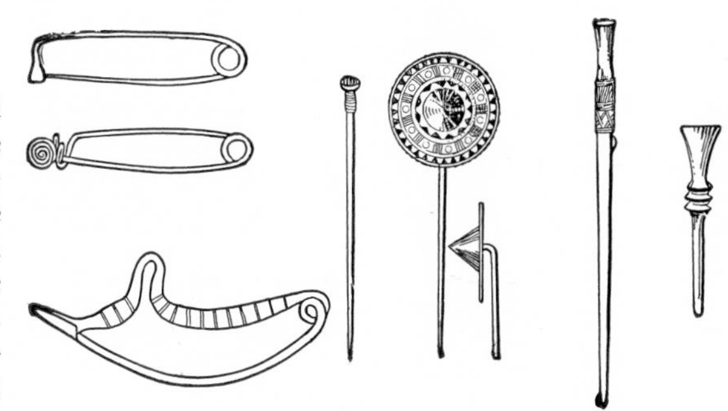

FIG. 15-3. Pins and safety pins (fibulae). These forms appeared for the first time in the Bronze Age, but some of them continued in use to the Iron Age and beyond. (Courtesy of Peabody Museum, Harvard University.)

any of the common cold materials. Also, metal can be made with narrower and sharper points without danger of breaking, as in the case of pins and needles. It was necessary to combine the qualities of coiling and sharp pointing before the first safety pin, known archeologically as a *fibula*, could have come into being. Once the trick was learned, man went in for an amazing degree of elaboration. Fibulae were made in great numbers and in all sorts of sizes and shapes (Fig. 15–3). Quantities of brooches and clasps were manufactured on similar principles.

Among the early uses to which metal was put was the production of weapons and agricultural implements that called for sharp, yet sturdy and durable, cutting edges. The superiority of metallic blades for such purposes was promptly grasped, especially by farmers and soldiers, and copper celts, knives, daggers, swords, scythes and sickles were produced in abundance. Methods of hafting remained to be worked out. An interesting series of metal celts can be arranged to illustrate various solutions to the problem. Early celts are flat and very much like those of polished stone. These were presumably wedged into the cleft of a handle, and may have been secondarily tied in place. Other metallic forms have raised sides that form a constricted channel into which a shaft can be tightly forced. Still others combine this feature with a horizontal bar or *stop ridge*, designed to keep a handle from slipping too far down. Most elaborate of all are *palstaves*, in which the sides rise and meet each other to form a hollow socket. Some palstaves also have a ring added at the side to make doubly sure of a tight haft by wedging and tying. (For illustrations of various kinds of celts, see Fig. 15–4.)

Despite the wide range of new possibilities that the qualities of liquefied copper put at man's disposal, its softness made the continued use of pure copper impractical. For this reason it was soon displaced by a combination of copper and tin. This step was based on yet another advantage of metallurgy, because by melting together two or more metals a blend or *alloy* can be made that has different qualities from any of the

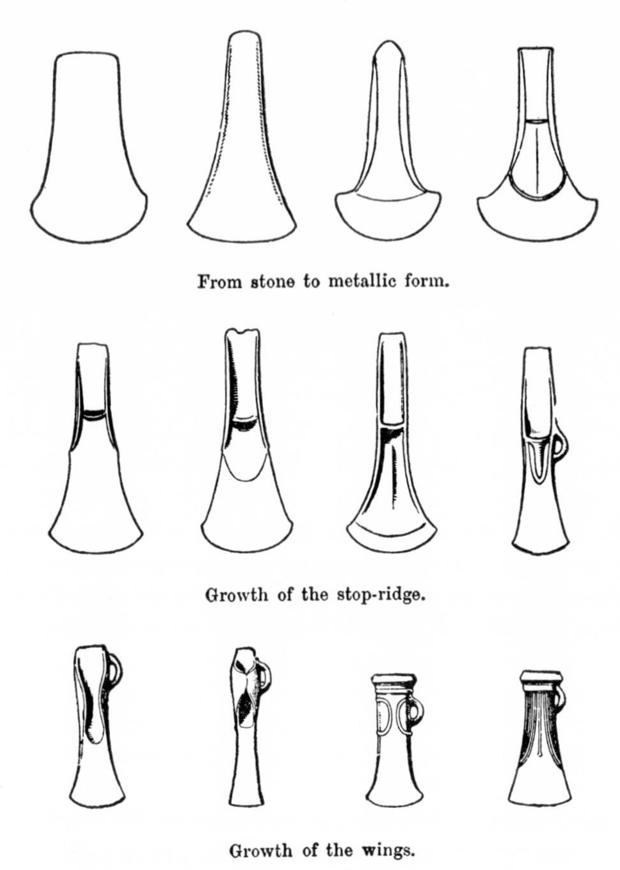

From stone to metallic form.

Growth of the stop-ridge.

Growth of the wings.

FIG. 15-4. From flat celt to palstave. Various kinds of metal celts are illustrated. They are arranged in logical order to show all the stages from flat shapes to ringed palstaves. (Courtesy of British Museum.)

contributing materials. Bronze, the first alloy to come into wide use, added hardness and toughness to copper without detracting from its attractive properties. Very early specimens reveal great uncertainty as to the best proportions of tin to copper; but later a formula of about 10 percent of tin and 90 percent of copper became almost universal.[5] One must not forget that bits of stone, ivory, or cold metal can be pounded into softer materials like wood or leather, but in such cases there is no fusion of properties, and each cold substance retains its

[5] Too little tin makes bronze tough but hard to cast, and too much tin makes bronze very brittle. For the best results the percentage of tin should vary according to the object that is being made.

distinctive nature. Only molten materials can be truly blended into alloys.

SOME RESULTS OF COPPER-BRONZE USE

When we were dealing with the Neolithic it was pointed out that specialization probably began as the range of arts and crafts increased. During the Copper-Bronze Age there is no longer any uncertainty about the growth of specialists. Among other things, it was not long before whatever sources of free metallic copper may have existed on or near the earth's surface were exhausted. It then became necessary to mine copper ore. Successful mining called for prospectors trained to recognize hidden cuprous deposits, miners to extract the ore, and smelters and refiners to separate the pure metal from its associated impurities. Even after these operations had been carried out, it was no trifling matter to acquire the skill and equipment needed for metallurgy. No individual could possibly perform all the necessary activities by himself, and anyone who wanted to make or acquire copper articles had no choice but to depend on others. Thus personal self-sufficiency, which was highest in the Old and Middle Stone Ages, began to fade in the Neolithic, and dwindled still further during the Copper-Bronze era.

Much the same is true of community self-sufficiency, particularly after bronze had replaced pure copper. It so happens that deposits of both copper and tin very seldom occur in the same locality. Hence, practically every society that advanced into the Bronze Age found itself compelled to import either copper or tin, or both. Thus was started an export-import business, and thus did community self-sufficiency reach a close. So much importance was attached to the metal trade that it always tended to become either a government monopoly or a private enterprise regulated by the state.

In order to secure the raw materials that were required for bronze many things were necessary, chief of which was a surplus of something valuable that could be exchanged for tin or copper. By 3000 B.C., methods of mixed farming had improved to such an extent in parts of the Eastern Mediterranean Zone that well-favored settlements had the wherewithal to engage in long-distance trade. We must not forget that those who made long journeys by land had to stop at times for rest and refreshment, and that living accommodations had to be built into all vessels that made distant sea voyages.

Extensive traveling also gave a new impetus to knowledge. Importers had to know where the supplies they wanted were located, and they had to learn ways of reaching the exact spot and getting home again. If trips were to be overland, an elementary knowledge of *geography* was essential. One had to know what rivers, lakes, forests, mountains, or deserts would be encountered, and which were the best routes to take. If travel was to be by water the art of navigation had to be understood. In either case, there was also the need of providing a suitable means of transportation—animal-drawn vehicles for land, and boats propelled by oars or sails for travel by water. It is no mere coincidence that the rise of such intellectual pursuits as *map-making* and *astronomy* came into being at the very time when the ingredients for bronze were being sought.

Still other important consequences resulted from the establishment of export-import trade. No one would risk sending a load of valuable goods for the purchase of expensive raw materials unless his cargoes were protected. In minimum terms, this meant that voyagers conveying costly loads had to take along armed guards or soldiers. When goods went by sea, marines were sent along to fight off would-be robbers. Here begins the tie-in between business and the armed forces that is still of great concern today.

Before many decades had elapsed it was found to be inefficient to send heavy loads back and forth to complete a single transaction. Instead of relying on elementary barter, systems resembling *coinage* were devised, by means of which a great deal of value could be encompassed in a small item. Bars of silver were first used for this purpose in western Asia. Their worth depended on weight and there was much worry over sharp practices of adulteration and short-weighting. Later, when true coins, such as *shekels,* replaced clumsy bars of precious metal, traders accepted them only if they were confident of the stability of the governments that issued them. From the beginning, coinage was recognized to be a public rather than a private function, linking economics and politics.

As commerce continued to expand there was a strongly felt need for systems of weights and measures. Every dealer had to know how large a return he could expect for a given amount of goods. The principle of so much of this for so much of that, which underlies all trade, cannot operate across societies or nations without standardized units of values, weights, and measures. And standardization along these lines cannot develop without *mathematics.* This was not the only practical application of mathematics in the early Metal Ages. Measures of distance were essential to geography, and the sciences of astronomy and navigation also had to have mathematical foundations.

With the rise of big business came a further need, too, for precise notation. Records of all sorts had to be accurately kept to prevent chaos, and neither detailed maps nor charts could be prepared without a means of writing. Frequently, too, identifying marks for owners were indicated in the Near East by impressions made with *seals.* Seals could also be used symbolically, as when a bull stood for power or virility, but sometimes they were purely decorative. Some seals were flat, some cylindrical, and both sorts were pictorial and carved out of hard material. At best, like signet rings, they had only restricted meanings, usually pertaining to a particular person, but they could not express all the details of a transaction. For this it was necessary to have true writing, based on a *phonetic alphabet.* A phonetic alphabet implies that certain graphic symbols stand for particular sounds, making it theoretically possible to put into writing whatever meaningful sounds a given spoken language utilizes. In Mesopotamia, with perhaps a parallel development in Egypt, true writing is found prior to 3000 B.C. The earliest Mesopotamian records were made by cutting or impressing wedge-shaped characters into soft clay tablets (Fig. 15–5). Because of the wedge-shaped characters this

FIG. 15-5. Model of a Mesopotamian clay tablet. A sharp-pointed stylus is thought to have been used for incising the cuneiform writing at the top. The scene below was made by pressing a seal into the soft clay of the tablet before it was baked. (E. Chiera, *They Wrote on Clay*. Chicago, 1938. Courtesy of University of Chicago Press.)

writing is called *cuneiform*.[6] When the clay tablets were baked, the cuneiform inscriptions became permanently fixed. Thousands of complete or fragmentary tablets containing cuneiform writing have been dug up by archeologists from ancient settlements in western Asia, and there are specialists who can read many of the antique scripts. Their translations reveal that a large proportion of the earliest written documents dealt with business, and smaller percentages are known to have been concerned with politics and religion.

One of the fascinating aspects of archeology is to observe how a number of apparently unrelated traits may be combined to help form a new device. An extraordinary instance of the process is to be found in the formation of a *calendar*. Whether based on movements of the sun, moon, stars, or the planet Venus, all calendars depend on some knowledge of astronomy coupled with mathematics. To keep accurate track of the passage of time, based on measurable activities of heavenly bodies, it is necessary to be able to write. So, in a sense, the calendar may be regarded as a combination of astronomy, mathematics, and writing. Its earliest uses, too, were composite, ranging from religious interest in the heavens to the commercial importance of knowing the length of time involved in completing a business transaction. From the days of the Copper-Bronze Age, man has been sensitive to the passing of time, and our own culture is often called time-bound.

Learning to write and read was a long and laborious process which ordinary folk did not try to master. To serve them there arose a specialized group of *scribes*, each of whom, in Mesopotamia, had to learn about 2000 signs. Professional scribes exchanged their skills for the necessities of life. They worked for illiterate individuals, as well as for the state and its rulers, temples and their administrators, and business men. For the latter they drew up agreements which were signed with the seals of contracting parties in the presence of witnesses. Contracts were binding and there were regular courts of law to see that their terms were carried out. The equivalents of our phrases, "Put it in writing," and "I'll sue you," were everyday features of Mesopotamian Copper-Bronze Age life.

A few additional comments may help to bring about a fuller appreciation of the significance of writing. Were it not for the prior development of suitable tools, particularly for drawing and carving, there is not much chance that any form of writing would have arisen.

---

6 Many additional details are to be found in E. Chiera, *They Wrote on Clay*, Chicago, 1938. For a good, popular account of the development of writing, see David Derringer, *Writing*, New York, 1961.

Once it has developed, writing speeds up the building of culture because it helps to prevent loss of ideas or experiences and so contributes to the formation of an ever-growing stockpile of enduring human knowledge. What is put down in writing acquires permanence and stands an excellent chance of being more accurately preserved than something handed down by word of mouth. Whatever is written can easily outlast the lifetime of the author; with the help of translation and copying it can be spread throughout the world; and when signed with an official seal or signature it has greater authenticity than a verbal statement. If a letter carrier in the United States were to tell a young man orally that he had been drafted, the chances are that he would not be taken seriously. Not so if the postman delivered a written letter, officially signed, that contained exactly the same words.

For the student of culture growth the development of writing is of the utmost importance. With the help of written statements, one can learn the range of ideas, values, symbol systems, and abstract concepts that once prevailed in an extinct society. Archeologists working in historic periods are not confronted with the necessity of trying painfully to deduce these intangibles from material remains, and the record of the past emerges in greater detail and clarity than ever.

Concluding remarks

Even so brief a synopsis as has been given in this chapter serves to bring out the complexities of Copper-Bronze Age life. Mention has been made, no matter how scantily, of miners, prospectors, smelters, metallurgists, traders, travelers, drivers, innkeepers, sailors, soldiers, marines, geographers, astronomers, mathematicians, scribes, lawyers, judges, rulers, and priests; to say nothing of agriculturalists, stock breeders, potters, weavers, wagon makers, boatbuilders, and merchants. No one of the specialists could have been a full-time farmer, and no full-time farmer could have doubled as a true specialist. Social distinctions based on wealth and occupation, as well as on sex and age, are everywhere in evidence; there is a tremendous increase of ornaments among the rich; and differences between rural and urban folk come into prominence. Everyone who lived in a Copper-Bronze community was directly and deeply affected by the new technology and its consequences, but metal was so scarce and expensive that only a fraction of the populace regularly used copper and bronze; and the average person's material culture continued to be not much more than Neolithic.

Selected References

Breasted, James H., *The Conquest of Civilization,* rev. ed., New York and London, 1938, Chaps. 1–5.

Chiera, Edward, *They Wrote on Clay,* Chicago, 1938.

Childe, V. Gordon, *Man Makes Himself,* London, 1936, Chaps. 6 and 7.

Cline, Walter, "Mining and Metallurgy in Negro Africa," *General Series in Anthropology,* No. 5, Menasha, Wis., 1937.

Delaporte, Louis J., *Mesopotamia,* London and New York, 1925.

Hanfmann, G. M. A., "The Bronze Age in the Near East: A review article," *American Journal of Archaeology,* Vol. 55, 1951, pp. 355–65.

Kroeber, Alfred L., *Anthropology,* rev. ed., New York, 1948, Chaps. 12, 13, and 17.

Massoulard, E., "Préhistoire et protohistoire d'Egypte," *Travaux et Memoires, Institut d'Ethnologie,* Vol. 53, Paris, 1949.

Peake, H., *The Bronze Age and the Celtic World,* London, 1922.

Randall-MacIver, R., *Villanovans and Early Etruscans,* Oxford, 1924.

Speiser, Edward A., *Excavations at Tepe Gawra,* Philadelphia, 1935.

Woolley, C. Leonard, "Ur Excavations," *Publications of the Joint Expedition of the British Museum and the Museum of the University of Pennsylvania to Mesopotamia,* Philadelphia, 1934.

Metal Age Cultures of the Old World

CHAPTER 16

COPPER-BRONZE CULTURE IN WESTERN ASIA[1]

A sage who was living around 2000 B.C., and who was conversant with the entire world as it was known in the fourth and third millenniums B.C. (4000–2000 B.C.) would have been sure of the fact that the latest advances of culture were to be found in the neighborhoods of Mesopotamia, Egypt, and the Indus River valley of northwestern India. By comparison with these centers, the rest of Africa and Asia was certainly backward; Europe, any wise man of that time would have said, was too far behind ever to count for much; and as for the Americas—what were they? Anyone nowadays who is disturbed by the lack of progress in the underdeveloped regions of the world should remember and find solace in the errors of past judgments. Inasmuch as the Western world got its start toward dominance in the Copper-Bronze Age by diffusion from the Eastern Mediterranean Zone, especially from Mesopotamia, we shall present an account of that area before touching lightly on its neighbors.

At various places in Mesopotamia, not far from Mosul, archeologists have uncovered remains of what seems to have been an extensive Age of Copper (Chalcolithic). Above these materials are objects showing a transition to the use of bronze. The excavations indicate that the

1 Much of this synopsis is based on C. L. Woolley, *The Sumerians*, Oxford, 1929. There are a great many works dealing with this region and the Sumerians; and *Sumer* is the name of a journal that publishes numerous articles on ancient times in and around Mesopotamia.

full Copper-Bronze way of life in Iraq began in the north, perhaps above Bagdad. In those days southern Mesopotamia was probably too wet and swampy for human habitation, but shortly after 3500 B.C., some of the waters receded and in due time the region came to be known as *Sumer* and was settled by people called *Sumerians*. Everything about Sumerian origins is obscure, but the fortunate circumstance that they wrote on clay, coupled with the diligence of archeologists and other scholars, has led to the decipherment of their language and a detailed knowledge of how they lived.

Before long Sumer was divided into city-states, including Biblical Ur, Nippur, Lagash, and others. Each had its own territory, the boundaries of which were jealously guarded and sometimes fought over in large-scale wars by soldiers occasionally armed with metal weapons. Every city-state had its own ruler and local deity. The rulers were intimately associated with their respective municipal gods, and in some cases came to be identified with them. Many later notions of the divine right of kings can be traced back to Sumerian concepts. Theoretically, the deity owned all the land pertaining to his city and the ruler and lesser officials were supposed to administer it on his behalf. Each god dwelt within an elaborate temple built by several hundred laborers, at least some of whom were expert masons, bricklayers, and carpenters. Not only did a temple house sacred images and kings and their attendants, but it was also the custom for a great deal of business to be transacted in its name. Not until Christ drove the money-changers out of the temple was it considered wrong to mix religion and profits.

Sumerian scribes customarily had temple connections. They wrote and kept accounts in cuneiform, which evolved afterward into the Phoenician script from which our own alphabet was ultimately derived. Similarly, they kept track of weights and measures in a way that provides a basis for some of our own methods of reckoning. Sumerians used a sexagesimal system, based on units of 60, a number which can be evenly divided by 1, itself, and 2, 3, 4, 5, 6, 10, 12, 15, 20, and 30. Therefore, whenever we tell time by seconds, minutes, and hours, sentence offenders to 30, 60, or 90 days, or navigate with a compass marked into 360 degrees, we are unconsciously following in the footsteps of the ancient Sumerians who long ago disappeared from history.

It was the same Sumerians who first applied precise mathematical calculations to astronomy. They identified and named most of the planets, worked out their movements, tried to predict eclipses, and hitched navigation to the stars. In each of these spheres we have built modern science on a Sumerian groundwork. Of course they made serious errors when judged by present standards, and there is no denying that much of their information was applied to the discredited pursuits of fortune-telling and astrology, but there is also a lasting quality to many of their accomplishments.

Without question the Sumerian achievements in material culture are most impressive. They made tremendous forward strides in farming techniques, animal domestication, pottery manufacture, weaving, metallurgy, and architecture. Wood and stone have always been scarce in southern Mesopotamia, so for erecting buildings they used mud and clay skillfully, packing it into wooden forms to make sun-dried brick, and baking it in kilns to produce true, waterproof bricks. It is the Sumerian use of temper that gave rise to the Biblical admonition that brick cannot be made without straw. In Mesopotamia, too, it is believed, was invented the principle of the arch, whereby a curved, self-supporting structure can be constructed. As is to be expected, the finest buildings were temples, homes of rulers, and public monuments, often situated atop massive man-made mounds of earth (*ziggurats*) (see Fig. 16–1). Architects prepared blueprints for the erection of great buildings, some of which were several stories high. Commoners had to be content with living on the flats in small, squarish huts of reeds, thatch, and mud.

FIG. 16-1. A restored ziggurat at Ur. This restoration shows how one of the impressive, artificial mounds probably looked at the height of Mesopotamia's Copper-Bronze Age. A public building has been erected on the top. (Courtesy of the Museum of Anthropology, The University of Michigan.)

There is proof of town planning, and public drains, for which professional builders were held responsible, were in use in the cities.

While the Sumerians were the pioneers of advanced culture in southern Mesopotamia, they were not the sole inhabitants of the area. Shortly after 3000 B.C. *Semitic* names begin to show up frequently in the records, although prior to that date the Semites were found chiefly in the north.[2] Around 2300 B.C. a Semitic ruler named *Sargon* overran and united all of Mesopotamia. The invaders absorbed the elements of Sumerian culture and their priests even learned the rival tongue for use in their own rituals. Surviving bilingual texts that were used in sacerdotal schools show that this is an early example of religious conservatism, whereby one language is used in daily life and a more ancient one is retained for worship.

Sargon's empire did not long endure following his death and for several centuries no one power dominated the whole of Mesopotamia. Then, about 1700 B.C., *Hammurabi* rose to prominence and again put the Semites in control. He is rightly famous on several counts. When he made his capital at Babylon he had its local city god, *Marduk,* elevated to the highest theological position in the country, thus putting Marduk before all other gods and instituting a Semitic trend to monotheism. He also ordered a compilation and codification of existing laws in the area. When completed, the results were known as the *Code of Hammurabi,* which tradition says was handed to him by the sun-god. This code contains almost all of the precepts later set forth in the Ten Commandments, and also establishes such principles as "an eye for an eye, and a tooth for a tooth." Hammurabi likewise is credited with having set up legal procedures which are, in several respects, ancestral to our own. Witnesses were sworn, perjury was punished, judicial decisions were enforced, and appeals could be made from lower to higher courts.

Within the span of the Copper-Bronze Age in Mesopotamia there developed a cult centered around heavenly deities, whose worship was universal throughout the nation, rather than simply local. A very popular national pair consisted of *Ishtar* (the planet Venus) and her husband-lover, *Tammuz,* god of vegetation. Annually, Tammuz died and went to the underground home of the dead, from which he was returned and restored to life the next spring through the efforts of Ishtar. Their story became the source of the Greek tales of Venus and Adonis and, in the opinion of sober scholars, the cult of Tammuz played a direct part in spreading ideas of annual rebirth or resurrection, thus influencing the origins of Christianity.

---

2 Anthropologists identify Semites by language only and not by race or religion. Both Arabs and Hebrews speak Semitic tongues and are Semites.

THE COPPER-BRONZE AGE IN EGYPT[3]

Egypt's Copper-Bronze culture presumably evolved at the same time and along the same general lines as Mesopotamia's, but there are few facts available to explain the steps by which Egypt became more isolated from world events. The two countries were surely in touch with one another in Copper-Bronze days and ideas diffused back and forth. Even so, they continued unlike in countless respects. Egyptian rulers were more directly deified, and Egyptian writing differed in being *hieroglyphic.* This means that it consisted of rows of pictorial symbols that probably stood for objects, ideas, or sounds. From the beginning Egypt also had a system of cursive writing, which used lines that were joined into a connected script. It was inscribed with ink on wood, papyrus, or pottery. In its more formal aspect, the cursive writing was called *hieratic* and was used by priests, whereas in its lay form it was known as *demotic* (Fig. 16–2). Like the Sumerian, Egyptian writing came to have all the elements of a phonetic alphabet, but the two systems used completely different sounds and signs and Egyptian was not taken over by any of the European languages.

Again like Mesopotamia, Egypt accumulated a vast body of astronomical lore and an associated store of mathematical knowledge. The Egyptians developed a decimal system of reckoning, but they did not advance as far into higher mathematics. Egypt, however, did formulate a 365-day solar calendar which, it is generally agreed, is the direct forerunner of ours.

Specialists and workmen closely similar to those of Mesopotamia arose in Egypt, but the things they produced were quite distinctive. For instance, Egyptian artisans originated the manufacture of *glass* and the *faïence* method of decoration. There was a good deal of foreign trade with the same consequences as in Iraq; and similar social divisions were to be found between poor and rich, urban and rural dwellers, specialized craftsmen and farmers, rulers and subjects, and priests and laymen.

One outstanding difference is the Egyptian emphasis on the cult of the dead. As early as 3000 B.C. all of Egypt was united under a ruler named *Menes.* Some of his family's tombs have been excavated and their contents are extraordinarily rich. From the time of Menes, efforts were made to preserve the physical remains, at least of deceased royal per-

[3] J. H. Breasted, *The Conquest of Civilization,* New York and London, 1926; and J. A. Wilson, *The Burden of Egypt,* Chicago, 1951, are the chief sources for this section.

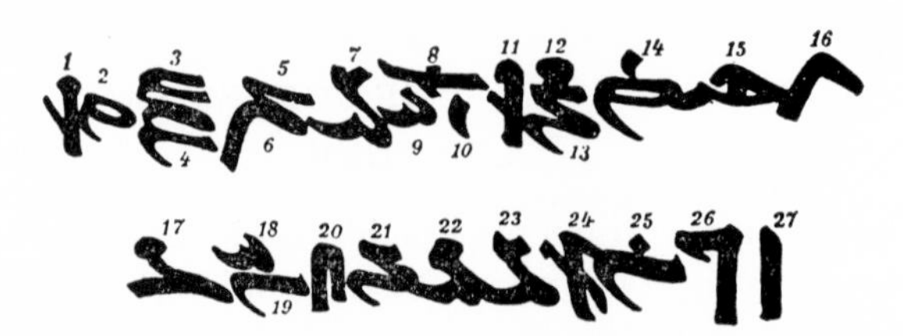

Now if we transcribe these into hieroglyphics we obtain the following:

1.	a reed	11.	see No. 1
2.	a mouth	12.	a knee bone (?)
3.	a hare	13.	see No. 2.
4.	the wavy surface of water	14.	a roll of papyrus tied up
5.	see No. 4	15.	an eye
6.	a kind of vessel	16.	see No. 6
7.	an owl	17.	a goose
8.	a bolt of a door		
9.	a seated figure of a man	18.	see No. 9
		19.	see No. 4
10.	a stroke written to make the word symmetrical	20.	a chair back
		21.	a sickle

FIG. 16-2. Ancient Egyptian writing. The cursive, hieratic, priestly form shown at top is made up chiefly of demotic, hieroglyphic symbols. Many of the correspondences are shown in this figure. The hieroglyphic writing of ancient Egypt should be contrasted with the old cuneiform writing of Mesopotamia, as shown in Fig. 15–5. (Courtesy of the Museum of Anthropology, The University of Michigan.)

sonages, by embalming or mummification; and to the same complex of beliefs belong the customs of pyramid building and obelisk construction. As the wealth and power of the rulers grew their funeral monuments increased in grandeur, until a climax was reached in the *Great Pyramid of Cheops,* dated around 2600 B.C., which measures 755 feet on a side and towers to a height of 481 feet.

Copper-Bronze Age Culture in Crete

It was inevitable that some of the great cultural achievements of ancient Mesopotamia and Egypt should have diffused to other parts of the

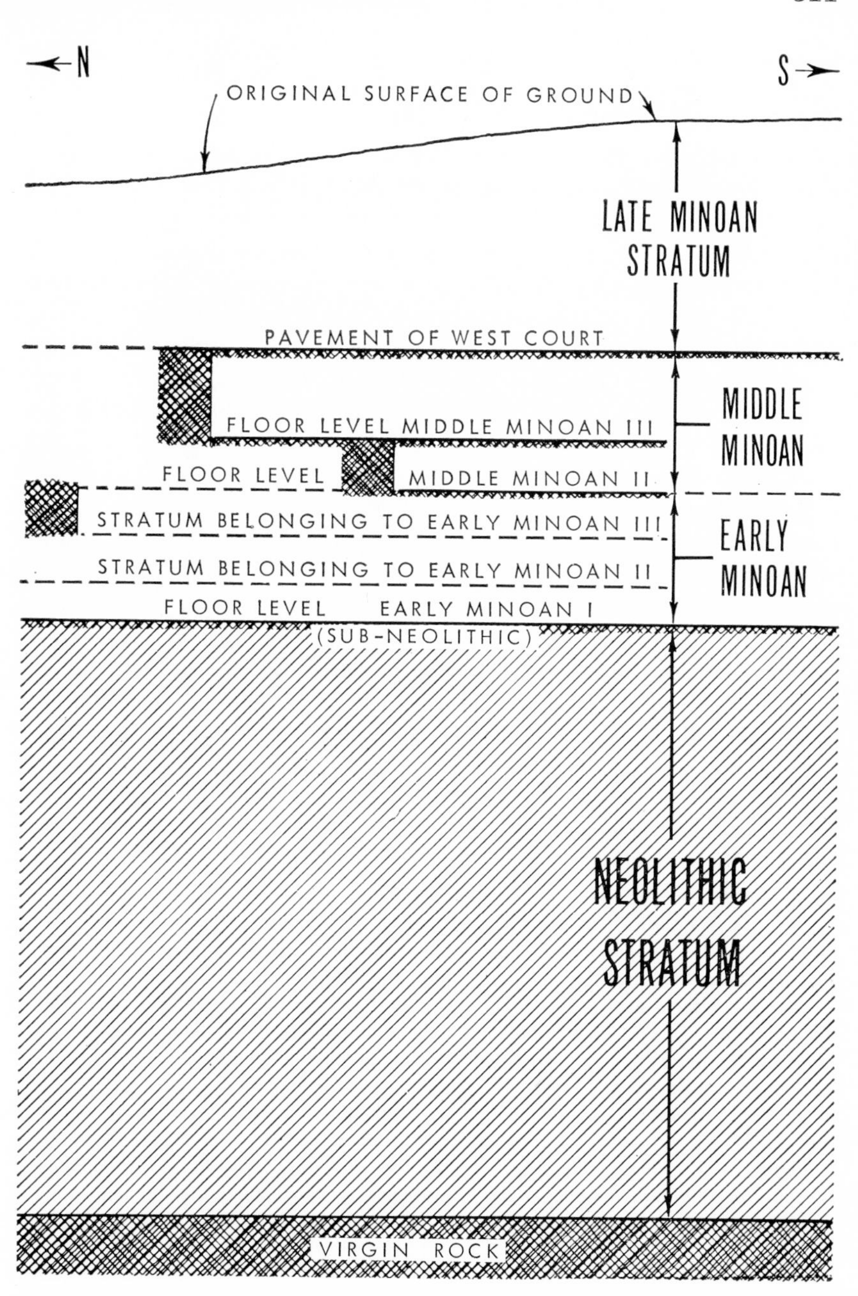

FIG. 16-3. Stratigraphy at Knossos, Crete. The brilliant Copper-Bronze Age (Minoan) culture comes after a long Neolithic period. (Courtesy of the Museum of Anthropology, The University of Michigan.)

Eastern Mediterranean Zone, but nowhere did the diffused traits, particularly some from Egypt, flourish as brightly as they did on the island of Crete.

The origins and all the sources of Cretan culture are extremely hard to untangle, but archeological excavations have revealed evidence of a long-lasting Neolithic period, which gave place to a brilliant Copper-Bronze Age civilization (Fig. 16–3). The Cretan phase, during which the metallurgical use of bronze was known, was named *Minoan* by Sir Arthur Evans, the renowned British archeologist. Evans recognized Early, Middle, and Late stages, each of which has three subdivisions. Broadly speaking, and covering its entire range, Minoan culture is believed to have started about 3500 B.C., and to have lasted in the neighborhood of two thousand years.

Although many Cretan sites have been investigated, the most thorough studies were made at Knossos by Evans. At this place Sir Arthur found the remains of several edifices, the most imposing and elaborate of which he called "The Palace of Minos." (See Fig. 16–4.)[4] It consisted of a cluster of rooms or buildings grouped around a squarish courtyard. Some of the structures were multistoried, and there were often ingenious arrangements for admitting light and air. Some places even had facilities for storing water and for drainage. The palace seems to have housed craftsmen who were skilled in the manufacture of pottery and other Copper-Bronze Age pursuits. Fresco painting, sculpture, and goldwork

[4] The original report came out in a series of volumes. See Sir Arthur Evans, *The Palace of Minos,* London, 1921 ff.

FIG. 16-4. (Opposite). The Palace of Minos. Top: Restoration of the northern entrance to the Copper-Bronze Age palace at Knossos. The restoration brings out the grandeur and beauty of this imposing structure. Middle: A Minoan shrine. Within the palace at Knossos there was found a chamber that was dubbed "The Shrine of the Double Axes." Double axes of stone are displayed on a ledge, together with presumed idols. Many objects and portrayals indicate that the Minoans venerated or worshiped the bull, perhaps for its virility and strength. The double axes were probably conventionalized representations of bull horns, and may be connected with the "horns of consecration" that are often shown on holy persons and gods in this area. The containers in the foreground probably held offerings. Bottom: Double axes in the Eastern Mediterranean Zone. These double axes always appear in a ceremonial context. All the figures are from Egypt, except the one on the extreme right, which is from Crete. They indicate the importance of diffusion in the Eastern Mediterranean Zone in Copper-Bronze times; and these examples serve once more to link the occurrence of double axes with the horns of a bull. (Top and middle figures courtesy of the Museum of Anthropology, The University of Michigan. Bottom figure from H. R. H. Hall, *The Civilization of Greece in the Bronze Age,* London, 1928. Courtesy of Methuen & Co., Ltd.)

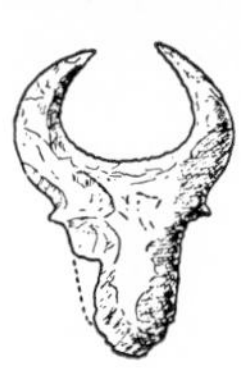

are only a few of the arts and crafts that were brought to astonishing heights.

With so many accomplishments to its credit, it is not surprising that Minoan culture included the art of writing. Sir Arthur Evans distinguished two varieties, which he called, "Linear A" and "Linear B." For several decades they remained undeciphered, but in 1952 Michael Ventris, ably assisted by John Chadwick, announced the decipherment of "Linear B."[5] It turned out to be an ancient form of Greek. Tablets with "Linear B" inscriptions have also been found at Mycenae in Greece.

Apparently, while Minoan culture was flourishing in Crete, a related way of life was going on in nearby Greece, on the mainland of Europe. The contemporary Greek culture is called *Helladic,* and is generally subdivided into the same stages as Minoan. Helladic culture is found at several places, but one of its greatest centers was at Mycenae. Nevertheless, Mycenae never achieved the same brilliance as Crete (see page 318). Only after Minoan culture had collapsed did mainland Greece rise to world prominence.

HARAPPA CULTURE IN INDIA[6]

Up to about forty years ago, scholars knew of no Copper-Bronze Age culture that was either as old or as brilliant as those of the Eastern Mediterranean Zone. Then, beginning in 1922, a series of excavations was started in northwestern India that brought forth astounding evidence of a mature Copper-Bronze culture, which may have existed as early as about 3000 B.C. Its remnants were found in or near the valley of the Indus River and are particularly impressive at the sites of *Mohenjo-daro* and *Harappa* in Sind. From the latter site the remains are often referred to as the *Harappa Culture.* The two great centers give proof of a highly urbanized way of life that lasted for considerably more than a thousand years. Each city was successively rebuilt a number of times, yet their building arrangements, methods of construction, and artifacts show remarkable uniformity throughout all the centuries of their occupation.

---

5 Ventris died soon after the decipherment of "Linear B." His work was carried on by his collaborator. See J. Chadwick, *The Decipherment of Linear B,* Cambridge, England, 1958. See also L. R. Palmer, *Mycenaeans and Minoans,* London, 1961.

6 Those who wish fuller information on this topic are advised to read the original report by J. H. Marshall, *Mohenjo-daro and the Indus Civilization,* London, 1931; and at least E. J. H. Mackay, *The Indus Civilization,* London, 1935, and Sir M. Wheeler, "The Indus Civilization," *The Cambridge History of India, Supplementary Volume,* Cambridge, England, 1953.

Both cities contain structures of truly baked brick laid out along regular streets. Through these streets ran covered drains for carrying away household refuse. Some of the homes had rooms for bathing and had water flowing into them. The residents practiced in their own distinctive way all of the essential industries and arts known in the Copper-Bronze Age. Besides what was locally available, Harappa Culture abounds in materials that could have been procured only through a well-organized export-import trade. They traded with Mesopotamia, but were neither culturally nor politically dominated by western Asia. Indeed, they were so completely independent that their pictographic form of writing still remains their very own, for the plain reason that it has never been deciphered. About 400 characters, superficially reminiscent of Egyptian hieroglyphs, have been identified, but what they mean is an unsolved mystery.

To provide the city folk with food there must have been a large supplementary population of farmers. Barley was the principal cereal and was eaten solid or drunk as beer; wheat was raised, stored, and milled to flour for making bread; and cotton was cultivated and woven into cloth. Humped cattle were under domestication, and so also were humpless cattle, water buffaloes, goats, sheep, pigs, dogs, and asses. As usual, horses were later added to the list. Less certainly domesticated, but probably under human control, were the elephant and camel.

There is a curious lack of easily recognizable cemeteries or religious structures at Mohenjo-daro and Harappa, and it was formerly thought that there were no extensive fortifications, but later excavations indicate that some of the buildings may have been citadels.[7] One architectural feature at Mohenjo-daro has attracted much notice. It is a large bath or swimming pool, about 40 feet by 24 feet, with a well-paved floor of brick and a decided slope toward a drain in one corner (Fig. 16–5). That it was built to hold water may be taken for granted, but the purpose for which people bathed is a matter for conjecture.

Prior to the exciting discovery of Harappa Culture, the start of anything in India resembling modern life used to be dated at 1500 B.C. and attributed to a migration of Indo-European speakers (*Aryans*).[8] Now it is known that there had been a brilliant Copper-Bronze culture in the Indus valley some 1500 years earlier than the time of the Aryan invasion. The question then turns to the unexplained extinction of

---

[7] This view is strongly expressed in M. Wheeler, "Harappa 1946: The Defences and Cemetery R 37," *Ancient India,* Vol. 3, 1947, pp. 59–130.

[8] As in the case of Semitic, anthropologists regard "Aryan" as purely a linguistic term. There is no such thing as an "Aryan race," for many varieties of mankind speak Aryan tongues.

Harappa Culture. Some archeologists believe that it faded out in pre-Aryan days from internal or local causes, but others argue that Harappa Culture was terminated by the invaders of Indo-European speech.[9]

For one reason or another very little is known of the varieties of mankind that were responsible for the formation of the earliest Copper-Bronze cultures. About all that can be said without quibbling is that they were members of *Homo sapiens,* that the Caucasoid stock played

FIG. 16-5. "Great Bath" at Mohenjo-daro. In the foreground may be seen what is called "The Great Bath." Although its exact use is unknown, it is one of the most important remains of Harappa culture.

a major part, and that the Mediterranean race was strongly represented. The Negroid stock may have played a contributory role, at least in India, and possibly in Egypt; but the presence of Mongoloids is not attested, with the exception of the first Chinese Metal Age. China's Copper-Bronze phase can be dated from the Shang dynasty (about 1500–1100 B.C.), and many wonderful remains have been found at the Shang capital of *Anyang,* just east of the Yellow River's great bend.[10] There are signs of large cities, imposing rulers, elaborate tombs, a well-developed system of writing, the domestication of many plants and animals (not all of which were known farther west), a variety of skills in weaving and pottery-making, and excellent work in bronze devoted to some

9 Wheeler attributes the collapse of Harappa to the Aryan invasion.

10 For a recent archeological study of Anyang and the Shang dynasty, see C. Tê-k'un, *Shang China,* Cambridge, England, 1960. There is a discussion of Shang site excavations on pp. 1–17; and pp. 239–49 present a brief synopsis of Shang culture. This work also provides a fine bibliography.

domestic implements and an abundance of military and ritual objects. When one remembers how much later it came in time, there is an amazing parallel between China's Copper-Bronze Age and that of western Asia. Nevertheless, Anyang's late date sets it apart from the events we are tracing, and its connections with the Eastern Mediterranean Zone are entirely obscure.

COPPER-BRONZE CULTURE REACHES EUROPE [11]

One of the incidental results of the Copper-Bronze Age was a remarkable increase of the human population. As people spread out from the more crowded centers of the Eastern Mediterranean Zone, it was inevitable that some of them should go in the direction of Europe. Settlers went early to Crete and Cyprus, moved on to other islands in the Aegean Sea, and came at last to the peninsula of Greece. Influences from the populous areas were also spread by colonists or other migrants to Asia Minor, wherein was situated the city of Hissarlik, site of Homer's Troy. When it was found that sources of copper and tin were located in Hungary, Bohemia, Cornwall, and Ireland, commercial relations with those regions were started. The Copper-Bronze Age began to reach central Europe prior to 2000 B.C., and it slowly grew and spread to other parts of the continent along the Mediterranean Sea or the Danubian corridor.

Much of the credit for introducing metallurgy to Europe is assigned to the *Bell Beaker folk*. Their origins are indeterminate, but they show up in Spain somewhat earlier than 2000 B.C. They get their name from a distinctive form of pottery that resembles a bell in shape. These beakers, which may have been used to quaff beer, appear in great profusion, and were almost invariably placed in graves, together with copper daggers, copper awls, and a large variety of implements made from cold substances.

The Bell Beaker people traveled widely in Europe and their remains are often found in places where Megalithic culture had spread during the Neolithic. They even penetrated the British Isles, where their culture is strongly manifested. There they sometimes buried their dead under elongated mounds called *long-barrows*, and at other times they made burials under *round-barrows*. A few similar barrow graves belong

[11] For an elaboration of this subject see V. G. Childe, *The Bronze Age*, Cambridge, England, 1930.

to Britain's Neolithic, but they become much more abundant in the early Metal Ages.

Between 1800 and 1400 B.C. Greece received specialized craftsmen from the island of Crete, as well as from places in the Aegean Sea, and from Asia Minor. The city of *Mycenae* was one of the very first Greek communities to gain renown in those days, and its success was due to the absorption of Cretan (Minoan), and other Eastern Mediterranean Zone influences. By 1400 B.C. Mycenae was in a position to reverse the trend and to dominate Crete and send its own exports to Troy, other communities in Asia Minor, the Eastern Mediterranean Zone in general, and as far off as Italy, Sicily, and the British Isles. Improved methods of land and sea transport helped to speed up communications and trade, and Mycenaean ships are known to have reached a length of 100 feet, and were capable of carrying about 150 people.

Yet Mycenae itself never attained the splendor of the great Copper-Bronze cities of Africa, Asia, or Crete. It was highly militaristic and was enclosed by ramparts of huge stones, to the style of which the name *Cyclopean masonry* has been given. Only a small area was enclosed, within which the bodies of great personages were placed in domed structures known as *beehive tombs*, but commoners were buried in cemeteries outside the Cyclopean walls. Implements of war predominate among the ruins of Mycenae and much importance was attributed to long rapiers of bronze. Light war-chariots drawn by trained horses were greatly prized by the wealthy and powerful; and while officers had some metal equipment, ordinary soldiers fought on foot with inferior Stone Age weapons as befitted vassals of their overlords. A great deal of the archeological material corresponds to descriptions found in Homer's epic of the Trojan War and his works are judged to provide a reflection of the life of those days.

Mycenae, as was said earlier, represents the first emergence of Greece or any other European mainland area among world cultural leaders. However, it was doomed to collapse when raided by backward people who ultimately acquired a knowledge of metallurgy and its correlated arts and crafts. By the time that Greek culture was fated to rise to the great heights of its classical period in art, architecture, literature, and philosophy, a thousand years were to elapse and the new attainments would have little connection with the earlier Mycenaean Age.

Iron makes its entrance

Somewhere around 1500 B.C., people living in the vicinity of present-day Armenia discovered how to manufacture things of iron. They did all they could to keep their knowledge hidden from others, but they used the new metal for weapons and as their armies made conquests the secret was automatically disclosed. Among the first to exploit the advantages of iron were the *Hittites,* followed soon after by the *Assyrians.* Both the Hittites and the Assyrians found the great and wealthy Copper-Bronze centers of the Eastern Mediterranean Zone extremely tempting targets for attack, and were soon coming down on them "like the wolf on the fold." The successes of the Iron Age invaders were attributable not only to their fighting ability and superior arms, but also to the internal collapse of the older societies. Assuredly, the Copper-Bronze Age communities carried within their own social systems the seeds of destruction. Throughout their existence objects of bronze remained out of reach of the general populace and wealth tended to become concentrated in the hands of a few. Such was the case, too, with all the associated advances of knowledge and industry. Commoners worked hard, paid heavy taxes, and supported the state in many ways, but got pitifully little in return. By and by, rulers came to rely not on masses of loyal citizens but on slaves and mercenaries. No wonder they could not offer strong resistance to invasion and attack.

Within a few centuries after 1500 B.C., every one of the great Copper-Bronze centers in Mesopotamia, Egypt, Crete, and India, had collapsed; and even in far-off China the Shang dynasty was soon to be overthrown by the Chou. A kind of Dark Ages followed, but the accomplishments of the early Metal Ages remained to form a platform on top of which the Iron Age was built. The period of transition lacks the glitter and color of the mature Copper-Bronze Age, to the extent that it gives the impression of having moved backward, but in the long run cultural progress was still being made as new and more modern forms of group living emerged.

In strictly technological terms, it was not easy for iron to displace bronze. Above all, it was necessary for new metallurgical skills to be acquired. Because of its internal composition iron does not readily lend itself to casting, either in simple molds or by the lost-wax method; and cast iron is often too brittle to be practical. Not until methods of *forging* (repeated pounding while hot) and *tempering* (sudden alternations of heat and cold) were worked out, could sturdy implements be made. Even so, forging and tempering remained free-hand techniques, requiring a strong operator who could turn out only one object at a time. Other drawbacks were the quantities of fuel needed and the tendency of pure iron to rust. On the other side of the ledger, the new substance was far more abundant than copper, and even more so than tin. It could also be used by itself, thus making it much cheaper than bronze

Moreover, iron is tougher than bronze, and when it is mixed with a small amount of inexpensive carbon it becomes steel and is still harder, as well as rust-resistant. Suffice it to say that it was not long before the advantages were found to outweigh the disadvantages, with the consequence that because it was so cheap and so much more readily available, it made possible for the first time the everyday use of metallic implements. Iron was indeed the poor man's metal. With the use of metallic tools, forests and timber could more easily be cut, plowing and cultivating practices could be improved, every soldier in an army could be well-equipped, and cheap household instruments and ornaments became available to almost everyone.

The late start of the Iron Age provided time for two Copper-Bronze traits to mature to a point where they could achieve widespread distribution. Writing, thanks to simplification of the phonetic alphabet, became less of a highly specialized craft. Universal literacy was far from being attained but many ordinary folk learned to read a little and to write their names, and small merchants began to find that they could keep their own accounts. Coinage, too, was brought to lower social levels than ever before. Coins of small denomination were minted, making it easier for people of little wealth to buy and sell, undertake to save for the distant future, pay taxes more conveniently than in kind, and so participate to some extent in the money economy of the total community. Without any formal planning the Copper-Bronze Age had turned into an era of aristocrats, and the Iron Age was to witness the rise of the common man.

Iron Age Cultures of Europe

The complexities of Iron Age archeology, supplemented as they are by a wealth of historical documentation, are exceedingly difficult to summarize. Instead of trying to treat the entire Old World, therefore, American anthropologists have fallen into the habit of singling out for examples two of the best-known sites in central Europe. The older, called *Hallstatt*, was discovered in Austria; and the more recent, *La Tène*, gets its name from a place in Switzerland. It may be assumed that the knowledge of working with iron reached some parts of Europe by 1000 B.C., but it did not become widespread on that continent for several centuries. Hallstatt culture is customarily dated from 800–400 B.C., and La Tène runs from 400 B.C. to A.D. 1.

Most of the originally identified Hallstatt material was found in a huge cemetery that was excavated over a stretch of twenty years starting in 1847. The graveyard is located at the scene of an ancient salt-mining center, close to one of Europe's oldest iron-working areas and not far from a connection with the basin of the Danube River. Burials were about evenly divided between unburnt and cremated, but there are slight indications from the associated grave furnishings that upper class and wealthier folk were the ones who practiced cremation. Early Hallstatt represents a transitional stage of culture, for many objects of bronze as well as iron pertain to it. Despite a later increase of iron materials, Hallstatt never in its active years showed such traits as great cities, elaborate architecture, wheel-made pottery, coins, or writing. It is an odd twist of fate that a folk whose graves have long endured should have left so few traces of their regular habitations. A place in France, which had a Hallstatt form of culture, provides evidence that the people lived in rectangular huts made of perishable materials and surrounded by earthen ramparts. Just the same, next to nothing would be known of the Hallstatt were it not for the objects left in cemeteries.

Several types of swords, emphasizing the transitional nature of Hallstatt, have been recovered. The earliest ones were long, heavy, and made of bronze. Then follow imitations in iron, and shorter swords with the pommel branching into two horns or *antennae*. Daggers were also common (Fig. 16–6), and there were many iron knives with blades that folded into a handle like a modern jackknife. A type of bucket, *situla,* made by riveting together sheets of bronze, occurs frequently; and there was a great variety of pottery, skillfully made by hand and often painted with black or red geometric figures on a yellowish slip. Enameled bronze (bronze coated with a glassy surface) appears for the first time, and bronze bracelets with inlays of iron were in vogue. Fibulae of bronze or iron were stylish in the mature Hallstatt, and there was a limited use of amber, coral, gold, and glass.

Attempts that are none too satisfactory have been made to subdivide Hallstatt into successive periods on the basis of variations in burial customs, sword and dagger types, and fibulae and pottery styles. The best division tentatively sets apart an early phase with big swords of bronze or iron and no fibulae, from a later stage featuring short, antenna-handled iron swords, and a variety of fanciful fibulae. In general terms, representations of Hallstatt culture have been found scattered through a wide zone of central Europe from Hungary to Spain, but the Iron Age did not reach northern Europe and the British Isles until some centuries later.

The type station of La Tène, the second phase of central Europe's Iron Age, is situated in the eastern end of Lake Neuchatel, Switzerland.

It is often associated with speakers of Celtic languages. Explorations began at La Tène in 1858 and were carried on sporadically for several decades. A period of four centuries, ending on the verge of the Christian era, is thought to span the years that La Tène was occupied. From the nature of the objects recovered, Paul Vouga has been led to the conclusion that the place had been a military establishment, with im-

FIG. 16-6. Iron Age daggers from Hallstatt (after von Sacken and MacCurdy). Both daggers at the right have antennae handles. The third one from the left is made entirely of iron, but the one at the extreme right has a bronze handle. Hallstatt swords were of the same forms as the daggers.

portant trading connections. His opinion was based on the finding of exceptionally large numbers of iron swords and other weapons. Shields and helmets were also common, and much stress was laid on what we would call military insignia.

Apart from weapons, La Tène culture reveals a profusion of coins, originally issued in many places, fibulae of bronze, iron, and gold, and an abundance of bracelets, wheel-made painted pots, glass beads, and objects of enameled bronze. Made of iron were a large number of tools and utensils, including axes, knives, hammers, saws, and agricultural and fishing devices (Fig. 16–7). That there was an increase of accumulated wealth is indicated not only by stocks of coins, but also by the first large-scale appearance of locks and keys. Shears and scissors are other objects that came into common use in the La Tène, and there is a wide range of tweezers, razors, ornaments, and trinkets. Burial in the ground was the rule throughout most of the period, but cremation appears before

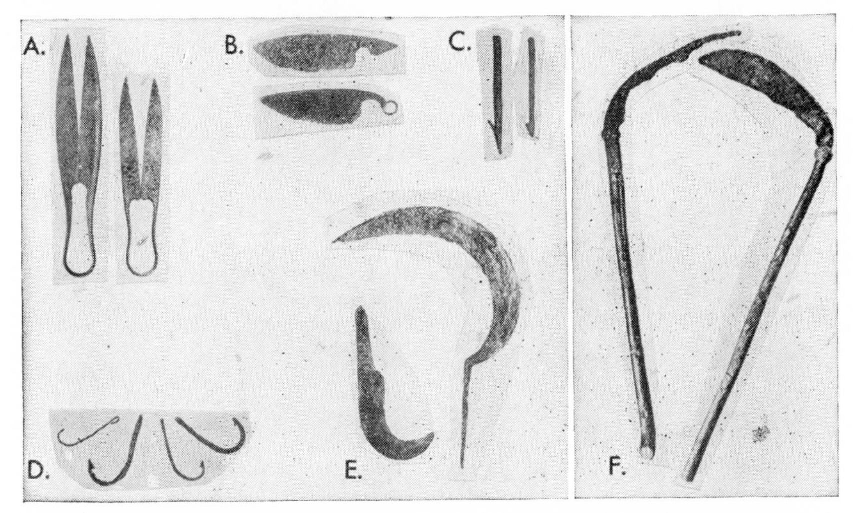

FIG. 16-7. Nonmilitary Iron Age tools (after MacCurdy, following Vouga). A. Scissors or shears. B. Razors. C. Harpoon heads. D. Fishhooks. E. Sickles. F. Scythes. (Courtesy of Peabody Museum, Harvard University.)

its close. Important men were interred with their chariots, and one famous grave of this sort also contained wine, several varieties of meat, iron spits, and a great carving knife (Fig. 16–8). Wine seems to have been imported from Italy or Greece, and historic records state that wily Greek traders were quick to realize that they could drive better bargains if they got their customers drunk.

During the 500 years prior to the Christian era, the world's most important historical events continued to take place not in central or western Europe but in Greece and the Eastern Mediterranean Zone. Darius, the Great, of Persia, had by 500 B.C. subjugated all of western Asia and was looking for more worlds to conquer. Greece was the only European nation of the day that seemed worth bothering about, and in 491 B.C. Darius sent a huge fleet of 600 ships against Athens. After unchallenged initial successes, the Persians in 490 B.C. reached Marathon, where they were soundly beaten at the hands of a confederation led by Athenian Greeks.

FIG. 16-8. An Iron Age chariot burial. This presumed warrior from the Iron Age was buried under a two-wheeled chariot, with food and implements. The small rectangle in the foreground contained the remains of horse trappings. (Courtesy of British Museum.)

It is beyond the scope of this volume to trace the rise of classical Greek culture that followed soon after Marathon. However, for the benefit of those who may look upon the archeologically established Iron Age as something distant and unconnected with modern times it may be well merely to list, with their dates, a small handful of the well-known historic figures who lived in late Hallstatt or La Tène times. Herodotus, father of modern history, died in 425 B.C.; Hippocrates, father of modern medicine, was born in 460 and died around 370; the great playwright, Sophocles, lived from 496(?) to 406; Socrates' life ran from 469 to 399; the everlastingly famous Aristotle was born in 384 and died in 322; the short but important lifetime of Alexander the Great fell between 356 and 323; Cicero lived and died between 106 and 43; and Julius Caesar was born in 100 and died in 44 B.C. So did the Iron Age witness the shift of world leadership from the Eastern Mediterranean Zone to Europe, and thus did it bring mankind to the threshold of our era.

As one views the whole march of culture from its beginnings in the Old World to the start of the Christian era, it becomes apparent that it was undergoing constant development as a unified whole. When archeologists first uncovered the evidence of the great antiquity of culture, they were so impressed with the noteworthy achievements that occurred at particular times and places that they put great emphasis on each of the stages through which man's culture had passed. Thus, the phases were emphasized at the expense of the totality of human culture. Today, however, there is a feeling that one should learn to regard culture as a whole, with each stage representing a period on a continuum. The older approach has—for the most part—been presented here, partly because the new attitude has not yet crystallized, partly because a consideration of the phases is vital for an understanding of what happened in the past, and partly because the bulk of earlier archeological writings would lose their meaning unless readers knew about the stages through which culture is believed to have passed.

Selected References

Brew, James O., "The Metal Ages: Copper, Bronze, and Iron," in H. L. Shapiro, ed., *Man, Culture, and Society,* New York, 1956, pp. 111–38.

British Museum, *A Guide to the Antiquities of the Bronze Age,* Oxford, 1904.

———, *A Guide to the Antiquities of the Early Iron Age,* Oxford, 1905.

Chadwick, John, *The Decipherment of Linear B,* Cambridge, England, 1958.
Childe, V. Gordon, *The Bronze Age,* Cambridge, England, 1930.
Evans, Sir Arthur J., *The Palace of Minos at Knossos,* London, 1921 ff.
Frankfort, Henri, *Kingship and the Gods,* Chicago, 1948.
Hawkes, Christopher, F. C., *The Prehistoric Foundations of Europe to the Mycenean Age,* London, 1940.
Mackay, Ernest J. H., *The Indus Civilization,* London, 1935.
Marshall, Sir John H., *Mohenjo-Daro and the Indus Civilization,* London, 1931.
Palmer, Leonard R., *Mycenaeans and Minoans,* London, 1961.
Tê-k'un, C., *Shang China,* Cambridge, England, 1960.
Wheeler, Sir Mortimer, "The Indus Civilization," *The Cambridge History of India, Supplementary Volume,* Cambridge, England, 1953.
Wilson, John A., *The Burden of Egypt,* Chicago, 1951.
Woolley, Sir Charles L., *The Sumerians,* Oxford, 1929.

Man and Culture in the New World: Part I

CHAPTER 17

NEW WORLD VERSUS OLD WORLD

Despite the abundance of material already presented, almost nothing has been said about the evolution of man and culture in the extensive territories of the Americas. From the point of view of learning the main steps leading to the formation of *Homo sapiens* and of becoming acquainted with the broad outlines of his cultural progress it may be enough to limit one's self to the Old World, but to arrive at a better understanding of the varieties and complexities of human behavior it is necessary to know something of the New World as well. Not that there is any direct contradiction between the events that took place in the two areas, but there is a profound difference in one detail after another. It is only by examining the differences that a student of anthropology can gain an insight into the range of biological and cultural activities that may be found in dissimilar environments. An impartial and comprehensive science of man cannot be formulated if one hemisphere of the globe is left out of consideration.

Because of circumstances that are still inexplicable there was no hominid evolution in the Americas, even though the general pattern of biological development followed much the same course up to the Primates. Lemurs and tarsiers both were well represented in the American Eocene, and at a later date platyrrhine monkeys also made their appearance. At this stage the evolution of Primates in the New World seems to have come to a halt. Nowhere in the Americas has anyone ever found a verifiable specimen, fossil or living, of any catarrhine monkey or ape—always excepting importations from abroad. There is also a total absence of presapiens hominids, which lends further support to the contention that man did not originate in America. Not even Neandertal man, whose varied remains show up throughout the Old World, has made an appearance in the New. And yet, there were millions of Indians present when Columbus arrived. There seems to be no way of getting around the conclusion that man had entered the New World from the Old, at some time after he had evolved into *Homo sapiens*. By then, it will be remembered, culture had progressed so far in the Eastern Hemisphere that it is unlikely that cultural evolution in America should have started from scratch. Instead, the first migrants are thought to have brought with them a way of life that corresponds roughly to Upper Paleolithic.

Whether or not the first Americans remained in touch with their homelands in the Old World is a moot question. Archeologists in this country are reluctant to say that all contact was immediately broken, yet, as they study the evidence it looks very much as if the great bulk of later American culture went through an independent evolution in isolation. For example, a good number of groups moved into a Neolithic stage, but instead of relying on Old World beasts they domesticated such New World creatures as the alpaca, llama, and turkey. Even these had only a restricted distribution in pre-Columbian days, and aboriginal America's limited use of domesticated animals provides one of its sharpest distinctions from the Neolithic in the Old World. In this hemisphere the horse was never domesticated, and no draft animal was widely utilized.

On several other scores there are such wide contrasts as to strengthen the belief that almost all of the Neolithic of America was independently evolved. Take, in this connection, the matter of agriculture. In one spot or another the prehistoric Indians learned to raise numerous crops, including many kinds of maize or corn, several varieties of beans, squashes and pumpkins, tomatoes, cocoa, manioc or cassava, tobacco, white and sweet potatoes, and cotton, only the last two of which were then known anywhere in the Old World. Much the same may be said of pottery. Neolithic peoples in the New World manufactured an incredible variety of ceramic objects, but only a restricted number of their forms and decorations can be matched in the Eastern Hemisphere. There was also a big difference with regard to rotary power. Some American Indians may have known the principle of the wheel; but at no time before Columbus was the concept put to practical use except in the making of spindle whorls and drills. Beyond that, the rare instances of wheels are limited to little things that might have been toys.

One of the most startling revelations of American archeology is the astounding cultural advance that was made once or twice by an essentially Neolithic people. For instance, the *Maya Indians* of Guatemala and Yucatan, and the *Toltec-Aztec* of Mexico, who were for all practical purposes Neolithic, nevertheless had an amazing collection of traits which, throughout the Old World, do not appear until the maturer phases of the Copper-Bronze Age.

Prior to 1492 there was a Copper-Bronze Age in the New World, but its effective range did not extend very far beyond the territorial limits of *Nuclear America* (see page 344). It attained its highest peak among the so-called *Inca Indians* of Peru and Bolivia. Only the Inca had some craftsmen who regularly used an alloy of copper and tin, and even they did not make large quantities of everday implements of bronze. A few tribes in Ecuador and Colombia worked with other mixtures or alloys, and the Maya and some others dealt with molten gold and silver; but none of the latter groups seems to have utilized bronze to an important extent. One must not jump to the conclusion that America's Copper-Bronze Age was an exact duplicate of the Old World's, except that it came later in time. In some regards it was alike, but neither in writing, mathematics, nor the use of a calendar did the Copper-Bronze Inca equal the attainments of the basically Neolithic Maya.

By way of another contrast with the Old World, the aboriginal metallurgists of America never learned to utilize iron. Whether they would have developed an Iron Age had it not been for European conquest and colonization will never be known. In any event, it is certain that the American Indians were the more readily defeated because they lacked such cultural items as metal weapons, wheeled vehicles, and domesticated horses.

When it is compared with the Old World story, the evolution of culture in pre-Columbian America appears greatly compressed in time and scope. In time it extended from about 20,000 B.P. to A.D. 1492, and in scope it ran from a sort of Upper Paleolithic beginning to the Copper-Bronze Age. Within these limits it reveals much diversity and complexity, and drives home the lesson that culture is a universal but highly varied phenomenon of mankind.

MAN COMES TO AMERICA

If *Homo sapiens* did not evolve in the New World he must have entered from the Old. This unequivocal statement of fact, innocent as it seems, has given rise among American archeologists to a series of long-lasting, sometimes acrimonious, and completely unresolved debates. Prominent questions that await definitive answers include: Just who were the first people to have come? When did they arrive? Precisely where did they come from? What aspects of culture did they bring along? These broad queries can be expanded or broken down into numerous more detailed ones that are still harder to answer, but it will serve our purpose to examine the main four in broad terms.

The problem of who the first Americans may have been is complicated by the fact that archeologists have as yet found no skeletal remains directly associated with the oldest recognizable artifacts. In other words, there have been discovered ancient specimens of human workmanship, but there is no way of telling who made them. Since the middle decades of the last century, reports have occasionally been made of skeletal remains supposedly pertaining to Pleistocene man, but in nearly every instance the claims were subsequently modified or rejected. Until the time of his death, Aleš Hrdlička led a stubborn and usually successful campaign to refuse the label of Pleistocene antiquity to any hominid specimen, particularly if it bore a resemblance to living Indians. Today, there is complete willingness to accept as valid any Pleistocene human relics, regardless of their appearance, provided only that they can be accurately dated by geological, radiocarbon, or other scientific methods.[1] Just the same no candidate for the honor of being the first American has been unanimously nominated, to say nothing of having been elected.

If one turns from the unsolved problem of the very earliest arrivals to questions of somewhat later inhabitants, he is a little better off for reliable information. By making a stratigraphic study of successive skull types at Pecos, New Mexico, E. A. Hooton was able to demonstrate that the prehistoric residents of that abandoned village were a composite rather than a unified group, and that the earliest strains were long-headed (dolichocephalic) and non-Mongoloid.[2] Much more recently, Georg K. Neumann, of Indiana University, has been making an exhaustive survey of human remains found in archeological deposits, in an effort to reconstruct the racial history of pre-Columbian America. His terminology is original and entirely different from Hooton's, but he also finds that the first known folk were physically varied, longheaded, and non-Mongoloid.[3]

On the basis of present-day knowledge, scholars accept the prob-

[1] For a discussion of this controversial problem see, with the citations he makes, T. D. Stewart, "The Development of the Concept of Morphological Dating in Connection with Early Man in America," *Southwestern Journal of Anthropology,* Vol. 5, 1949, pp. 1–16.

[2] E. A. Hooton, *The Indians of Pecos Pueblo,* New Haven, Conn., 1930.

[3] G. K. Neumann, "Archeology and Race in the American Indian," in J. B. Griffin, ed., *Archeology of Eastern United States,* Chicago, 1952, pp. 13–34.

ability that the peopling of the New World began with the arrival of sapiens strains, and was followed by an indefinite number of waves of migration that lasted over many centuries. J. Louis Giddings, of Brown University, an archeologist with much experience in the Arctic, believes that the earliest movements of people between the continents were not one-way, but that groups of "Polar Men" wandered back and forth between Asia and America before lasting settlements were made in the Western hemisphere. James B. Griffin, of the University of Michigan, thinks that men might have traversed the Lena Valley to the Arctic, and then moved along the Arctic and into America. In any case, the later permanent arrivers in the New World tended to occupy the interior hearts of the continents while the earlier settlers moved to the margins. Last, or nearly so, to come on the scene were the ancestors of the modern Eskimo. As more and more people reached America there was a general but not universal increase of broadheadedness (brachycephaly) and Mongoloid characteristics. This ancient situation is still reflected in the present. Most native groups are classed as Mongoloid by virtue of skin and eye color, hair form and distribution on the body, and cheekbone configuration; but, on the other hand, Asiatic Mongoloids have a high incidence of blood group B, whereas American Indians are extremely low in B. However, it must never be forgotten that the American Indians are not at all identical and that many subvarieties can be distinguished among the living tribes.[4]

The date of man's entrance into the New World would be entirely open to question if anthropologists had to rely only on skeletal fragments. Luckily, some estimates can be made from the occurrence of humanly manufactured artifacts. Several of these have been dated by a combination of techniques, with the result that nearly everyone accepts an entrance date of around 20,000 B.P.[5] This leads to speculation about the environmental conditions that prevailed at the time, especially in the locality that served as the original gateway.

On the score of place of entry there is comforting agreement. Only a rare dissenter, almost never a trained anthropologist, objects to the

---

[4] W. S. Laughlin, ed., *Papers on the Physical Anthropology of the American Indians,* New York, 1951.

[5] The entire question of prehistoric man's first arrival in the Americas is now being re-examined. There is a marked tendency to push the date further and further back into the past. A strong protest against the acceptance of the customary dates was published by George F. Carter in *Pleistocene Man at San Diego,* Baltimore, 1957. On the basis of some archeological discoveries, Dr. Carter argues for an entrance date of 100,000 years ago. Even though Americanists expect dates earlier than 20,000 B.P. to become acceptable in the future, they regard Carter's estimate as extreme.

When one is dealing with the New World, prehistoric and pre-Columbian are practically synonymous. Both terms refer to anything earlier than 1492.

contention that man came to America from northeast Asia, by crossing the Bering Straits into Alaska. A few disturbing details remain to be clarified before high probability can be converted to established fact, but in most respects the hypothesis of a Bering Straits approach is scientifically supported. At the time in question North America was most likely in the latter phases of the Wisconsin glaciation that came toward the end of the Pleistocene in the New World. Geological and related studies have shown that neither northeastern Siberia nor Alaska was then heavily covered with ice. Nor did the waters of the Bering Straits provide a serious obstacle. The straits are only about 57 miles wide at one spot; they are narrow enough for the American shore to be seen on clear days from parts of the northeastern Asiatic coast; they are broken up by islands that limit open water to twenty-five miles or less at a stretch; there were probably seasons of winter when crossings could have been made on solid ice; and there may have been a land bridge between the two continents in late Pleistocene times.

Although the theory of a Bering Straits gateway is most widely accepted, it is not the only one that has been proposed. Migrations across the Atlantic have been postulated on one basis or another from Wales, western Asia, Egypt and other parts of Africa, or from mythical places like Atlantis or Mu. Not one of these suggestions is backed by trustworthy proof, and none, with the exception of a Norse movement around 1000 B.C., is taken seriously by American anthropologists. In a rather different category are the hypotheses of ancient trans-Pacific movements to other New World regions than Alaska. Enough evidence has been accumulated to establish the possibility that now and then a boatload of navigators from islands in the South Pacific may have reached a spot on the western shores of the Americas, but it is highly improbable that they ever arrived in sufficient numbers or early enough to have become ancestors of the American Indians or the founders of their ways of life.[6]

When it comes to the question of what kind of culture the first occupants of America brought with them, there is again no clear-cut answer. Whatever they had that was intangible or perishable cannot be

---

[6] In spite of its author's frank disclaimer, published at the end of his book, some readers of Thor Heyerdahl's *Kon-tiki* are of the opinion that he proved the possibility of a reverse migration from Peru to Polynesia. Anthropologically, the voyage of the Kon-tiki proved next to nothing. Heyerdahl has since expounded his ideas more fully in *American Indians in the Pacific,* New York, 1953.

In an effort to disprove Heyerdahl's theory, Captain Eric de Bisschop sailed a craft in the opposite direction, from Tahiti to Chile. His exploit is described in E. de Bisschop, *Tahiti Nui,* New York, 1959. His vessel was constructed according to Polynesian specifications, whereas Heyerdahl's raft was built on supposedly ancient Peruvian lines.

recovered, and whatever they have left behind of a durable nature can tell only a partial story at best.

Failing the discovery of actual specimens, recourse has been made to speculative reconstruction. The late A. L. Kroeber attempted to reconstruct the elements of original New World culture on the basis of items that have been universally reported among the known tribes. Kroeber believed that traits common to every one of the Indian groups may well have been retained from the culture that was brought here at the beginning. His list of material items includes stone implements made by pressure or rubbing, bone or horn objects fashioned by polishing, knowledge of hafting, control of fire, making of baskets or nets, use of the spear thrower or bow, and possession of tamed (domesticated?) dogs.[7] Such reconstructions, no matter how close they may come to the mark, do not suit present-day Americanists. They insist, with good reason, that all reconstructions of America's past must be based entirely on the actual findings of archeologists.

To sum up, American anthropologists are fairly well agreed that man came to the New World by crossing the Bering Straits from northeastern Asia to Alaska about 20,000 B.P. Several waves of immigrants followed the first arrivals, bringing in diversified physical features that became increasingly Mongoloid. The Pleistocene's Wisconsin phase was in a late stage when the earliest migrants came, and their culture was about on a level with Europe's late Paleolithic. After they had taken up residence in the New World they may have received a few influences from the Old, but on the whole most of their later achievements in cultural development seem to have been independently evolved in the Americas.[8]

---

[7] A. L. Kroeber, *Anthropology,* rev. ed., New York, 1948, p. 778.

[8] James B. Griffin, University of Michigan, in "Some Prehistoric Connections between Siberia and America," *Science,* Vol. 131, 1960, pp. 801–12, expresses the opinion that the earliest American culture resembles eastern Siberian in some respects. He thinks that there then followed, at least in the Eastern Woodlands of the New World, a long period of indigenous developments before there was a resurgence of Siberian, and possibly other east Asiatic influences, during a millennium starting about 1500 B.C.

On the other hand, Chester S. Chard, University of Wisconsin, who has closely followed the excellent and extensive work of Russian archeologists, does not believe that anything found in eastern Siberia is early enough to have been ancestral to American culture. Chard's views are stated in "New World Origins: A Reappraisal," *Antiquity,* Vol. 33, 1959, pp. 44–49.

The Russian stand is given, in part, in S. I. Rudenko, translated by Paul Tolstoy, *The Ancient Culture of the Bering Sea and the Eskimo Problem,* Toronto, 1961. For a more comprehensive treatment, see A. L. Mongait, *Archaeology in the USSR,* M. W. Thompson, trans., (Penguin), Baltimore, 1961, and H. N. Michael, ed., *Studies in Siberian Ethnogenesis,* Toronto, 1962.

Early cultures in the Americas[9]

While there is much confusion and vagueness regarding the origins of culture in the New World, it is certain that there was no cultural uniformity after a beginning had been made. There might have been a common base at first, but once people found themselves in different environments within the Americas, they were bound to fashion different tools and to develop different habits. Accordingly, it is impossible to present one single story that tells how culture grew in all of the Western Hemisphere. Just the same, certain stages of development do seem to have been reached at particular times, and when these stages are put into a chronological sequence, they serve to indicate how culture developed in America.

Our story begins with a poorly defined stage of indiscriminate *food-gathering*. We do not know much about this postulated stage, and only a handful of Americanists believe in its existence. A place called Tule Springs, in Nevada, which has been radiocarbon dated at 22,000 B.P., has yielded the best available evidence for a food-gathering phase. At this time these people had flint choppers, scrapers, knives or projectile points, and worked splinters of bone. It is likely that they combined food-gathering activities with hunting.

As a rule, most archeologists prefer to attribute the beginnings of culture in the Western Hemisphere to small bands of east Siberian hunters who crossed the Bering Straits in the pursuit of game. This suggests the existence of a land bridge or of very shallow water so that the animals and their pursuers could have come across. Little is definitely known about these hunters. Apparently, they made a number of assorted lithic implements, but they seem to have relied heavily on stone points, pressure-flaked in the form of a lance head, and therefore called *lanceolate*. These stone points were probably affixed to long shafts, and may have been hurled with atlatls or spear throwers. Enough lanceolate projectile points have been found associated with the bones of extinct mammals to suggest that their makers were hunters of such big beasts as mammoths, mastodons, American camels, wild horses, and ancient bison. Quite often, stone implements suitable for scraping hides accompany the lanceolate points.

The most likely manifestations of this ancient New World hunting

---

9 The organization and content of this and the next two sections have been greatly influenced by Gordon R. Willey's article, "New World Prehistory," *Science*, Vol. 131, 1960, pp. 73–86.

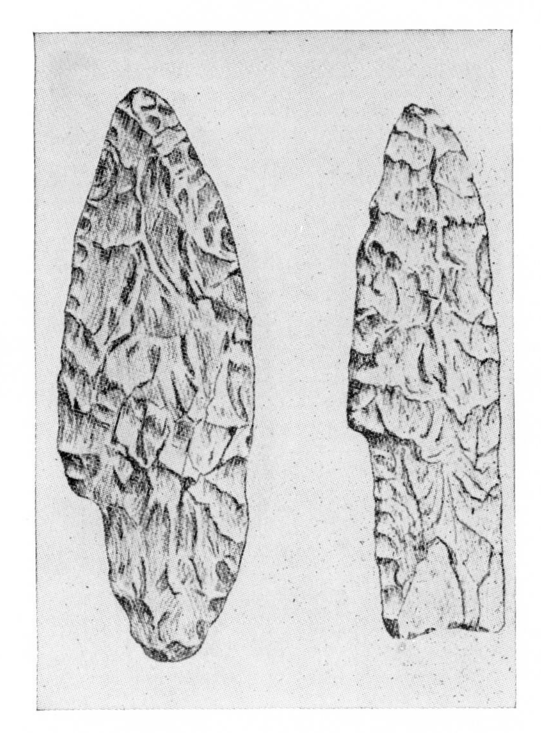

FIG. 17-1. Sandia projectile points. The notch or shoulder at one side of each point is typical. Notice the small channel at the base of one point. (From H. M. Wormington, *Ancient Men in North America,* rev. ed., Denver, 1949. Courtesy of the author and the Denver Museum of Natural History.)

culture have been found scattered through the high plains ranging from Texas and eastern New Mexico into Arizona, and from Colorado into northern Mexico. One of the most carefully studied sites was found at Sandia, New Mexico. Within a limestone cave situated in the northern Sandia mountains, the archeologist Frank C. Hibben, of the University of New Mexico, found signs of three clearly separated occupation layers, the oldest of which contained nineteen Paleolithic implements, now known as *Sandia points* (Fig. 17–1). They are well made, slightly reminiscent of Solutrian workmanship, and notched at one side to produce a shoulder. Despite a few claims to the contrary, Sandia points are believed to have had a very narrow distribution.[10]

Some time after the days of the Sandia point makers, around 10,000 B.C., the last of the Wisconsin glaciers withdrew, big-game hunting spread more widely than ever, and some bands of men began to migrate ever farther from the Bering Straits. Hunters of guanaco even penetrated all the way to the Straits of Magellan at the tip of South America by 7000 B.C. At this stage, the principal implements made of stone are known as

[10] George Agogino is now reinvestigating the original Sandia cave. His studies should throw much additional light on the time and nature of the culture represented by this site.

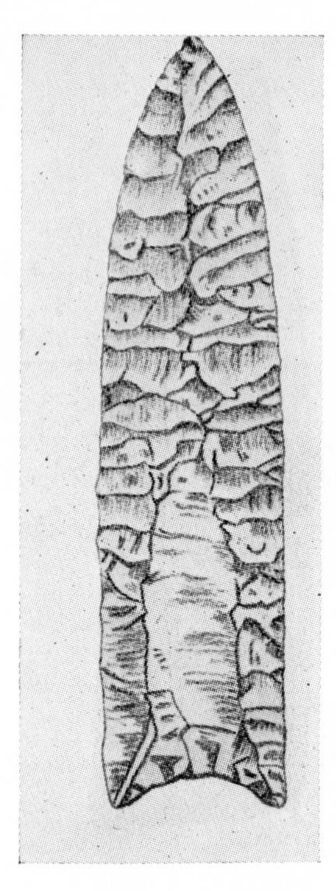

FIG. 17-2. Clovis point. These projectile points are made of stone. The fluted channel is better developed than in Sandia points, but not as fully formed as in Folsom points. (From H. M. Wormington, *Ancient Men in North America,* rev. ed., Denver, 1949. Courtesy of the author and the Denver Museum of Natural History.)

fluted points. They are called "fluted" because they have a channel or groove running from the base up the length of the point.

Fluted points occur in two major varieties. Although there is no complete agreement the one that seems to be somewhat the older is called *Clovis.*[11] These *Clovis fluted points* (Fig. 17–2), may be as much as 3 or 4 inches long and, in contrast with Sandia points, they have close analogies with a widespread range of materials throughout the Americas. There is nothing comparable to them in the Old World.

A somewhat younger contemporary of the Clovis fluted point, and possibly a descendant from it, is the *Folsom point* (Fig. 17–3), which has been dated around 9900 B.P. Recognition and acceptance of *Folsom Culture* make up one of the most dramatic chapters of American archeology. The story has so often been told that it need not be repeated in detail.[12] Suffice it to say that from 1926 on, first at Folsom, New Mexico, and later

[11] Excavations were made at Clovis around the mid-1930's, first by Edgar B. Howard, and later by John L. Cotter. A detailed geological examination was carried out by Ernest Antevs in 1934.

[12] A good summary may be found in F. H. H. Roberts, Jr., "The Folsom Problem in American Archeology," *Annual Report for 1938,* Smithsonian Institution, Washington, D.C., 1939, pp. 531–46.

at the Lindenmeier site in Colorado, as well as elsewhere, repeated discoveries have been made of a highly characteristic stone and bone industry that was produced by hunters of an ancient form of buffalo, *Bison antiquus*. Well over 6000 lithic objects have been recovered at Lindenmeier alone, and a quantity of bone artifacts has been excavated, but not a speck of any *Folsom Man* has ever come to light.

Among the assortment of implements found, the Folsom point stands out as the most significant artifact of the culture. It is a small

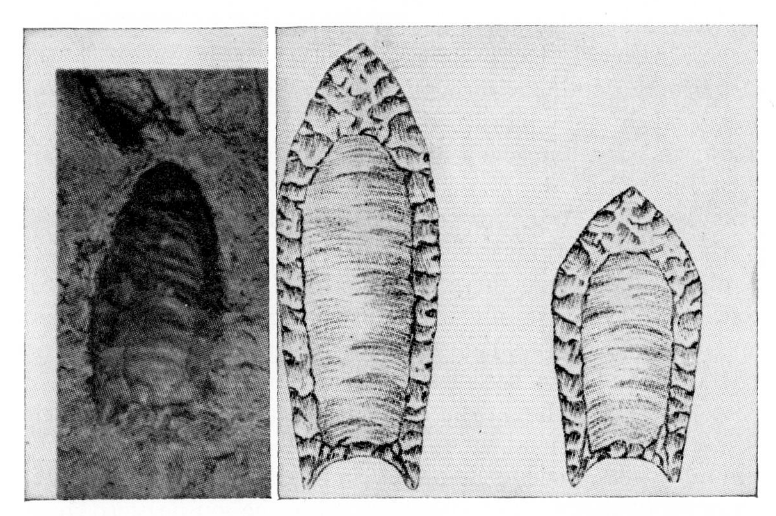

FIG. 17-3. Folsom points. Left: The original Folsom point photographed *in situ*. It is shown exactly as it lay when first discovered. Center and right: Two varieties of the Folsom point. Each has well-developed fluting, and a concave base from which "rabbit ears" project. (From H. M. Wormington, *Ancient Men in North America*, rev. ed., Denver, 1949. Courtesy of the author and the Denver Museum of National History.)

point, with a curved base and a slightly rounded tip. It is not as heavy as the Clovis point, and the two kinds of implements are never found side by side.

That fluted points represent a high and distinctive peak of lithic workmanship in America is readily admitted by all, but there is still doubt as to why the channels were made. Perhaps, as has been surmised, the fluting lessened the weight of the stone point, gave it greater penetrating power, and made it easier to haft. These are reasonable conjectures, but they have never been proved. After the time of Folsom, fluting begins to fade out and ultimately disappears.

Although it is occasionally held that what is called *Paleo-Indian*

Culture[13] prevailed at this time in the East while the *Desert Culture*[14] spread through the West, the term Paleo-Indian has also been suggested for both regions, and has been applied to all those early Americans who hunted mammals that are now extinct. This would include the makers of Sandia points and the manufacturers of fluted points, whether Clovis or Folsom. As thus used, no specific date is attached to the term Paleo-Indian, nor does it have a racial or linguistic connotation. It pertains only to a stage of culture during which lanceolate or fluted points were widely used.

While the Paleo-Indians lived primarily by hunting, it should not be assumed that they had no interest in plants. This interest is believed to have become dominant during the *Altithermal* period, starting around 5000 B.C., when many parts of the New World, especially in the West, grew hot and dry, and many Pleistocene mammals shrank in numbers or died out.[15] Only the Plains, east of the Rockies in North America, and the Pampas of Argentina remained suitable for hunters. Thereupon numbers of New World inhabitants entered on a stage of *food collection.* This phase differs from the earlier food gathering in that it involves more effective exploitation of local environments, and the development of adequate technological equipment. Hunting continued wherever possible, but it tended to become secondary. Food collection usually applies to wild plants, but it can also refer to the collection of shellfish. On the whole, some food collectors were able to build large and stable communities and sometimes they accumulated great material wealth.

In one of the increasingly arid spots, in the southeastern corner of Arizona and adjacent New Mexico, there lived in early Altithermal times a people whose remains suggest that they were more interested in gathering wild vegetal products than in pursuing game. Archeologists know about them from objects found at several spots, all of which may be

[13] This entire topic has been extensively reviewed and discussed in R. J. Mason, "The Paleo-Indian Tradition in Eastern North America," *Current Anthropology,* June, 1962. Mason suggests that Clovis points may be quite old in parts of the eastern United States, and that, contrary to prevailing opinion, they may even prove to have been ancestral to the Clovis points found further west. He believes Paleo-Indian culture to have begun between 12,000 and 13,000 B.P.

[14] In large sections of the West, from Oregon to Mexico and from California to the Rockies, many sites reveal what is called the Desert Culture. It may have started as early as 9000 B.P. The Desert Culture usually features short, broad blades in a number of styles, milling stones, choppers, and a variety of vegetal and wooden objects. Hunting and gathering were the principal subsistence pursuits. For further details, see J. D. Jennings, "Danger Cave," *Memoir No. 14, Society for American Archaeology,* 1957.

[15] It is possible that intensive hunting speeded up the extinction of some large mammals, but this point is in dispute among American archeologists.

said to represent the *Cochise Culture* (Fig. 17–4). Only the very earliest phase is of comparable antiquity with Folsom.[16] Relative lack of devotion to hunting is inferred from the absence of projectile points, although one must not rule out the possibility that these might have been made of perishable substances that have since disintegrated. On the other hand, reliance on wild seeds, nuts, fruits, and berries is brought out most clearly by the presence of grinding stones similar to those known from later times to have been used for preparing plant foods. The principal early tools consist of thin, flat, milling stones, the whole class of which are called *metates* in American archeology. Whatever was put on a milling stone was crushed or ground with a rubbing stone, *mano,* which, in the earliest level of Cochise Culture, was small and evidently meant to be held in one hand only. Both the metates and manos were made of sandstone.

As temperatures climbed in the Great Plains the heat was accompanied by drought, but far to the east there was enough rainfall to stimulate the growth of grass and forests and to make the area increasingly attractive to settlers. There thus arose in the present territory of the eastern United States, most of which is called Eastern Woodlands, a phase of culture that is known as *Early Archaic.* It is typified by small groups of Indians who knew neither how to grow crops nor how to make pottery. Many habitations were made near water courses and relics of weirs, nets, and hooks point to great interest in fishing. There is good proof, based on the frequency of stone mortars and pestles, that the Early Archaic people relied more heavily on plant foods than their Paleo-Indian predecessors; and this circumstance has led some writers to propose a connection between Early Archaic in the eastern United States and Cochise Culture in the Southwest.

A subsequent period sometimes identified as *Late Archaic* in the Eastern Woodlands may be regarded as transitional between Paleolithic and Neolithic. It extends in time from about 3000 to 1000 B.C. and is featured by the introduction of a host of new items, some of which might have been brought in by a fresh wave of short, stocky, broad-headed migrants from Asia. These include a profusion of polished stone celts, adzes, and banner stones.[17] Also found are tubular objects of clay

---

[16] For an account of the three phases that make up Cochise Culture, consult E. B. Sayles and E. Antevs, "The Cochise Culture," *Gila Pueblo, Medallion Papers,* No. 29, 1941.

[17] In the earlier days of American archeology scholars were puzzled by finds of stone objects with winglike projections extending from a central perforation. Their purpose was unknown, but it was surmised that they might have been carried on staffs like banners, hence the name. Modern archeologists look on them as weights connected with the use of spear-throwers.

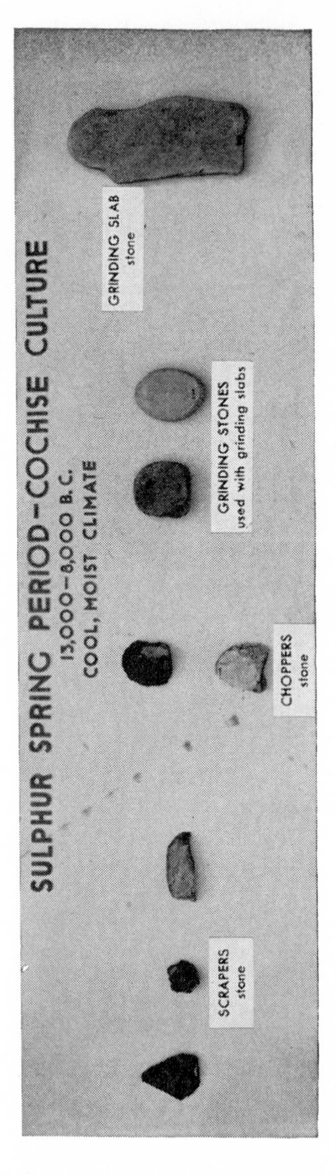

FIG. 17-4. (Above and Opposite). Stages of Cochise culture. The Sulphur Spring period corresponds, roughly, to the same antique time when Folsom projectile points were being made. (Courtesy of the Chicago Museum of Natural History.)

or stone that have been tentatively identified as pipes. Copper was imported from the vicinity of the Great Lakes,[18] and steatite (soapstone) bowls were carried as far as the Lower Mississippi Valley.

---

[18] Copper objects were not uncommonly made and used in the New World by people of Stone Age culture. *Annealing* was a favorite technique. Annealing calls for the pounding of heated, but not molten, copper. A degree of tempering or toughening can be achieved by subjecting the metal alternately to heat and cold.

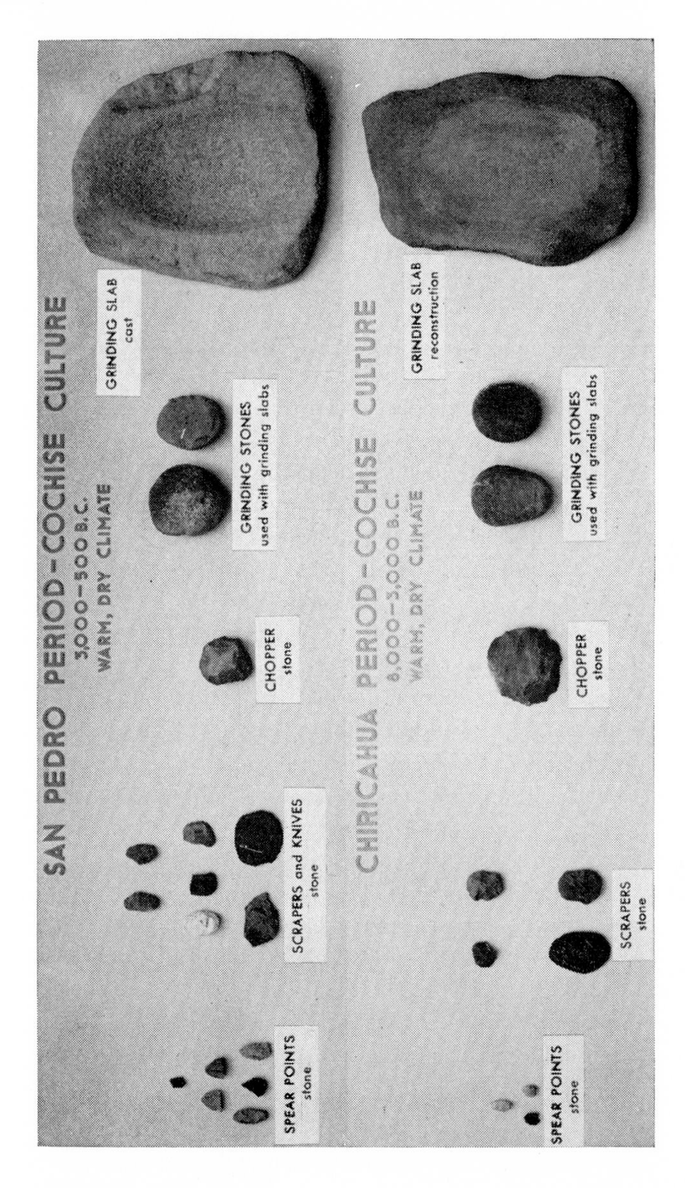

Although the New World's food-collecting stage is most clearly revealed in a limited number of places, the way of life was apparently widespread. Large shell mounds, suggesting at least partially sedentary societies, have been found along both coasts of North and South America. Then, too, in certain areas of the western United States, some food collectors subsisted primarily on fish and acorns. Accordingly, archeologists can show that food collecting took many forms.

Incipient cultivation

As was the case in the Old World, many groups in America went from a Paleolithic to a Neolithic stage, but some tribes never took up a New Stone Age form of culture. This is true not only of peoples living in extremely cold climates unsuited for crop cultivation, but even of some societies whose lands were later adapted to agriculture by European settlers. Again, as was true of the Old World's Mesolithic, pottery was occasionally produced by noncultivators;[19] and, conversely, instances have been reported of farming populations that had no pottery.[20] American archeology drives home the lesson that the domestication of plants and the making of pottery may appear separately. Nonetheless, despite some exceptions, it seems to have been the customary rule throughout the world for a ceramic industry to accompany agriculture. Within the last millennium before Christ the stage was set in the New World for the Neolithic and incontrovertible proof of its existence soon becomes available.

The New World's shift from food collecting to true agriculture was probably a long and slow development. *Incipient Cultivation* has been proposed as a suitable name for the period of transition; and four independent or partially independent centers are now recognized. The oldest seems to have been located in the vicinity of Mexico; another appears to have existed in Peru; a third may well have been in the Amazon-Orinoco drainage, where *manioc,* a root plant, came to be grown; and the fourth may have been centered in the valley of the Mississippi.

Incipient Cultivation refers to a stage in which the domestication of plants was known, but in which agricultural products made up only a small part of a society's subsistence patterns. Traditionally, the oldest cultigen in the Western Hemisphere has been traced to *Bat Cave* in New Mexico.[21] Corncobs found in Cochise-like refuse at Bat Cave have been dated between 3500 and 2500 B.C. Not only are the dates uncertain, but

---

19 A. Serrano, "The Charrua," *Handbook of South American Indians,* J. H. Steward, ed., Washington, D.C., Vol. 2, 1949, p. 194. The Eskimo likewise provide an excellent example of a nonagricultural folk who knew how to make pottery.

20 J. B. Bird, "Excavations in Northern Chile," *American Museum of Natural History, Anthropological Papers,* Vol. 38, No. 4, 1943, p. 307. Bird expresses the caution that the occurrence of agriculture without ceramics, weaving, or basketry may be accidental.

21 Bat Cave was excavated for Harvard University by Herbert W. Dick. For his report, see "Evidences of Early Man in Bat Cave . . . ," *Indian Tribes of Aboriginal America,* Proceedings of the 29th International Congress of Americanists, Vol. 3, 1952, pp. 158–63.

there is even a question as to whether the maize was actually cultivated. The cobs are so tiny, and the corn shows so many wild botanical characteristics that there is some doubt as to whether it was grown or merely collected.

A somewhat stronger case for Incipient Cultivation was made by R. S. MacNeish, at *Tamaulipas* in semiarid, northeastern Mexico.[22] Even in very early levels he found traces of domesticated squash and other plants, though the general cultural context resembled that of most food collectors in desertlike environments. Later, there is definite evidence of domesticated beans followed by the appearance of primitive maize. But even as we approach 3000 B.C. the cultivated plants are estimated by MacNeish to make up less than 10 percent of the food supply. The precise relationship between Bat Cave and Tamaulipas corn is uncertain, but most Americanists regard Tamaulipas as being closer to the unknown spot where maize was first domesticated.

FARMING VILLAGES, AND THE CONCEPT OF NUCLEAR AMERICA

As we get beyond 2000 B.C. there appear in the New World increasingly numerous full-scale villages, whose inhabitants relied very much on farming. In spite of the fact that such villages show diverse local or regional traits, all of them may be said to be variations of a single agricultural theme, in which the growing of maize played a key part.[23] Naturally, American archeologists are eager to learn everything possible about the formation of these villages; and they are most anxious to track down the origin of corn. In spite of their desires many questions remain unanswered, and the beginnings of corn domestication are obscure and subject to conflicting opinions.

As one surveys the New World it becomes unavoidably apparent that the highest prehistoric levels were attained by the Toltec-Aztec-Maya, who lived in Mexico (including Yucatan) and Guatemala, and by

---

22 R. S. MacNeish has published several papers on his work at Tamaulipas, but a reasonably complete and detailed account may be found in "Preliminary Archaeological Investigations in the Sierra de Tamaulipas, Mexico," *Transactions of the American Philosophical Society,* Vol. 48, Part 6, 1958.

23 There is a growing belief, exemplified by G. R. Willey, that true farming villages had only a limited number of original sources and that most of the communities drew their inspiration, if not their actual materials, from the same few centers.

the Inca of Peru and the vicinity. It has been proposed to call all of this vast area "Nuclear America"[24] and to recognize within it a northern center in Mexico and a southern center in Peru. There are a goodly number of close parallels between the two centers, and each had a similar development. At each end of Nuclear America high culture began with a *Formative* period that started within the last millennium before Christ. There then followed a climactic, *Classic* phase that fell within the time span of A.D. 1 to 1000. In both areas the high attainments of the Classic phase gradually petered out and a *Post-Classic* stage began around A.D. 1000. The Post-Classic shows an overall decline of culture, which is particularly noticeable in the fine arts.

Between the northern and southern high points of Nuclear America there has always been considerable interchange, although experts are frequently puzzled about the routes that were taken. If we accept an original entrance for man across the Bering Straits, the earliest direction must have been from north to south. Furthermore, it is now held that maize was domesticated in or near the northern periphery of Nuclear America, and that knowledge of its use was transmitted in all directions, including the south. Around 715 B.C., however, when fully domesticated corn reached Peru, many traits and influences began to move in the opposite direction, from south to north.

With respect to the growth of culture in the New World, Nuclear America seems to have played a role comparable to that of the Eastern Mediterranean Zone in the Old World.

SOME NEOLITHIC HIGHLIGHTS NORTH OF MEXICO

North of Nuclear America areas of advanced culture developed in the Eastern Woodlands and in the southwestern United States. Each zone came to rely on cultivated maize; and, while people in the Eastern Woodlands worked in solid metal, neither area had any knowledge of full-fledged metallurgy.

In terms of its basic economy *Early Woodland*, which began early in the Christian era, may be looked upon as a continuation of the generally nonagricultural Late Archaic (page 339). Tubular pipes were ground from stone and positively associated with tobacco smoking, large

[24] A full treatment of this important topic may be found in G. R. Willey, "The Prehistoric Civilizations of Nuclear America," *American Anthropologist*, Vol. 57, 1955, pp. 571–89.

earthen mounds were constructed over the bodies of the dead,[25] woven cloth made its first appearance, and copper was being used for ornaments. Pottery-making seems to have begun in the northerly ranges of Early Woodland, where the first forms resemble styles known from northeastern Asia. It is very interesting that pottery preceded agriculture by several centuries, and that ceramics may have come from the north whereas farming might have come from Nuclear America to the south.

Around A.D. 600 the eastern United States entered on a *Middle Woodland* period, whose cultural climax was reached in the *Hopewell* phase. The most active centers were in southern Ohio and the Illinois Valley, and a noticeable lag in development is revealed in sites to the southeast and along the Gulf Coast. Probably, the Hopewell people were farmers who raised the three most basic North American crops—corn, beans, and squash. These were supplemented by game, fish, and wild edible plant products. An ample food supply is attested by the large sizes of permanent settlements, the building of enormous earthworks for socioreligious purposes rather than for practical considerations such as defense, and the rich flourishing of art in forms and styles that were so standardized as to suggest the presence of specialists. Pipes of polished stone are abundant in Hopewell remains and reach an exceptional degree of elaboration. Many are made like a platform, on which there is often carved a realistic effigy of an animal within whose body the bowl is to be found (Fig. 17–5).

Pottery-making was a featured activity. Hopewell vessels were grit-tempered, gray-buff in color, and decorated with bands or rows of incised, impressed, or stamped designs. There are exceptionally fine pieces, showing no signs of practical use, that are judged to have served in sacred contexts; good, carefully fashioned wares that show evidence of restricted utility; and ordinary cooking pots that are customarily ornamented with impressions from a cord-wrapped paddle, and are sometimes equipped with feet.

Production of ornaments must have been a major activity. Copper was cleverly handled, without being liquefied, and was made into a great many forms. Sheets of mica were used whole or cut into complex

---

[25] Mounds of many different kinds have been found throughout the New World. They are very abundant in the eastern half of the United States. They were initially regarded as mysterious and attributed to the work of a strange, mound-building "race." They still puzzle archeologists, but are now treated like any other feature of a particular way of life. Much attention has been attracted by *effigy mounds* whose outlines were formed to resemble the shape of an animal. Many effigy mounds exist in the Great Lakes region and in the Ohio Valley. A fuller discussion of several of these points may be found in G. I. Quimby, *Indian Life in the Upper Great Lakes,* Chicago, 1960, pp. 85–88, *et passim.*

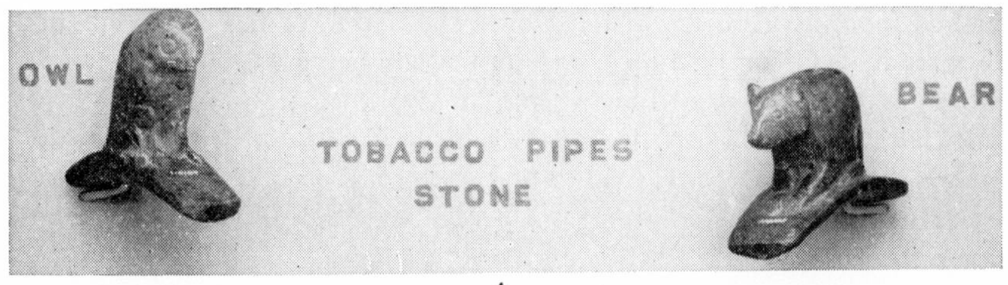

A

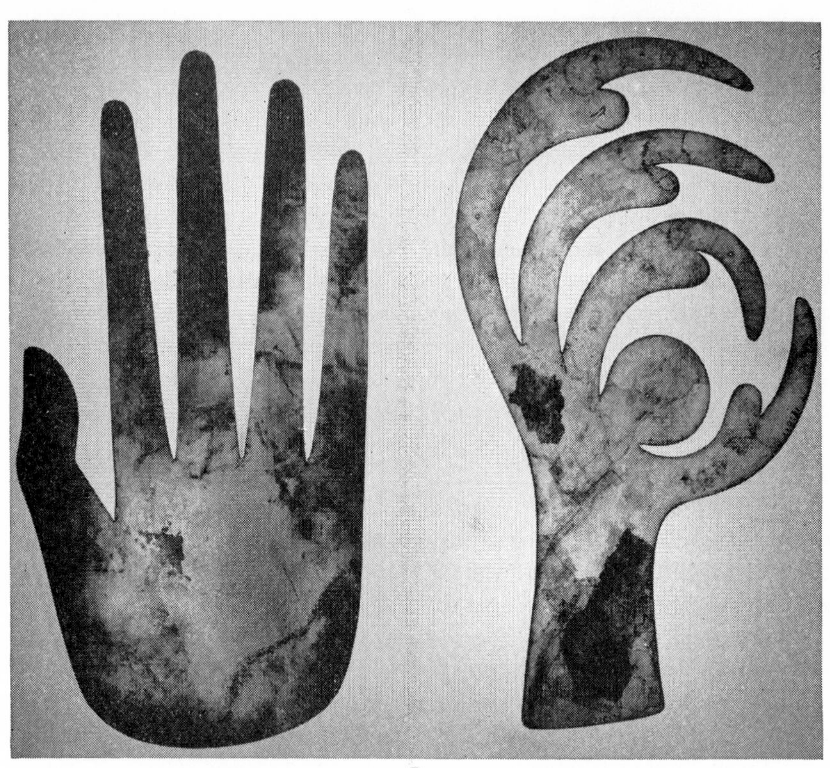

B

FIG. 17-5. A few artifacts of Hopewell culture. A. Two varieties of platform pipes. B. A human hand and the foot of an eagle, made of mica. (Courtesy of the Chicago Museum of Natural History.)

geometric or realistic figures; and decorative objects in great profusion were made of pearl, silver, shell, bone, animal teeth, stone, and human skeletal parts. Much of the finest art work is found in graves, and Hopewell culture reveals a variety of burial customs. Corpses were placed sometimes in log tombs and sometimes on platforms; some graves were lined with woven mats and some with sheets of mica; many bodies were buried under cone-shaped mounds of earth; and others were cremated in clay basins.

Somewhere about A.D. 1000 the great Hopewell phase of Middle Woodland underwent decline and was succeeded by a less well-known stage that may be called *Late Woodland.* This probably had only a short, transitory existence before it was absorbed or replaced by an eastward spread of the Mississippi pattern that lasted into historic times. Most authorities at present believe that cultural events in the eastern United States during the last centuries of American prehistory show a strong parallel with what was happening in the Southwest. There are so many things common to both areas that a connection seems perfectly logical. Sites are known from Texas and Oklahoma, the inhabitants of which may well have served as intermediaries between the two major Neolithic zones north of Mexico, but numerous details await clarification.

A second important zone of Neolithic culture north of Mexico seems to have begun within an extensive area in the drainage of the San Juan River, near the four corners where the boundaries of Arizona, New Mexico, Colorado, and Utah meet. It is known as the Southwest, and occupies a unique position in American archeology. Much of the territory comprises a high plateau and there are many arid spots where perishable materials may last for amazingly long periods. In addition to an abundance of artifacts, plant and animal remains, and dried-out bodies loosely called mummies, the Southwest provides a record of continuous occupation from early prehistoric times to the present; and tree-ring dating often makes possible an accurate means of timing events and climatic conditions. It was in the Southwest that most of the leading American anthropologists did at least some of their field work two or three generations ago.

Within the Southwest archeologists were first attracted to the vicinity of the four corners, where some spectacular ruins, like Betatakin, awaited scientific investigation. After an initial phase of devotion to detailed reports of particular sites, efforts were made to formulate a synthesis that would apply to the whole region. A sequence was established that was marked into three preceramic periods called *Basket Maker I, II,* and *III,* followed directly by five fully developed Neolithic stages known as *Pueblo I, II, III, IV,* and *V.* Not long after this scheme had been proposed students working at a distance from the four corners began to find material that did not fit into the Basket Maker–Pueblo pattern. It was then decided to rechristen the latter as *Anasazi,* to rename the various stages, and to restrict their application to the plateau terri-

A

B

C

tory of the four corners.[26] At least three other subregions have been recognized for other parts of the Southwest,[27] but we shall limit ourselves to a synopsis of the Anasazi.

Archeologists fully expect that the start of Anasazi will some day be traced back to an antecedent culture of the type indicated by Sandia, Folsom, or Cochise. Meantime, it is assumed that around the opening of the Christian era the early Basket Makers began to frequent the plateau country around the four corners. They were longheaded Indians who supplemented the hunting and gathering of food by growing corn and, possibly, squash. They hunted deer and smaller game with spears and atlatls. Their agricultural implements were simple *dibbles* or wooden digging sticks about 3 or 4 feet long and beveled or pointed at one end, as well as flat metates and manos of stone. They may have kept turkeys and they certainly had domesticated dogs, whose ancestry has been traced to Asia.

About A.D. 500, *Modified Basket Maker* culture (formerly Basket Maker III), begins in the same general region as the earlier stage. Throughout this period subterranean *pit houses* were in use and some groups even congregated into what may be called small villages. During this stage, too, religious chambers known as *kivas*—usually circular, but occasionally squarish—were built underground, apart from the living quarters.

Although Modified Basket Maker culture continued most of the older ways of life, it also made a number of innovations. Farming seems

---

[26] The more recent terminology is explained in F. H. H. Roberts, Jr., "Archeology in the Southwest," *American Antiquity*, Vol. 3, 1937–1938, pp. 3–33. A somewhat similar but fuller account occurs in E. H. Morris, "Archeological Studies in the LaPlata District," *Carnegie Institution*, No. 519, Washington, D.C., 1939, pp. 8–44.

[27] The most distinctive and by all odds the most accepted of these subdivisions, called *Hohokam*, is centered along the Gila River and its vicinity in southern Arizona. Somewhat less clearly distinctive is the *Mogollon-Mimbres* manifestation of southwestern New Mexico and adjacent southeastern Arizona. Even less distinct and less certain of acceptance as an individual stage is the *Patayan*, whose remains are distributed along the Colorado River Basin, south of the Grand Canyon of Arizona.

These archeological subdivisions are discussed in Irving Rouse's essay in A. V. Kidder, *An Introduction to the Study of Southwestern Archaeology*, New Haven and London, 1962.

FIG. 17-6. Variations of pueblo locations and structures in the Southwest. A. Pueblo Bonito was situated in the open at Chaco Canyon, New Mexico. It was probably built after Pueblo III had begun. B. Montezuma's Castle was located in rock shelters on the sides of a steep cliff near Campe Verde, Arizona. (Courtesy of Chicago Museum of Natural History.) C. Awatovi was perched on a high mesa, close to the modern Hopi pueblos in Arizona. (From *American Antiquity*, Vol. 3, 1937. Courtesy of J. O. Brew.)

to have been more intensively carried on, more varieties of corn were grown, and beans were added to the former crops. Bows and arrows gradually replaced atlatls, and small stemmed projectile points and notched axes were introduced. But the most important novelty was the manufacturing of pottery. The earliest pieces were of a plain, gray color, shaped by coiling within a basket and hardened in the sun without actual firing. Where the idea of potmaking originated among the Modified Basket Makers is not known, but before long numerous styles had developed, all hand fashioned by coiling. Similar lines of cultural progress appear to have been followed throughout the *Developmental Pueblo* (formerly Pueblo I and II) stage until the *Great Period* (Pueblo III) began around A.D. 1000. Among other things the Indians of this date started to move out of small villages and to congregate in massive, terraced buildings, as may be seen at pueblo Bonito or Mesa Verde, that contained up to a thousand rooms. The huge pueblos were made of stone masonry and were several stories high.[28]

Not all of the Indians in the San Juan district moved into the huge, terraced structures and not all of the massive pueblos were identical. Apart from differences in their modes of construction, a few of the huge buildings, such as the cliff houses at Montezuma's Castle in Arizona, were erected among overhanging rocks on ledges high up the walls of steep cliffs; others, like pueblo Bonito in the Chaco Canyon of New Mexico, were located on level spots, out in the open; and some, like Awatovi near the Hopi villages of Arizona, were built on flat-topped mesas, far above the surrounding plain (Fig. 17–6).

From every point of view the Great Period marked the highest peak of Anasazi culture, but its brilliance was not long-lasting. Signs of a decline by about A.D. 1300 are evident throughout the neighborhood of the four corners. The large pueblos were abandoned one after the other and fell into ruin, arts and crafts declined, groups of Indians wandered over the countryside, and a shift of population took place southward, toward the Little Colorado and the Rio Grande Rivers.

Whatever its causes of decline may have been, the Great Period was followed by a *regressive* stage (Pueblo IV), which later underwent a *renaissance* (Pueblo V) south of the original Anasazi center. Although Pueblo culture never again recaptured its earlier exuberance, it did not fade completely away, and many of its former traits were retained. Villages continued to be built in large, communally inhabited blocks of contiguous rooms, often facing an open court or plaza within which

[28] Pueblo, when spelled with a capital refers to a generalized aspect of Anasazi culture. When written with a small letter it signifies a particular structure, town, or tribe.

were dug underground kivas, now customarily square and never exceptionally large. Natives living along the Rio Grande learned to make new kinds of glazed pottery, and there was lively trade not only among various local communities but even as far off as the Mississippi Valley. A large number of the towns founded after 1300 have persisted into modern times, having survived the Spanish conquest of the sixteenth century and the westward expansion of the United States. Many of these Indian villages, which are, in general terms only, related to the more ancient cliff dwellings, still function actively, and have kept a good measure of their prehistoric culture. It is for this reason that serious anthropologists as well as curious tourists continue to visit ruins like Betatakin, pueblo Bonito, and Mesa Verde, as well as Zuni, Laguna, Acoma, Santo Domingo, Taos, San Ildefonso, the Hopi towns, and other famous pueblos.

Selected References

Armillas, Pedro, "History of Land Use in Arid and Semi-arid Regions: Ancient America," *UNESCO series in the arid zone program,* n.d. (mimeographed prepublication copy).

Brew, James O., "Archaeology of Alkali Ridge, Southeastern Utah," *Papers of the Peabody Museum of American Archaeology and Ethnology,* Harvard University, Vol. 21, Cambridge, Mass., 1946.

Griffin, James B., ed., *Archeology of Eastern United States,* Chicago, 1952.

———, "Some Prehistoric Connections between Siberia and America," *Science,* Vol. 131, 1960, pp. 801–12.

Haury, Emil W., *et al., The Stratigraphy and Archaeology of Ventana Cave, Arizona,* Tucson, Ariz., and Albuquerque, N. Mex., 1950.

Kidder, Alfred V., *An Introduction to the Study of Southwestern Archaeology,* New Haven, Conn., 1924.

———, *An Introduction to the Study of Southwestern Archaeology,* New Haven and London, 1962.

Krieger, Alex D., "New World Culture History: Anglo-America," in A. L. Kroeber, ed., *Anthropology Today,* Chicago, 1953, pp. 238–64.

Martin, Paul S., *et al., Indians before Columbus,* Chicago, 1947.

Neumann, Georg K., "Archeology and Race in the American Indian," in J. B. Griffin, ed., *Archeology of Eastern United States,* Chicago, 1952, pp. 13–34.

Sayles, Edward B., and Antevs, E., "The Cochise Culture," *Medallion Papers,* No. 29, 1941.

Willey, Gordon R., "New World Prehistory," *Science,* Vol. 131, 1960, pp. 73–86.

———, "The Prehistoric Civilizations of Nuclear America," *American Anthropologist,* Vol. 57, 1955, pp. 571–89.

Wormington, Helen M., "Ancient Man in North America," rev. ed., *Museum of Natural History,* Denver, 1957.

———, "Prehistoric Indians of the Southwest," *Ibid.,* 1947.

Man and Culture in the New World: Part II

CHAPTER 18

THE ESSENTIALLY NEOLITHIC MAYA

Generally accepted criteria of Metal Age culture do not readily apply to the pre-Columbian Maya and Aztec. Some Maya artisans hammered ornaments of gold and fashioned "sleigh bells" of copper; and Aztec craftsmen attained the art of casting liquid copper and gold by the lost-wax (cire-perdue) method, but experts freely admit that these Indians failed to go beyond what may be called metallurgical infancy because they seldom handled molten metal and never manufactured utilitarian metallic implements. Thus, it seems most logical to describe them as essentially Neolithic. On this level they went far beyond the achievements of any of the more northerly tribes.

Although the origins of Maya culture are lost in obscurity, it is conceded that it had become completely Neolithic centuries before that stage was reached in the eastern and southwestern United States. Sylvanus G. Morley,[1] leading Maya specialist at the time of his death, was of the opinion that the ancestors of the Maya had acquired knowledge of ceramics and plant cultivation during the first millennium before Christ. He divides the succeeding epochs of Maya culture into an *Old Empire,* ranging from A.D. 317 to 987, and a *New Empire,* which endured in one fashion or another from 987 to 1697. Since, by his own admission, the term "empire" is misleading–inasmuch as the Maya were never

[1] Much of this section is summarized from S. G. Morley, *The Ancient Maya,* Stanford, Calif., 1956.

grouped into one large and unified political division—we shall speak only of *Early* and *Late Maya* periods.

Early Maya culture is believed to have had its beginnings in the lowlands of north central Peten, in Guatemala, at a time when the region was so densely forested that farmers repeatedly had to clear and burn over the land. Despite this difficulty, the Early Maya found it possible to achieve surpluses of food and other goods, thus furnishing the setting in which the more highly specialized features of the culture could flourish. Crops of maize, beans, squash, pumpkins, sweet potatoes, tomatoes, and cassava (manioc) were raised. In addition, many wild fruits and nuts were gathered and chili peppers, allspice, coriander, and vanilla were cultivated for seasoning and flavoring. Game was hunted in the forests, and the plumage of birds and the skins of deer and jaguar were used for making fine cloaks and sandals. Cocoa was grown in quantity and was made into the universally popular drink of chocolate. Among the most important nonedible plant materials were mahogany and cedar wood for building, liana vines for tying, gourds for containers, tobacco, rubber, and copal resin for incense. From their environment the Early Maya also secured in abundance building stone, lime, and gravel. There is no doubt of their favorable situation, nor of the intelligence with which they took advantage of natural resources. Maize was their staff of life, and figuratively speaking, the basis on which they built their remarkable culture.

Early Maya society was highly organized. There were numerous city-states, each headed by an hereditary ruler, descended in the male line, who was the leading power in civil, religious, and military affairs. He appointed town and village chiefs who, together with priests and special councilors, formed an advisory body. Most of the administrators were related to the ruler and constituted a nobility. Of equal or even higher status were the priests, who were divided into grades on the basis of function. Commoners came next and were the actual builders of the great monuments that were the glory of the Maya. At the bottom of the social scale were slaves, some of whom were born to that condition whereas others came into it as prisoners of war, criminals, or orphans.

Architecture and sculpture—using wood, stone, and clay—were among the major arts and crafts, and wooden mallets and polished stone celts were the most important tools. According to Morley, the years from about 730 to 880 saw the greatest development of all pre-Columbian times in New World sculpture. Also, pottery was made in huge quantities and in greatly varied styles. No cloth of the Early Maya period

FIG. 18-1. Some aspects of Maya culture. A. A ruined temple at Uxmal, in Yucatan. B. The lower half of a carved stela in Chichen Itza, Yucatan. It shows the feet of a warrior, trampling on Ahpuch, the god of death. C. A few examples of Maya hieroglyphics.

has actually been recovered, but from artistic representations it is known that elaborate cotton garments were in wide use. Basketry, too, is known only indirectly. Flint chipping, the handling of precious and common stones, and work with feathers all reached high levels, but metallurgy was little practiced.

In terms of material culture, the most amazing accomplishment of the Early Maya is the erection of imposing assemblages of high pyramids, massive stairways, colorful temples, carved monolithic columns (called *stelae*) (Fig. 18–1), and ceremonial ball courts.[2] Yet, the material achievements are more than matched by the intellectual heights reached in particular by the priesthood. A system of writing was devised, in which carefully made figures (*glyphs*) stood for ideas or sounds. Neither connected, cursive writing nor a true phonetic alphabet was developed, but Maya hieroglyphics command special attention because they were part of an essentially Neolithic way of life. Most of the writing was concerned with dates and religion,[3] and here again there is reason for wonder and admiration. The Maya had an original sign for zero, with the help of which the value of a digit changed according to its position, just as we recognize the differences between 5, 50, 500, and 505. Mathematics was geared to astronomy, and together with writing they made possible a reliable calendar in which accurate corrections were made for leap years. Not content with a single calendar, the Early Maya kept simultaneous track of a sacred year of 260 days and a secular year of 18 months of 20 days, plus 5 unlucky days at the end. New Year's Day in the two systems fell together every 52 years, and was the occasion for special ceremonials.

Brilliant though it unquestionably was, the culture of the Early Maya declined in 987. As in the case of the Great Pueblo collapse in the southwestern United States, many reasons have been advanced to explain why all the old cities were abandoned, but no one knows what really happened. At the time that the earlier localities were being evacuated, the culture was kept alive and later brought to a genuine renaissance in northern Yucatan, which had been only marginal in the earlier phase. There was some mingling with peoples from central Mexico and there were some innovations in religion, lesser arts and crafts, metallurgy, and architecture, but basically, Late Maya culture is a continuation of the Early period.

---

[2] S. G. Morley, *op. cit.*, pp. 312–81.

[3] Most of the Maya dates can be read by experts, but there are two different schemes for relating the system to the Christian calendar. See Morley, *op. cit.*, pp. 259–311 and pp. 457–62.

TOLTEC-AZTEC CULTURE

Distinctive though it was, the manner of Late Maya life was not devoid of outside influences and must be seen in the light of what was taking place in the Valley of Mexico, wherein Mexico City is situated. These happenings were part of the record of events in what anthropologists term *Meso-America,* a major portion of which includes the Valley of Mexico, Yucatan, and Guatemala. Human habitation and culture in Meso-America may reach back to the end of the Pleistocene.[4] Then follow several stages until about 200 B.C., when there starts a Formative horizon roughly contemporaneous with the time when Early Maya culture was beginning to emerge in Guatemala. During the Formative, many people were clustered in large metropolitan communities. Great pyramids were constructed, doubtless with religious implications, and forward strides were made in writing, astronomy, mathematics, the calendar, pottery manufacture, and other arts and crafts. These developments, together with a tightly knit social structure, were advanced in the Classic horizon, which comes between 400 and 900 (at the same time that Early Maya culture was reaching its peak), and were carried still further in the Valley of Mexico during the *Toltec Period* (A.D. 900–1200). This period saw the introduction of metalwork in gold, silver, and copper;[5] worship of the feathered-serpent, *Quetzalcoatl*; new architectural details in the construction of public monuments; use of hieroglyphic writing; and other fine attainments (Fig. 18–2). During Toltec days a Mexican-Maya combine ruled northern Yucatan. Thereafter, about 1200, the culture of the Toltecs declined, and not long afterward the Aztec became their cultural heirs. The Aztec made themselves rulers of the Valley of Mexico, brought the older achievements to a head, and were the dominant power against whom the Spanish conquerors struggled to ultimate victory.

Superficially, Aztec culture was closely parallel to that of the Maya. There were similar systems of writing, architecture, economic life, social organization, and calendar manipulation. In each respect some important differences are to be found, but the greatest distinction

---

[4] The summary of cultural events in Meso-America is based on A. Caso, "New World Culture History: Middle America," in A. L. Kroeber, ed., *Anthropology Today,* Chicago, 1953, pp. 226–37.

[5] It is possible that the arts of metalwork were transmitted to the Valley of Mexico from outside regions. See, especially, the works of A. Caso dealing with Monte Alban; and S. K. Lothrop, "Archeology of Cocle, Panama," *Memoirs of the Peabody Museum of American Archaeology and Ethnology,* Cambridge, Mass., Vol. 7, 1937.

FIG. 18-2. Examples of Toltec-Aztec craftsmanship. A. Front wall of the Toltec temple to Quetzalcoatl (the feathered serpent) at Teotihuacan, Mexico. B. Aztec artisans working (*left to right, top*) with feathers, gold beads, and stone beads. Below, a male carpenter, and a female weaver. (B. From T. A. Joyce, *Mexican Archaeology,* London, 1920.)

is one of emphasis. The Aztec were a more warlike people, who ruled their neighbors and demanded tribute. Warfare was given high place and was intimately connected with religion. Aztec gods required much human blood and the chief honor of a warrior was to provide captives for sacrifice. Numberless victims were marched, often with solemn pomp and ceremony, up imposing stairways crowned by temples and shrines. There, high above the throngs gathered for the spectacle, the victims were stretched backward over sacrificial stones and held by arms and legs while a priest slashed open the chest and pulled out the heart. Sometimes bodies were then rolled down the steps to be flayed, and sometimes the blood of a victim was mixed into cakes which the populace ate.

Trade, both foreign and domestic, was another important Aztec activity, and there was a formal class of merchants who traveled widely over Mexico bringing goods back and forth and acting secondarily as spies and intelligence agents. Regular, carefully supervised markets were held frequently and, while barter prevailed, there was also a medium of exchange in the form of highly prized cocoa beans. In the markets were made available the products of specialized artisans, who devoted their lives to perfecting particular crafts such as pottery, featherwork, carpentry, the making of mosaics of precious stones, or cloth weaving. Metallurgy was known and some remarkable ornaments and luxury items were made, but even for so major an Aztec pursuit as war, wooden swords edged with obsidian were used.

As an indication of the uneven development of the totality of mankind's culture, and of western Europe's failure to provide leadership at all times, it should be noted that even as late as A.D. 1519, when Cortez led a European army that conquered Mexico City, then called Tenochtitlan, he and his men were astonished by what they found. Never, except to some extent in Venice, had any of the Europeans seen so much wealth or so many and such splendid architectural monuments. Again and again the conquerors from Europe expressed amazement at the heights of culture attained by these "savage" Indians in the New World.

INCA OF THE COPPER-BRONZE AGE

While the cultures of the Toltec-Aztec and Maya were flourishing and exchanging some of their ideas and customs, another great New World way of life was being elaborated in South America. This culture is commonly described as *Inca,* although the term applies literally only to the ruler and his family, whereas the general populace are better identified as speakers of the *Quechua* language. The direction of Inca culture differed from that of Middle America, and it was the only one to make considerable use of bronze.[6]

At its peak the core of Inca culture was in the capital city of Cuzco, not far from the border of Bolivia high in the Andean mountains of Peru. In the fifteenth century A.D., Cuzco was the center of a remarkable social system that has been described as a benevolent dictatorship. Actually, it was closer to a form of despotism that was benevolent only to a small degree. Almost every act of a commoner's life was rigidly prescribed. Each man and woman who tilled the soil, as most of the people did, was given the use of a stipulated plot of state-owned land, was told where to live, what to grow, what subsidiary crafts to pursue, and how much work he was expected to do at a given age. In addition, each householder was heavily taxed and had to contribute years of military and labor service to the government. Even marriages were supervised by the ruler's officers, and if a population surplus developed at one spot the excess might be shifted to establish or fill out a colony elsewhere. Whatever aspect of the system could be called benevolent arose from the state's desire to keep all ordinary subjects at identical, but reasonable, levels of well-being. To this end if crops in one district were inadequate, sufficient food to compensate for the deficiency would be provided free of charge from government warehouses. These handouts were balanced by the gathering up of extra foodstuffs wherever a community exceeded the established quota. Only on regularly held market days were the plain folk given a chance, on a small scale, to buy or sell as they saw fit. Barter was the only form of exchange, for the Inca never invented a system of coinage.

By virtue of a form of society that was so carefully controlled from above, it was not difficult for Inca rulers to organize ambitious programs of public works and to maintain bodies of carefully trained specialists. Great city structures were built of stone by common laborers under the direction of professional architects, engineers, and master masons. Crowbars and levers of bronze or wood were employed during the process of construction, but hammers of heavy stone were the commonest tools. These, together with water, sand, and ample supplies of

[6] The treatment of Inca culture is drawn in part from J. H. Rowe, "Inca Culture at the Time of the Spanish Conquest," *Handbook of South American Indians,* J. H. Steward, ed., Washington, D.C., 1946, Vol. 2. pp. 183–330. See also L. Baudin, *Daily Life in Peru,* New York, 1962.

"elbow grease," were used to trim and polish the huge, stone building blocks, often of irregular shape, that had to be tightly fitted in place (Figs. 18–3, 18–4). A variety of palaces, temples, storehouses, forts, and other structures were erected, and a network of roads, superbly engineered, was built regardless of obstacles imposed by steep mountain grades or coastal deserts. Suspension bridges were skillfully placed over streams, and much effort and ability were expended in irrigation works, water control projects, and the construction of tremendous terraces that made it possible to farm the sides of mountains.

Inca society, in the last analysis, rested on an agricultural foundation. Maize was the staple at lower altitudes, and was often made into a fermented beverage called *chicha*. Intoxication was a regular part of ceremonial life. White potatoes, a grain called *quinoa,* and several other domesticated plants were of the greatest importance at higher altitudes. In one locality or another throughout the area, beans, peanuts, chili, tomatoes, avocadoes, lima beans, and many other foods were grown. From every point of view, the Andean area must be reckoned as one of the world's greatest sources of plant domestication. Besides raising crops of many foodstuffs, Inca farmers also grew cotton and coca, the basis of cocaine, and gathered wild grasses for thatch and cordage. By contrast with the manifold uses made of vegetal products, less importance was attached to animals. There was some hunting, but it was strictly regulated; fish were caught but seldom eaten by the average person; and a number of domesticated beasts were kept. Llamas were raised for their wool and flesh and also served as beasts of burden and for sacrifices. Alpacas provided wool, primarily; domesticated ducks were known; and dogs were numerous. Swarms of guinea pigs were allowed to roam through the households, acting as scavengers and providing the commonest source of meat available to ordinary folk. As compared with other New World tribes, the Inca people had a large list of domesticated animals, but even they made little use of them to supplement human labor and they had no beast trained for pulling.

The Inca manner of combining social and material aspects of culture may be understood from a consideration of the *Yana-kona* and *Aklya-kona*. The Yana-kona comprised a group of young men, taken into the service of the monarch. They were taught to fulfill numerous functions for the state, and some were even trained to hold minor administrative posts. There is also a possibility that they furnished metallurgists who worked for the ruler. Smiths dealt with gold, silver, copper, and bronze, for which tin was mined in Bolivia. Some utilitarian implements like knives, axes, chisels, hoes, and crowbars were

FIG. 18-3. A street in Cuzco, Peru. Cuzco was the ancient capital of the Incas. The walls are survivals of the excellent stone masonry that was an outstanding aspect of Inca culture. (Courtesy of the Chicago Museum of Natural History.)

FIG. 18-4. Cyclopean masonry in the New World. Another example of the great skill shown by the Indians of Peru in fitting together large blocks of irregular stone. The remains are from the so-called fortress of Sacsahuaman at Cuzco, and are usually attributed to the Inca. (Courtesy of the Museum of Anthropology, The University of Michigan.)

made, as well as needles, bells, and an amazing variety of decorative and ornamental objects. Artifacts of gold and silver were reserved for the Emperor and the highest nobility, and Cuzco palaces were filled with delicate figures fashioned from precious metals.

Aklya-kona was a class of young women, chosen for special care and training at an early age. A few were destined for sacrifice, most of them were dedicated to lives of chastity, and some were later given as concubines or wives to nobles or commoners, respectively. Under expert direction, some of the Aklya-kona were trained to weave the finest of fabrics for the use of the highest classes. Their skill has probably never been exceeded. They knew almost all of the techniques of weaving that have ever been invented, including methods of making brocades with gold and silver threads, embroidery, feather-ornamented cloth, and tapestries of excellent quality.

Inca genius and ingenuity may be found in almost every aspect of life, yet they never attained the intellectual levels of the Maya and Aztec in the fields of mathematics, astronomy, writing, and the calen-

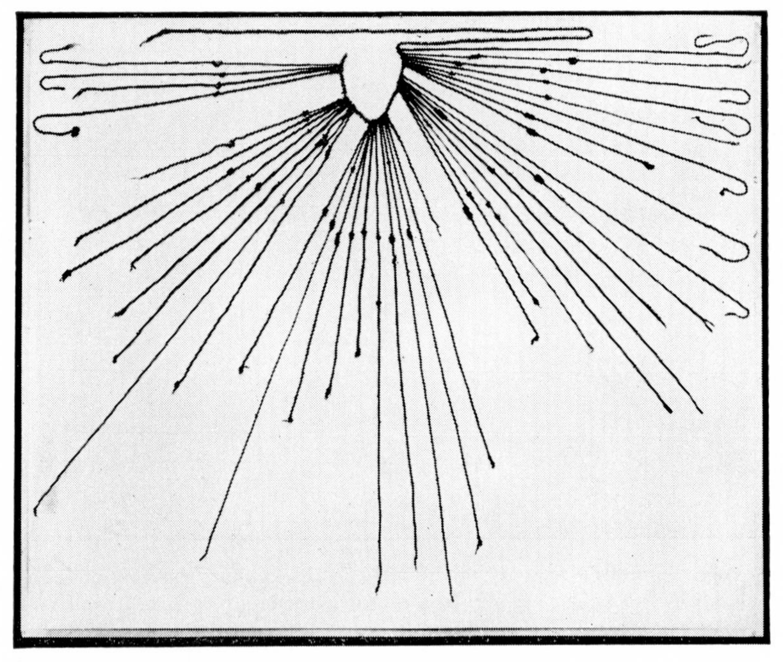

FIG. 18-5. A Peruvian quipu. Knotted strings served the Incas as accounting devices and comprised their method of keeping track of statistics. The Inca had no knowledge of true writing. (Courtesy of the Chicago Museum of Natural History.)

dar. Not that the Inca lacked all knowledge along these lines. It has been argued, for instance, that they understood the concept of zero, but in the absence of writing such a claim cannot be proved. They are known to have divided the year into twelve lunar months, each marked by a ceremony, but how they reckoned the remaining days of a full year is still unknown. In order to keep track of the multitude of details concerning the people they ruled so carefully, the Inca must have had a way of keeping records, but all that archeologists have found are the ingenious objects called *quipus* (Fig. 18–5). A quipu consists of a central cord to which are attached strings of varied make or color. Each string represents a class of objects, and knots tied along its length indicate numbers. With the help of quipus, administrators found it possible to keep track of all kinds of statistics, but the system could work only as long as some officials memorized what each quipu represented. At best, a quipu was useful only as long as its significance was remembered, like a handkerchief tied about one's finger. It was hopelessly inadequate as a way of recording data permanently.

THE END OF PREHISTORY IN THE NEW WORLD

Surely, one can see even from the brief treatment here given that the line of cultural development in the New World ran parallel to the Old in broad outline, but differed in one essential detail after another. In both vast areas there were similar origins in gathering and hunting stages, as well as in the manufacture and use of Paleolithic tools. These were followed by the entrance of some groups into Neolithic levels, and culminated in cultures that had acquired metallurgy.

As has been shown, the start of culture was a late phenomenon in the Americas. It was most likely derived from Asia at the outset, but was primarily carried independently forward until the first half of the sixteenth century. Conventionally, American prehistory is supposed to have come to an end in 1492, but a few decades actually elapsed before Europeans made any marked impact on aboriginal customs. When the blow fell, though, it struck hard. The primary motivations that inspired conquest from Europe were desires for treasure and native converts to Christianity. Inevitably this drew invaders to the most populous centers, which were also the wealthiest, and so a kind of battle plan was automatically formulated. The opening episode began in 1519 when Cortez confronted the Aztec at the present site of Mexico City. For all their administrative skill and efficiency, the Aztec had followed so aggressive a policy that they had made many enemies who welcomed an opportunity to retaliate by helping the foreign attackers. A long and bloody struggle followed, but in 1521 the Aztec were forced to succumb. Further south in Guatemala, and eastward in northern Yucatan, other Spaniards found no organized resistance among the descendants of the Maya, whose culture had disintegrated long ago. With the founding of Merida in 1542, the entire territory of the ancient Maya came under Spanish control. Today, several million full-blooded Aztec and Maya Indians continue to live in Meso-America, but they cannot read the ancient hieroglyphs, calculate the calendars, construct fine monuments, or manufacture the splendid products of the past.

What may have been a mere accident of history paved the way for the conquest of the Inca domain. Huayna Capac, the last great ruler, died suddenly in 1527 without having named a successor. Two half-brothers, his sons by different mothers, promptly engaged in a civil war to determine who should rule. When Pizarro arrived he cleverly took advantage of their bitter struggle, and managed to defeat them one after the other by 1532.

Shortly after, in 1540, Coronado undertook the first Spanish penetration of the southwestern United States. He met resistance occasionally, but was soon able to win at least the nominal submission of the natives. North of the Rio Grande there were no great stores of treasure to reward a conqueror, so little effort was made to subjugate the Indians thoroughly, and they continued to carry on much of their old culture even though they acknowledged the legal control of Spain. At the same time that Coronado was traveling through the Southwest, De Soto was leading an expedition into the Southeast. Here he found the Mississippi pattern of culture still flourishing, but his coming began to upset the established ways of native life; and when the colonization of the Eastern seaboard started, the old customs rapidly disintegrated. Much the same was true of the northeastern United States. The colonists who founded Jamestown in 1607, or who reached Plymouth in 1620, were confronted by tribes whose cultures were going concerns. But when colonial expansion started to move westward, aboriginal life quickly changed or vanished.

How diffusion operates

Within a hundred years after the discovery by Columbus there was not a region of high American Indian culture that had not been greatly influenced or submerged by Europeans. This century was not, except in rare cases, marked by good will or helpfulness on either side. From the standpoint of the Indians, the termination of nearly all of their old customs must have been a continuous tragedy. Yet, from a detached anthropological view, there is a lesson in cultural growth to be learned from the situation. At the cost, it must be admitted, of a deplorable amount of bloodshed and grief, each party's culture was enriched by the contact in several respects. Europeans learned to grow potatoes, maize, and tobacco; and Indians learned to raise wheat, barley, and oats. Europeans acquired knowledge of rubber and cocaine; and native Americans became acquainted with iron, steel, and wagons. Domesticated ducks and turkeys were introduced to the Old World; and the New found out about domesticated horses and cattle. Thus does the process of diffusion operate despite the basic hostility of the peoples concerned.

Much the same is true of the present moment. From some of our bitterest enemies we have learned to use such instruments of war as dive bombers, massive tanks, and powerful submarines. With equal alacrity, our opponents have hastened to adopt American contrivances, such as jeeps. Plainly, diffusion may operate in a climate of hate as well as in a friendly atmosphere. Traits can be added to two patterns of culture without subtracting from either one. When Europeans learned to grow white potatoes they added them to their existing crops without necessarily giving anything up; and when Indians discovered how to grow wheat they were not forced to sacrifice any of their traditional foods in exchange. In these respects, each side was a gainer and neither was a loser.

Post-Columbian contacts of Europe and aboriginal America also throw light on the way in which particular cultures grow. To some extent they develop from local inventions, but they also expand by accretions gained through diffusion. Indeed, if one takes a world view, existing cultures are found to have a much higher percentage of diffused elements than of independent inventions. If all borrowed items were suddenly to be removed from the established way of life of the United States it would eliminate such cardinal aspects as the English language, Judaism and Christianity, printing, coinage, and the wide range of useful plants that were first domesticated by the Indians of the New World.

Finally, we may note from the cultural interchange that took place after 1492 that all groups of *Homo sapiens* are potentially capable of assimilating each other's cultures. No biological or mental barriers stand in the way. Many New World Indians of our day live by standards that were derived from European sources in historic times. Some people say, without adequate thought or sufficient consideration of the facts, that the aboriginal Americans deserve lowly status because they are degenerate and unable to absorb the finer points of civilization. The opposite may be repeatedly demonstrated. Throughout the southwestern United States, where sizable native populations are still to be found, the Indians who stubbornly reject the ways of the Caucasoids are apt to be objects of admiration, curiosity, friendly interest, and benevolent concern. It is precisely those who have shown themselves most willing to absorb "white" culture who are most likely to be punished. Many a native youngster who has been well trained in a particular craft at a government school finds himself baffled on trying to get a job to discover that "Indians need not apply." Culturally imposed obstacles, it must be concluded, do far more to prevent the sharing of a given way of life than any supposed deficiencies of mind or body.

Selected References

Bennett, Wendell C., "A Reappraisal of Peruvian Archaeology," *Memoir, Society for American Archaeology,* No. 4, Menasha, Wis., 1948.

———, and Bird, Junius B., "Andean Culture History," *Handbook Series of the American Museum of Natural History,* No. 15, New York, 1949.

Caso, Alphonse, "New World Culture History," *Anthropology Today,* A. L. Kroeber, ed., Chicago, 1953, pp. 226–37.

Cressman, L. S., "Man in the New World," in H. L. Shapiro, ed., *Man, Culture and Society,* New York, 1956, pp. 139–67.

Hay, Clarence L., *et al.,* eds., *The Maya and Their Neighbors,* New York, 1940.

Morley, Sylvanus G., *The Ancient Maya,* Stanford, Calif., 1946.

Rowe, John H., "Inca Culture at the Time of the Spanish Conquest," in J. H. Steward, ed., *Handbook of South American Indians,* Washington, D. C., Vol. 2, 1946, pp. 183–330.

Steward, Julian H., ed., *Handbook of South American Indians,* six volumes, Washington, D. C., 1946–1950.

Tax, Sol., ed., *The Heritage of Conquest,* Glencoe, Ill., 1952.

Vaillant, George C., *Aztecs of Mexico,* New York, 1941.

Some Laws of Culture Growth

CHAPTER 19

By the dawn of written history, *Homo sapiens* had brought culture to such a stage that its usefulness was plainly evident. Once patterns of culture were originated, however, they proved to follow laws of their own, occasionally without reference to the wishes of the individuals who lived by them. At the same time, man could not completely shake off the age-old imperatives of the biophysicochemical world. The chemical substances within his body continued to act in their accustomed ways, the laws of physics still operated as they always had, and the dictates of biology had to be observed. It is because these forces are so firm and insistent that no pattern of culture can ever be purely random and that the values imbedded in any way of life can never be entirely arbitrary or capricious.

Students who are just becoming acquainted with the science of man frequently ask, "Why, apart from mere curiosity, should we have to learn so many details of man's cultural past?" This is a legitimate question, worthy of a careful answer.

Anthropologists do not find it difficult to justify their interest in the data of archeology, even when the subject leads back to times so remote that few facts are available and all interpretations are open to question. Unless one takes the indefensible position that modern culture sprang ready-made into existence without antecedents, he must be willing to study what came before in order to understand what is going on now. Without such understanding, we would have no inkling of the laws of culture growth, could make no predictions, and could establish no controls.

On one other important point at least, archeologists have already made a lasting contribution. No one knows, nor is anyone likely ever to discover, the stock or racial affinity of the very first fist-ax maker, potter, weaver, farmer, or metallurgist; nor is it probable that we shall ever learn the identity of the first person to have made use of a spear, bow and arrow, wagon, boat, alphabet, calendar, or coin. Archeologists have shown that no one race can truthfully take credit for having begun all these achievements, and that once they had become part of human culture they were utilized by all manner of people. From the start the building of universal culture has been a joint enterprise of mankind, and leadership in the movement has shifted without loss of progress from one region to another and from one hominid subdivision to another.

Archeology has also proved that everywhere on earth human beings have transcended the biophysicochemical realm and entered the sphere of culture. It has, in addition, brought to light the infinite variety of forms that particular cultures may take and has demonstrated how often a group of people in one locality may develop a way of life that is markedly different from that of their neighbors. It is easy enough to become bewildered by these facts and to come to the erroneous conclusion that the totality of culture is a chaotic hodgepodge that has followed no consistent pattern of development. But a discerning student of man must learn to recognize the unity that underlies the mass of differing details. Today it can be shown that from the beginning a number of consistent trends have been operating along regular and, therefore, predictable lines. Once the existence of these trends has been recognized, their past courses can be charted, and if they show steady movement in a given direction it may be forecast that they will, until diverted, continue to go in the same direction in the near future. Archeology makes one of its major contributions when it provides the data from which trends may be charted. It is convenient to talk of trends as moving consistently in one direction, but trends generally move in zigzag fashion.

All sciences pass through a preliminary fact-gathering stage, after which efforts are made to discover which phenomena regularly occur together. These observations lead to the establishment of scientific laws of cause and effect, which seek to describe the observed combinations and to explain how, when, and why they were formed. Then laws that are found to have been long operative in the past are used in forecasting the future. Thus, anyone who has again and again watched blue litmus paper turn red when dipped in acid can predict that on future occasions blue litmus will redden on contact with an acid. The longer and oftener one can observe the operation of a presumed law in the past, the more certainly can he foretell its future course. Under such conditions, prediction is no more than a projection into the future of a trend line observed in the past. So it is that anthropologists who want to know how culture is likely to act in the future must find out from archeologists how it has acted in the past. At the same time it should be recognized that some of these so-called laws of culture may be no more than a description of observed regularities that seem to prevail between phenomena.

In chemistry and physics, the particles that are studied must act and react in specific ways, and they have absolutely no choice. This is not true in biology, where there is a degree of choice, even if death is the price of a poor decision. When it comes to the sphere of culture, there is so much room for voluntary action or inaction that laws or basic trends are exceedingly hard to detect. Moreover, once a biophysicochemical law has been determined, it is assumed that it will go on operating the same way into the indefinite future. This, unfortunately, is not the case with sociocultural laws. For instance, around A.D. 1800 a working week of 84 hours was by no means unknown in the United States. Gradually the hours of work were reduced to 63, 56, 52, 44, and 40. Now there is talk of a 35-hour working week, and one union has already demanded 20 hours. On the basis of former happenings this looks like a manifestation of a law of diminishing hours of work. Yet, if such a trend continues indefinitely, it will some day reach the point of absurdity. We may applaud the reduction of working time to some extent, but what if the work week is cut to one hour, or twenty minutes, or ten seconds? At what point do we try to halt or even reverse a trend whose course can be so well plotted in the past? And how, if it should be desired, would we make an established trend move in the opposite direction? To some extent, as several observers have already pointed out, the "do it yourself" movement can be interpreted as a way of using up the excess of leisure that hangs heavy on the hands of many workers, but it must be admitted that such movements are no better than makeshifts when it comes to dealing firmly with the question of reversing a strongly directed trend.[1] Few social scientists have as yet begun to study universal trends of cultural behavior and too little information is available about many cultures, but enough is already known to justify the cautious formulation of a few tentative laws. These formulations, even though they may prove to be only temporarily valid, are among the most significant of the inferences to be drawn from archeology. Equally im-

[1] For another expression of this point of view, see the *New York Times Magazine,* June 28, 1959, p. 22.

portant is the fact that the recognizable and predictable trends which are here stated as laws can be shown to operate, not independently, but as integrated parts of one whole pattern of cultural evolution. Integration usually sounds like a good thing to us, but it can be a source of serious trouble when a pattern of culture must integrate, or keep in equilibrium, a number of conflicting forces.

An obvious clash arises whenever a hungry person is confronted with a forbidden food. He must, in all such cases, make a choice between observing biological or cultural values. He cannot, at the same time, observe both.

Or, take the case of a young American who was always a devoted son while he was single. As soon as he marries he can no longer remain an equally devoted son without making a poor husband. If he gives all his attention to his mother, he must neglect his wife; and if he is completely attentive to his wife, he must become at least partially neglectful of his mother.

These instances serve to illustrate only two of the kinds of contradictions that all systems of culture must try somehow to reconcile. In addition, every successful way of life must maintain a dynamic balance between forces of stability, conservatism, or inertia, and forces tending to change or disintegration. No pattern of culture is flawlessly consistent, and the best it can do is to have the sum total of its cohesive elements outweigh its disintegrative factors. With these matters in mind, we may now turn to a consideration of the laws that seem to be operative in the ways of life of all known societies.

THE LAW OF INCREASING RELIANCE ON CULTURE

For all the grave doubts that may beset the student of human origins, it has been established that on their very first appearance the earliest hominids could, perforce, have utilized only such biogenetically inherited mechanisms as their hands and feet. Presumably, they quickly came to make some use of sticks and stones that could be manipulated by the organs of their bodies, but as the archeological record of the Lower Paleolithic bears witness, they were slow in the beginning to develop an extrasomatic kit of tools. Thereafter they came to depend more and more on nongenetic equipment, and as they did, the law of increasing reliance on culture (Fig. 19–1) began to operate.[2]

[2] In order to keep the argument as unified and simple as possible, it will be assumed that every person has complete access to all the items available in his stage of culture. The reader must recognize that this is not the case in reality.

Admittedly, there must be an ultimate limit to this trend. Increasing reliance on culture cannot advance so far as to overcome the basic limitations of biology. No amount of culture can make human bodies fly by themselves, and in no culture can males bear and nurse babies. All of this may be true, but it is not easy to foresee when or where the ultimate limit will be reached. Already mankind has begun to make cultural implements which, in some respects, greatly exceed the potentials of the human body. One aviation expert has thus described the

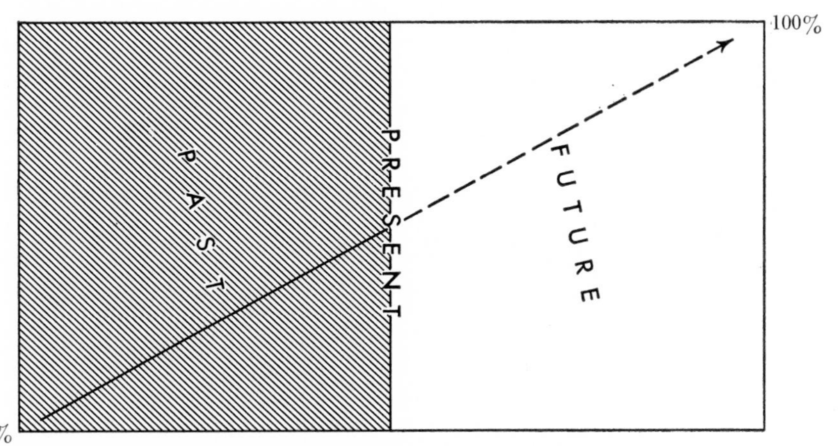

FIG. 19-1. The law of increasing reliance on culture. When hominids first appeared, they perforce had to get along with only their biological mechanisms. As time went on, however, they decreased their dependence on inherited, somatic devices, and increased their reliance on culture. Of course, *Homo sapiens* cannot rely entirely on culture because he cannot completely eliminate his biology. That is why so much of his behavior is really biocultural. The further in the past that one can see the direction of a trend, such as man's increasing reliance on culture, the more confidently can he project it into the future.

situation: "Our flying machines are rapidly approaching capabilities that are penalized rather than aided by the presence of a human pilot."[3]

The law of increasing reliance on culture does not stand apart from other trends of cultural development. Among other things it makes possible man's shift from dependence on brawn (biological strength) to trust in brain (cultural efficiency). It also helps to level out the differences between the sexes. Throughout the world it will be found that as cultures advance, sex differences tend to diminish, except in matters directly related to biology. Any middle-aged citi-

[3] This statement was made by J. H. Kindelberger, and was quoted in the *Ann Arbor News* for June 13, 1952.

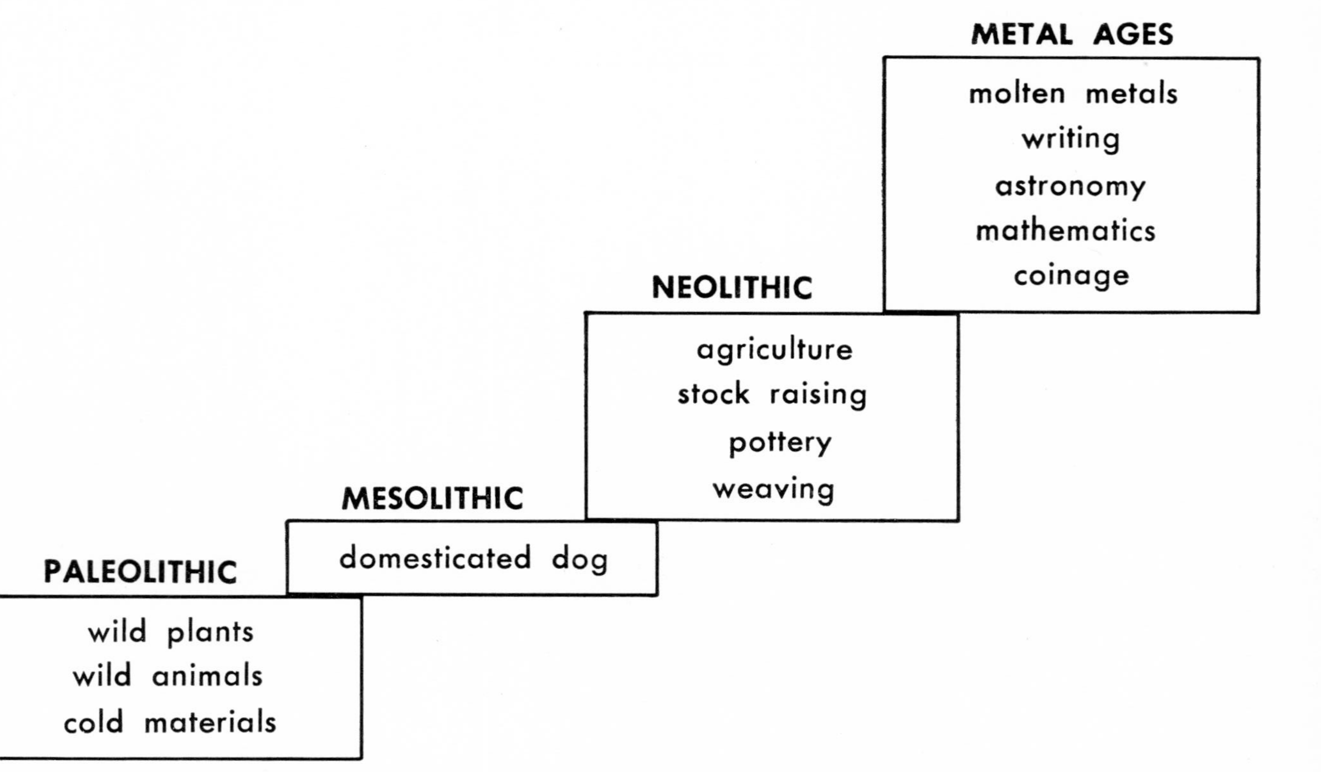

FIG. 19-2. The law of expanding use of natural resources. Although the figure illustrates man's expanding use of natural resources, it also brings out the additive nature of human culture.

zen of the United States can recall sociocultural activities that were once regarded as entirely masculine and are now carried on by individuals of either sex.

The law of expanding use of natural resources

It would not have been possible for man to have increased his reliance on culture had he not learned, as time went on, to make wider use of the raw materials provided by nature. This could have been accomplished only by the accumulation of knowledge, for no new ingredients have been added to the composition of the earth since its formation. Whatever original substances or organisms have at times been formed in laboratories have always been recombinations or refinements of older ingredients. Basically, man has had the same physicochemical resources available to him from the time when hominids first appeared. Until 12,000 B.P., *Homo sapiens* was able to utilize only a small fraction of his physical environment, not much more than the air around him, wild plants and animals, water, and a few substances that could be used while cold. Then, in the Neolithic, grass and farm lands that had had no particular value before became highly important for grazing and agricultural purposes; certain kinds of clay changed from detriments to valuable commodities for manufacturing pottery; and previously neglected fibers took on a new significance as the making of textiles developed. Later, metallic ores became greatly prized; and in our own day, the rapid march of culture has given previously undreamed-of value to once negligible items such as uranium.

While the law of expanding use of natural resources continually brings new materials to the fore, it also serves to render older things obsolete. The general point of this statement can be illustrated by an example from the United States. Around 1910, an investment in a municipally owned trolley system would have been regarded as safe and the purchase of automobile stock as reckless. Today only a lunatic could be persuaded to invest in trolley cars, and automobiles are considered safe, even though it is reasonably sure that they will some day be outmoded. Not all of the natural resources that were of prime significance to *Homo sapiens* in former times lose their value at the same rate of speed, and the use of some things continues to be retained for many centuries; but whenever an object loses its importance, its manufacture tends to become a lost art.

To chart the past operation of the law of expanding use of

natural resources (Fig. 19–2) is none too difficult, nor is it hard to foretell that some materials presently of little worth will some day turn out to have exceedingly high value. At the same time, it must be recognized, man's increasing ability to utilize the potentials of his environment has had much to do with increasing the speed of culture growth. Our era is distinguished for its amazing speed of culture growth, especially in the field of technology. Whether or not man will forever go on expanding his use of natural resources is a question that only the future can answer.

Since cultures grow only a little by means of local invention and very much through the agency of diffusion, quick progress is aided by the speed and frequency of contact between a given society and many others. With the modern perfection of means of communication, an item invented in one place can almost instantaneously be spread throughout the world. All societies with progressive cultures, whether on friendly or hostile terms, strive to keep in touch with one another, and the surest way to cultural decline is through a policy of isolation.

THE DECLINING PERCENTAGE OF INDIVIDUAL KNOWLEDGE AND ITS COROLLARIES

As the human ability to take advantage of a steadily mounting number of natural resources continues, the sum total or stockpile of knowledge available in a progressive society becomes too great for any one person to encompass. So there comes into play *the law of declining percentage of individual knowledge* (Fig. 19–3B). In order to understand how this

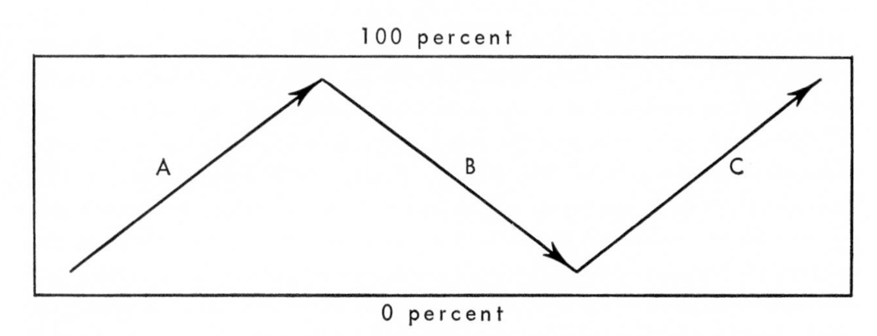

FIG. 19-3. Three interconnected laws of culture growth. A. The law of increasing specialization. B. The law of declining percentage of individual knowledge. C. The law of necessary cooperation. These three laws usually work together.

law works we must imagine a stage when every human male knew all there was for men to know, and when every female knew all that pertained to the members of her sex. Such totally unspecialized levels probably existed only at the dawn of cultural evolution, and at that time each individual may be said to have had 100 percent of all the knowledge available to his sex. For contrast, we have but to consider the present state of affairs in our own society. What man or woman of today knows how to raise and prepare all the food that he eats, fashion all the utensils and dishes needed for cooking and serving, make all the garments to be worn, build his own house, cure his ailments, and build and service his own radio, television set, refrigerator, and automobile? Far from knowing how to do all these things for ourselves, we rely on numerous others to do most of them for us. And to the extent that this is the case we exemplify the law of declining percentage of individual knowledge. It must be admitted that in our society and culture, one person, no matter how brilliant he may be, can have only a tiny fraction of the total knowledge to be found among all of us.

Whenever such a stage is reached in any society, the only way that its culture can be maintained is by a process of compartmentalization, which means that its stockpile of knowledge is divided up, with particular subgroups or specialists assuming responsibility for particular fractions of the total. Wherever the law of declining percentage of individual knowledge goes into effect, therefore, it is invariably accompanied by a *law of increasing specialization* (Fig. 19–3A). Once more, it is archeology that supplies the necessary proof. Neolithic communities always have more classes of specialists than those of the Old Stone Age; Metal Age societies have even more; and modern social units have the greatest numbers ever known in the history of mankind.

The law of declining percentage of individual knowledge, together with its corollary, the law of increasing specialization, gives firm support to the ancient jest that "a specialist is one who learns more and more about less and less." These laws also apply to tools, for the more highly specialized a tool is, the more restricted is its range of usefulness. No modern builder would want to erect a house with nothing but surgical instruments, nor would any normal patient voluntarily trust himself to a surgeon who operated with a butcher knife and a carpenter's saw.

The law of declining percentage of individual knowledge and the accompanying law of increasing specialization bring into action still another trend that may be described as the *law of necessary cooperation* (Fig. 19–3C). To prevent a very complex culture from collapsing, each individual participant must be assured of the cooperation of specialists who can fill in the gaps of his own knowledge. Where each person knows only a tiny percentage of his total culture, he cannot possibly insist on complete independence. So essential is mutual interdependence that it may not be left to chance. Hence social regulations that are designed to further the law of necessary cooperation are found in every advanced culture. We could no more maintain our way of life with a Paleolithic form of social organization than we could keep up our industrial production with Old Stone Age implements, techniques, and raw materials. Any society that fails to pay full attention to the law of necessary cooperation is bound to find its culture getting out of balance and veering toward disintegration.

THE LAWS OF CONSERVATION OF TIME AND OF HUMAN MUSCULAR ENERGY

Neither the expanding utilization of natural resources nor increase of specialization is a random matter. Consciously or not, each was developed in the interests of greater efficiency. No matter in how many ways efficiency may be defined and evaluated, it can always be measured with reference to material culture by standards of time consumption and the expenditure of human muscular energy.[4] Throughout the march of culture, an implement that could perform a given task in less time than its predecessor would, in the course of events, always displace the earlier tool. This is equivalent to saying that insofar as two instruments could do the same task, mankind has invariably selected the one that accorded with the *law of time conservation.*

More dramatic still is the *law of HME conservation.* This is one of the most clearly demonstrable and most surely predictable of all the laws of culture growth. The same principle applies whether one is dealing with a progression of cutting implements and weapons, from stone knives and fist axes to spears, bows and arrows, revolvers, machine guns, and atom bombs; or with the evolution of means of transportation from foot to horse, to automobile, to airplane. The primary determinant is the recognition, explicit or implicit, of the fact that more can be accomplished if mechanical efficiency is increased and the expenditure of HME decreased. We demand and praise effectiveness in our cultural implements, not in our biological structures. When our eyes begin to fail, we try to get adequate corrective glasses rather than resort to operations on our genetically inherited optical systems.

[4] As another instance of a labor-saving device, the letters HME will be used for the phrase "human muscular energy."

Even when analysis is restricted to a single technological device like an automobile, the law of HME conservation may be seen to operate constantly and consistently. The first automobiles manufactured had to be cranked by hand, at a considerable cost in HME. Today, they begin with the push of a finger on a starter. Shifting gears manually, which was once universal, is now an almost obsolete practice. Tires that had to be laboriously blown up on hand pumps are rapidly and effortlessly filled with air by the use of readily available pressure pumps. Even car windows that had to be raised or lowered by turning a handle can presently be operated by touching a button.

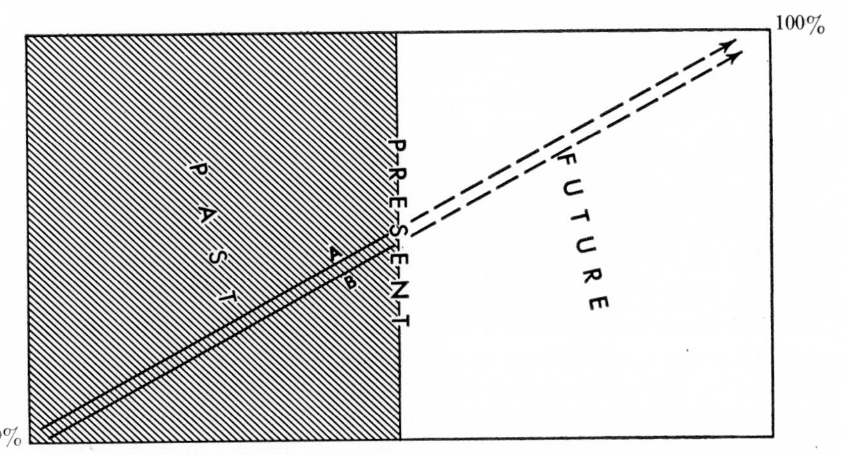

FIG. 19-4. The twin laws of conservation. A. The law of time conservation. B. The law of human muscular energy conservation. As culture grows, man consistently tries to save increasing amounts of time and human muscular energy.

In combination, the laws of time and HME conservation have worked, in the past, with unfailing certainty (Fig. 19–4). One may be positive that in the foreseeable future no invention will succeed if its use calls for an additional outlay of time and human effort. With equal assurance one can forecast that a time and energy-saving contrivance has an excellent chance of ultimate acceptance. No shrewd businessman can be persuaded to finance the production of anything that goes against this combined trend. As a matter of fact, a new item may not look or taste quite as nice as something it is trying to replace, but if it saves time and energy it stands a good chance of succeeding. So much importance does mankind attach to the laws of time and HME conservation that objects conforming to these principles are likely to be widely purchased even if their manufacturing and initial costs are high. Still, one can imagine a day when these trends may come to an end or be reversed.

Forces of culture and biocultural institutions

There is yet much to be learned about the laws of culture growth, but it is encouraging to know that a start toward understanding them can already be made. It is entirely unlikely that the first hominids to have used extrasomatic implements had any inkling that what they were doing had some connection with forces of culture, any more than they are likely to have known about the forces of biology, physics, or chemistry. In fact, so few highly sophisticated people of our own day have any awareness of the existence of abstract forces of culture that we must assume that early man had no knowledge of them. Yet much that he did was shaped by these forces.[5] Even at the beginning of hominid existence, there must have been at work forces of initiation that brought patterns of culture into being and forces of limitation that kept these patterns within definite bounds.

When fixed and repetitive responses to the forces at play in the building of a pattern of culture become established as customary ways of behaving, they form the basis for what social scientists generally have in mind when they speak of social, cultural, or biocultural institutions. Once they have come into being, the institutions of any society tend to have an independent existence and to follow their own rules. They are, therefore, legitimate objects for study, even if students have little interest in the forces that may have brought them into being. Institutions customarily include not only fixed ways of acting, but also the people who are expected to behave toward one another in prescribed, repetitive ways. Quite commonly, too, as in the case of religious institutions, set ways of acting are associated with particular kinds of external objects, such as garments, insignia, implements, or structures.

Rarely are institutions neutral in terms of being regarded by the members of the societies in which they are found as neither good nor bad. Far more commonly institutions are connected with *systems of values.* Not all societies develop the same institutions, nor do they all ascribe identical values to similar institutions. Likewise, as societies grow large, complex, and heterogeneous, some of their members come to live by one set of institutions and values, whereas others may live by

[5] It has even been maintained that man is a helpless agent in the grip of powerful forces of culture. In other words, the forces of culture express themselves regardless of what man thinks or tries to do about them. This view finds expression in L. A. White, "Man's Control over Civilization: An Anthropocentric Illusion," *The Science of Culture,* New York, 1949.

quite different ones. Variable though social or cultural institutions and systems of values may be when one compares group with group, they all stem from identical chemical, physical, biological, psychological, and cultural forces. These forces are relatively so invariable that their study promises to yield as much valuable information as an examination of biocultural institutions. On the other hand, we can expose and examine underlying forces only by studying the particular institutions through which they make themselves manifest.

THE INTEGRATED PATTERN OF CULTURE GROWTH—A RESTATEMENT

Man became a human being, entirely different from all other animals, when he began to contrive and rely upon nongenetically inherited and extrabodily equipment. At the outset, progress in this direction was slow and beginning hominid life was predominantly biological, but as one millennium succeeded another there was a marked increase of reliance on culture and a consequent playing down of dependence on biology. Still, reliance on culture would have remained woefully restricted if man had not learned to make continually greater use of his natural resources. As this aspect of human activity gained momentum, a point was reached wherein the stockpile of a society's fund of knowledge became too great for any one individual to handle entirely and classes of specialists arose as custodians of particular fractions of the whole. Then, to prevent its total culture from fragmenting into unconnected parts, each social unit found ways to enforce cooperation among its various members.

When trends or laws based on the march of culture in the past are charted, one major movement stands out—and that is in the nature of a joint trend devoted to the conservation of time and HME. What mankind does with the saved energy and time is not always clear. Some of it is doubtless used in the production of works of art; some is absorbed by recreation, amusements, and sports; and some is converted to nervous or mental activities. Not all of it is necessarily utilized in ways that are officially sanctioned by a particular society; but whether individuals approve or disapprove, there seems to be no way known of reversing the dual trend. Ever since *Homo sapiens* started to decrease his reliance on biology in favor of culture and to direct his efforts to the conservation of time and energy, he has continued to press toward these goals with very little deviation.

Selected References

Childe, V. Gordon, *Social Evolution,* London, 1951.

Clark, J. Grahame D., "Archeological Theories and Interpretation: Old World," in A. L. Kroeber, ed., *Anthropology Today,* Chicago, 1953, pp. 343–60.

Haring, Douglas G., "Science and Social Phenomena," *American Scientist,* Vol. 35, 1947, pp. 351–63.

Herskovits, Melville J., *Man and His Works,* New York, 1948, Chap. 7.

Lee, Dorothy, "Are Basic Needs Ultimate?" *Journal of Abnormal and Social Psychology,* Vol. 43, 1948, p. 391–95.

Linton, Ralph, *The Study of Man,* New York, 1936.

Opler, Marvin K., *Culture, Psychiatry, and Human Values: The Methods and values of a Social Psychiatry,* Springfield, Ill., 1956.

Steward, Julian H., "Cultural Causality and Law: A Trial Formulation, etc.," *American Anthropologist,* Vol. 51, 1949, pp. 1–27.

———, "Evolution and Process," in A. L. Kroeber, ed., *Anthropology Today,* Chicago, 1953, pp. 313–26.

Thompson, Laura, *Toward a Science of Mankind,* New York, 1961.

White, Leslie A., "Energy and the Evolution of Culture," *American Anthropologist,* Vol. 45, 1943, pp. 335–56.

Willey, Gordon R., "Archaeological Theories and Interpretations: New World," in A. L. Kroeber, ed., *Anthropology Today,* Chicago, 1953, pp. 361–85.

Zipf, G. K., *Human Behavior and the Principle of Least Effort,* Cambridge, Mass., 1949.

PART THREE

Cultural and Biocultural Behavior

Aims and Methods of Cultural Anthropology

CHAPTER 20

BASIC CONCEPTS AND DEFINITIONS

The principal concern of ethnographers, ethnologists, social or cultural anthropologists is the growth of culture and the interplay of living people with one another, with their physical settings, and with the sum total of their cultural phenomena. With the rare exception of hermits, human beings live in groups or societies, each of which calls for a number of regularly repeated acts of behavior and each of which has a distinctive set of values, often symbolic and nonbiological, that consciously or subconsciously regulates the conduct of its members.

There is no mathematically precise way of defining a society, but in broad terms it may be said to consist of a group of individuals of both sexes who reside in one locality, recognize the same administrative authority, regulate their lives according to the same openly expressed or hidden standards of values, and interact or cooperate for the attainment of common goals. On each score a considerable amount of variation is possible. Using the people of the United States as an example, one might question whether they constitute a single society. One might justifiably ask whether residents of northern Maine really follow the same way of life as the inhabitants of southern California around Hollywood, or whether the folk in Delaware truly interact with those in Idaho for the attainment of common goals. Only in times of great country-wide events, such as national elections or wars, are we conscious of any important degree of cooperation among all the citizens of the United States.

As it happens, many of the doubts that trouble students of large and complex communities are less grave in the case of those who deal with primitive societies, and ethnologists have traditionally worked with the latter. "Primitive" is also a difficult term to define, but anthropologists agree that it should not be taken to mean inadequate, immature, deficient, savage, or backward.[1] Perhaps one way to sense the anthropological concept of primitive with respect to groups is to begin with nonliterate, that is, with societies whose cultures do not include the regular use of a written language.[2]

Primitive societies differ from others in several essential aspects. The differences need not be caused by an absence of writing, but on the whole it has been found that each nonliterate society is small in numbers, relatively isolated, comparatively homogeneous in culture, and racially and linguistically much alike. Usually it occupies only a limited range of territory, with boundaries that are well-known and seldom transgressed. Within the territorial limits, outsiders are so rarely encountered that constant interaction with total strangers, so prominent a feature of our own lives, is seldom necessary. Living together with a restricted number of physically similar people who speak one's own language and whom one knows quite well makes cooperation for the achievement of common goals comparatively easy. Furthermore, a primitive community is likely to have a uniform religion. Rarely will it show divided allegiance to conflicting religious systems, or profound variations of symbolic values. Small, rather isolated societies, with fairly homogeneous forms of culture, are likely to function in such comparatively simple and direct ways as to provide an investigator with a chance to observe culture patterns in their entirety and to discover their underlying structures and interconnections, as well as to get at the mainsprings of peoples' actions. There is something comforting and satisfying in this situation. It affords a sharp contrast to the difficulties that must be overcome by those who study large, literate, culturally heterogeneous societies. These customarily have such complex systems of technology, economics, religion, politics, and social organization in general that it is very hard to find the principles according to which they operate. It might even be maintained that a budding social scientist ought to learn something of the simpler forms of human life in society before going on to analysis of more complex and complicated social structures.

---

[1] S. Tax, "'Primitive' Peoples"; and L. Mednick, "Memorandum on the Use of Primitive," *Current Anthropology*, Vol. 1, 1960, pp. 441–45, throw much light on the difficulties of defining "primitive."

[2] It is necessary to distinguish between nonliterate and illiterate.

Cultural anthropologists, then, attempt to discover and record the basic mode of behavior or pattern of culture that makes up a group's design for living together. It does not take much experience to realize that even within a small, relatively homogeneous society, more than one culture pattern must prevail. As an irreducible minimum, one is unlikely to find an identical way of life followed by grown males and females, and it is hardly to be expected that a single pattern guides the conduct of infants and adults. There is also little cause for surprise if one finds varying customs and standards being followed by those of markedly divergent social backgrounds, greatly advanced age, and widely different occupations or places of residence, even within a single territorial zone.

Since every society has a number of different designs for living, what is an ethnologist to describe? Should he report a number of culture patterns, each of which applies only to one particular subdivision of a society; or should he try to present a single, over-all pattern that may or may not be representative of all concerned? Anthropologists usually get around the dilemma by reporting in detail the commonest pattern of culture that applies to normal adults of either sex and by indicating whatever significant variations customarily apply to others. In the light of this practice, it must be realized that every pattern of culture that is reported is really a composite, made up of the ways of life of many individuals. It is, therefore, a kind of average, and like all averages it has to be carefully checked to make sure that it properly represents those who live in a particular society.

Social scientists other than anthropologists sometimes wonder why the latter appear to be preoccupied with primitive peoples and their forms of culture. Actually, as we shall see, many fieldworkers trained in anthropology have begun to study modern, highly literate, industrialized communities, and they have brought to their task some of the techniques and ideas drawn from their knowledge of primitive life. A surprising number of behavioral forms whose importance was first recognized in primitive tribes have been found to exist in modern societies; and numerous students of human life in nonprimitive settings have expressed their indebtedness for fresh insights to the contributions made by cultural anthropologists.

Then, again, studies of contemporary primitive societies have occasionally proved to be of value for filling gaps in the archeological record. For example, when we were dealing with the Old World's New Stone Age it was possible to describe many details of material culture, but only a little could be said of the intangible aspects of human behavior. Since essentially Neolithic societies still exist, one can sometimes understand from observing them how men and women probably behaved in the New Stone Age.

Before going further, a serious student of cultural anthropology must memorize three fundamental axioms of the science of man: (1) a total society has a distinct existence, quite apart from that of any of the individuals of whom it is composed; (2) every society seeks to perpetuate itself biologically through the birth of offspring to its members; and (3) every society strives to continue its patterns of culture indefinitely by teaching infants to know and accept its ways of life. On the basis of these axioms, reproduction becomes a social as well as an individual concern, and the establishment of long-lasting cultural traditions is not entirely a private matter. No society willingly looks forward either to biological or cultural extinction.

FIELD TECHNIQUES IN ETHNOLOGY

Unlike many other scientists, a cultural anthropologist cannot bring his subjects into a laboratory; instead, he must go to visit them wherever they may happen to reside. This may be inconvenient, but it has the advantage of giving him a chance to study a people's manner of living in its customary setting. Whenever possible, one should select for investigation a society whose culture gives promise of throwing light on some particular problem of social science. Before departing for the field, an investigator should familiarize himself with whatever has already been written about the group and region he is going to study.

When ethnology was in its infancy, the matter of making contact with a primitive folk was often a serious problem. Today there is hardly a tribe[3] left that has not become known to some government official, military officer, missionary, traveler, teacher, trader, or former anthropologist. Moreover, practically all primitive groups now number among their members some individuals who have received training in a European tongue. Intermediaries and interpreters are therefore customarily available and, in some cases, published materials may even contain linguistic information, prepared by previous investigators, by means of which it is possible to learn in advance a good deal about a language whose speakers have no means of writing.

Equipped with a background based on his reading and training, and aided by local residents who deal with the natives he intends to

[3] In this book, "tribe" is used synonymously with "primitive society."

study, an ethnologist nowadays rarely has difficulty in establishing contact with a primitive group. Whenever conditions permit, he makes arrangements to live right within the community whose customs he has come to investigate. Once settled down, a fieldworker is ready to begin the dual tasks of making himself acceptable to the point where his presence is taken for granted by his neighbors and of noting everything that goes on about him. An ethnologist quickly senses whether his subjects distrust writing in their presence or the taking of photographs, and he guides himself accordingly. No detail should be deliberately omitted from his notebooks simply because it seems trivial, for the commonplace often has greater value than the unusual in yielding understanding.

Collection of cultural data by an anthropologist in some ways resembles the collection of coins by a beggar. If a hundred people each give a beggar a nickel, no one of them feels that he has given more than a trifle, and each contributor would probably be surprised to know that in the end the beggar had received five dollars. So it frequently is with the ethnologist. No native need give him more than a scrap of information at a time, yet if the anthropologist diligently writes down all that he is told on a given subject, he may at the end of a field trip find that on many topics he has accumulated a sizable fund of valuable data of whose existence none of his informants may be aware.

Apart from recording all that he chances to see and hear, an ethnologist finds it wise to question selected informants on particular topics. When interviewing, he must avoid asking leading questions and must allow subjects to wander from the point of inquiry as much as they like. Digressions frequently prove more rewarding than straightforward answers. At first a fieldworker must rely on interpreters, but he should take pains to learn the native language as well and as promptly as possible, so that he gradually becomes less and less dependent on what translators choose to convey to him. Some workers supplement their data with answers to prepared questionnaires or standard psychological tests.

Most fieldworkers make use, in one way or another, of the *participant-observer* technique.[4] This implies that a man will seek to share in the activities of the male natives and a woman will try to take part in the daily life of members of her sex. The participant-observer method may yield relatively few data for the time spent, but it helps a fieldworker to establish good rapport. Also, it helps him to acquire some first-hand information and to learn to see things from the tribal point

[4] F. R. Kluckhohn, "The Participant-Observer Technique in Small Communities," *American Journal of Sociology,* Vol. 46, 1940, pp. 331–43.

of view. Critics sometimes object to this approach because they fear that it makes a fieldworker so much a part of the very thing he is studying as to deprive him of the detachment and objectivity essential to the scientific method. All that need be said in reply is that the danger appears greatest to those who have never tried to become participant-observers of a culture different from their own. A cultural anthropologist is in more danger of being kept an outsider who cannot get the local viewpoint than he is of being allowed to become too thoroughly immersed in the life around him. Overcoming the biases of one's own culture is a greater challenge than the risk of going native.

More than anything else, a student on a field trip must never forget that he is an unexpected and uninvited guest in a society made up of sensitive human beings whose system of values is entirely different from his own. His job is to learn all he can about the other culture and to adjust to native ways, not the other way around. Even though the period of living in a strange cultural world is temporary, all anthropologists agree that the effects are long-lasting and exciting.

Many years of research have made it clear that some topics are best avoided at the outset. It is improbable that the members of any society will be willing to discuss freely with a stranger their deep-seated religious beliefs or the intimate details of their sex life. A beginner is well advised not to plunge into such matters prematurely. Information of this kind may be sought indirectly, or after one feels that he has won the confidence of "his people." It is usually best to start field work with commonplace technological activities, with the collection of word lists, or with any other subject that is likely to be regarded as neutral.

THE PERSONAL TOUCH

Sooner or later the thought is apt to arise: why could not the operator of an excellent moving picture camera and a perfect sound recorder produce a better report of a primitive culture than an ethnologist? A moment's reflection should provide part of the answer. Many people are averse to being photographed, and even if everyone were willing it would be impractical to keep the needed equipment in continuous operation for months, possibly for a year or more. Besides, many activities take place indoors, at night, during periods of bad weather, or in spots where extraneous noises may drown out what is really important. Nor would a finished sound track convey much meaning to audiences that did not understand the native language. Furthermore, one must not forget that mechanical devices can record only sights and sounds, whereas an ethnologist uses all his senses.

No instrument has yet been invented that can make discriminating selections of ethnological materials, and a trained anthropologist can certainly pick out significant items of culture better than the most proficient of cameramen. Wherever possible a fieldworker does not fail to supplement his notes with photographs, but indiscriminate picture-taking can be more harmful than helpful. Similarly, many workers take sound recorders into the field, but once more the material to be recorded has to be carefully chosen.

Without an ethnologist to marshal facts into systematic order they remain a hopeless jumble. Coherence emerges only when similar data are fitted together according to a consistent scheme. The more clearly a worker knows ahead of time the kinds of problems he intends to study and the kinds of questions he plans to ask, the more certainly will his material lend itself to adequate classification and intelligent analysis. Above all, it is the function of an ethnologist to make his data meaningful to others. The success of a published monograph can best be measured by the light it throws on the behavior of people in a given society and by the extent to which its material makes possible the building of new theories pertaining to the universal workings of human behavior.

How do you know you're right?

Any inferences drawn from field data are bound to be wrong if the original material is faulty. Consequently, it is up to every ethnologist to make sure that the information he publishes is as correct as possible. There are several ways of achieving reasonable accuracy. No one of them is self-sufficient, but together they serve to keep a worker from making gross errors.

The most common practice is to question *multiple informants* on the same topic. There is no way of telling in advance whether a native is representative of his society or abnormal in some way, or whether he is truthful, willing to talk, and competent to speak on the subject under study. Accordingly, it is wise for a field investigator to question several informants. The informants should be as varied as possible, and they should be unaware of what others may already have said. If the statements of multiple informants show much agreement, the investigator may feel fairly certain that he is getting at the truth. If there is marked disagreement, he must note the fact and try to figure out what it signifies. Material obtained from a single informant is always suspect.

There is also a need for checking the *internal consistency* of one's data. If, to cite a hypothetical case, an anthropologist discovers that his informants insist that their society never indulges in violence, yet finds in his notes frequent instances of assault and murder, he is faced with a marked lack of internal consistency and must seek its explanation.

Another method of avoiding mistakes is to make sure that one's description of a way of life covers *the yearly round.* All peoples practice different customs at various seasons. Ideally, a worker should stay in the field at least for a whole year, but if this is impractical he should make certain to obtain from informants full accounts of the group's behavior all through the yearly round.

The author has long been an advocate of still another device for insuring accuracy, which he calls the *divided field-trip.* Essentially this means that an ethnologist should make more than a single visit to a society under study. Even if his total time in the field is limited to a few months, he would do well to leave the area for a while and to return to it after a lapse of time. The outstanding value of the divided field-trip is that it enables an anthropologist on his later visit to overcome some of the deficiencies of the first. On his initial arrival he might, without knowing it, have been introduced by someone whom the natives heartily disliked; he might unwittingly have dealt with unreliable informants; he might sometimes have been told deliberate untruths; his very presence might have been resented; and he might, through ignorance of local customs or beliefs, have offended some members of the community. All these faults are capable of being remedied on a return trip. Now the ethnologist may join the society without any intermediary; he knows which informants are apt to be cooperative and trustworthy and which had better be diplomatically avoided. Few people are able to remember and repeat long after whatever deliberate misstatements they may earlier have made; if he has previously acted properly, he will find the community pleased to have him return; and he is most unlikely to give offense through ignorance of the society's symbolic values. On the whole, the advantages of the divided field-trip are so varied and numerous that they far outweigh the disadvantages of losing a few working days in the field. Besides what has already been mentioned, the divided field-trip gives one an undisturbed chance to study his notes carefully, to discover such inconsistencies as may require further checking, to find out which topics have not been sufficiently investigated, and, in general, to lay plans based on the knowledge already obtained for a more adequate research program when work is resumed.

Cultural configurations

Comparative studies of numerous cultures teach us that the major features of any society's institutionalized way of life neither stand by themselves nor fall into a shapeless arrangement. This can be illustrated by the construction of a model that stands for a cultural configuration. It may not be possible to make a single figure that is satisfactory to every social scientist, but something fruitful may be achieved even if only the minimum essentials are represented. However, although the idea of making a model may be accepted, there still may be a measure of disagreement with regard to its shape. Some may wish to picture a culture pattern as a pentagon, with one side each devoted to man's dealings with his environment, interpersonal relations, religion, language, and value system. Others may consider values to be subsumed under religion, and may, accordingly, prefer to show a way of life as a square or rectangle. Still others, including the writer, in their search for absolute minimums, would reduce the figure further and give it graphic representation as a triangle. Far more important than the actual number of lines or sides used is the fact that in the construction of any model, the parts should always be linked together, for the various facets of biocultural behavior never remain separate but always form a connected pattern in which the parts are usually adjusted to each other.

When examining a *biocultural triangle* (Fig. 20–1), one must imagine a spring placed at each juncture where two lines meet. This will make it easier to appreciate why heavy pressure on, or a marked change in the size or direction of any one side is bound to induce changes in the total configuration. Stated graphically, a biocultural triangle may look like this △ at one stage and like this ◺ at another.

If it be true that the three principal segments of our figure interlock, then it makes little difference, in a specific culture, at which spot an investigator starts his studies. A careful follow-up of any lead should take him all around the three sides of the figure. For instance, an ethnologist is unlikely to arouse resentment if he shows a friendly interest in the daily work of a potter. Without fail, his inquiries will deal with the subject of raw materials and will thus take him well into the Man⟷Environment aspects of the tribe's culture; after which it is but a simple step to seek information on the potter's personal background. This will include questions about the sex, age, and relationship of the potter's teacher, the age when training began, and other attributes of Man⟷Man conduct. Quite often, too, it will be found that some pots are made specifically for use in sacred contexts, and that design elements on others have religious significance.[5] By following such leads,

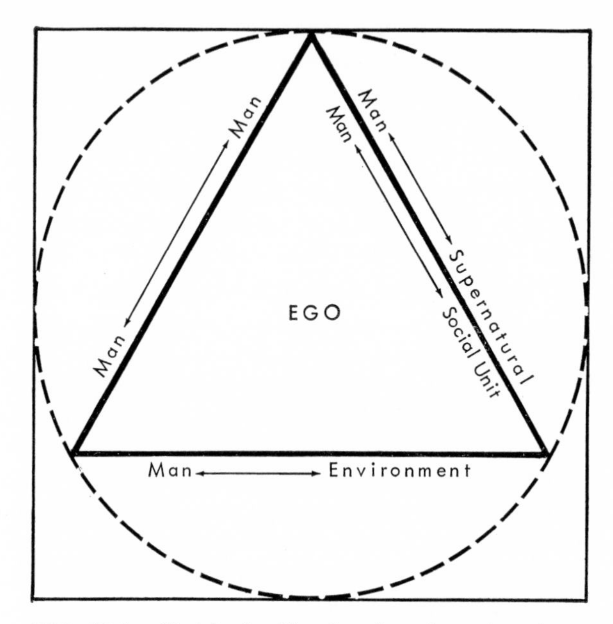

FIG. 20-1. Model of a biocultural configuration. As an Ego grows up in any society, he learns to conform to the biocultural triangle within which he is reared. This triangle, however, cannot be a random matter, but must conform to the laws of biology, which are fixed for all mankind and which are indicated by the circle which encloses the triangle. Nor can the laws of biology be random, for they cannot exceed the limits of physics and chemistry (shown by the external square).

fieldworkers can gain valuable information about a tribe's Man⟷Supernatural beliefs. This example demonstrates how all parts of a biocultural triangle may fit together and shows how an alert investigator may learn much about social and religious customs even if he starts out with simple questions about the technique of pottery making.

[5] R. L. Bunzel, *The Pueblo Potter,* New York, 1929, p. 92. Figs. 1 and 2 show pottery bowls intended to hold sacred prayer meal; and a design element on Fig. 4 is interpreted as a prayer for rain.

The reality of culture patterns

Those who doubt the reality of abstract concepts may wonder whether culture patterns actually exist. It can be shown that they do, even if the people most directly affected by them do not happen to be consciously aware of their existence. Let us take an example from American food habits. Suppose a wealthy but eccentric individual decided that he wanted a breakfast of beet soup, raw oysters, and sassafras tea; in what restaurant could he get them? At the opposite extreme, Americans who order fruit juice, eggs or cereal, toast, and coffee may feel that they are expressing their personal desires, but restaurant keepers know that a pattern is being followed. Probably the most successful restaurateurs are those who most completely anticipate the patterned food habits of their patrons. What chance of success would a restaurant owner in the United States have if he catered to the unexpected whims of rich eccentrics, but failed to stock stand-bys like toast and coffee?

Life in society would be just about impossible were it not for the existence of regularly patterned and therefore predictable ways of behaving. They are usually taken for granted by individuals, and they do not always function without a degree of variation; but think how difficult life would be if a person never knew what forms of behavior to expect from a spouse, parent, child, or neighbor. To appreciate this point one has only to compare the assurance that an individual feels when he says, "I know how to handle him. I can anticipate every move he'll make," with the distracted state of mind of the person who is forced to say, "I can't do a thing with him. I never know what he'll do next."

Some of the most interesting but difficult problems of social science are to determine how patterns of culture get started or become changed. It can be shown that forms of culture are sometimes modified by innovators and at other times in response to forces of their own, without the noticeable efforts of any identifiable person. A. L. Kroeber and Jane Richardson have suggested, in this connection, that styles in women's clothing may change in cyclic fashion,[6] without reference to the wants of their wearers or the whims of dress designers. Unfortunately, the implications of this topic have not yet been fully explored. Despite the manifold problems of interpretation that await analysis, modern fieldworkers invariably base their programs on the assumption that patterns

[6] A. L. Kroeber and J. Richardson, "Three Centuries of Women's Dress Fashions, a Quantitative Analysis," *Anthropological Records*, Vol. 5, No. 2, 1940.

of culture do exist. To a large extent, whether or not they realize it, people are *culture-bound* in every society.

OVERT, COVERT, AND MATTERS OF EMPHASIS

A number of the greatest difficulties involved in ethnological studies grow out of the simultaneous existence in one society of a number of divergent, and sometimes contradictory, sets of ideas. Clyde Kluckhohn drew attention to an important aspect of this problem when he discussed *overt* and *covert* patterns of behavior.[7] By modifying his usage slightly, we may designate as overt standards those somewhat idealized notions that one consciously thinks of as typical of his culture, and which are promptly recited in response to questions. Covert patterns may represent equally realistic guides to conduct, but one is less sure to be immediately aware of them and is less likely to express them readily in words. Something of the difference between them is reflected in our sayings about preaching one thing and practicing another, but when we make a contrast of this sort there is usually a hint of deceit. Such is not the case in the distinction between overt and covert with which we are dealing. One does not have to be a liar or a hypocrite to say that a given way of behaving is typical of his culture, but to act most of the time according to a different pattern. An illustration based on our own culture should serve to make the point clear.

Suppose one were to ask an average American, comfortably seated at home, if he would risk about two thousand dollars' worth of equipment, plus his own and his family's lives, merely to save a minute or two of time. The overt reply would unfailingly be in the negative; yet, anyone who has observed average Americans driving cars would realize that on the road they act according to a covert pattern favoring the values of great speed and daring that is the opposite of their overt responses. This is the very sort of unspoken contradiction that a trained anthropologist must always be prepared to detect.

When they are viewed in their entirety, biocultural configurations sometimes reveal different kinds of emphases. One society may reward with prestige and honors all manifestations of strongly aggressive conduct, but another may frown upon and punish aggressors. The late Ruth

[7] C. Kluckhohn, "Patterning as Exemplified in Navaho Culture," in L. Spier, *et al.*, eds., *Language, Culture, and Personality,* Menasha, Wis., 1941, pp. 109–30.

Fulton Benedict in her famous book, *Patterns of Culture,* to illustrate this point selected certain societies whose ways of life reflected strongly marked differences in basic attitudes. She described as *Apollonian* those forms of culture that showed high regard for sobriety and restraint, and she called *Dionysian* those honoring intemperate and reckless behavior.[8]

Certainly it is true that some cultures have a dominant tone that seems to color the activities of their participants. Orthodox Jewish males who lived in eastern Europe during the nineteenth century were Apollonian to the extent that they could achieve the most treasured honors of their communities only if they were great scholars who devoted themselves to the study of Old Testament writings and their commentaries.[9] At about the same period of history, far off in the Great Plains region of the United States, the Crow Indians favored Dionysian modes of action and reserved their highest admiration and rewards for men who were daring fighters.[10]

Since the publication of *Patterns of Culture* other cultural anthropologists have pointed out that Ruth Benedict drew her evidence for domination by a single cultural motive from only a few idealized behavior traits, in a very small handful of carefully selected societies. Far more often, it is argued, group ways of life reveal the influence of multiple motivations. Morris E. Opler, of Cornell, has suggested that instead of having one guiding principle most cultures are organized around a number of interrelated themes.[11] Whichever may be the proper view, it is now fully recognized that varying culture patterns, or their parts, do show different emphases in setting up standards of approved behavior for the members of particular societies to follow, and every fieldworker should become aware of whatever emphases seem to prevail in the culture he is studying.

---

[8] R. F. Benedict, *Patterns of Culture,* Boston, 1934. The terms and concepts, "Apollonian" and "Dionysian," were borrowed from Nietzsche. Benedict also inaugurated a trend, still followed by an occasional anthropologist, toward differentiating "guilt" from "shame" cultures. In the former, an individual feels uneasy if he becomes aware that any of his actions deviates from the approved moral code of his group; in the latter, a person regards transgressions lightly unless he happens to be caught.

[9] M. Zborowski and E. Herzog, *Life is with People,* New York, 1953, p. 74, *et passim.*

[10] R. H. Lowie, *The Crow Indians,* New York, 1935, p. 215.

[11] M. E. Opler, "Themes as Dynamic Forces in Culture," *American Journal of Sociology,* Vol. 51, 1945, pp. 198–206. A year later Opler further elaborated some of his ideas in "An Application of the Theory of Themes in Culture," *Washington Academy of Sciences,* Vol. 36, 1946, pp. 137–66.

The danger of biocultural unconformity

Because the values of biology and those of culture can, and occasionally do, run counter to each other, there arises a source of potential conflict in human affairs that is entirely missing in the activities of other animals. As long as a society's ways of life correspond reasonably well to the biogenetically determined requirements of its individual members there need be little difficulty, but if a group's symbolic or cultural values diverge widely from basic biological considerations, a *biocultural unconformity* develops, which is a possible source of great danger (Fig. 20–2).

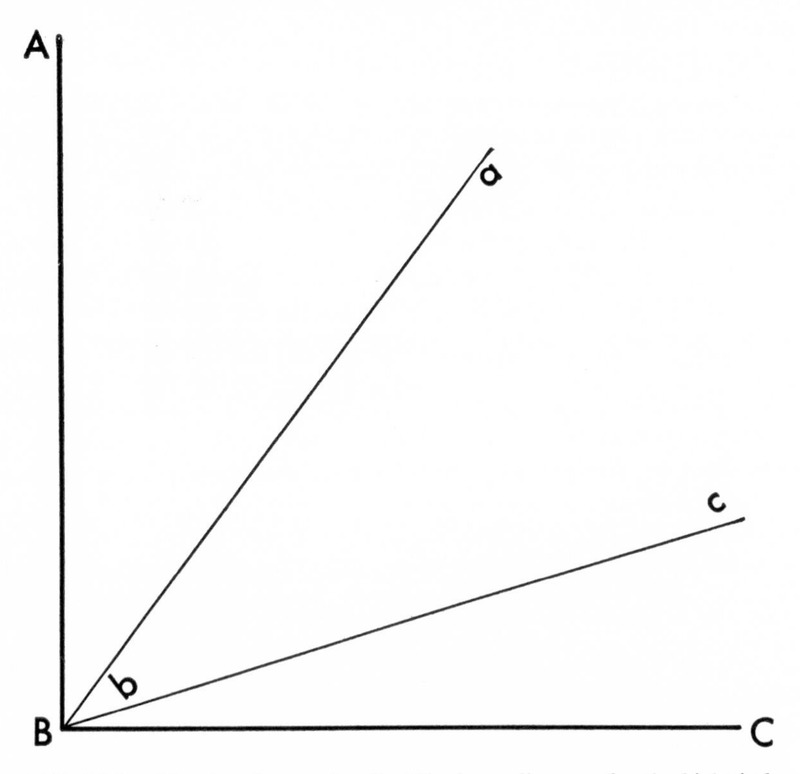

FIG. 20-2. Biocultural unconformity. The heavy lines are for the biological forces that underlie human behavior and the light lines represent cultural responses. Trouble spots arise whenever ab diverges from AB, or when bc is too far removed from BC. The further the gap between them, the greater is the likelihood of trouble.

Several aspects of Euro-American life illustrate the grave importance of this principle.

Many agencies in the United States, including all branches of medical practice, are dedicated to the saving and prolongation of human life. Our system of cultural values gives high esteem to these objectives. Every time a life is saved or mortality rates are lowered we are inclined to cheer. Tables, such as the one in Fig. 20–3, showing a steady rise of life expectancy in the United States, make us very proud. What we often

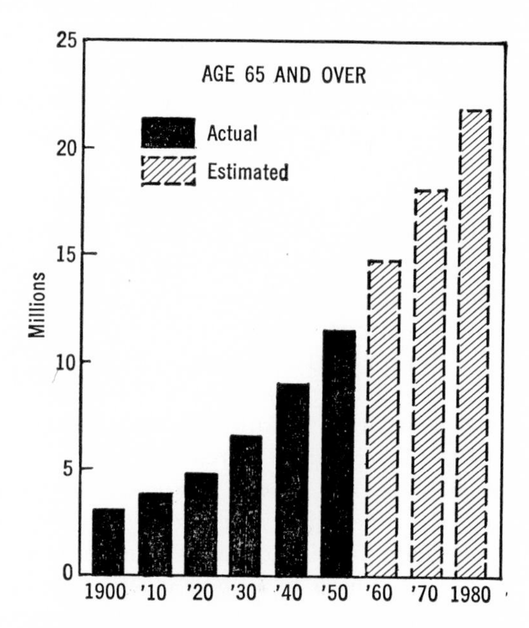

FIG. 20-3. Increase of older people in the United States. Actual figures are indicated by solid columns; projections into the future are shown in the stippled columns. (Courtesy of U.S. Department of Labor, Bureau of Labor Statistics.)

overlook is the patent fact that these accomplishments are limited to matters of biology and are not always accompanied by cultural advances in the treatment of the aged. Illogically, we are making a successful biological effort to produce, for the first time in our history, a large and growing body of oldsters, but culturally we do not know what to do with them.

Much the same applies to many patients in mental hospitals. Thanks to some splendid and dramatic advances in therapy, the staffs of many institutions annually cure thousands of disturbed persons who were once regarded as incurable. Unfortunately, there still persists in our society a *cultural stereotype* that makes something shameful of mental disease. Consequently, many patients who have become physically well continue to remain in hospitals because they are culturally unwanted by their relatives and friends.

Biocultural unconformity may also manifest itself in a society's attitudes toward parenthood. Every normal adult desires sexual intercourse at one time or another, and every social unit wants to have children born to its members. Yet, each group approves of sexual relations not indiscriminately but only between certain people under specified conditions, and it sanctions the birth of children only to selected persons. It is a quirk of biocultural behavior that sociocultural approval may be given to these activities quite apart from the biological fitness or readiness of the individuals most concerned.

Hardly any society chooses to make a theoretically vital distinction between those who are physically best suited to beget children and those who are best equipped to rear and train them. With pitifully few exceptions, an untested and unproved assumption is made that those who produce children are competent to raise them. Hence, in practice, no distinction is drawn between biological parenthood and what may be called cultural parenthood. Only a few modern nations, especially the USSR and Israel, are reported to have tried separating some features of biological from cultural parenthood, but at the moment no reliable information on the success of their efforts is available.

Two aspects of juvenile delinquency in the United States may be better understood, at least in part, in the light of the difficulties that may arise from biocultural unconformity. At present we do not know all the biochemical ingredients and interactions that are contained in each body, but enough is known to suggest that no two persons are exactly alike[12] and that the ingredients that compose one's body may have some bearing on one's temperament and, accordingly, on his behavior.[13] There is a good chance, therefore, that people are greatly varied even at birth, yet our school system fails to take account of this variability. All children in the United States must, by law, attend school until about the age of 15 or more. No consideration whatsoever is given to the possibility that some children may be biologically well-suited to this cultural requirement, whereas others might be better fitted, biogenetically, for roaming outdoors. If this be so, there is no use in lament-

---

12 The promise of getting badly needed information along these lines is held forth in the researches of recent workers who call themselves chemical anthropologists. Preliminary physiological investigations suggest that the adrenal glands of professional basketball players pour out excessive amounts of epinephrine, whereas hockey players produce unusual quantities of norepinephrine. The former seems to go with alertness, and the latter with aggression and combativeness. These conclusions are tentative.

13 Sheldon and Eleanor Glueck, *Physique and Delinquency,* New York, 1956, pp. 226–27, have found that mesomorphic, somatotonic youngsters, who are muscular and active of body, are the most likely to run afoul of the law.

ing the restlessness of some children in classrooms or their indulgence in truancy. Since youngsters cannot change their inherited biologies, it would seem wiser for societies to modify their cultural requirements and to make them more flexible in order to eliminate some of the sources of biocultural unconformity.

More dramatic still are those aspects of biocultural unconformity that constantly arise in the United States from our attitudes toward sexual relations. Boys and girls throughout the world reach sexual maturity somewhere around the age of 15, and for the next 5 years males, especially, are at the height of their potency and desire. During those very years our ways of life provide not a single culturally approved outlet. Youthful marriages are deprecated, particularly for men, and are often unfeasible for economic or other reasons; irregular love affairs, or the "sowing of wild oats," are so frowned upon officially that they are often punishable as illegal; consort with prostitutes is forbidden and widely condemned; and homosexuality, sodomy, and masturbation are considered thoroughly despicable. On the score of sex, then, our culture is entirely unrealistic and illogical, permitting a wide gap to open up between the facts of biology, particularly as they apply to young men aged 15 to 20, and the cultural values that these self-same young men are taught to hold high. Small wonder that the statistics of criminality show that the age group in question gives far more than its proportionate share of trouble. It would be naive to assume that young adult males commit only crimes of sex, for psychologists have shown that sexuality can be sublimated or directed into numerous channels. It is too bad that we have no way of determining the number of antisocial acts that may originate from biocultural unconformity. And it is a disturbing fact that wherever biocultural unconformity may cause a young person to "go wrong," it makes little difference if he comes from an unbroken good home or a broken bad one. Biological impulses are so universal and persistent that youngsters can "go wrong," regardless of their family backgrounds.

Biocultural unconformity poses a threat to stability not only when one deals with the operations of whole societies, but also when one considers the reactions of particular individuals to the patterns of culture within which they grow up. It is a fact that biocultural configurations vary widely in the traits that societies most esteem and reward, and it is equally true that babies differ in their ability or willingness to accept restrictions and to tolerate frustrations. Over the years it always happens that some infants are better suited for life in one type of system than in another.

In all cases where there is likely to be a discrepancy between innate temperament and cultural values, an individual finds himself facing a dangerous situation. If he forces himself to conform to his society's standards, he must run the risk of internal or personality maladjustment; but if he permits himself to follow inborn leanings that run opposite to his group's approved forms of behavior, he is in danger of external conflicts with his fellow men.

Thus, the threat of biocultural unconformity confronts each of its potential victims with an insoluble dilemma. Luckily, few people and few patterns of culture run to extremes. Most individuals have mixed temperaments, and most ways of life offer widely different means of achieving success. Among us, for instance, a great scholar, actor, artist, business executive, or professional athlete, can live equally well. Beyond question, one of the advantages of living in a big, culturally heterogeneous community is that its code provides a variety of satisfactions for all manner of persons.

Selected References

Benedict, Ruth F., "Anthropology and the Abnormal," *Journal of General Psychology,* Vol. 10, 1934, pp. 59–80.

———, *Patterns of Culture,* Boston, 1934.

Bennett, John W., "The Study of Cultures: A Survey of Technique and Methodology in Field Work," *American Sociological Review,* Vol. 13, 1948, pp. 672–89.

Henry, Jules, and Spiro, Melville E., "Psychological Techniques: Projective Tests in Field Work," in A. L. Kroeber, ed., *Anthropology Today,* Chicago, 1953, pp. 417–29.

Kluckhohn, Clyde, "Patterning as Exemplified in Navaho Culture," in L. Spier, *et al.,* eds., *Language, Culture and Personality,* Menasha, Wis., 1941, pp. 109–30.

———, "The Place of Theory in Anthropological Studies," *Journal of the Philosophy of Science,* Vol. 6, 1939, pp. 328–44.

———, and Kelly, William, "The Concept of Culture," in Ralph Linton, ed., *The Science of Man in the World Crisis,* New York, 1945, pp. 78–106.

Kluckhohn, Florence R., "The Participant-Observer Technique in Small Communities," *American Journal of Sociology,* Vol. 46, 1940, pp. 331–43.

Kroeber, Alfred L., and Kluckhohn, Clyde, "Culture," *Papers of the Peabody Museum of American Archaeology and Ethnology,* Vol. 47, No. 1, Cambridge, Mass., 1952.

Murdock, George P., "The Common Denominator of Cultures," in R. Linton, ed., *The Science of Man in the World Crisis,* New York, 1945, pp. 123–42.

Opler, Morris E., "Themes as Dynamic Forces in Culture," *American Journal of Sociology,* Vol. 51, No. 3, 1945, pp. 198–206.

Paul, Benjamin D., "Interview Techniques and Field Relationships," in A. L. Kroeber, ed., *Anthropology Today,* Chicago, 1953, pp. 430–51.

Man's Relations with His Physical Environment

CHAPTER 21

LET'S EAT!

Like those of other animals, the bodies of human beings are made up of protoplasm, which is not equipped either to store indefinitely or to replace from within itself the ingredients necessary to sustain life. This means that, without fail, members of *Homo sapiens* must regularly get from some external source whatever their bodies need. Adequate amounts of oxygen in the air, as well as those solids and liquids customarily consumed as food, generally provide each individual with all that he requires to live and function properly. We have here the source of a universal aspect of all cultures, for no way of life can endure if it fails to deal satisfactorily with the problem of providing its carriers with a sufficient supply of oxygen and food. Yet no two societies have exactly the same eating and drinking preferences. Truly has it been said that one man's meat is another man's poison.

In a few cases the bodies of other persons can provide much that an individual needs. Suckling babies every where derive most of their nourishment from their mothers or wet nurses; and cannibals sometimes consume the bodies of other humans for food. But the period of nursing never makes up more than a small fraction of an average life span; and anthropologists have found real (as opposed to ceremonial or symbolic) cannibalism to have been important only in restricted parts of Africa, in the tropical areas of the New World, and on some of the South Sea Islands. Far more commonly, human beings get what they need in the way of oxygen, food, and drink, not from one another but from their physical settings. So incontrovertible is this requirement and so unfailing is this practice that man's interrelations with his environment must form the base of every biocultural model or configuration.

Oddly enough, although we are dealing with an essential biological necessity for all mankind, the evaluation of food as good or bad is often illogical or nonlogical, according to the scheme set forth on page 16.[1] There is no society known, including our own, that has first made a thorough scientific analysis of all the nutritive elements in its environment and has then given preference to those items that were shown to be best suited to man's bodily needs. Instead, cultural anthropologists find everywhere the existence of food preferences based on symbolic, man-made values that may have nothing to do with nutrition as such. A poor family of Caucasoids in the United States might bewail its inability to afford meat, but would nevertheless reject a gift of plump, nutritious gophers, which Navaho Indians regard as a delicacy. Even cow's milk, which is widely held to be an excellent food, was until recent years despised by Chinese, Koreans, Japanese, and other residents of the Far East. As late as 1934 the writer knew a tribesman, hospitalized with an advanced case of tuberculosis, who insisted on returning to his native village because he was sure the hospital attendants were trying to poison him by making him drink milk.

Symbolic values are so basic to the use of all human foodstuffs that as many shortages are due to the scarcity of culturally approved items as are due to a genuine lack of nutriments. While World War II was being fought, teams of scientists tried to persuade Allied peoples whose customary rations were in short supply to substitute other highly nourishing foods. In practically every case where the substitution failed to conform to culturally determined standards of taste and texture it was strongly resisted, in spite of scientific assurances of its nutritional value.[2] An interesting example of the same principle turned about is the practice of a soft drink company which retains an attorney who can eat various insects without harm. Whenever a suit is brought by a plaintiff claiming to have been made ill by a bug in his drink, the lawyer eats a similar specimen to disprove the claim. Apparently, juries are so impressed by this feat that they fail to consider the possibility of culturally induced damages and therefore dismiss the case.[3]

---

1 A good deal of information about the acquisition and preparation of foodstuffs by particular tribes may be found in R. L. Beals and H. Hoijer, *An Introduction to Anthropology,* rev. ed., New York, 1959, Chap. 11; and E. D. Chapple and C. S. Coon, *Principles of Anthropology,* New York, 1942, pp. 127–38, 142–97, *et passim.*

2 Lately, in an effort to isolate all the components of taste, experimenters served chicken under gray or green lights. Although the food was identified for them, subjects found its looks so distasteful that they could not eat it.

3 On June 27, 1953, the *Ann Arbor News* carried an Associated Press dispatch describing the victory of a lawyer who ate a cockroach in court.

There is no edible substance to which seemingly arbitrary cultural values cannot be assigned. Sometimes foods come to be regarded as better suited for men or women, without reference to the actual physical differences of the sexes. A cultural concept, unknown in our society but known in western Asia and widespread among Indian peoples of Latin America, is the notion that foods may be hot or cold regardless of their temperature or physiological properties. One of these nonlogical classifications lists as cold such diverse items as mutton, fish, maize, rice, chocolate, bread, butter, milk, sugar, and barley beer; whereas hot foods include beef, turkey, sweet potatoes, coffee, mangoes, and chick-peas.[4] People may cling to beliefs of this sort long after the basis for the classification has been forgotten. Anthropologists cannot always explain the origin of the hot or cold concept, but they can show that it is cultural and not biophysicochemical. George M. Foster has tentatively traced some of these notions to the teachings of Hippocrates and Galen. They are likely to be associated with a belief that various ailments are hot or cold. Quite often, in such cases, cures are thought to be brought about by resort to opposites, so that cold remedies and foods are used against hot illnesses, and vice versa.[5]

Foods may also be socially ranked as high or low. Sometimes this may be determined by expense, which may rest on a nutritional base, as when cream costs more than milk. Just as often, high-class foods may be more costly but of less nutritional value, as in the case of polished and unpolished rice. Other rankings may disregard economics and biological worth altogether. Many American housewives would be ashamed to serve guests a Sunday dinner of hamburgers and onions instead of chicken and potatoes, even though the former might conceivably be more expensive and nutritious than the latter. As an experiment, the writer asked five Japanese to rank a list of assorted foods in the order in which a traditional Japanese would have preferred to serve them to an honored visitor. All of them, as might have been anticipated, placed rice first. That they were thinking in terms of cultural values is made clear by the fact that a nutritional study of the same foods ranks rice last.[6]

[4] J. Gillin, "Moche: A Peruvian Coastal Community," *Smithsonian Institution, Institute of Social Anthropology*, No. 3, Washington, D.C., 1945, p. 54.

[5] G. M. Foster, "Relationships between Theoretical and Applied Anthropology: A Public Health Program Analysis," *Human Organization*, Vol. 11, 1952, p. 8.

[6] The list of foods, presented to Japanese informants in alphabetical order, consisted of barley, beef, chicken eggs, milk, and rice. The biological or nutritional evaluation of these foods is taken from R. J. Williams, *What to Do about Vitamins*, Norman, Okla., 1945, pp. 50–54. I am indebted for this reference to my colleague, James N. Spuhler.

There are as many variations of eating etiquette as there are food preferences. Despite the simple fact that the final aim of all feeding customs is to put food into the mouth, societies favor an incredible series of preliminary maneuvers. Another important distinction between biologic and cultural factors can be made on this score. It is a stark fact that the etiquette of eating seldom goes beyond the point where food is swallowed. Thereafter, in all societies, the matter of digestion becomes a biological activity, virtually free of cultural controls. To some extent cultural ideas may interfere with the biochemistry of digestion, but such interference is never a matter of fixed etiquette. The reason etiquette regulations are limited primarily to the realm of culture is that their values and procedures are man-made. Accordingly, they are subject, at least in theory, to human control. Basic biological processes, by contrast, are unalterable and are not subject, even in theory, to man's complete control. Hence, rules of etiquette tend to be inoperative in matters of biology.

Rarely does one find a culture pattern that gives high value to the serving of food in the same vessels in which it was prepared. Instead, human beings almost without exception try to eat their food from containers other than cooking vessels. As a matter of fact, there are many people who pride themselves on the expensive array of extra items, like serving plates and table coverings, that they interpose between the preparation and consumption of food. Yet, it must be admitted that such highly prized objects have only doubtful value when it comes to the basically biological needs of ingesting and digesting nutritious substances. In contrast to those Euro-Americans who feel that correct dining demands a wide assortment of utensils, many inhabitants of eastern Asia can get by with a pair of simple chopsticks. Well-mannered Hindus eat with freshly washed hands from individual trays, but many American Indians dip into common bowls with unwashed hands. Some societies regard postprandial belching as good form; others as bad; Americans as variable. Among us a burp in polite company is a matter for apology, but a loud reverberating belch may be a matter for prideful boasting in a group of masculine beer drinkers.

Extrabiologic attitudes toward food are well brought out in a consideration of prescribed forms of restraint. Many societies have differing schedules for taking meals, and individuals learn to adjust their wants to cultural norms. Virtually never, except for babies fed on demand, are the proper times for eating left to the cravings of individual appetites. No matter how ravenously hungry a well-bred American may be, it would never occur to him to rush into a kitchen and begin eating before a hostess was ready to serve. Similarly, in distant Tierra del

Fuego, a half-starved Ona woman may be eager to pounce on a guanaco brought home from the chase by her husband, but etiquette prescribes a pause and a show of indifference before cooking operations may begin. Obviously, in all cases of this kind, symbolic, cultural values carry far more weight than the pangs of hunger. Much the same applies to matters of quantity. The amount that a person consumes is not always commensurate with his appetite or the needs of his body. Eating or abstaining out of politeness are very real habits.

That food customs are directly connected with other aspects of a biocultural triangle may be readily shown. Eating together at social gatherings or celebrations like weddings always has strong sociologic implications, and the feeling that no party can be successful unless food is served is widespread. Perhaps a trifle less apparent, but equally common, is the use of food as a symbol of social status. The positive aspect, indulgence in luxury items that are not necessarily nutritious, is well known to all, but fewer people are aware of a negative side, conspicuous waste.[7] In our culture we look down on those who serve portions rigidly measured to the number of diners. Covertly we feel that more than exactly enough food ought to be offered. A similar notion is carried to even greater extremes among the Trobriand Islanders who live near New Guinea. One of their principal staples is the cultivated yam, and on occasion farmers display heaps of yams, many of which form a surplus and will be allowed to rot. Not only is this an expression of conspicuous waste, but it is also a measure of social standing, for convention decrees that no native may pile up as many yams as does the village chief.[8]

The manner in which all three segments of a biocultural triangle are interconnected is further exemplified by the manifold religious implications of food. Practically universal are the beliefs that some substances may fittingly be offered to supernatural powers, usually in the form of sacrifices, and that foods blessed by deities or religious officers have great extranutritional value for humans.

Almost all cultures, too, incorporate a religious notion that certain foods are prohibited or taboo to ordinary men and women.[9] Sometimes the prohibitions admit of no exceptions, and sometimes they apply only at particular times or under special circumstances. In our sophisticated society the existence of religious food taboos frequently causes embar-

---

7 As here used, the concept is modified from Veblen's original usage. See M. Lerner, ed., *The Portable Veblen,* New York, 1948, p. 136.

8 B. Malinowski, *Argonauts of the Western Pacific,* second impression, London, 1932, p. 61.

9 The common occurrence of food taboos, whether generally cultural or specifically religious, has been studied in F. J. Simoons, *Eat not this Flesh,* Madison, Wis., 1961.

rassment. Because of the high cultural value we ascribe to being rational and logical, many of our religious people are reluctant to admit that they subscribe to taboos which have been aptly described as based on culturally standardized unreason. Accordingly, they make great efforts to rationalize their beliefs. Some Christians maintain that Lenten prohibitions reflect a time when it was dangerous to eat in the spring foods that had been stored from the preceding fall. Along similar lines there are Orthodox Jews who argue that they do not eat pork because it may anciently have caused illness in hot countries.

When viewed in the light of all the food taboos involved in the faiths mentioned, these explanations prove to be unsatisfactory. They do not explain why many Christians who eat meat regularly on Thursdays and Saturdays must abstain on Fridays, and they fail to throw light on the Jewish custom of allowing dairy products to be consumed immediately before meat, but not directly after. Religious attitudes toward diet are extraordinary phenomena of culture and are not always brought into line with biology. Their persistence into the twentieth century serves to demonstrate how consistently man gives preference, short of inducing death, to cultural rather than biological values. At the same time, the contradictions involved in so many of man's attitudes toward food show why it is necessary to think of each pattern of culture as maintaining a dynamic equilibrium between oft-conflicting forces.

DWELLINGS AND OTHER STRUCTURES

Housing is another essential aspect of material culture that is part of man's interaction with his external surroundings. By learning to build and occupy houses, man lessened the need of making biological adjustments to the weather. To the extent that habitations keep out rain, frost, wind, and direct sunlight, they serve to stabilize the environmental conditions under which mankind must live. As is the case with all biocultural activities, different societies may erect different kinds of dwellings even if they happen to reside in an identical setting. On a joint reservation in Arizona, the Hopi Indians occupy rectangular dwellings of stone and adobe, traditionally clustered into communal pueblos, whereas the Navaho live in individual, dome-shaped structures (*hogans*), made of heavy timbers and earth (Fig. 21–1).[10] Cultural values always

[10] For further information on variations of house types, see Beals and Hoijer, *op. cit.*, 328–34; Chapple and Coon, *op. cit.*, pp. 194–210; and E. A. Hoebel, *Man in the Primitive World,* New York, 1949, pp. 115–30.

A B

FIG. 21-1. Differing house types in one environment. In Arizona and New Mexico the stone and 'dobe terraced structures of the Pueblo Indians (A) contrast vividly with the timber and earth hogans of the neighboring Navaho (B).

dictate which of a range of available materials a group will select for building, and there is no established rule that enables one to predict from the nature of a region the kinds of houses that its occupants will construct.

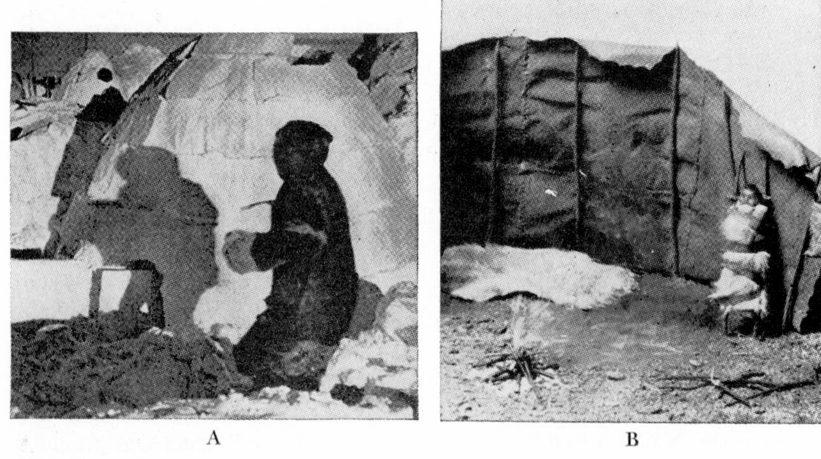

A B

FIG. 21-2. Contrasting types of houses in very cold environments. The snowhouse (igloo) of the Arctic Eskimo (A) is very different from the Ona windbreak (B) in Antarctica. By our standards, the Eskimo house is infinitely more logical. (A—G. de Poncins, *Kabloona.* New York, 1941. Courtesy of Reynal & Hitchcock, Inc. B—Bureau of American Ethnology.)

What is true of building materials is also true of architectural styles and household furnishings. Physical environments never compel the use of a given shape or size, although they may impose limitations on the choice of substances employed. Anthropologists can show numerous illustrations of housing practices that, in terms of our logic, make clever adjustments to their setting, but they can also point out examples of dwelling styles that appear to be out of keeping with their surroundings. Eskimo igloos are excellent adaptations, by our standards, to Arctic lands where snowfall is heavy, but the windbreaks of the Ona near Antarctica fail to keep out the bitter cold to which these people are subjected for many months of the year (Fig. 21–2).

Occasionally, specific methods of building homes or of making furniture become so thoroughly identified with particular societies that minute details of construction may be used for tracing tribal movements or contacts.[11]

Like houses themselves, certain aspects of home furnishings are institutionalized responses to biophysicochemical forces. Even the most scantily furnished of dwellings are likely to contain: (1) cooking vessels, dishes, dining implements; (2) chairs, stools, cushions, or mats; and (3) beds or their equivalents. The first items reflect ways of satisfying hunger. The next set, on which people sit, kneel, squat, or recline when they want to rest, are necessitated by the fact that the muscles involved when standing become strained and weary in time and achieve relaxation when a person lowers his body. As to beds, it is an observable fact that all normal human beings must sleep for a part of each day, although physiologists have not yet determined precisely why sleep is necessary. Simply because some aspects of household furnishings can be shown to satisfy biophysicochemical needs, it does not follow that all of them do. Esthetic, social, and religious considerations may likewise be important in this connection.

---

[11] In this connection cultural anthropologists usually call attention to use of the *false*, or *corbeled, arch* as opposed to the *true arch*. Corbeled arches are constructed by a system of overlaps, so that the sides stick out and serve as counterweights to the arch or vault. The need for sidewise projections makes a corbeled arch appear massive and clumsy, with a good deal of solid construction in relation to the area of free space. Corbeled arches presumably originated in the Copper-Bronze Age in Greece, and independently among the Maya Indians in the New World. From these centers the trait seems to have diffused widely.

True arches are built in such fashion that their parts are self-supporting, especially when a *keystone* has been slipped into place. They do not require massive counterweights at the sides, so that they can be slender and graceful. Mesopotamia is generally accepted as their place of origin in the Old World, and in the New World the principle of the true arch is found among some of the Eskimos, who managed to construct vaulted igloos without counterweights.

Structures that are meant for living quarters are found universally, but almost equally common are supplementary buildings devoted to other purposes. These, too, may vary in materials employed, methods of construction, elaboration or ornamentation, contents, size, and shape. Again, like residences, they may show varying degrees of compliance with the natural environment.

The clearest reflection of man's relations to his environment is to be found in the uses to which supplementary buildings are put. Commonest of all are those designed for storing surplus foods, tools, and equipment, or raw materials to be used in manufacturing various things. Places for sheltering and feeding domesticated animals are widespread, and so, too, are working arrangements that may vary from mere covered platforms to elaborate factories. Less widely distributed, but very important on many Pacific islands, are distinct outbuildings for the preparation of meals.

As to the interactions of man to man with respect to structures that are not homes, the best examples are clubhouses of various kinds. Some are for the exclusive use of adult men, some are open only to members of a *secret society,* and others may be reserved for women. Special living quarters for unmarried warriors comprise an outstanding feature of Masai culture in northeastern Africa; and large, communally maintained guesthouses are found regularly through southeast Asia. It is often difficult to decide whether the functions of a building should be classified as social or religious (Fig. 21–3). In a great many parts of the primitive world, for instance, females are expected to resort periodically to menstrual lodges, but this requirement is usually connected with a supernatural fear of blood. *Sudatories* or *sweat houses* are also very common, and their use, too, generally has socioreligious implications.

More clearly religious in purpose are buildings in which major supernatural activities are regularly held. These may not be as elaborately constructed in primitive societies as are many churches, cathedrals, temples, synagogues, mosques, and shrines, but they serve much the same purpose. When they are not clearly differentiated from dwellings, observers unfamiliar with a particular culture may fail to recognize them as houses of worship, but members of a given society will ordinarily detect some form of symbolism by which to identify them. Even when they are built with the same kinds of materials and along similar lines as homes, such places will be regarded as sacred because they are supposed to house deities or because of the rites that are known to be held within them. On the other hand, buildings with primarily religious functions, such as the *kivas* of the Pueblo Indians (Fig. 21–3), may be used as informal masculine clubhouses when no rituals are in progress.

FIG. 21-3. Nondwelling structure. Left: An outside view of a Hopi kiva at Oraibi. Below: Inside a kiva. Kivas are traditionally a part of Pueblo culture. Their primary use is to house religious exercises, but at other times they are masculine clubhouses.

Herskovits has shown us how the structures and furnishings of the Bush Negroes in Guiana, South America, touch on many aspects of their patterns of culture.[12] As he describes the situation, these natives live in rectangular, gabled houses, woven of palm fronds. Each dwelling unit is part of a complex of structures, and a number of such complexes constitute a village. Doorposts of village elders are carved with symbolic designs, and men of wealth store their possessions in secondary buildings with open sides of latticework. All who please may look in, but only males related to the owner may enter, on pain of death from a potent charm. Even so brief a synopsis indicates ways in which materials taken from the environment are linked with social and religious factors.

Clothing customs

There was a time when the human habit of wearing clothing was unfailingly attributed to the promptings of comfort, modesty, the sex urge, or love of decoration. Then ethnologists began to report numerous instances of garments that were inadequate for comfort by our standards, that deliberately exposed body parts which Euro-Americans sought to conceal, or that appeared to Westerners hideous rather than ornamental. Examples also came to light of women who wore alluring garments or accessories, yet rejected the advances of all males. In many parts of the world a woman would be embarrassed to be seen without an item, like a lip plug, that we might regard as largely ornamental, but would not feel ashamed at the exposure of her body. (See Fig. 21–4.) Cases are also known where the body is painted instead of clothed. (See Fig. 21–5.)

It is now agreed that the origins of clothing habits are obscure and that various motives may prevail in different cultures. Garments sometimes are used to keep their wearers warm and dry, but they may also be worn, as are summer furs, for purely symbolic reasons. Aboriginal Australians are occasionally said to betray deficient mentalities because they may wear too little for warmth even when thick pelts are available. With equal reason, these natives might wonder about the mentality of Occidentals who wear far too much when it is almost unbearably hot.

Although human jaws, teeth, or hair may be worn (usually as ornaments) in many societies, body parts never make up a complete garment. There is thus brought into play another aspect of man's relation to his physical setting. Plants and animals are always counted upon to supply needed raw materials. Nor should it be overlooked that all tools used

[12] M. J. Herskovits, *Man and His Works,* New York, 1948, pp. 217–220.

in the making of clothing likewise originate in the natural environment.

Habits of dress seldom fail to have sexual, chronological, or socio-

FIG. 21-4. Kirdis woman, with lip plug. This young African woman is going to market. She is unconcerned about the nudity of her body, but she is wearing a string of beads and a lip plug. (From Edward Weyer, Jr., *Primitive Peoples Today,* New York, 1959. Courtesy of the author, E. Häberlin, and Doubleday & Co., Inc.)

logical connotations (Fig. 21–5). Sometimes the differences have demonstrable biological bases, but this is not always the case. The movement of zippers toward the rear of skirts in our society may be related to the fact that women's forearms are anatomically different from men's, so

FIG. 21-5. Clothing customs among the Witoto. The Witoto Indians live in the tropical forest of the Amazon drainage. Men, women, and children all dress differently. On festive occasions, in particular, adult women use painted decorations in place of garments that conceal body parts. (Courtesy of Paul Fejos and Bureau of American Ethnology.)

that they can more easily reach back, but biology utterly fails to explain why skirts are worn by females in societies like ours, but by males in other places, such as in parts of China or New Zealand. Makers of articles of clothing also tend to be of one sex or the other, and many of the body movements that distinguish males from females are associated with the making and wearing of different garbs. To an American, a strong man knitting dainty garments is always a comic figure.

Important distinctions of rank, wealth, occupation, and status are often expressed, likewise, in ornaments, insignia, accessories, or hair styles. During the Copper-Bronze Age in Mesopotamia only priests were allowed to wear beards, and Buddhist religious officers always have shaved heads. Unmarried females among the Hopi traditionally had their hair done up in circular buns (butterfly wings) at the sides of the head, but married women wore their hair in two braids (Fig. 21–6); and a Muslim bride in Persia always wore special regalia (Fig. 21–7).

Throughout eastern Asia fans and umbrellas of many kinds had marked sociocultural significance, and in Malaya a man felt improperly dressed without a daggerlike weapon conventionally known as a *kris*. The kind of kris—particularly its handle—gave an immediate clue to the wearer's status. Commoners had to be content with plain handles, but men of the upper classes went in for elaborate handles, featuring inlays of pearls, gold, or other precious materials. Possibly related to the Malay custom of wearing a kris was the Japanese tradition that permitted aristocratic warriors, *samurai,* to carry two swords. This privilege was so highly regarded that never did a samurai forget to carry his swords and never did he carelessly put them aside. Commoners in old Japan were never allowed to wear swords.

Headgear often played an important role in setting apart one unit of society from another. In ancient China and Japan there were formal ceremonies, sometimes conducted by the emperor in person, that granted honored people the right to wear a particular kind of hat or cap that showed where they stood in the social hierarchy. Americans are inclined to disregard the cultural implications of head coverings, but even so they associate mortarboards with academic commencements, and they know that graduates of nursing schools go through an impressive capping ceremony.

Study of clothing customs always leads an investigator into the field of supernaturalism. Religious officers customarily wear distinctive (and often archaic) garments, particularly when they are performing their rites, and lay worshipers may put on special clothes, such as the prayer shawls of Orthodox Jewish men, while attending services. Quite

FIG. 21-6. Hair styles of Hopi women. Left: Girl with her hair in "butterfly wings," worn by unmarried females. (Courtesy Bureau of American Ethnology.) Below: Woman grinding corn. The two braids at the sides of her head indicate that she is married. Her face is dark, presumably because it was smeared with purplish corn meal. The cut of her dress exposes her left shoulder and breast. (Courtesy American Museum of Natural History.)

commonly, religious symbols are worn as mute prayers by laymen, and Lumholtz once described the Tarahumara Indians of northern Mexico as being literally clothed in prayer.[13] Cultural conventions regularly prescribe gestures or body motions connected with wearing apparel during worship, as when Hindus or Moslems take off their shoes in sacred

FIG. 21-7. A Muslim bride. An Iranian bride is pictured in the costume typical of her status. She bears two lighted candles that symbolize long life. (Courtesy Three Lions.)

places, while Christian males bare their heads and Jewish men cover them. Such usages must be classed as nonlogical, for all attempts to rationalize them prove unconvincing except to members of the faith that practices them.

[13] C. Lumholtz, *Unknown Mexico,* New York, 1903, p. 827.

TECHNOLOGY

Industrial arts form a major portion of every society's *material culture.* Anthropologists generally study them under the heading of *technology.* Ingredients are so seldom drawn from the human body that the topic always becomes an integral part of any effort to understand man's relations to his environment. The commonest arts and crafts, in addition to those concerned with food, shelter, household furnishings, and clothing, are devoted to the manufacture of domestic utensils (including pottery and basketry containers), agricultural implements, weapons and cutting tools, and means of transportation.[14] Careful consideration of the materials used, working processes, correlated implements, and methods and styles of decoration provides a large body of factual data that cultural anthropologists find of the utmost importance for making comparative studies.

Never does the technological aspect of a group's material culture stand by itself. Commonest of all sociologic connections is a division of work between men and women, ordinarily described as *sexual dichotomy.* In practice, this means that each society sets aside the teaching and performance of some occupations for males and reserves others for females. When these culturally assigned activities have been in operation for a long time, they come to be so intimately associated with a particular sex as to give the impression that they are biologically determined. Thus, in our society, we are inclined to think that women are better suited than men for sewing with needle and thread, baking cookies, dusting furniture, diapering babies, or nursing the sick. To whatever extent this may be true, it is much more likely the result of cultural conditioning than of biology. This may be seen from the number of men who are professional bakers, tailors, nurses, and valets; from the great changes of female occupations, without attendant changes of body structure or function, that have taken place in the last fifty years; and from the fact that the same pursuit may be feminine in one society and masculine in another. Tilling the soil is women's work in the Bororo tribe of South America, but farming is a major occupation of men among the Pueblo Indians of North America. Surely, it is not because of anatomical differences that the making of bark cloth is the work of males in African Uganda but is left to females in the Polynesian Islands

[14] Specific details on each of these topics may be found in the previously cited works by Chapple and Coon, Beals and Hoijer, and Hoebel. For a study of the interplay of material culture and nonprimitive ways of life, see C. R. Walker, *Modern Technology and Civilization,* New York, 1961.

of the eastern Pacific. Except in terms of culture, it would be impossible to explain why the Hopi Indian men of northeastern Arizona weave rugs, dresses, and blankets, whereas all weaving among the neighboring Navaho is done by women (Fig. 21–8).

Sexual dichotomy has an effect on a group's way of life similar to

FIG. 21-8. Sexual dichotomy in weaving. Men are weavers among the Hopi, but women do all the weaving among the neighboring Navaho. (Left: Courtesy Chicago Natural History Museum. Right: Courtesy Museum of Anthropology, University of Michigan.)

that of specialization. It enables different people to devote themselves to different aspects of community living, and it demands cooperation if each sex is to benefit from the labors of the other. This helps to explain why technological and material considerations, rather than "love," are so often primary factors for the arrangement of marriages. As a Hopi Indian once said to a "white" bachelor who had just announced his forthcoming wedding, "Good. Now you'll have someone to cook for you."

In the case of all cultural phenomena, biological factors set definite limitations to the assignment of tasks for the two sexes. After all, it would be nonsensical to deny that only female bodies are capable of conceiving, bearing, and suckling infants. Because of these inescapable physical facts, the duties of women tend to center about home and family, and rarely are women expected to roam as widely as men or to carry out the principal tasks on which the very life of a community depends. Even here, though, surprises sometimes await a Euro-American investigator. In a small number of societies, tasks that to us appear quite important, difficult, or burdensome are assigned to females, despite their occasional biologically determined infirmities.

Religious factors may also control a person's occupation. In the case of the Plains Indians who used to inhabit the United States east of the Rocky Mountains, young men were supposed to seek visions during which the spirits dictated their future careers. Every now and then a youth who was thoroughly masculine would find himself ordered to do the work of a woman. In a number of Amerind tribes, men who dressed and acted like females were known as *berdaches.* Cases of this sort show that it is improbable that sexual dichotomy is always based on anatomical factors. Instead, they establish a strong presumption that patterns of work, except in matters directly concerned with the biology of sex and reproduction, are determined on the basis of symbolic, cultural values.

WHAT MAN GIVES TO HIS ENVIRONMENT

So far in this chapter, attention has been focused on what human beings draw from their physical setting, but man also gives things to the area about him. Ordinarily, what he gives most systematically consists of body wastes. All hominids must draw into their lungs great quantities of air that contains oxygen, and must exhale carbon dioxide, which the vegetation around them utilizes. Equally universal is the human need to eliminate waste products, either as urine or feces. In most societies these substances are discarded and allowed to interact at random with the soil and the atmosphere; but in Asiatic countries east of India, body wastes, euphemistically termed *night soil,* are utilized as fertilizer and are even placed directly on plants that later serve as food. Only a few Euro-American groups with highly advanced technologies remove from bodily excretions all substances that are harmful to human beings before giving them to the environment.

Many differing cultural values may be associated with the act of elimination. Our society holds up as an ideal the separation of the sexes and privacy. Other societies may separate the sexes but show less regard for privacy. Still others may seem unconcerned on either score.

One must not jump to the conclusion that people who appear indifferent to urination or defecation are necessarily immodest. Anthropologists have learned to give due weight to the phenomenon of *cultural blindness.* By this is meant any custom which induces people not to register or remember what their eyes see. Many a man in the primitive world observes a female in the act of elimination, but his brain records no apparent impression of what he has seen. In such cases, the phenomenon of cultural blindness may be just as effective for preserving modesty as are locked toilets.[15]

Wastes eliminated from the body are by no means the only things that men and women give to their physical settings. Garbage, ashes, broken or discarded implements of all kinds, and the bodies of the dead are some of the other objects that people regularly donate, directly or indirectly, to the environments in which they live. Nor should we overlook the important fact that farmers, especially, are likely to add to a particular locality more water, insecticides, and soil nutrients than nature provides. All in all, it is easy to demonstrate that man takes from but also gives to his environment.

Selected References

Chapple, Eliot D., and Coon, Carleton S., *Principles of Anthropology,* New York, 1942.

Du Bois, Cora, "Attitudes Toward Food and Hunger in Alor," in L. Spier, *et al.*, eds., *Language, Culture, and Personality,* Menasha, Wis., 1941, pp. 272–81.

Forde, C. Daryll, *Habitat, Economy, and Society,* New York, 1934.

[15] Cultural blindness need not be restricted to the excretory process. In our society men whose eyes are perfectly sound are apt completely to forget what manner of clothes were worn by people whom they had seen only a few moments ago. Psychologists recognize that human perception is not merely a matter of sound optics, but that it also involves the cultural conditioning and temperament of a viewer.

Foster, George M., "Relationships between Theoretical and Applied Anthropology: A Public Health Program Analysis," *Human Organization,* Vol. 11, 1952, pp. 5–16.

Gillin, John, "Moche: A Peruvian Coastal Community," *Smithsonian Institution, Institute of Social Anthropology,* No. 3, Washington, D.C., 1945.

Goldschmidt, Walter, *Man's Way,* New York, 1959, pp. 110–19.

Mead, Margaret, *Male and Female,* New York, 1949.

Morgan, Lewis H., "Houses and House Life of the American Aborigines," *Contributions to American Ethnology,* Vol. 4, Washington, D.C., 1881.

Richards, Audrey I., *Hunger and Work in a Savage Tribe,* London, 1932.

Sayce, R. U., *Primitive Arts and Crafts: An Introduction to the Study of Material Culture,* Cambridge, England, 1933.

Singer, Charles, *et al., A History of Technology,* Vol. 1, New York and London, 1954.

Williams, Robert J., *What to do about Vitamins,* Norman, Okla., 1945.

Culture and Environment

CHAPTER 22

CULTURAL DETERMINANTS OF ENVIRONMENTAL USE

One of the most striking aspects of human behavior is man's universal unwillingness to deal with his external environment in purely biophysicochemical terms. Other animals when motivated by the force of hunger, let us say, interact directly with their physical settings to procure whatever biology tells them to eat. For *Homo sapiens,* considerations of biologic worth are not enough. Wherever we choose to look, we find people rejecting or ignoring some things and utilizing only selected items from the region they inhabit. These are chosen in accordance with the symbolic values that prevail in their society's way of life. Man, therefore, interposes a set of cultural institutions between any such biological force as hunger and the external environment that might satisfy it.

This kind of behavior may give hominids many satisfactions, but it may also endanger their existence. That is to say, culture may increase or expand man's utilization of his environment under some circumstances; but it may, under other conditions, greatly restrict his use. We know that human beings do not eat raw grains or cereals but that cooking makes their use possible. Similarly, many tribes in the northern half of South America consume large quantities of a poisonous form of *manioc.* Only when the poison has been thoroughly squeezed out by a cultural device (Fig. 22–1) does this kind of manioc become suitable for human consumption. These examples show how culture may enlarge the utility of some things that man gets from his surroundings. Nevertheless, to get a fully rounded picture of the situation, one must give due recognition to the fact that cultural values may also seriously diminish man's use of his environment. This is the case whenever food taboos restrict unlimited use of the nutrients provided by nature.

What applies to foods is also true of clothing habits. No society gives equal value to all the materials that could be used for making

FIG. 22-1. Manioc press or squeezer. Poisonous manioc is grated and put into a flexible press. When the stick at the base is twisted, the press contracts and squeezes poison from the manioc. With the help of such devices many South American tribes can grow and use poisonous varieties of manioc. Thus does a cultural device make possible a greatly expanded use of the natural environment. (Courtesy of the Museum of Anthropology, the University of Michigan.)

garments. Clothing made of paper, burlap, and silk is commonly evaluated in terms other than availability, utility, cost, or biological efficiency. Cultural considerations likewise apply, of course, to man's use of construction materials or of resources needed for manufacturing.

To the extent that a pattern of culture cuts down on what is available, it helps to create a potential source of trouble. Thus, many a traditional Chinese has starved to death in the presence of milch cows because his culture tabooed the use of milk; and many a Hindu has suffered from lack of meat within sight of a sacred cow.

From what has already been said on the subject of man's dealings with his environment, it should be apparent that human beings never live in a world of bare physical objects. Everything about them may have a symbolic value. Invariably, people learn to hold culturally standardized ideas about their physical setting, and every social unit makes the environment a part of its system of ideas.

SEX, AGE, SOCIOECONOMIC STATUS, AND LOCALE

Culturally approved ways of behaving are never exactly the same for all the individual members of a society. What is considered proper for the wealthy and powerful may well be regarded as improper for the poor and powerless. Nor are cultural values likely to remain unchanged throughout a person's life span. In homely language, it makes a world of difference if a child soils itself at 9 months or 9 years of age. Many an American parent does not hesitate to place a 6-month-old daughter over his shoulder and to aid her to burp in the presence of onlookers; but who ever heard of assisting a 16-year-old girl to burp publicly? Except where simplification is essential, it is inaccurate to speak of a single pattern of culture that regulates the interactions with the environment of a total society. An example relating to dress should help to make clear what is meant.

If, with reference to American society, one were to say, "I know a poor 30-year-old mother who makes all the clothing that her 5-year-old daughter wears," the remark would cause little comment. How different the statement sounds, though, when we change some of the factors involved.

It is easy to imagine the amazed reaction of hearers to the remark that, "I know a wealthy 30-year-old father who makes all the clothing that his 5-year-old daughter wears." And the surprise of the listeners would reach a peak if someone said, "I know a 5-year-old daughter who makes all the clothing that her 30-year-old mother wears."

This indicates how likely it is that the human utilization of environment is delimited not by one over-all set of symbolic values, but by a number of value systems, each of which may apply to the behavior of different persons. Rough parallels regarding behavioral differences for differing groups of individuals are not unknown in infrahuman societies, but their variations probably rest on physical rather than on biocultural distinctions.

An evolving society is likely to increase in numbers and expand in territory. A tendency toward fragmentation arises as the process continues, with the result that the residents of particular regions or neighborhoods, as well as other distinct units, may form subgroups with customs that can be designated as *subcultures*. If the values of the subcultures are in agreement with those of the larger culture within which they exist, no special difficulties need arise. Unluckily, this is not always the case. As an example, our overall culture frowns officially on men who have many love affairs, but in some subgroups a man who has "a way with women" may be esteemed and admired. Ideas of this kind underlie our references to the right and wrong sides of the railroad tracks.

It is when the symbolic values of a local subculture diverge widely from those of the dominant way of life that trouble is most likely to follow. Nudists and polygamists may run afoul of the law even when their behavior is perfectly acceptable in their own communities. Many a person who lives up to the values of his subculture finds himself arrested for failing to observe the values of the greater society to which he belongs. The need of reconciling overall standards with those of subcultures comprises one of the most troublesome problems in all large societies.

Hardly anything gives more point to the existence of numerous subcultures within the confines of a single society than consideration of *statuses* and *roles*. Most societies are inclined to rank their members on a scale of some sort, giving high status to certain individuals and low status to others. As the late Ralph Linton pointed out, status may be *ascribed* or *automatic*, or else it may be *achieved*. Typical of the former are those cases in which a person is born as a noble or an aristocrat. Indicative of the latter are self-made men and women. Opportunities to achieve desirable statuses may serve as safety valves for those who are dissatisfied with their ascribed status.

With each status, whether it be ascribed or achieved, goes a fixed way of behaving; such behavior Linton has termed a role. Unless a person acts in the manner considered proper for his status, his rank in a society may go unrecognized. Nor is the behavior unrelated to objects originally drawn from a society's external environment. People of high status are expected to dress and eat differently from those of low, to dwell in different kinds of houses or neighborhoods, and to carry or wear distinctive objects or insignia. As Melville Herskovits tells us, an aristocratic Dahomean from west Africa was distinguished from an inferior by the facts that he wore sandals, walked in the shade of an umbrella, smoked a long pipe, and proudly handled his great togalike cloth and wand of office.[1]

We can go a step further. Each adult, regardless of his status, is usually expected to play a variety of roles in his society. A man may be a warrior at one time, a husband at another, and a farmer at a third. Seldom does a grownup find it hard to slip quickly from one role to another. In fact, we are likely to make fun of a person who cannot read-

---

[1] M. J. Herskovits, *Man and His Works*, New York, 1948, p. 210.

ily change his behavior to suit changing circumstances. We find it amusing when a professional baseball player tries to maintain professional standards while playing "catch" with a young son, and we ridicule a college professor who "lectures" to his wife. We do not expect a single pattern always to guide the behavior of a normal human being.

As a general rule, the higher a person's status the less likely is he to exert much muscular energy, particularly in his dealings with the environment. Chinese gentlemen of old cultivated exceedingly long fingernails to show that they never had to work hard with their hands. We, too, differentiate between manual laborers and white-collar workers. In keeping with the policy of holding in low esteem whatever savors of animal biology, we give small salaries and assign low status, in the vast majority of cases, to those whose occupations call for purely physical exertions.

A group of people sharing similar statuses form a *class*. Ordinarily, a class implies a degree of *sociocultural mobility*, which means that a person can somehow achieve the status of a class different from the one into which he was born. A class thereby differs from a *caste*, which usually has fixed boundaries that cannot be crossed after birth. As we know it from India, whose caste system has been best described, a person who is born in a caste must stay within it for life, marry another member of the same caste, and practice only the occupation that his caste has traditionally followed. Under modern conditions of rapid technological change, the caste system is breaking down in many parts of India.

Culture areas

Long before the numerous patterns that make up any group's way of life were adequately recognized, many anthropologists, particularly in America, used to divide the world into a number of *culture areas*. Such classifications were originally made to enable museum visitors to envision, with the help of native specimens, how different peoples lived in various portions of the globe. Arrangements of this kind generally rested on the expressed or implied assumption that people living in a single environmental zone would develop distinctive ways of life,[2] or, conversely, that

[2] The best available treatment of this aspect of the topic may be found in A. L. Kroeber, "Cultural and Natural Areas of Native North America," *University of California Publications in American Archaeology and Ethnology,* Vol. 38, 1939. It must not be thought that Kroeber is simply an economic or environmental determinist of the type that believes a given setting inevitably produces a given way of life.

Clark Wissler is generally credited with having originated the concept of culture areas.

no culture pattern could succeed if it failed to utilize the materials provided by its immediate setting. Assuredly, one would have to search far and wide to find examples of people who refused to interact, more or less directly, with the natural habitats in which they lived. Very few wooden houses are likely to be built in a region where timber is unavailable. It is certainly true that many customs appear alike in one part of a continent but change markedly as one turns to a distant region; yet modern anthropologists feel that the generalizations involved in the culture area concept are too broad to be useful except for very limited purposes. Members of many societies may use identical or nearly identical environments in greatly varying ways; and, sometimes, remarkably similar things are to be found among people who dwell in vastly different settings. Another important criticism rests on the difficulty of establishing precise lines of demarcation that show where one environmental region ends and another begins.

Some anthropologists used to establish culture areas primarily but not always entirely on the basis of single items, such as the principal food-getting techniques or the kinds of house types that prevailed in various spots (Fig. 22–2).[3] Once more, it would be hard to deny that the environment sets limits on what a society can utilize for food, shelter, clothing, and other requirements. Certainly, it would be ridiculous to expect desert dwellers to try to live on fish. Nonetheless, the principle of culture areas is today used very cautiously because it underemphasizes the ingenious ways in which people may select different things from similar settings, and because it fails to take into account the important part played by adherence to differing sets of symbolic values.

At the time when the concept of culture areas loomed large in the thinking of many American ethnologists, efforts were occasionally made to derive the relative ages of various traits from their distribution within or between the culture areas in which they were found. Generally speaking, the tacit assumption was made that each item of culture originated in one spot or center and then spread to the periphery. On this basis the trait in question must have been older in its place of origin and more recent elsewhere. This method of analysis, occasionally known as the age-

[3] See *The American Indian,* by Clark Wissler, rev. ed., New York, 1938, for the Western Hemisphere. For the Old World, see M. J. Herskovits, "A Preliminary Consideration of Culture Areas in Africa," *American Anthropologist,* Vol. 26, 1924, pp. 50–56; E. Bacon, "A Preliminary Attempt to Determine the Culture Areas of Asia," *Southwestern Journal of Anthropology,* Vol. 2, 1946; A. L. Kroeber, "Culture Groupings in Asia," *Southwestern Journal of Anthropology,* Vol. 3, 1947, pp. 322–30; and H. W. Krieger, "Design Areas in Oceania," *Proceedings of the United States National Museum,* Vol. 79, 1932, pp. 1–53.

area concept, has fallen into relative disuse because it is often difficult to determine where a given cultural item originated, because the centers and peripheries of assorted culture areas are far from clear, and because

FIG. 22-2. Culture areas, based on the distribution of typical structures in the aboriginal New World. Many diverse kinds of structure were built in pre-Columbian times in various regions or areas of the Americas.

questions of population stability and of trait persistence and distribution are anything but settled.[4] A further problem arises from the difficulty of determining whether a complicated cultural activity, such as farming,

[4] A critical discussion of the age-area concept is given in M. T. Hogden, "Change and History," *Viking Fund Publications in Anthropology,* No. 18, 1952, pp. 116–21.

should be treated as a single unit or as a *trait complex,* comprised of a combination of distinct but related items. Moreover, under the heading of *stimulus diffusion,* Kroeber has discussed the possibility that an idea might be diffused from one zone to another, but that it might be expressed in entirely different forms in the two regions concerned. It would be impossible in the light of Kroeber's illustrations to deny that stimulating ideas can spread as well as can material objects; but where the same concept leads to the development of two or more different things, it is extremely hard to trace what has actually spread from one place to another. A further difficulty arises from the fact that nonmaterial traits may have a vastly different distribution from those material items that are thought to have spread from the same source.

For all the criticisms that may currently be leveled against it, the culture area approach was a useful construct when it was first developed. Not only did it make possible the orderly arrangement of much heterogeneous material that had previously remained unorganized, but it also served to draw attention to the basic fact that, for all their varied approaches, human societies cannot endure unless they enter into successful relationships with their immediate surroundings. More than one student of culture is of the opinion that exploitation of the environment —particularly in terms of the food quest—may be a major factor in the formation of human societies. Some would even go so far as to say that friendly relationships, such as the sharing of food or other goods with nonkindred, has led to the emergence of ever-larger political aggregates. We presently believe so firmly in the interrelationship of levels of technology and levels of social organization that we expect to find only small bands with rudimentary forms of material culture occupying a sparse region. Never do we find large empires under these conditions. Moreover, if the members of two societies live in similar environments and follow similar pursuits with similar tools, they are likely to worship similar deities. All of this implies that within the limits of any given culture area one is likely to find only a restricted number of biocultural configurations.

Archeologists, as well as some ethnologists, still utilize the culture-area concept, but in modified form. They customarily think in terms of *phases,* arranged in chronological order to show evolutionary trends if one phase is thought to have grown out of an earlier one. Among contemporary American archeologists there is much talk, also, of *co-traditions.* Co-traditions refer to the shared relationships to be found, through time, between entire phases or whole cultures, rather than between single elements. As is to be expected, one cultural continuum, with each phase growing out of the preceding one, is most likely to be found within the limits of one culture area. However, archeologists caution us that it is possible for people with a given cultural tradition to influence others by migrating from one culture area to another.[5]

As a general trend of cultural evolution, to which, admittedly, some exceptions can be found, the smaller the size of a society, the lower will be its level of technology and the more directly and biologically will its members interact with their environment. There will also be less specialization and more egalitarianism. In addition, the total membership of a small unit of mankind will devote a greater part of its time to food pursuits.

The concept of *territoriality,* which may some day turn out to be closely related to the notion of culture areas, has of late been given serious consideration by a number of biologists. They have found that fish, reptiles, birds, and many mammals show *territorial* behavior. In most cases, this is connected with the driving off of intruders, even of the same species, if they are judged to be rivals of the occupants for sex partners. As to Primates, they too sometimes exhibit characteristics of territoriality, according to those who have studied Primate life in the wild. The concept of living a certain way in a particular region seems to be so basic to many animals that something resembling the culture area notion has been postulated for the forerunners of *Homo sapiens.*[6]

CULTURAL MODIFICATIONS OF ENVIRONMENT[7]

It has been said that a society's environment remains stable except under extraordinary conditions. This statement cannot be true if people are constantly interacting with their settings. Quite apart from drastic shifts that may be brought about by such nonhuman agencies as temperature and rainfall fluctuations, volcanic eruptions, floods, droughts, and ero-

---

[5] A fuller discussion of this point may be found in I. Rouse, "Culture Area and Co-Tradition," *Southwestern Journal of Anthropology,* Vol. 13, No. 2, 1957.

[6] M. Bates, *The Prevalence of People,* New York, 1955. Extremists, not including Bates, would link all aspects of nationalism, such as military defense of national boundaries, with the notion of territoriality. See R. Ardrey, *African Genesis,* New York, 1961.

The problem of territoriality is discussed by H. P. Hediger, "The Evolution of Territorial Behavior," in S. L. Washburn, ed., "Social Life of Early Man," *Viking Fund Publications in Anthropology,* No. 31, New York, 1961, pp. 34–57.

[7] This subject has been comprehensively treated in W. L. Thomas, Jr., ed., *Man's Role in Changing the Face of the Earth,* Chicago, 1956.

sion, there are a number of environmental changes that can be traced to cultural activities. In fact, it may be stated as a general rule that the more advanced is a group's technology, the greater are the alterations of physical setting that will be made. Thus gatherers, hunters, and fishers make relatively few lasting changes in their environment; farmers and herders make more; and members of highly industrialized societies make the most. Man may even go so far as to change his environment in ways that may be detrimental to his future welfare, as when he engages in careless plant-gathering practices, indiscriminate use of grazing grounds or water resources, or large-scale mining operations.

There are other cases wherein a society's whole way of life is affected by its interactions with its environment. The best known of such instances are those in which farming methods so exhaust the soil that people are forced to move themselves or their farms periodically, and to become what cultural anthropologists call *shifting cultivators.* Likewise, settled communities which depend on wood for fuel, house construction, and other purposes, face a critical situation when nearby sources of timber become depleted. The Iroquois-speaking Indians who lived east of the Appalachian Mountains provide a case in point. Although they used to inhabit permanent settlements, they were in the habit of moving their villages approximately every twenty years in order to be closer to a forest. Indeed, when they first made contact with European colonists, they are said to have asked if the colonists had come to a strange country because they had run out of wood in their homelands.

There is still another kind of interplay between culture and environment, by means of which certain unchanging features of a landscape may achieve a greatly altered significance through the agency of a group's level of culture. Let us suppose that a steep mountain peak, 8000 feet high, stands midway between two communities. As long as the two settlements have no means of travel except foot, the peak imposes a well-nigh insurmountable barrier to intercourse between them. If a road comes to be built over the mountain and animal-drawn conveyances or riding horses become available, the barrier grows less insurmountable. With the advent of power-driven vehicles, the difficulties of communication dwindle still more; and for those who can use aircraft, an 8000-foot peak is no obstacle at all.

What is true of mountains likewise applies to oceans, wide streams, broad deserts, and dense jungles. In each case the environmental feature may remain exactly as it was, but its functional significance will vary with different stages of culture. The ultimate effect is the same as if it were the landmark itself that had changed. That is what is really meant when people speak of the shrinking of the globe or when Americans refer to the dwindling of the oceans that separate them from the Old World. Any environment with which human beings interact should be regarded from a dynamic rather than from a static point of view.

Motor habits

One of the most intriguing approaches for studying man's relationships with his environment, as well as cultural conditioning and other topics, lies in the field of *motor habits.* This phrase may refer to customarily patterned movements of the body or any of its parts, that are much alike for all the members of a sex or social group. It often refers to the ways in which the people of a particular society have learned to manipulate their physical settings, or else it may refer to the ways in which the members of a society customarily handle objects or materials that were drawn, originally, from their external surroundings. Motor habits may pertain to the way in which people put on, wear, or handle garments, employ all kinds of tools, roll cigarettes, grasp the handle of a kettle, use a knife and fork, or sit on a sheepskin stretched on the ground. Some

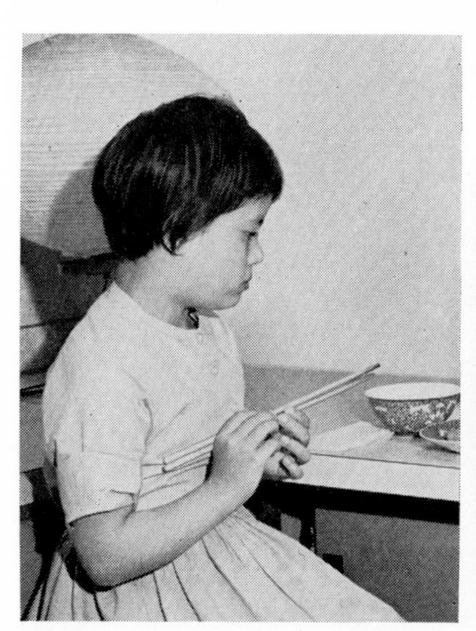

FIG. 22-3. Comparative motor habits. The difference between the Korean girl eating with chopsticks (right) and the American girl (left) looking doubtfully at her chopsticks suggests that different motor habits may result from differences of cultural training and habit rather than from differences of anatomy. (Left: Courtesy of Eck Stanger and *The Ann Arbor News.* Right: From A. Goodfriend, *Something Is Missing,* New York, 1955. Courtesy of the author and Farrar, Straus, and Co., Inc.)

writers think that gestures and facial expressions may belong in the same category. To illustrate only a few of these habits, American woodworkers push planes away from their bodies, but Far Eastern carpenters pull planes toward them; all Hopi Indians roll cigarettes by moving the thumbs upward, but Navahos turn their thumbs down; Americans pick up and pour from a teakettle with the palm down, but Japanese grasp and use it with the palm up. Residents of India mean "yes" when they shake their heads halfway in the manner that Euro-Americans use to signify the negative, and in some parts of Italy people are summoned by moving the fingers with the palm out, much as when we wave goodbye; but in other parts of the same country, people are called by using the hand with the palm in, just as we do.

Motor habits are usually different for each sex in a given society or subculture. This is connected with sexual dichotomy. As men and women are taught to deal differently with their environments, they learn to use their bodies in different ways. In some cases the motor habits that distinguish the sexes are outgrowths of biology, but often they are not. Thus, biology may dictate that only women must learn the actions that go with the nursing of babies, but there is nothing in biology that forces women to wash dishes.

FIG. 22-4. Bathing a baby in New Guinea. The manner in which parents handle a baby while it is being bathed is often standardized for an entire tribe. In this way motor habits may provide a clue to a group's identity. (Courtesy of Asia Press, Inc.)

An adult who may be eager to change his accustomed way of life by adopting an entirely new culture often finds that acquisition of correct motor habits gives him more trouble than anything else. In times of war, spies who could otherwise pass for enemy nationals are likely to give themselves away by mistakes in motor habits. We usually look quite awkward when we try to eat with chopsticks (Fig. 22–3), but most Far Easterners are clumsy when they try to eat with knives and forks. Only

FIG. 22-5. The anthropology of posture. Sitting customs usually involve a variety of objects that were taken, originally, from a society's physical environment. At the same time, all members of a society or of any of its subgroups, such as groups of differing status, are culturally conditioned to hold and use their bodies in prescribed ways. (From Gordon W. Hewes, "The Anthropology of Posture," *Scientific American*, Feb. 1957. Courtesy of the author and editor.)

those who have made a detailed pursuit of this fascinating topic are aware of the extent to which seemingly individual body movements prove to be standardized within the limits of particular patterns of culture.[8]

Gregory Bateson and Margaret Mead, as well as Ray Birdwhistle, are among those who have made many studies and interpretations of the way in which various peoples move and use their bodies.[9] Margaret Mead even believes that it is possible to identify different patterns of culture by analyzing single activities, such as the bathing of babies (Fig. 22–4). An interest in the interplay of body motion and culture pattern has led Gordon W. Hewes to make investigations all over the world of what he calls "the anthropology of posture." He regards the ways in which men and women hold and utilize their bodies to be biocultural activities, compounded of human anatomy and culture (Fig. 22–5). Many rugged individualists are amazed, when shown pictures of the motor habits that prevail in their societies, to discover how culture-bound they really are.

Selected References

Bates, Marston, *The Prevalence of People,* New York, 1955.

Bateson, Gregory, and Mead, Margaret, *Balinese Character,* New York, 1950.

Birdwhistle, Ray L., *Introduction to Kinesics: An Annotation System for Analysis of Body Motion and Gesture,* Louisville, 1952.

Herskovits, Melville J., "A Preliminary Consideration of the Culture Areas of Africa," *American Anthropologist,* Vol. 26, 1924, pp. 50–63.

Hewes, Gordon W., "The Anthropology of Posture," *Scientific American,* Vol. 196, No. 2, 1957.

Hoebel, E. Adamson, "The Nature of Culture," in H. L. Shapiro, ed., *Man, Culture, and Society,* New York, 1956.

Kroeber, Alfred L., "Cultural and Natural Areas of Native North America," *University of California Publications in American Archaeology and Ethnology,* Vol. 38, 1939.

LaBarre, Weston, "The Cultural Basis of Emotions and Gestures," *Journal of Personality,* Vol. 16, 1947, pp. 49–68.

Linton, Ralph, *The Study of Man,* New York, 1936, Chap. 8.

[8] Many further details may be found in LaBarre, "The Cultural Basis of Emotions and Gestures," *Journal of Personality,* Vol. 16, 1947, pp. 49–68.

[9] See, for example, G. Bateson and M. Mead, *Balinese Character,* New York, 1950.

Rouse, A. Irving, "Culture Area and Co-Tradition," *Southwestern Journal of Anthropology,* Vol. 13, No. 2, 1957.

Thomas, William L., Jr., ed., *Man's Role in Changing the Face of the Earth,* Chicago, 1956.

Wissler, Clark, *The American Indian,* rev. ed., New York, 1938.

Interpersonal Relations

CHAPTER 23

A CHILD IS BORN

The second leg of our biocultural triangle is devoted to the relations that exist between a man and his fellows who live in the same society.[1] Interpersonal arrangements are just as essential a part of any group's way of life as is the need for people to interact with their environments. Such arrangements, too, have undeniable biologic foundations. Again, genetically inherited forces that impel each person to deal with others are invariably channeled by each society into cultural institutions that are valued as good, whereas violations are branded as bad. Relationships between human beings, therefore, are truly biocultural; and when they are institutionalized, they may serve as guides to conduct either for particular individuals, such as a chief, or for groups of people, such as all fathers or all mothers.

Barring the restricted possibilities of artificial insemination, adoption, or the recruitment of new members from the outside, a society can perpetuate itself indefinitely only through the continuous operation of sexual reproduction. Consequently, each social unit's pattern of culture must make adequate provision for the birth of children among its members. Every normal female, regardless of whether she is an opera singer, waitress, stenographer, or professional athlete, is a potential mother; and every normal male is a potential father. Just the same, no society is content to leave the bearing of offspring to chance or to the powerful urgings of sheer biology. A balance is always struck between

[1] As used by anthropologists, man is synonymous with *Homo sapiens* and includes representatives of both sexes. This has given rise to the oldest joke in the profession —a definition of anthropology as "the science of man, embracing woman."

the total range of a group's potential for begetting and bearing offspring and a set of cultural restrictions on parenthood. Popular writers sometimes make sensational references to widespread sexual promiscuity among native peoples, but ethnologists have never found a group whose way of life permitted completely unregulated relations between the sexes.[2]

What they do find is a widespread difference of moral values or standards. Some tribes allow a great deal of premarital license; others insist on prenuptial virginity, especially for girls. Some demand that cousins must marry; others forbid such unions. There is no uniformity of symbolic attitudes toward mating among mankind, but some features are universal. All societies distinguish socially permissible marital relations from other forms of sexual activity, all have culturally based preferences for the selection of proper mates, and all specifically forbid cohabitation between certain individuals. The most widespread of all prohibitions, *incest regulations,* are designed to prevent intercourse between parents and their children and between *siblings* (brothers and sisters). Historically, only Peru, Egypt, and Hawaii apparently permitted some brothers and sisters to mate and have offspring, but even in these places permission was not granted to the entire society. Instead, it was limited to members of ruling families. Ethnologists are unable to explain in detail how incest rules first arose, but it can be shown that they tend to be cultural rather than biological in character.[3] Again and again, people who happen to be unaware of their relationship may be attracted to one another and engage in copulation, only to be overwhelmed with shame and dread if they later discover that they are close kin. If the horror of incest were entirely biological, forbidden unions could not take place and there would be no need of cultural regulations to prevent them.

Marriages may be encouraged or prohibited on many grounds. Almost anything—kinship, race, religion, economic status, degree of

---

[2] It was once believed that human society had evolved by stages, one of which was promiscuity. This concept has been discarded.

Another outworn notion called for a stage of group marriage, in which a number of men had equal rights to a number of women. Anthropologists have never found cases of group marriage.

[3] For an exposition of this viewpoint, see L. A. White, "The Definition and Prohibition of Incest," *American Anthropologist,* Vol. 50, 1948, pp. 416–35.

There is a possibility that something somatic may underlie incest. Observers of rhesus monkeys in the wild have reported no cases of mother-son sexual relationships. Nothing can be said of fathers and daughters because paternity cannot be determined among wild creatures. There are no reports on brother-sister couplings.

education, place of residence, or occupation—can be used as a basis for discriminating for or against the choice of mates. When ethnologists describe a custom that compels people to marry within a given unit, they call it *endogamy*; whereas a rule that forces individuals to find spouses outside a particular group is known as *exogamy*. These terms may apply to a total society or to any of its subdivisions. In Western societies most marriages are *endogamous* with respect to nationality and religious affiliation, but they are *exogamous* with regard to the family circle.

So many diverse forms of approved cohabitation are known that anthropologists have trouble in agreeing on a single definition of marriage. Most widely accepted, at the present moment, is a statement to the effect that marriage consists of the socially sanctioned union of one or more men with one or more women. Implied in such a definition, but not directly expressed, is the added fact that any children born of such a union will be recognized as "legitimate" and will be entitled to the care and training that will fit them to live in the society where they were born. Looked at in this way, we find that throughout the world wedding regulations are designed not only to direct sexual activities into culturally approved channels, but also to encourage the propagation and rearing of children. The long-drawn-out helplessness of human infants is an inescapable fact and parents, particularly mothers, are everywhere charged with the responsibility of caring for babies at least until they can look out for themselves. If no parent is available a substitute, or *surrogate,* must be provided. In the words used by an Araucanian Indian from central Chile when we were discussing the problem of getting wet nurses for an orphan, "Nohow will they let the baby starve!"

Scientists have not yet determined the proper classification of the craving for offspring. As far as an individual is concerned, it may very well be the result of a combination of biological, psychological, and cultural elements, and in primitive societies sterile couples are particularly likely to be unhappy and to seek natural and supernatural help. In addition to anyone's personal desires, there is also the interest of society as a whole. Society never allows parents to do away with their children just as they please, and punishment is generally greater for one who illegally subtracts a person from a social group than for one who adds a member to it, no matter how disapproved may be the manner of propagation. Openly or tacitly, every social unit is pleased when children are born to its members, although under special conditions, usually involving shortages of food, *infanticide* may be allowed.

SYSTEMS OF RECKONING KINDRED

As was pointed out in the preceding section, marriage regulations almost universally forbid certain kin to mate and they quite often prescribe the union of other relatives. Wedding rules and methods of reckoning kindred are thus seen to be closely associated and to be basic to every society. An anthropological convention divides ways of naming relatives into *descriptive* and *classificatory* categories. Descriptive systems, like ours, are supposed to use a separate term for designating each particular relative, usually in the direct line of one's descent, such as his father or mother. Classificatory arrangements never restrict the use of a term to a single individual, but unfailingly employ one term to designate a class or group of persons, some of whom are lineal kin and others collateral. Thus, for example, the term for father might be applied both to one's father and to the father's brothers. Even if we grant that there is usually some overlap between the two methods,[4] it is still true that occidental societies show a strong tendency to use descriptive terminology, whereas primitive groups reveal a marked preference for classificatory systems.

The manner in which a society identifies and labels relatives is known as its *nomenclature system.* This is an integral part of its *kinship system*; and it can readily be diagramed as a genealogical table. Because each person is variously related to a number of people, as when I call "uncle" the selfsame man that my father calls "brother," ethnologists find it helpful to present each kinship system from the viewpoint of one particular individual. This personage is labeled *Ego* and customarily represents an average, adult male.

People in Euro-American societies generally trace kinship *bilaterally,* through the mother's and father's lines alike, but in a great many primitive cultures relationships are reckoned *unilaterally,* or *unilineally,* by way only of one parent. Where kinship is unilaterally counted through males, the kinfolk make up a *patrilineal clan,* or *gens*; where kinship is unilaterally reckoned through females, the relatives comprise a *matrilineal clan,* or *sib.* A clan may be defined as a named group of relatives who trace their descent in one sex line from a common ancestor or ancestress. All *clanmates* are taught to believe that they have a common ancestry, even when their supposedly shared lines of descent can-

[4] Kroeber years ago drew attention to the fact that we group several different individuals under the designations of aunt or uncle, and that as many as 32 different persons may be called cousin. See A. L. Kroeber, "Classificatory systems of relationship," *Journal of the Royal Anthropological Institute,* Vol. 39, 1909, pp. 77–84.

not be genealogically established. It should be noted that clans are likely to persist for many generations, whereas families are always in greater danger of dying out.

Clans are sometimes found to be subdivided into *lineages* (Fig. 23–1). A lineage may be described as a segment of a clan, between whose members informants believe actually demonstrable ties of descent exist. Occasionally, trouble arises in trying to separate a clan into its component lineages. This may happen when a field worker has decided that a certain clan contains two distinct lineages headed, let us say, by two

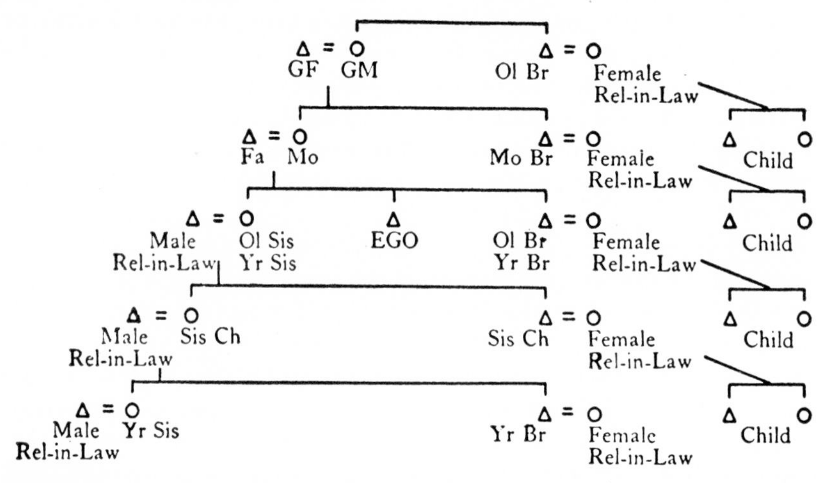

FIG. 23-1. A Hopi (Crow) lineage. The diagram shows his mother's matrilineal lineage, from the viewpoint of a male *Ego*. All members of *Ego's* own clan and lineage are connected by short, vertical lines that indicate descent ties. (Courtesy of Fred Eggan.)

presumably unrelated individuals, *x* and *y*. If, on the basis of later information, it develops that *x* and *y* are really siblings and have the same parents, a clan that was once said to have two lineages would turn out to be composed, in actuality, of a single lineage. Despite the danger of such confusions, anthropologists generally try to distinguish lineages from clans, because in some societies lineages are plainly recognized and in others a clan honor or object may be found to be transmitted not within the entire clan but within only a particular segment or lineage of it.

Since they are believed to be descended from the same personage, lineage or clanmates of the same generation are frequently regarded as brothers and sisters and are forbidden to intermarry. As a rule, their line is supposed to have been established at some time in the dim past when their original founder mated or had an intimate experience with a supernatural personage, plant, animal, object, or celestial body—ordinarily but not invariably identified as a *totem*—whose name the clan bears and with which it feels itself to be intimately connected. This connection may be expressed by the right to utilize certain names, by a symbolic design that may be used only by members of the appropriate clan, or else by rituals intended to increase the numbers of the totem, or by taboos forbidding *clansfolk* to injure, kill, or eat representatives of their totem. By way of a concrete example, the members of a Rabbit clan may all have rabbit names, may not marry one another, may look upon rabbits as siblings, perform ceremonies for the multiplication of rabbits, wear rabbit designs, abstain from rabbit hunts, mourn slain rabbits, and refuse to eat rabbit meat. In some cases clans may also have religious, political, or economic attributes, such as common ownership of lands, houses, ceremonies, or rights to chieftainship.

As for clan methods of designating kindred, two principal variants are widely recognized. Patrilineal clans that have separate terms for mother's brother and father's brother, but which unite under a single label mother's brother, mother's brother's son, mother's brother's son's son, and so forth, are said to use the *Omaha* system (Fig. 23–2). Matrilineal clans that distinguish mother's sister from father's sister, but which group together the father's sister and her feminine descendants through females (Fig. 23–3), are said to use the *Crow* system.[5] In each of these instances, students must come to realize, the lines that set some of the generation levels apart are occasionally disregarded in the terminology. There are thus at least two features common to classificatory forms of kinship nomenclature that are not found in ours. Where many clanmates are called by one and the same term, an adult *Ego* may find himself with a whole cluster of fathers, mothers, and grandparents; and some of these may be mere infants.

To an ethnologist from a Western society on his first field trip, it comes as a shock to have an adult point out a small child as his father or grandfather, but this is a logical outgrowth of any kinship system whose means of labeling kindred sometimes disregards generation lines. Similarly, it strikes us as incredible that a grown man should not know the identity of his real mother, but in certain of the classificatory arrangements under discussion no distinction in terminology need be made between the mother and her sisters. The result is that the women whom we call mother and aunts may become confused. Whatever complexities may arise from such usages are compensated by the ease with which surrogates take over the functions of a missing parent. A child

[5] Kinship terminology is called *bifurcate-merging* when some relatives are clearly set apart while others are grouped together. For much additional information on all the points treated in this chapter, see R. H. Lowie, *Social Organization,* New York, 1948.

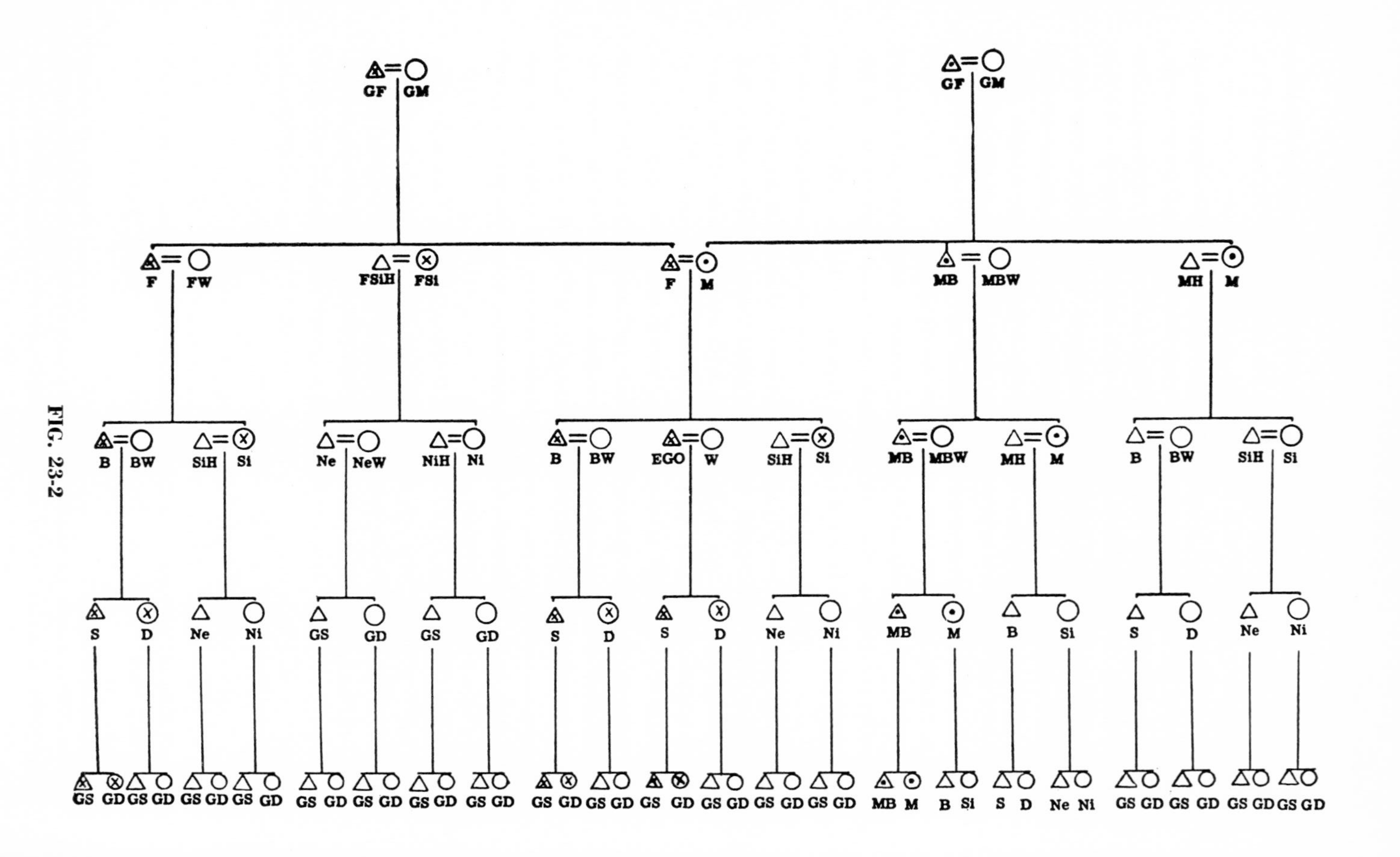

GF GM
GF GM
F FW
FSiH FSi
F M
MB MBW
MH M
B BW
SiH Si
Ne NeW
NiH Ni
B BW
EGO W
SiH Si
MB MBW
MH M
B BW
SiH Si
S D Ne Ni
GS GD GS GD
S D S D Ne Ni
MB M B Si
S D Ne Ni
GS GD GS GD GS GD GS GD
GS GD GS GD GS GD GS GD
GS GD GS GD GS GD GS GD GS GD GS GD
MB M B Si S D Ne Ni
GS GD GS GD GS GD GS GD

FIG. 23-2

who has learned to call and regard as mothers many women is very likely to accept one of them as a true parent in the event of the death or loss of his natural mother.

Broadly speaking, the easiest way to grasp the workings of any clan system of kinship nomenclature is to start with the premise that within a clan all persons of the same sex and approximate generation are identically designated. Where such practices exist, *Ego* is likely to call his father and all of his father's brothers, "father"; his mother and all of her sisters, "mother"; his own agemates, "brothers and sisters"; and their offspring, "children." There are numerous variations of the basic clan method of labeling relatives, but their type names and distinctive characteristics may safely be left to specialists.

In many instances a number of clans are found combined into larger groupings known as *phratries*. As a rule, a *phratry* may be defined as an unnamed exogamic unit consisting of two or more clans. Quite often, but not always, the members of a phratry share all the rights and obligations of their constituent clans. The earliest American student of primitive kinship, Lewis H. Morgan, believed that phratries arose from the segmentation of clans either as a result of migrations or through the pressure of numbers. On the basis of his own field work, the writer inclines to Morgan's point of view. On the other hand, Robert H. Lowie —who was a very astute student of the topic—favored the concept that phratries arose when originally unrelated clans merged for some purpose such as the carrying out of a ceremonial obligation. In either case, the definition of a phratry holds good as given.

If an entire tribe is divided into two parts, each of which is generally exogamous, each half is called a *moiety*. A moiety may thus consist of a number of phratries or else of a multiplicity of clans and their component lineages.

Kinship terms may be used in direct address, as when we say, "Father, I want to tell you something." They may also be used for reference, as when we say to a third party, "I told something to my father." Another usage, rare among us but often found in primitive societies, is

FIG. 23-2 (Opposite). The Omaha kinship system. In this figure and the one immediately following, the triangle stands for a male, the circle for a female, the equal sign for a marriage, and a vertical line for descent. The letters represent English words, so that "F" is for father, "Si" for sister, "MBW" for mother's brother's wife, "Ne" for nephew, "Ni" for niece, etc. An x designates members of *Ego's* own clan, and a dot indicates members of *Ego's* mother's clan. The Omaha system is associated with patrilineal clans or strong patrilineal emphasis. *Ego's* father and *Ego's* father's brother are merged, but *Ego's* mother's brother is differentiated by a separate term. *Ego's* mother's brother's male descendants are merged under a single term, thus overriding generation levels.

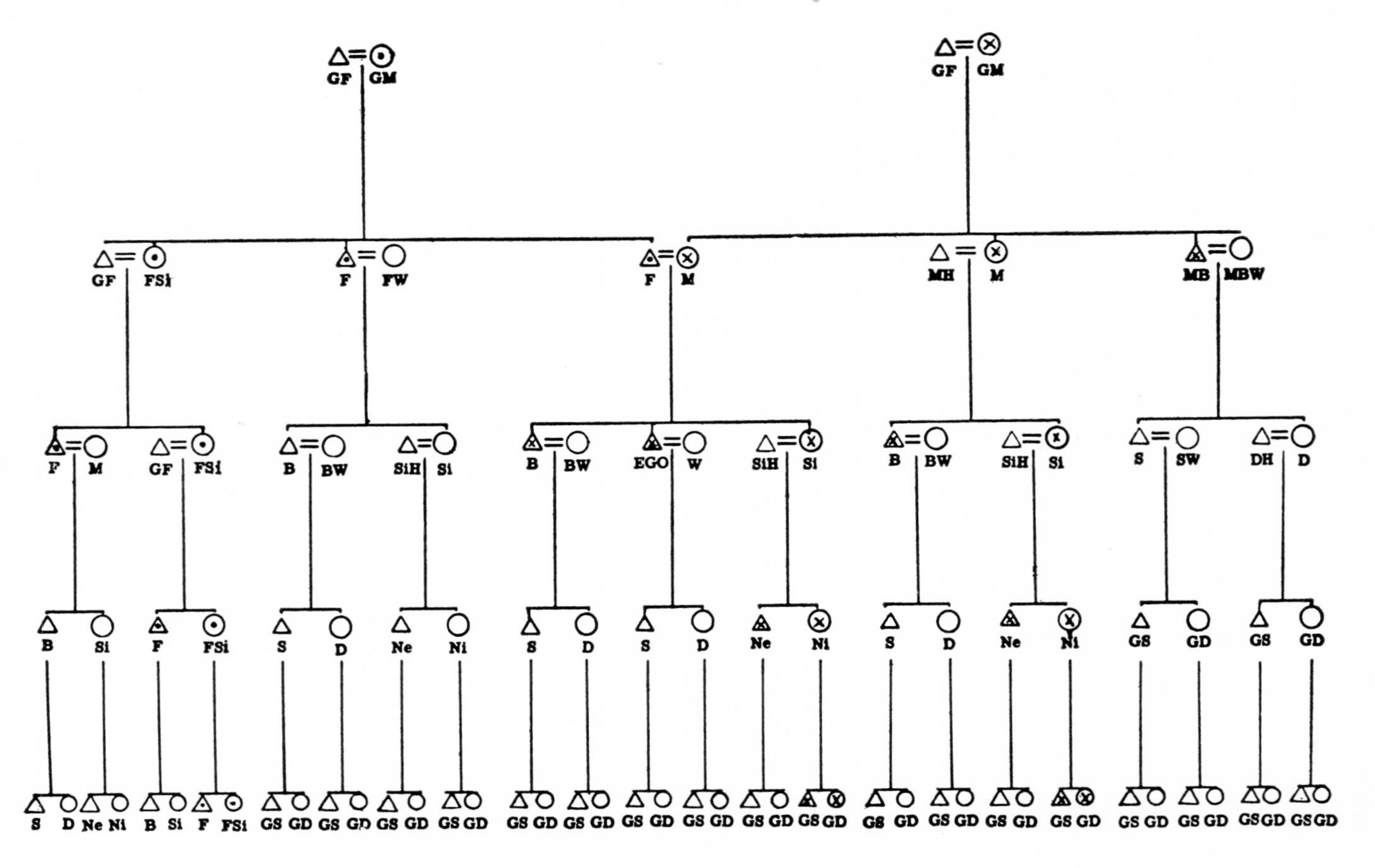

GF GM
GF GM
GF FSi
F FW
F M
MH M
MB MBW
F M
GF FSi
B BW
SiH Si
B BW
EGO W
SiH Si
B BW
SiH Si
S SW
DH D
B Si
F FSi
S D
Ne Ni
S D
S D
Ne Ni
S D
Ne Ni
GS GD
GS GD
S D Ne Ni
B Si F FSi
GS GD GS GD GS GD GS GD
GS GD GS GD GS GD GS GD GS GD GS GD
GS GD GS GD GS GD GS GD
GS GD GS GD GS GD GS GD

FIG. 23-3

called *teknonymy*. Teknonymy means that a person is identified by stating his relationship to someone else. So a wife might inquire for her husband by asking, "Where is my son's father?" Or a little boy might say, "I'm going to play with my sister's son."

More than one system of kinship nomenclature may operate simultaneously. Men in the United States regularly apply the term "brother" to a male sibling, to a fellow member of a fraternity, and, sometimes, to a masculine coreligionist. In primitive societies, bilateral modes of labeling kin may operate side by side with unilateral practices. One highly important result is that family and clan ties may both be recognized. Where matrilineal clans are found, a man very rarely joins his wife's clan at marriage. Consequently, he is usually of a different clan from his wife and offspring, yet his children will call him "father" and will acknowledge him as their male parent. When important clan functions are being held in a matrilineal society of this kind, a man may be excluded from his wife's and children's group, but in daily life he need not be treated as an outsider.

Whatever may be a society's method of designating kin, therefore, it will generally be found that full importance is given to a father, mother, and their unmarried offspring. These relatives comprise the unit widely known as the *primary, limited, conjugal,* or *nuclear family.* A society's habit of labeling kindred along only one sex line does not mean that the nuclear family is being overlooked or slighted. The pull of bilateral family ties within a unilateral clan structure was forcibly brought home to the author during a study of a village split that broke the Hopi pueblo of Old Oraibi into halves in 1906. With rare exceptions, conjugal or nuclear family groups sided together and unilateral clan loyalties were almost entirely disregarded. Only four married couples out of several hundred were separated by the split. As among the Hopi, it will be found that throughout the world, recognition is likely to be given to the bilateral nuclear or conjugal family, even if it is interwined with a unilateral segment of a social structure.

There are many writers who believe that the nuclear family is so nearly a universal feature of human societies that they regard it as having been derived from those of man's animal forerunners whose bodies come closest to his in build and function, particularly with respect to a year-round ability to perform the sex act. This ability would have induced a male, it is often argued, to have remained permanently with a

---

FIG. 23-3 (Opposite). The Crow kinship system. This is found associated with matrilineal clans or wherever a society has a strong matrilineal emphasis. *Ego's* father's sister is distinguished from his mother's sister, but all *Ego's* father's sister's female descendants are merged in the terminology, thereby disregarding generation lines.

female, and might thus have been the basis for the formation of family groups. Assuredly, many interesting and fruitful suggestions for an understanding of the noncultural aspects of family life in *Homo sapiens* can be obtained from careful observation of infrahuman Primates, but one must use such data with great care. Modern scientists do not believe contemporary man to be directly descended from any of the living Primates, and human families are so full of cultural, symbolic overtones that it seems self-evident that only limited understanding can be achieved from studies made of cultureless creatures.

One of the major functions of the nuclear family in human societies is to teach youngsters the details of the way of life to which they are expected to conform. Families thus have an important educational aspect by means of which patterns of culture are transmitted from one generation to another. Many other people ordinarily supplement the training that parents give their children, but even if no one else lends a hand the parents are expected to bring their offspring up properly.[6] A child gets its cultural bearings, so to speak, within the confines of its nuclear family, and therefore this unit is sometimes called the *family of orientation.*

Two other kinds of families are known to cultural anthropologists. One, found especially among the Hindus, is called a *joint family.* Its base consists essentially of a number of nuclear families, all related in one sex line and all sharing a common residence; but servants and other nonrelatives may also live under the same roof. Sometimes, a similar grouping of kinfolk and retainers, generally called an *extended family,* may be found, with each of the related nuclear families occupying a separate home. When the consanguineous members of a joint or extended family trace their descent unilaterally, as they often do, they are hard to distinguish on this score from clans or lineages.

CONSANGUINITY AND AFFINITY

Regardless of what system of kinship nomenclature a society uses it will be found that each person's relatives are connected with him by "blood"

---

[6] In former times, parental teachings in Africa were often supplemented at a *bush school.* Here youngsters were taught many of the ways of their people. Quite often they were told upon "graduation" from the bush school that thereafter their actions would reflect not only on their immediate families, but also on their entire tribe. This point is elaborated in Prince Modupe, *I Was a Savage,* New York, 1957, pp. 11, 28, *et passim.*

or marriage. "Blood" ties, whether they be real or fictitious, are described as *consanguineous,* and relationships through marriage are called *affinal. Consanguinity* is supposed to denote descent from a common parent or parents, but in many cases it cannot be proved and has to be assumed. Primitive people are much less likely than Euro-Americans to insist on proof of "blood" connection, and they make little effort to separate real from fictional consanguineous kin. A husband is assumed to be the father of his wife's children, even if the wife is known to have been occasionally unfaithful. Nonetheless, primitive folk do not take the ties of "blood" lightly, nor are they indifferent to the links established through marriage. It is everywhere recognized that when two people wed they develop a new set of relationships not only between themselves but also among their respective kinfolk. This is no trivial matter, and many wedding customs express a sense of reluctance on someone's part whenever a marriage takes place. The gravity of entering into a new set of affinal relationships is one of the reasons why the blessings of a deity, also known as *supernatural sanctions,* are sometimes sought at weddings.

Primitive attitudes toward the birth of offspring are likely to be based on practical considerations as well as on emotion. Feelings of love for children are as prevalent as they are among us, but factors that we submerge or fail to recognize may be more openly expressed. There is no failure to realize that a consanguineous line can be maintained only by sexual reproduction, even though some earlier writers have expressed opposite views, and where offices or property must pass on only to "blood" relatives the extinction of a consanguineous unit may be deplored as a tragedy. This is all the more true since the economic costs of having babies are negligible in primitive societies. It does not cost much, if anything, for medical help; and nonliterate people have no cause to dread the expenses of education. Formal schooling hardly exists, and informal instruction is freely given as occasion warrants. Moreover, children are very often the equivalent of old-age insurance. Many an aging pair finds it comforting to realize that they have numerous progeny who will look after them as a matter of course. Unwanted or rejected children are exceedingly rare in the primitive world.

The acceptance of affinal relatives is another matter, for one never knows how they will turn out, and they do not have to be involuntarily accepted from birth as do consanguineous folk. Yet, the operation of incest and exogamic regulations makes it necessary for each social division to take a chance on some outsiders when it comes to choosing spouses. A degree of unwillingness to undertake the hazards of matrimony may be expressed by individuals in the form of *ceremonial coyness,* as when a prospective bride or groom is expected to make a show of resistance; or else it may be reflected in an entire group's behavior. This may be inferred from the variety of ways in which two social units that have once succeeded in providing each other with mates will continue to do so as long as possible. Such customs, known to all ethnologists, as having two brothers marry sisters, or the *levirate,* whereby a widow marries a brother of her late husband, or the *sororate,* which permits a man to marry a sister of his deceased wife, or the requirement that a son must take over his dead father's spouse or spouses may all be interpreted as efforts to keep in force affinal bonds that have already been established.

The loss that one group sustains when a member marries and moves away is compensated as a rule by the other's payment of goods, money, or services. When it is a girl's consanguineous kindred that receive compensation, it goes by the name of *bride price*;[7] whereas recompense received by the groom or his relatives is known as a *dowry*. An unusual form of bride price once practiced by Bantu-speaking tribes in south Africa was known as *lobola.* By this arrangement a number of heads of cattle were given when a girl was married. Her brother then used them to get himself a bride. One can imagine the complications that followed in the event of a divorce.

One or two instances of true *wife capture,* in which men regularly carry off brides without prearrangement or payment, are authentically reported. More often, however, as in the case of so-called "mock rape" among the Araucanians of Chile, all details for the capture of a bride are settled in advance, the bride and her people make only a token show of resistance, and adequate compensation is later provided. Very seldom does a wedding take place in primitive society without an attendant transfer of valuable items, and in some instances marriage payments prove to be costly and highly involved transactions.

KINSHIP BEHAVIOR, AND MORE ON MARRIAGE

Kinship systems not only stipulate how relatives are to be labeled, but also prescribe forms of correct behavior between various sets of kin. Each recognized degree of relationship carries with it certain rights and privileges, as well as a number of duties and obligations. Knowledge of these functional requirements is what gives life to the study of kinship

[7] In several societies, if a young man cannot afford to pay for a bride, he may be allowed marital privileges while he donates a stipulated amount of labor to his wife's parents.

systems, for in this way the cultural anthropologist comes to understand how different people—for instance, mothers and daughters, or fathers and sons—are expected to act toward one another in repetitive, prescribed ways.

Among the most important regulations affecting the behavior of kinfolk are those pertaining to marriages. Practically universal in primitive societies is the aforementioned rule of exogamy that forbids clanmates to wed or to have sexual relations. Almost as common, except in Moslem societies, is an incest taboo directed against the mating of *parallel cousins* (offspring of two brothers or of two sisters). Such a prohibition is sometimes counterbalanced by a society's stated preference for *cross-cousin* marriage, which unites the children of a brother with those of his sister. In communities where this custom prevails, young cross-cousins of opposite sex may be brought up with the notion that they are potential mates, and they are sometimes allowed a large measure of intimacy that may go as far as nonmarital intercourse.

Lesser degrees of familiarity are sometimes permitted to individuals of different sex, and may also pertain to members of the same sex. Such familiarity may be institutionalized into *joking relationships.* Joking relationships ordinarily refer to standardized forms of familiarity in speech or action that prevail between particular kinds of relatives. In a few societies brothers and sisters habitually tease and joke, but more often grown brothers and sisters are taught to treat each other with formality and circumspection. R. H. Lowie believed that joking relationships were most common among potential mates,[8] but Fred Eggan and Sol Tax, of the University of Chicago, are inclined to regard the joking relationship as affording relief for some of the restraints and tensions caused by other features of a kinship system.[9]

Plural Marriages and Concubinage

We are so accustomed to thinking of marriage in terms of our own concepts that it is easy for us to overlook the great variety of attitudes that may exist in other cultures. Americans, whose sense of morality stems from Judeo-Christian teachings, find it very hard to avoid the feeling that a society that permits an individual to have multiple spouses at one time is somehow inferior and wanton. An ethnological report of a wife

[8] R. H. Lowie, *Primitive Society,* New York, 1920, p. 102.

[9] F. Eggan, ed., *Social Organization of North American Indians,* Chicago, 1937, p. 76.

who nags her husband into taking another partner never fails to strike an American as being so incredible as to appear ludicrous. Yet plural marriages of one sort or another are widespread in primitive society.

When a man is allowed to have multiple wives the custom is termed *polygyny,* but if a woman is permitted to have more than one husband concurrently it is called *polyandry.* Together these customs are known as *polygamy.* Cultural anthropologists have found polygyny to be exceedingly common, but polyandry is reliably reported only among the Toda of southern India, in parts of Tibet, and in a few other places.

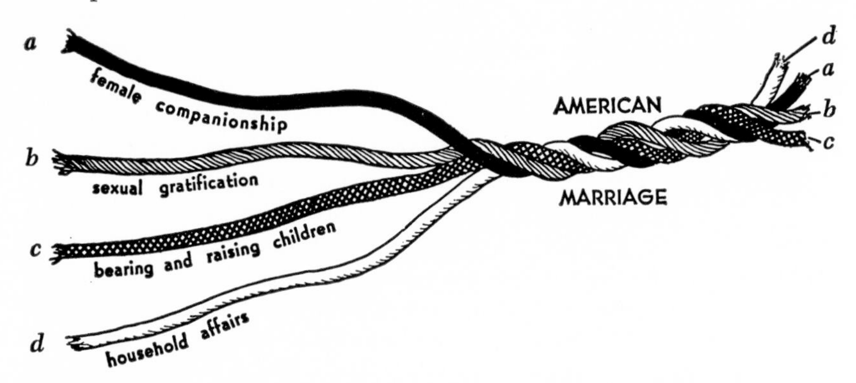

FIG. 23-4. The rope of American marriage. From an American husband's standpoint, the rope of marriage consists of at least four separate strands. Other societies may combine the same or other strands in different ways. Sexual gratification, and the bearing and rearing of children are the two factors that most commonly occur.

Marriage customs are not unitary but may better be likened to a rope that consists of independent strands braided together to form a single object (Fig. 23–4). Varying societies do not always select the selfsame strands for weaving the rope of marriage, and it is difficult for us to realize that each of the various segments may be assigned by a man to a separate wife.

To be more specific, Occidental men expect one wife to have at least four functions: (a) to gratify her husband's sexual desires, (b) to bear and rear his children, (c) to conduct his household affairs, and (d) to provide him with feminine companionship. We find it difficult to realize that these four elements of marriage are separable and that it is possible for each of them to be entrusted to a separate woman. Lenape Indian men, around Delaware, are said to have practiced polygyny, with each wife serving a different purpose. One woman was chosen primarily as a sex partner; another's main duty was to rear offspring; and a third acted as a housekeeper.[10] The classical Greeks, too, are reported to have separated child raising and housekeeping from the purely sexual aspects of marriage.[11]

A man's spouses, even within a culture that freely permits polygyny, do not necessarily have equal status. Much more commonly, the first wife is regarded as the principal one. She outranks the others and generally has charge of running the household in which she resides. This was the case in ancient China, where a man's first wife had the greatest prestige and dominated all other females who might come to share her home through marriage to males who resided therein. Since, however, the only true test of a successful marriage by Confucian standards was the birth of a male heir, a Chinese woman who failed to bear a son fully expected her mate to take secondary wives or concubines.[12] In many parts of Africa, on the other hand, even a mother of many sons might scold her husband for neglecting to marry additional wives who would relieve her of difficult household chores.

Long before the publication of the Kinsey reports, men had come to realize that the sexual desires of their wives did not always correspond to their own. Some of the difference may be a matter of biology, for a young man's desires tend to be continuous and steadily persistent, whereas a woman's are more apt to be variable and cyclic. This depends, it is thought, on *hormone* production, which varies at different stages of the menstrual cycle. In any event, male and female sexual wants do not always coincide. From this point of view, it would be easy to explain why some well-to-do Frenchwomen cheerfully help prepare their husbands to spend a night with a mistress. Unfortunately, this would not explain why females from other societies tend to be less cheerful under similar circumstances. Within the scope covered by the French example, sexual activity can be separated from other aspects of marriage, but the phenomenon is anything but customary and universal and it appears to be culturally rather than biologically conditioned. This interpretation is supported by the former customs of the Nayar of southern India, among whom a woman lived for only a few days with her husband, after which she might openly dwell with a lover.

When it comes to the separation of providing feminine com-

---

[10] An account of Lenape customs is given in W. Ritchie, "Pre-Iroquoian Occupations," *Rochester Museum of Arts and Sciences,* 1944.

[11] E. F. Borgatta and H. J. Meyer, eds., *Sociological Theory,* New York, 1956, p. 218.

[12] It would be unrealistic to think that Chinese men took concubines solely for the purpose of begetting sons. Still, a child born to a concubine might by a legal fiction be claimed as her own by a barren wife. The difference between a secondary wife and a concubine usually depended on the woman's social standing.

panionship from other wifely duties, old Japan furnishes an excellent example. Men who could afford it were expected to seek female companionship, not always including sexual indulgence, from the professional group of entertainers called *geisha.* While some geisha undoubtedly granted sex favors to selected patrons, they were not as a class synonymous with prostitutes. Thanks to the geisha, Japanese wives were not called upon to perfect the arts of keeping men company and making witty conversation. And when a geisha married, she no longer kept up her old skills but concentrated on meeting the other requirements of a good Japanese wife.

Nor are the values associated with the strands of a marriage rope fixed for all time. It is not at all unexpected if sexual matters loom large in the early days of a marriage, but if other-sex companionship becomes more important in old age.

If one takes a world view, it turns out that multiple matings are highly variable. Sexual impulses may underlie many of them, but they are neither the entire nor the only reasons for entering plural wedlock. Sometimes a man's social or economic position demands that he marry a number of women, and sometimes a man's status goes up with each additional woman that he weds. On the whole, multiple marriages among human beings prove to be complicated biocultural arrangements, of which all the motivations have not yet been scientifically determined.

Living together

As soon as a marriage has been made, the newlyweds must face the problem of where they should live. Only three possibilities are widespread under normal conditions. A bridal pair may settle in a place that is new to each of them (*neolocal residence*), they may go to live where the groom resides (*patrilocal,* or *virilocal, residence*), or they may settle in the vicinity of the bride's home (*matrilocal,* or *uxorilocal, residence*). Although it occurs less often, mention should also be made of *avunculocal residence.* In its commonest form it requires a man and his wife to live in the home of his mother's brother. Where avunculocal residence is practiced, a man expects to become his maternal uncle's and not his father's heir.

Because of the strong sentiments of attachment that a person develops for the place where he was raised and for the people among whom he grew up, the choice of habitation that every wedded pair must make is a matter of grave concern. So, too, is the distance and availability of the new site with reference to the old. Ralph Linton has urged ethnologists to take pains to indicate the precise degree of isolation from a parental home that postmarital residence entails, but unfortunately his advice has seldom been followed. Among some tribes the rules of postmarital residence are variable, and in others a period of dwelling with one set of in-laws is followed by a term of living with the second set. Frequently, the birth of a first child to a couple signals the time for a change of residence.

Perhaps of still greater significance is the question of whether a bride and groom establish an independent household or join an already existing residential unit occupied by the parents and other relatives of either the husband or wife. When merging into a single unit takes place the custom may aptly be described as forming a *unilocal household.* Valid distinctions may thus be drawn between patrilocal and matrilocal arrangements that are either unilocal or *multilocal.*

Unilocal habitation cannot fail to exert a profound influence on the married pair and on any offspring that may be born to them. If the custom is consistently followed in a patrilocal setting, it inevitably leads to the formation after several generations of a social unit consisting of a man, his sons, grandsons, and so forth, together with their respective spouses and unmarried daughters. The males will form a permanent nucleus, occupying the same quarters from birth to death, bringing wives in from outside, and sending their daughters off at marriage. Where matrilocal customs prevail, the same results will ensue with the sexes reversed. The exact correspondence of such residential units to patrilineal or matrilineal clans was first noted many years ago, and there is a good likelihood that the unilateral classification of kindred was originally based on ties of common residence rather than on bonds of consanguinity.[13]

Another feature of unilocal residence is the hardship it imposes on one party to a marriage. In a matrilocal society, the women are so firmly placed in their households that they can, if they choose, make their husbands feel like privileged boarders who can be dismissed at will. When a man is divorced in such societies he usually reweds, goes to live with a married sister, or returns to the house of his mother. Conversely, in such patrilocal societies as that of the Araucanians or of the traditional Chinese, it was a girl who was uprooted from her natal home at marriage and who found herself forced to live out her adult life among strangers. In settings of this kind young brides often found

[13] A detailed discussion of this topic may be found in M. Titiev, "The Influence of Common Residence on the Unilateral Classification of Kindred," *American Anthropologist,* Vol. 45, 1943, pp. 511–30.

themselves unhappily subservient to their mothers-in-law, or forced to show the greatest of respect to their fathers-in-law. Chinese literature is full of stories concerning the difficulties of recent brides in dealing with their mothers-in-law; and among the Araucanians, older women who had previously married into the same patrilocal household frequently watched over a new wife to keep her from running away or committing suicide. Dominance and supervision by older people is impossible where neolocal residence is the rule.

One of the commonest methods of preventing undue familiarity among relatives who are forced by residence customs to live in close proximity is to prescribe a great show of respect or *avoidance.* This may take many forms, of which the most widely found is the custom, avidly seized upon by Euro-American comedians, of the *mother-in-law taboo.* In reality, there is nothing amusing about a mother-in-law taboo in primitive society, because its violation arouses the displeasure of one's tribesmen and may even cause serious illness or death. This is the case among the Navaho, where a woman's married daughters live in nearby *hogans,* and yet their husbands are forbidden either to speak with or to look upon the mother of their wives. Among the Navaho, childless brides or young children serve as intermediaries and warn people who might inadvertently violate the prohibition. Nevertheless, instances are known where a man's sickness is attributed to the fact that either he or his father once broke the mother-in-law taboo. Avoidance regulations, similar to the mother-in-law taboo, may be applied to other relatives, as is said to be the case among the Cubeo Indians of South America, who are reported to have a brother and sister-in-law taboo.

Kinship systems, including both the methods of labeling relatives and the prescribed forms of behavior that regulate their conduct, are so diversified and so basic to an understanding of social structures that they have been eagerly studied by ethnologists for the better part of a century. To date, the most widely used approach has rested on the assumption that primitive groups designate kindred according to some method of real or assumed "blood" or genetic connections. Most of the traditional students of kinship have assumed that since every child must have a father and a mother, ties of descent have always provided the basis for a kinship system. This is not invariably the case. It was recognized long ago that native peoples are not always interested in "blood" or descent, and it goes without saying that they are entirely unaware of genetic transmission.

In the light of these facts, it seems best to look upon kinship systems as parts of each group's culture; and, like other aspects of culture, designations of relationship may be symbolic as well as real. Looked at in this way, kinship nomenclature may be regarded as another human "invention." Ties of descent are not apparent to the naked eye, and it is not at all unusual to find in the primitive world ceremonies that are designed to establish and proclaim the kinship relations (including parenthood) of a newly born child. That an infant and the other members of his society might not otherwise know a baby's father is an old, old notion among us. That is why we think little of it when we read that a man has to perform some public action in order to declare and acknowledge his paternity. We are likely to think, however, that the biological bonds of mother and babe are so close that kinship relations between them must be automatically established. This is far from being the case, for there is absolutely no sure way that a mother can recognize her own infant. Among us, many a woman is delivered in a hospital and is hazy or unconscious at the exact moment of parturition. Under such conditions, relationship ties cannot and do not begin between a mother and her child until someone in the conventional garb of a hospital attendant hands a neonate to a just-delivered woman. Thus, it is not improper to say that motherhood as well as fatherhood is a sociocultural "invention."

Very often, in analyses of kinship, we fall into the habit of assuming that use of a given term, such as "father," triggers a fixed sort of behavior or role. It is equally possible for the reverse to be true, namely, that a man may be called father because he behaves toward *Ego* in a certain way. Thus, kinship terms may be applied to people who regularly help or feed one, quite apart from matters of descent and regardless of whose genes one happens to carry. Once again does the matter of physical space enter in, for no man or woman can possibly act as a parent unless he is, at least on occasion, within reach of a child. Parenthood at a distance is absolutely impossible in any society.

A sharper distinction than is customarily made needs to be drawn between *natal kin,* who comprise one's relatives by "blood" and who are *involuntarily* acquired at birth, and the marital or affinal kin whose selection is made *voluntarily* in postnatal life, as a result of someone's choice. Natal kin can then be further subdivided into those who customarily share a common habitation with a newly born *Ego* and those who do not. If such a subdivision is made, it will be found that incest taboos apply to those of one's natal kin and their offspring who, under aboriginal conditions, might have been expected to have lived in *Ego's* household when he was born.

A masculine *Ego,* to avoid making an incestuous marriage, must take a spouse from a household different from the one in which he has resided from birth. If it is admitted that primitive people are reluctant to establish marital bonds with a great scattering of persons, the safest course for our hypothetical *Ego* to follow would be to marry someone from the same household whence came his mother or his father. In a matrilocal society a male *Ego* would thus wed his father's sister's daughter, and in a patrilocal setting he would marry his mother's brother's daughter. This system is known as *unilateral cross-cousin marriage,* and accords with Crow kinship nomenclature in the first instance, and with Omaha terminology in the second.[14]

Besides providing a different way of trying to understand the wide prevalence of cross-cousin marriage in primitive societies, and in addition to whatever value it may have for explaining certain ways of designating kindred, the method of analysis in terms of space and common residence may also contribute to a better understanding of the phenomenon that ethnologists know as *alternate-generation harmony.* By this it is meant that people in a grandparental generation are warm and kindly to their grandchildren, whereas those in successive generations, that is, parents and offspring, may develop tension and strife. Sometimes grandparents and grandchildren, because of cross-cousin marriage, fall into exactly the same social divisions. This may facilitate the harmony of alternate generations. In the case of people like the African Ashanti, this factor gains additional importance from the native belief that the spirit of a deceased grandparent can be reborn only in a child resulting from cross-cousin marriage.[15]

One further point should be kept in mind when dealing with the mating of cross-cousins. Incest taboos forbid a sister and a brother to become parents of the same children, but through the operation of cross-cousin marriage they become parents-in-law of one another's offspring.

A unit, such as a clan, that contains a mixture of real and assumed kin gains in cohesion if its members live near one another. Thus, when the patrilineal clanmates of the Kota of southern India lived along particular streets, the clan system was very strong. When, however, relatives began to live anywhere in a Kota village, the clans weakened, and finally died out altogether.

For all that has already been discovered, there is much yet to be learned about primitive kinship. Recent students are thinking along

---

[14] An elaboration of the viewpoints expressed in this section may be found in M. Titiev, "The Importance of Space in Primitive Kinship," *American Anthropologist,* Vol. 58, 1956, pp. 854–65.

[15] *Idem.*

lines that were unknown to their predecessors and building their analyses on ideas put forward by their forerunners.[16] Some of them are focusing attention on *kinship sets,* which may be defined as categories of relatives bound together by one or more relationship ties. Others take the position that no terminological analysis is complete unless it partitions the whole universe of kin types into as many segments as there are terms of relationship, with each segment corresponding exactly to the range of a single term. Dissatisfaction has been expressed with egocentric charts that may lead to the analysis of a kinship system,

1 parent's parent	2 child's child
3 parents' parent's sibling	4 sibling's child's child
5 parent	6 child
7 parent's sibling	8 sibling's child
9 parent's sibling's child	10 sibling

FIG. 23-5. A new style of kinship diagram. This arrangement can be used in the study of kinship sets. It eliminates the use of *Ego,* and it is not modeled on genealogical or descent lines. Contrast figures 23-1, 23-2, and 23-3.

primarily in terms of everyone's relationship to one person, *Ego*. Professor Service, in another connection, has even suggested that the use of terms such as "Omaha" and "Crow" may serve to crystallize older concepts and may thus stand in the way of fresh analyses.

Different kinds of diagrams are displacing the conventional charts, which look like genealogical tables (Fig. 23–5), and fresh outlooks are everywhere in evidence. These developments show that cultural anthropologists still regard the study of primitive kinship to be of prime importance for an understanding of human behavior.

[16] See for example, M. S. Edmonson, "Kinship Terms and Kinship Concepts," *American Anthropologist,* Vol. 59, 1957, A. F. C. Wallace and J. Atkins, "The Meaning of Kinship Terms," *American Anthropologist,* Vol. 62, 1960, pp. 58–80, and E. R. Service, "Kinship Terminology and Evolution," *American Anthropologist,* Vol. 62, 1960, pp. 747–63.

Selected References

Edmonson, Munro S., "Kinship Terms and Kinship Concepts," *American Anthropologist,* Vol. 59, No. 3, 1957, pp. 393–433.

Eggan, Fred, ed., *Social Anthropology of North American Indian Tribes,* rev. ed., Chicago, 1955.

Fortes, Meyer, *The Web of Kinship among the Tallensi,* London, 1949.

Goodenough, Ward H., "A Problem in Malayo-Polynesian Social Organization," *American Anthropologist,* Vol. 57, 1955, pp. 71–83.

Karpadia, K. M., *Hindu Kinship,* Bombay, 1947.

Kroeber, Alfred L., "Classificatory Systems of Relationship," *Journal of the Royal Anthropological Institute,* Vol. 39, 1909, pp. 77–84.

Lévi-Strauss, Claude, "The Family," in H. L. Shapiro, ed., *Man, Culture, and Society,* Chap. 12, New York, 1956.

———, *Les Structures Elémentaires de la Parenté,* Paris, 1948.

Lowie, Robert H., *Social Organization,* New York, 1948.

Morgan, Lewis H., "Systems of Consanguinity and Affinity of the Human Family," *Smithsonian Institution, Contributions to Knowledge,* Vol. 17, No. 218, Washington, D.C., 1870.

Murdock, G. Peter, *Social Structure,* New York, 1949.

Radcliffe-Brown, A. R., "The Social Organization of Australian Tribes," *Oceania,* Vol. 1, 1930.

Schneider, David M., and Gough, Kathleen, *Matrilineal Kinship,* Berkeley, Calif., 1961.

Service, Elman R., *Primitive Social Organization,* New York, 1962.

Titiev, Mischa, "The Importance of Space in Primitive Kinship," *American Anthropologist,* Vol. 58, 1956, pp. 854–65.

———, "The Influence of Common Residence on the Unilateral Classification of Kindred," *American Anthropologist,* Vol. 45, 1943, pp. 511–30.

Some Nonkinship Aspects of Social Organization

CHAPTER 24

KINDRED AND STRANGERS

Primitive people always differentiate between relatives, no matter how they are identified and labeled, fellow villagers or neighbors, and total strangers. The latter are generally so seldom encountered that there may be no established ways of dealing with them. At the opposite end of the scale, etiquette rules may be exceedingly detailed and may call for very lengthy preliminaries before one deals with strangers. In some parts of the Orient, it is expected that three days will elapse before a stranger states his business.

Those of us who are accustomed to dealing regularly with strangers and who habitually entrust our lives to strangers—as we do whenever we take a bus or a plane, ride in a train or a taxicab, eat in a restaurant, or sail in a ship—often fail to appreciate the full impact of a stranger's appearance among a closely knit group of isolated people.

When the State of Israel was receiving migrant Jews from all parts of the world, the question of dealing with strangers became a practical matter. European Jews who applied for housing had no trouble in giving officials their names, the size of their families, and similar information. Oriental Jews, on the other hand, found themselves embarrassed and uneasy when they had to give personal information to strange receptionists. They could not bring themselves to reply quickly even to routine questions, and they often caused long delays simply because they were unaccustomed to dealing promptly with strangers.

It is not surprising that under conditions of isolation, strangers are regarded with a mixture of fear and hostility. Conversely, most primitive societies deliberately foster an attitude of belonging together among fellow tribesmen. Tribal initiation ceremonies are often designed, in part, to strengthen a youngster's feeling of belonging to his group. The more unified a society feels, the more likely is it to be reserved or hostile to strangers. However, such feelings do not inevitably lead to conflict with outsiders. Civil wars, usually following a breakdown of traditional social organization, are not entirely unknown in the primitive world. Wars may also be fought either for aggrandizement or else to safeguard one's territory or economy; and in a number of instances, warfare may be regarded more as a means of gaining honors than as a way of expressing aggression against others. The Plains Indians of North America are famous for the frequency with which their young men went on the warpath, but study of their customs shows that men fought more to gain the esteem of their fellows than to inflict damages on their enemies.

Many of the Plains tribes had regulated grades of prestige to be won in war. One of these systems is widely known as *counting coup*, and higher honors were gained, because of the degree of daring involved, for touching a live foe than for slaying an enemy. Similarly, some of the same tribes gave high prestige, starting in the sixteenth century, to a successful horse thief. Once again the boldness of the feat far outweighed any other considerations. It was much more honorable to steal one horse that was tethered within an enemy encampment than it was to drive off a number of horses whose owners were nowhere in the vicinity.

Some cultural anthropologists, including the famed student of kinship, G. P. Murdock of Pittsburgh University, believe it can be demonstrated that warfare is, on occasion, closely connected with polygyny. If warriors are successful, he believes, they may carry off enemy women and force them to become secondary wives. But if a war goes badly, many men are likely to be killed, whereupon the survivors may marry several of their tribeswomen to keep them from going entirely husbandless. When warlike tribes are pacified, the sex ratio returns to normal and tends to approximate one to one. Thereupon, monogamy is likely to replace polygamy, a change that illustrates the operation of an internal force of culture as opposed to such external pressure as might result from the teachings of Christian missionaries.

In terms of overall social organization, distaste for strangers is often counterbalanced by a fear that groups of kindred may become so thoroughly self-sufficient that they will deal only with one another, to the detriment of the total community. An equilibrium must be struck in this matter, as in many others, whether or not people are consciously aware of the need.

Considerations of this sort may help us to understand why incest regulations and other forms of exogamy are so widespread in human societies. If they do nothing else they force the near of kin to seek mates from other groups, weakening kinship ties and enforcing a degree of cooperation with other social units. In a broad evolutionary sense, the more primitive a society is, the more likely are its individuals to depend on kin for everything; and the further "advanced" a society is, the less apt are its members to limit their interactions to kindred.

Associations

Apart from the involuntary links of consanguineous relationships that await each child at birth, and different from the affinal bonds formed at marriage, there exist in primitive societies a large number of ties arising from membership in voluntary *associations*. They may be entered at different times, at various ages, in divergent ways, and for a variety of reasons. Joining may be purely optional or may result from social pressures that are so strong as to leave an individual little or no choice. Admission to associations may depend on the biological factors of sex or age; on general considerations of culture like rank, prestige, or marital status; on specific elements, such as occupation or the possession of a given amount of wealth; or on a combination of all three, as in the case of masculine, unmarried warriors. For all their diversity, associations show three virtually universal features. They are almost never made up entirely of consanguineous or affinal kin; each is exclusive because it never admits all the people of a given society; and each develops strong bonds of attachment among those nonkin who are admitted to membership. The variety and complexity of primitive associations may be demonstrated by several examples.

The Cannibal Society of the Kwakiutl Indians[1]

One of the most colorful areas of the aboriginal New World ran along the Pacific seaboard of Canada. This is the region described in anthropological literature as the Northwest Coast. Here, among others, lived the Kwakiutl Indians, whose customs were carefully studied by Franz Boas in the decade prior to the start of the present century.

During the summer season, the social organization of the Kwakiutl was based on ties of descent that sorted the people into clans. In the

[1] F. Boas, "The Social Organization and Secret Societies of the Kwakiutl Indians," Washington, D.C., 1897.

winter months, however, there prevailed an entirely different grouping, which depended on membership in secret societies. Individuals from each clan had a number of these societies from which to choose, but one of the most popular and highly regarded was the *cannibal* society, *hamats'a* (see Fig. 24–1).

Young men entering the cannibal society were whisked away early

FIG. 24-1. A cannibal dancer. Among the Kwakiutl Indians of the northwest Pacific coast, the cannibal society, *hamats'a,* was very popular. Members dressed in elaborate costumes when they danced in public. (Courtesy of the Museum of Anthropology, University of Michigan.)

in the course of the rites. For four days they were kept in total seclusion. At this time they were supposed to be visiting the home of their unit's guardian spirit, who taught them certain songs, dances, and other bits of sacred and tribal lore. While they were absent, their sponsors, usually their own fathers, were expected to provide feasts for their society mates. At the end of four days the initiates were lured back to the everyday world and entered the dance hall in a state of frenzy, because they were supposedly possessed by their guardian spirit. As cannibals, the novices bit people and acted madly until they were calmed down by the older men of their fraternity. Thereupon they sang and danced, presumably in the fashion learned from their guardian spirit, and gradually they again became integrated with the daily world.

Boas believed that the cannibal society was originally connected with warfare. In more general terms, however, all the secret societies of the Kwakiutl seem to have fulfilled a number of similar purposes. Each group sought to emphasize its spiritual origins and tried to strengthen itself by re-enacting its traditional way of behaving. At the same time, it also saw to it that its initiates learned some of their tribal mysteries but also came to accept the everyday values of the tribe. Finally, membership in a secret society invariably encouraged strong bonds of fellowship among nonkin and served clearly to differentiate the initiated from the uninitiated.

Masai Warriors' Societies[2]

Under aboriginal conditions, the Masai occupied a portion of east Africa. Each male, soon after attaining puberty, was subjected to *circumcision*. All those who had gone through the operation in any four-year period were combined into a *warriors' group*, which acquired a distinctive name and the right to use special insignia (Fig. 24–2). For an indefinite time the members lived in a special structure, away from their families, together with paramours. The latter were unmarried women of about the same age as the warriors, and who had in the last four years been subjected to *clitoridectomy*, an operation that involves an incision of the clitoris. After a dozen years or so, individual members of the warriors' group would begin to leave the common habitation, marry, and settle down in the expectation of becoming tribal elders. When the last of a warriors' group had taken these steps the unit was officially dissolved, but the former members retained their distinctive name and continued to share a few common interests for life.

Crow Indian Military Societies[3]

Quite different in nearly every way were the *Lumpwoods* and *Foxes*, two military societies that were very popular among the Crow Indians who used to live in the Plains area of the United States. Each was led by elected officers who were distinguished warriors, and every spring the leaders invited about a dozen promising young men to join

---

[2] A. C. Hollis, *The Masai*, Oxford, 1905, p. xvi, *et passim*.

[3] R. H. Lowie, *The Crow Indians*, New York, 1935.

FIG. 24-2. Members of a Masai warriors' group. These men lived together as long as they remained unmarried. During this time they formed a distinctive unit within their society. (Courtesy of British Information Services.)

their organization. Membership was for life, and each society had exclusive rights to the use of a characteristic song and dance. Members lived at home and were permitted to marry, their wives sharing in a few of the feasts and other public functions. From time to time each association would serve as a police force, and feats of military daring were regularly performed for the greater glory of one's club. Fierce rivalry prevailed between Lumpwoods and Foxes, and once a year each side paraded in public whatever mistresses it had made among the wives of the rival outfit. Convention forbade a cuckolded husband from punishing his spouse or betraying anger, but in most cases a faithless woman soon found herself abandoned both by her lover and her mate. Membership in the Crow military societies was so greatly coveted that, if a man died, his family brought pressure to have him replaced by a relative.

Banks Islands Sukwe[4]

On the Banks Islands of the western Pacific every man sought to join the *Sukwe* society. Admission might be had at any age upon pay-

FIG. 24-3. A *gamal* on the Banks Islands. Within such structures members of the Sukwe society held their meetings. Each gamal was partitioned into graded units, one for the members of each degree. Trespass into a higher section was punishable by death. (Courtesy of Cambridge University Press.)

ment of a fee of shell money to those who already belonged. The Sukwe met in a clubhouse (*gamal*) of its own in each village, and the structure functioned as a combined recreation hall, dining room, and dormitory for men only (Fig. 24–3). All gamals were carefully partitioned into graded sections, and no man dared enter a higher section than his own on pain of death. Members of each subdivision prepared and ate meals together, and it was every man's ambition to get into the highest branches of Sukwe. Since heavy payments had to be made for each advance, few natives got to the very top. Those who did were held in the greatest esteem. For a man to be out of the Sukwe altogether was a social dis-

[4] W. H. R. Rivers, *The History of Melanesian Society,* Cambridge, England, 1914, Vol. I, p. 61 ff.

grace, and those who remained in the lowest grades for life were regarded as failures. Stories of success on the Banks Islands, comparable to our tales of going from rags to riches, are told about men who overcame obstacles to reach the highest levels of Sukwe.

The Hopi Indian Marau Society[5]

As the examples already summarized indicate, a majority of associations in the primitive world are designed for men, but women's

FIG. 24-4. Marau dancers. The Marau was the most popular of the three associations for women among the Hopi. In their public performances, the members of these associations always ranged themselves in circular form. (Courtesy of the Chicago Natural History Museum.)

groups are not unknown. Among the Hopi Indians of northeastern Arizona, every town or pueblo has its populace divided into a number

[5] H. R. Voth, "The Oraibi Marau Ceremony," *Field Columbian Museum, Anthropological Series,* Vol. II, No. 1, Chicago, 1912.

of secret societies, each of which is responsible for conducting an important ceremony for the good of the tribe. Many of these associations have lapsed, but a few remain active. At the village of Old Oraibi there used to be three feminine associations, of which the most popular was the *Marau*. Admission was entirely voluntary and was almost never denied when requested. Despite the ease with which it might be joined, the Marau was a highly regarded aggregation of females. It had its own kiva at Old Oraibi, carried out its own initiations, performed secret rites for the promotion of rainfall, good crops, health, and fertility, and annually staged a public dance in distinctive costume (Fig. 24–4). In the eyes of the Hopi, the Marau observances were a regular part of the ceremonial

FIG. 24-5. A Duk-Duk assembly. On New Britain, in Melanesia, the Duk-Duk was an important secret society. Its members dressed in elaborate costumes, very different from their daily wear. (Courtesy of the Museum of Anthropology, University of Michigan.)

cycle and the prayers of the women were as greatly prized as those of the men.

Additional associations are well known, and a full account of their operations would reveal a bewildering profusion of details. Because participation is practically never limited to kin, membership in associations cannot help but create bonds that cut across ties of relationship and serve to knit firmly together many unrelated members of a society. Some associations carry on strictly practical activities, but even then they usually bring a splash of color and excitement into the lives of their community. People everywhere seem to enjoy opportunities to get away from their customary surroundings and routine duties, to learn secrets not shared by their fellows, to perform strange actions and rituals, and to wear elaborate costumes that differ greatly from conventional garb (Fig. 24–5).

Institutionalized friendship

In our society, friendships occasionally play the part that relationships do in primitive societies; and in modern Japan there is a popular proverb, capable of being variously translated, that says in effect: "A friend close at hand is better than a relative far away."

For all our recognition of the value of friendship, though, our type of society has never thoroughly institutionalized it. In many regions of Africa, however, as well as on a number of south Pacific islands and in other parts of the primitive world, dealings with friends are systematically regulated and play an important part in holding together unrelated members of a society.

It is not at all uncommon for institutionalized friendship to bind together for life two unrelated members of the same sex. Such men or women pledge themselves to cooperate at all times. The use of these alliances as a substitute for kinship connections is well brought out in a consideration of the Plains Cree Indians of Canada.[6] Among them, two boys who pledged friendship would address each other's parents as father and mother; and if one died, the survivor always lived for a time in the home of his deceased friend, where he was regarded as an adopted son. Likewise, should two friends become married, their wives would call each other sisters, as do the wives of true brothers.

Most widely publicized, although it occurs but sporadically in primitive society, is the custom known as *blood brotherhood*. In one form, practiced in medieval Europe and in parts of Africa, the principals would draw blood from their arms, allow it to mix in a container, then drink the contents. Other people may not establish blood brotherhood quite so literally, but in all cases something is done publicly to show that the two parties, and sometimes all their relatives as well, are henceforth to be regarded on the same basis as real "blood" kin. Customs of this sort emphasize the importance that many societies attribute to the need for establishing close bonds among those who are not automatically related by descent.

---

[6] D. G. Mandelbaum, "Friendship in North America," *Man*, Vol. 36, 1936, pp. 205–06.

A different way of establishing close ties is an institution comparable to *godparenthood,* which is known to various native peoples of Latin America as a *compadre* relationship, and which may call for such fixed and long-lasting patterns of behavior among those concerned as to lead to the formation of what have been termed *"padrino groups."*[7] Where the institution of *compadre* is highly formalized, very little is left to chance. *Godparents* take their obligations seriously and come much nearer than is often the case among us to acting like substitute parents to their *godchildren.*

Resembling the foregoing is the custom—found among various American Indian tribes of the Southwest, who live in towns, or *pueblos* —of establishing ties of quasi-kinship between a child and its *ceremonial parents.* As a rule this term refers to an individual and one of his relatives of the opposite sex, who sponsor a youngster's admission into a *sodality,* or secret society, which performs an important rite. Parents do not lightly select a ceremonial father or mother for their offspring. They are so conscious of the fact that the person chosen may be called upon to act as a parental surrogate that they weigh his qualifications very carefully.

Somewhat less telling is the primitive habit of recognizing *age groups* or *age sets.* Recognition may be completely informal or highly systematized. It is based on the idea that people of the same sex and approximate age are somehow alike and ought to develop the solidarity of a social group. Actually, many males and females of a given age are subjected to similar codes of behavior and share many experiences that serve to bind them together. Where age groups are explicitly recognized, the members are usually expected to help and befriend one another whenever necessary. In some instances societies anticipate that agemates will act together, and they may even go so far as to assign tasks to be carried out by an age group, like a Masai warriors' unit, rather than by particular individuals.

Thus, it appears that each biocultural triangle may be faced with the need for striking an equilibrium between opposing forces. Bonds of kinship are never allowed to become all-sufficient. This compels people, for the good of society as a whole, to develop mechanisms by means of which warm and close ties can be established among those who do not happen to be kin.

---

[7] E. H. Spicer, *Pascua, A Yaqui Village in Arizona,* Chicago, 1940, pp. 91–116. In some parts of Middle America similar groups are called *compadrazgo.* More details are given in G. M. Foster, "What Is Folk Culture?" *American Anthropologist,* Vol. 55, 1953, pp. 159–73, especially p. 167.

Primitive Law[8]

If a social unit wishes to keep itself going, its pattern of culture must contain something approximating a legal system. That is why cultural anthropologists do not regard primitive societies as anarchical even when they lack formal agencies for making and enforcing laws. By definition, nonliterate peoples cannot have written judicial codes, and it is most unusual to find them with clear-cut legislative and executive bodies. Nevertheless, their standards of conduct are usually known to all, and punishment for offenses committed is not rare.

Law enforcement implies a degree of social compulsion, tinged with a threat of authorized physical force, that makes an individual regulate his personal conduct to comply with the values, norms, or mores of his group. It is as though each society said to its members, "Conform, or be punished." Beyond the acceptance of this universal concept there is no world-wide agreement on what constitutes a violation of proper conduct or on the punishment to be inflicted. The cultures of some societies permit and even encourage forms of behavior that other groups may severely condemn. Many tribes use nothing more than shame or ridicule for holding people in line. A distinction may be drawn between groups that have something approaching a *state*, which exercises controls through the agency of bodies of *police* or other formal enforcement units, and tribes whose social controls are effective only through the operation of traditional usages as expressed in public opinion or reaction. It is never easy to draw a fine line between these two types of society, or between those nonconformists whose deviations are subject to some form of punishment and other nonconformists or innovators whose departures from established codes become accepted as models for new ways of behaving.

Once in a while, laws are based on considerations of biology. For instance, only females have sexual organs that are capable, in theory, of being penetrated at all times. For this reason, all legal systems recognize that rape and criminal assault can be committed only against women. Except for a greatly restricted number of such cases, legal regulations appear to be based more on symbolic, cultural values than on matters of biology; and some biocultural traits, as has already been indicated, may even give the appearance of running counter to biology.

---

8 E. A. Hoebel, of the University of Minnesota, is one of the foremost anthropologists specializing in primitive law. For his presentation of some of the points made in this section, see E. A. Hoebel, *Man in the Primitive World,* rev. ed., New York, 1958, Chap. 27.

Thus, it is obvious that men everywhere are incapable of bearing offspring, yet some societies, notably in the tropical portions of South America, practice the *couvade,* a custom in which men do the lying-in after their wives have given birth. In extreme forms of the couvade, males may even pretend to undergo the pains of labor and may simulate parturition.

In some parts of Africa, as among the Kikiyu tribe, girls might be "married" to a woman. If girls were unstable or were the mothers of bastards, they were often willing to pay a bride-price in order to secure a "husband" or a "father" for their children. All that was needed was a legal fiction, whereby a female became masculine.

Then, again, in any society men are likely to be stronger of physique than most women, but where such cultural mores as mother-in-law taboos prevail, a bold and powerful man may be genuinely afraid even to glance at his wife's mother. Another instance of the power of cultural convention is found on the Banks Islands. Some wives undoubtedly henpecked or dominated their husbands at home, but never would any woman have dared to follow her spouse into a men's club-house.

On the whole, as these cases make clear, cultural determinants play a greater part than biological factors in establishing what customs individuals of either sex are expected to observe.

Perhaps the most widespread of all legal regulations are those concerned with the sanctity of *property rights* and of *human life.* Property may be intangible, such as a design or tune; it may have such real value, as would a well-made spear; or its worth may be symbolic, as in the case of shell money. Moreover, property may be individually or collectively held, and it may be either zealously guarded or freely loaned. Such factors make little difference. In all of these instances there is present a concept of ownership, and violations of proprietary rights are punishable.

Since no society likes to face extinction, it follows that there will always be laws to prevent the killing of people, especially if they are members of one's own group and still capable of parenthood. A small percentage of tribes allow infanticide or permit the killing of the very aged or the hopelessly sick, but most societies regret the loss of a member under any circumstances. Distinctions may be drawn for all kinds of reasons between abortion, infanticide, suicide, murder, and various degrees of manslaughter, and some means of causing death may be condoned while others are not. In our society, the safest tool for a killer to use is an automobile, and a gun is probably the most unsafe. Should an intoxicated man shoot several people, he might be charged with murder and executed if found guilty; but if a drunken driver kills an equal number of people, he may be found guilty of involuntary manslaughter and sentenced to a relatively light prison term.[9] Other societies may make different discriminations. In many tribes a man who kills an adulterous wife caught in the act may not even be charged with any offense at all, but if he is thought guilty of having bewitched a woman he may be put to death.

There is no universal touchstone, either, for evaluating how severe the same form of punishment will be judged to be by peoples of different cultures. Cutting off the nose of a culprit might be regarded as unbelievably brutal in one society and as moderate in another. A slap across the face would humiliate and infuriate an adult male in the United States, but would have been taken in stride by a recruit in the Imperial Army of Japan. We might regard social ostracism as light punishment for a serious offense, but most primitive groups would tend to consider rejection by one's fellows as a fate worse than death.

Responsibility for carrying out retribution seems to follow a definite trend when one compares various social systems. Where cultures are relatively primitive, the matter of inflicting punishment on offenders is likely to be left to the kinfolk of those who were injured; but in societies and cultures of greater development and complexity, the administration of justice is entrusted more and more to impersonal agencies or nonrelatives. In simple societies a murderer may be called upon only to pay a fixed sum, *weregild,* to the surviving kin of his victim. In other cases a murder may start a *blood feud,* in which bereaved relatives try to kill an equivalent member of the other side's kinfolk. On the whole, punishment for murder is likely to be more drastic in modern than in primitive societies.

Methods of evaluating evidence and determining guilt are also highly variable. They may range from a tendency to regard as guilty anyone against whom an accusation is brought to very elaborate procedures for weighing evidence, and even to provision for the punishment of those who bear false witness. A favorite device is to subject a suspect, and occasionally his accuser as well, to an *ordeal.* Much as they may differ in details, all ordeals are based on the setting up of a trial

---

[9] *The Detroit Free Press,* October 20, 1950, p. 12, carried a story of a youth who, while drunk, drove through a red light and crashed into a car, killing two people and one of his own passengers. He was convicted of "involuntary manslaughter."

On April 30, 1962, the *Ann Arbor News* carried an account of a driver who caused a woman's death by making a left turn directly in front of her oncoming car. The police booked him on a suspicion of negligent homicide. Had he killed the same woman with a gun the charge would have been more severe.

or contest situation in which victory is always supposed to go to the innocent. Whether the test consists of being immersed in water, grasping a white-hot iron, plunging the hand into boiling water (Fig. 24-6), drinking poison, swallowing a hard crust, or trial by combat, the underlying idea seems to be that an incorruptible power, usually regarded as supernatural, will make its decision clear by allowing the guilty party to suffer injury or defeat. That mortals might "frame" the ordeal situation to favor or condemn a particular party is an idea that could be

FIG. 24-6. An ordeal by hot water. Among the Ifugao, in the Philippine Islands, guilt was often determined by subjecting a suspect to an ordeal by hot water. It was believed that an innocent person would be unharmed by such a test. (Courtesy of the Museum of Anthropology, University of Michigan.)

entertained only by an unbeliever. The swearing of *oaths* and a variety of divinatory practices are other ways of asking supernatural powers to determine the guilt or innocence of accused persons.

Whatever other attributes they may have, all legal systems are meant to help hold a society together and to maintain its accustomed way of life by preventing conflicting interests from coming to an open clash. Here obedience to law and patriotism or loyalty to one's social unit fuse into a single concept. The law-abiding person, whether primitive or not, is expected to put his social responsibilities above his personal interests, and so, too, is the patriotic individual. In this connection the highest legal authority in most primitive societies is vested in the headman or chief, who is also the tribe's political leader. When so much power is lodged in a single personage, he is likely to be equated with a deity, and thus the notion of divine rulers is exceedingly common. Under these conditions, violations of the accepted mores of a tribe may be regarded at one and the same time as political crimes and religious sins. It should occasion little wonder that an investigation of this aspect of man's relations to man in a primitive society regularly brings a student to a consideration of man's dealings with the supernatural, for orderly, patriotic, and religious conduct are constantly blended.

A REVIEW OF MAN'S RELATIONS TO MAN

Man's interactions with his fellows cover a host of topics, but they fall into a systematic arrangement if viewed in the light of the axioms that every society has a real existence, and that all societies, as well as individuals, seek to maintain themselves and their cultures indefinitely. Sexual reproduction is the only way, directly or indirectly, of continuously replenishing the supply of human beings that constitute a social unit, and on this point biological factors cannot be disregarded. All normal females are capable of bearing children, and every society encourages them to have offspring under regulated conditions. Cultural considerations also affect the recognition and naming of kinfolk. Every anthropologist realizes that consanguinity may be assigned as well as inherited. A Toda baby in southern India accepts as its father whatever man ritually presents its mother with a bow, regardless of whose genes the baby actually carries. Until modern times the Chinese considered all who had the same surname to be "blood" kin and forbade them to marry even if no trace of genealogical connection could be established. On the other hand, we must not forget that wherever unilateral systems of kinship nomenclature are in force, even "blood" relatives as close as one's own father or mother might, under some circumstances, be left out of the reckoning.

Primitive societies show a marked preference for the use of classificatory terminology, for unilateral methods of labeling kin along only one sex line, and for the occasional overriding of generation lines. Occidental societies generally employ descriptive terms and trace relationship bilaterally, by way of both the father's and the mother's lines. Accordingly, unilateral groupings such as lineages and clans, sometimes clustered into phratries or moieties, are commonplace in primitive society but rare or nonexistent elsewhere. Two of the best-studied systems of unilateral descent terminology are the Omaha and Crow, but others are known to specialists.

Even when a tribe labels kindred unilaterally, however, it is likely to give some recognition to nuclear family groups consisting of both parents and their unmarried offspring. Nuclear family units, since they include fathers as well as mothers, are usually bilateral, but their existence may be recognized even in societies that use unilateral methods of nomenclature.

All social groups differentiate between consanguineous relatives, supposedly bound together by involuntary ties of descent, and affinal kin who become joined to an *Ego* through someone's marriage. In all societies, too, the matter of postmarital residence is of great importance. Primitive peoples often, but not always, expect newlyweds to live with or near the same sex line that is used for labeling relatives. Thus, although a few exceptions are known, patrilocal residence goes hand in hand with patrilineal descent, and matrilocality is most commonly found with matrilineality. As societies evolve toward more modern conditions, newly married couples tend more and more to establish independent, neolocal residences away from the kin of either principal.

Marriage customs everywhere consist of the weaving together of numerous, individual strands. Differences arise because various societies combine different strands in a variety of ways. If there is an evolution of marriage practices, it runs from assorted kinds of polygamy to monogamy, and the cessation of warfare may provide one stimulus for this trend.

To be successful, every society's way of life must strike a balance between encouraging bonds of cohesion to develop among some of its members and preventing tightly knit groups from giving up their allegiance to the social whole. Bodies of close relatives, such as natal kin, are particularly prone to form self-contained and self-sufficient cliques that may threaten to become independent of the rest of their society. As a rule, incest and other exogamic regulations, membership in scattered associations, institutionalized friendships, authorized dealings with strangers, and connections with trading partners[10] are enough to over-

---

[10] Primitive societies carry on a great number of varied forms of trade. Some of these, like *silent trade,* in which goods are put out on trust and trading partners never see each other, have no deep sociological implications. On the other hand, in the *kula,* which is probably our best-known and best-written account of an elaborate trading system, there are countless socioreligious factors. It is evident that many ties developed among the members of a kula expedition. Simultaneously, as Malin-

come the dangers of large-scale segmentation. Then, too, individuals must occasionally be held in line for the good of the total society. This can ordinarily be accomplished through legal restrictions and appeals to patriotism. Where such measures prove insufficient, recourse may be had to supernatural beliefs that reinforce sociocultural sanctions and so help to bring about the formation and intensification of strong bonds of attachment to one's total society.

Selected References

Boas, Franz, "The Social Organization and Secret Societies of the Kwakiutl Indians," *Report of the U.S. National Museum for 1895,* Washington, D.C., 1897.

Hoebel, E. Adamson, *Man in the Primitive World,* rev. ed., New York, 1958, Chap. 27.

———, *Primitive Law,* Cambridge, Mass., 1950.

Hollis, A. C., *The Masai,* Oxford, 1905.

Lévi-Strauss, Claude, "The Social and Psychological Aspects of Chieftainship in a Primitive Tribe: The Nambikuara," *Transactions, New York Academy of Sciences,* series II, Vol. 7, 1944, pp. 16–32.

Lowie, Robert H., *Primitive Society,* New York, 1920, Chap. 10.

Malinowski, Bronislaw, *Argonauts of the Western Pacific,* London, 1922.

Mandelbaum, David G., "Friendship in North America," *Man,* Vol. 36, 1936.

Rivers, W. H. R., *The History of Melanesian Society,* Vol. 1, Cambridge, England, 1914, pp. 60–79.

Spicer, Edward H., *Pascua, A Yaqui Village in Arizona,* Chicago, 1940, pp. 91–116.

Voth, H. R., "The Oraibi Marau Ceremony," *Field Columbian Museum, Anthropological Series,* Vol. II, No. 1, Chicago, 1912.

owski tells us, "though transacted between tribes differing in language, culture, and probably even in race, it is based on a fixed and permanent status, on a partnership which binds into couples some thousands of individuals. This partnership is a lifelong relationship, it implies various mutual duties and privileges, and constitutes a type of inter-tribal relationship on an enormous scale." (B. Malinowski, *Argonauts of the Western Pacific,* New York, Dutton Everyman Paperback, 1961, p. 85.) The kula is an outstanding feature of the Melanesian Trobriand Islanders, whose customs Malinowski has carefully described.

Growing Up in a Culture

CHAPTER 25

Not so long ago it became apparent that something vital was being omitted from traditional studies of culture in terms of models or biocultural configurations. It seemed clear to some ethnologists that scant attention was being paid to the individual men and women who, in all instances, were the sole carriers and transmitters of patterns of culture. It was felt particularly that the impact of culture on the personalities of specific individuals was being neglected. If every human being must learn to adjust his behavior to the sanctioned values of his society, certain anthropologists held, the very process of adjustment could not fail to have a weighty effect on everyone's adult personality.

Today there is increasing reluctance to deal with biocultural configurations as if they existed in a vacuum. More and more attention is being devoted to efforts to understand what happens to the personalities of individuals as they learn to conform to the culture patterns that prevail in their societies. To be truly valuable, these studies require detailed investigation into the lives of many particular persons. Resort to generalities, averages, or types is considered of small worth in this kind of approach. A host of modern anthropologists, including Kluckhohn, Mead, Benedict, DuBois, Hallowell and Linton, whose names are among those best known to the general public, have made important contributions toward an understanding of the ways in which socially sanctioned mores affect the conduct and temperaments of specific persons. Kluckhohn has neatly characterized this aspect of the science of man as being concerned with the "person-in-a-culture."

All researches into personality formation owe much to the hypotheses so convincingly advanced by Sigmund Freud. Even those who most violently disagree with parts of his teachings or methods are likely to take for granted some of his ideas. Over the years many criticisms have been made of Freud's concepts, but a number of his most fundamental tenets have never been proved wrong. This is certainly not the place for a complete review and evaluation of Freudian doctrine, but two of his cardinal points have stimulated a great deal of research on the part of numerous anthropologists. These are the concept of infantile sexuality, which seems to be inborn and which perpetually seeks gratification, not necessarily intercourse and orgasm; and the notion that feelings of love, hate, anger, and frustration that are experienced in early life may be buried for years before expressing themselves overtly in ways that may not directly reveal their true causes. These features of Freudian doctrine have led investigators to devote much attention to child-rearing customs and, since toilet training and weaning are widely interpreted as inducing frustration or resentment in babies, great stress is laid on studying these practices in varied societies. It is true that a few students of man have read far more meaning into toilet training and swaddling habits than the average cultural anthropologist considers to be justified. Nonetheless, it is generally agreed that the experiences of early childhood are likely to play important parts in the formation of adult personalities.

It is customary to use *projective tests* for determining those grievances, resentments, hatreds, delights, or loves that an individual may never speak about, yet may carry below the level of his conscious thoughts and attitudes. These tests fall into several groups. One type asks a subject to perform tasks, such as drawing a man or a horse, wherein the things that he emphasizes or omits may provide clues to his innermost traits of personality. Another kind confronts a person with a series of vaguely defined pictures, based on inkblots or deliberately ambiguous sketches, which the subject is asked to explain or interpret in any way that he pleases. Other sorts of projective tests require a subject to judge the behavior of people in standardized situations, such as that of a man who beats his wife; or to tell what values or associations a given list of words brings to mind.[1]

Answers obtained from projective tests have been found to reveal about a person many things that lie below the threshold of his consciousness. A number of ethnologists now give projective tests as part of their research programs in the field. Sometimes they turn the results

---

[1] Best known of the tests based on indefinite pictures is Murray's Thematic Apperception Test (TAT). Standardized inkblots are used in Rorschach tests. A discussion of this subject may be found in H. H. and G. L. Anderson, *An Introduction to Projective Techniques,* New York, 1951.

over for analysis and interpretation to third parties, and in a surprising number of cases psychologists unfamiliar with the individuals and cultures concerned have made diagnoses of personality that closely agree with the independently formed judgments of the field workers.

A few psychologists and psychologically oriented anthropologists go so far as to try to explain the nature of culture itself as a reflection of individual personality traits. This reflects a time when the emphasis on war, for instance, which characterizes numerous societies, was attributed to the workings of a "death instinct" in the populace. Most modern scholars are reluctant to make such assumptions, and the origins of cultural emphases are usually left unexplained. Contemporary anthropologists are content to agree that each newly born child is faced with a pre-existent society and culture to which it must learn to adjust its built-in, biogenetically inherited mechanisms. Put another way, it amounts to saying that every baby must learn to conform to its society's sanctioned patterns for group living. What is called *learning theory* is thus involved, and to this vital subject many research workers have turned their attention. A common interest in learning theory is only one of several fruitful mergers between cultural anthropologists and psychologists.

Another area of joint activity concerns the awareness that the psychological potentials of a human being can be realized only if he is given the chance of interacting with other representatives of *Homo sapiens.* Ordinarily, these representatives will be found to stand in definite relationships to a child and to accept the obligations of attending to his physical needs and of teaching him the systems of values that are essential ingredients of their way of life. Through the combined efforts of all concerned, the sum total of the cultural norms of his social unit is brought home to a neonate, and as he grows older he becomes increasingly aware of the forms of behavior that are expected of him. Anthropologists and psychologists subscribe to the belief that an individual's personality can be understood only if one knows as much as possible about his teachers and about the whole cultural system in which he lives.

THE PROCESS OF ENCULTURATION

Although there are a great many definitions of culture, it is generally agreed that cultural concepts cannot be transmitted through genetic inheritance. Thus each child must start to learn the culture of its group after it has emerged from its mother's body. In any study of neonatal development, therefore, an anthropologist must begin with the assumption that a child is born with a set of complicated biological organisms but without a shred of culture. However, from the first moment of its birth a human baby begins to feel the impact of culture—in the way it is delivered, the mode in which its umbilical cord is cut and tied, the fashion in which it is washed and handled, and the manner in which it is swaddled or clothed.[2] At first it is passive, but somewhat later a newly born infant begins to be actively biocultural, and as it matures, in a country like the United States, it will find itself playing down the purely biological aspects of its conduct and stressing cultural values. It is as though each child began postnatal life as a 100 percent biological mechanism and thereafter tried to reduce its biological conduct to a hypothetical vanishing point. In reality, of course, biological activities can never be totally eliminated from human behavior.

For the process of adjusting individual responses increasingly to a society's patterns of culture, Melville Herskovits has chosen the fitting name *enculturation.* Enculturation or, as it is sometimes called, the *socialization* of a child, may be regarded as the manner in which each society molds the genetically controlled organization of its neonates to a set of pre-existing cultural norms.[3]

If it be granted that a baby's very first activities in postnatal life cannot be other than biological, it follows that many of its earliest experiences with the process of enculturation will be restrictive or frustrating. Tribes differ in responding to the desires of babies, but no matter how eager societies and their cultures may be to satisfy infantile demands, there is no group of human beings that drops everything instantaneously to feed a child at the first sign of hunger, allows it absolutely unlimited freedom of muscular movement, or everlastingly permits it to excrete when and where it will. Sooner or later each child must learn to eat, move, and eliminate in accord with the culturally determined set of rights and wrongs that prevails in its society. No doubt neonates differ in the degree to which they can tolerate restriction, but no human infant can completely avoid developing some feelings of displeasure or hostility as it reacts to enculturation. There is an assumption that a child reared under easygoing conditions that hold in check very few of its activities, cater to its wants, and permit toilet training and weaning to occur without signs of grown-up impatience

---

2 An interesting account of neonatal reactions and behavior is given in H. Thoms and B. Bliven, Jr., "What Is A Baby?" *McCall's,* January, 1957, p. 38, *et passim.*

3 A fine study of some of the problems involved in this process, analyzed from a psychological point of view, is presented by P. H. Mussen and J. J. Conger, in *Child Development and Personality,* New York, 1956.

or distaste, will develop into a well-adjusted adult. Unfortunately, there has been little proof of the truth of this assumption.

Studies of enculturation may throw new light on such traditional Freudian concepts as the important *Oedipus complex*. Hitherto it has been assumed that a male child got so much loving attention from his mother that he grew up to hate his father as a rival whom he hoped to displace in his mother's affections. Now it can be shown that a baby also resents the *enculturators* who impose cultural checks on his actions. In the vast majority of known societies the biological or quasi-biological parents of an infant are its earliest and most important enculturators, but this need not always be the case. Theoretically, at least, a neonate may grow up to hate his enculturators, but may have no resentment at all toward his father.

Most of the requirements of enculturation are patterned similarly for all normal children of comparable age, sex, social background, and place of residence. They are so regularly repeated that they can be predicted without much difficulty by any competent observer who is well acquainted with a particular society and its culture. Thus, we know that all girls among us will be taught not to reveal their breasts when wearing street dress, and we anticipate that boys will show an interest in athletics. Furthermore, these undiscriminating, patterned regularities of conduct may be imposed even on children who have been subjected to unexpected conditions, as when an American youth is injured so severely that he can neither play nor watch sporting events. Such random experiences, in conflict with inflexible behavior patterns, may place a severe strain on the formation of individual personalities, yet the demands of cultural conformity are so relentless that something approximating normal adjustment is expected despite all handicaps.

All in all, the process of enculturation may be envisioned as a continuum marked into a number of stages (Fig. 25–1). The first stage, labeled "A," shows a neonate beginning to move away from the strictly biological condition in which he was born. Throughout the beginning phases of this stage an infant is the helpless and passive recipient of whatever forms of culture its handlers may choose to impose upon it. At this time, too, a baby cannot be made significantly aware of its sex, socioeconomic status, religious affiliation, or locale. Only gradually does it become conscious of the differences that these and similar factors may cause or imply. Nor, at the outset of postnatal life, can the adult members of a society place too many restrictions on a neonate's behavior. Gesell and others have satisfactorily shown that physical maturation proceeds by degrees in infancy, one step at a time. Accordingly, it would be impossible to toilet train a youngster before his brain was capable of giving the appropriate orders to those mechanisms that control the bladder and sphincter muscles.

Children born into any society must go through a stage "A." What differs from one group to another are the detailed forms of the culture that will be imposed on a neonate, the manner in which they will be applied to him, the severity with which transgressions will be punished and the time when a child is assumed to have entered stage "B." Wherever, figuratively speaking, a social unit may decide to end the first stage, and no matter how unobtrusively or indefinitely a crossline may be

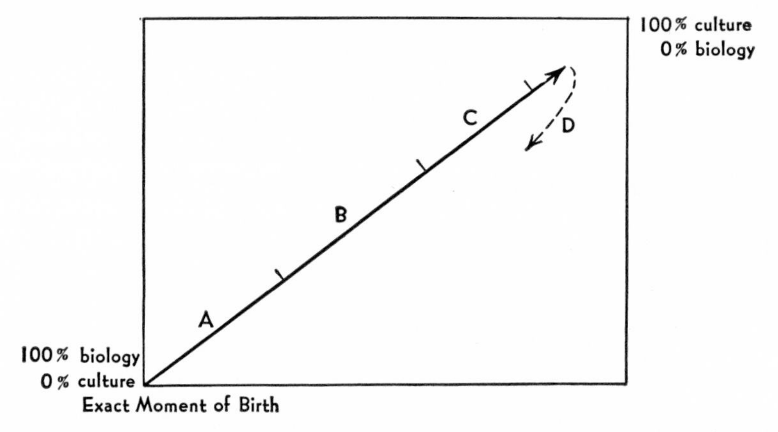

FIG. 25-1. The process of enculturation. In every society each neonate must go through the process of enculturation. This is divided into four stages. "A" stands for infancy, "B" for adolescence, "C" for adulthood, and "D" for old age. It should be noted that in each society "A" has the highest percentage of biological behavior and that "D" reverts somewhat toward "A."

placed, it always represents a critical threshold, after crossing which a child is no longer expected to behave as it did in "A." This is what underlies the remark, so often heard in our society, that runs somewhat as follows: "Cut it out, you're not a baby any more!"

Of course, many of the growing-up experiences of a baby may occur at different times. In any society, infants are likely to be weaned at one time, to begin to talk at another, and to complete their toilet training at a third. Nevertheless, all of these things ultimately reach a culminating point, and each society recognizes when a child has moved from "A" to "B." In Greece, for instance, coffeehouses are masculine preserves, yet young girls regularly play in them. Then comes a day when a girl becomes aware of her sex, and from that time on she never enters a coffeehouse. In a similar way, a very young boy among us unhesitatingly accompanies his mother to a ladies' room; but a time always arrives when he becomes self-conscious and insists on going to a men's room. Such examples illustrate what is meant by the critical thresholds that divide into stages the continuous process of enculturation.

Broadly considered, stage "B" of Figure 25–1 covers the period of adolescence. This is always a difficult stage because a twofold series of changes is taking place simultaneously. Not only is the body undergoing numerous alterations, involving no one knows how many physical strains and stresses, but at the same time an adolescent must conform to a new set of cultural forms. Too often are adults likely to underestimate the cultural trials and tribulations of adjusting to stage "B." No grownup would view without alarm the necessity for changing his manner of speech, as well as his food and clothing habits, methods of movement, and so forth. Yet, we blithely expect every adolescent to talk, eat, dress, and move in a fashion that is recognizably different from that of a baby. Of course, the changes required in "B" are not immediate. Time is generally allowed for these changes to take place, and youngsters are usually forewarned that they will someday have to modify their habits, but even so it is no trivial matter to adjust to so many changing ways of life at the same time that one's body is in a state of turmoil.

There is a danger, too, at the close of this stage, that the end of biological adolescence may not coincide with the termination of cultural adolescence. To be explicit, we assume that a child will become a biological adult several years before our country permits him to vote. Some of these discrepancies may lead to biocultural unconformity.

Stage "C" may be said to represent full maturity and is usually marked by marriage. Once more a degree of variation exists in establishing this threshold, but again every society insists that adult behavior must be clearly different from adolescent conduct, and that everyone must "act his age!" In some ways the transition to "C" is less difficult than the move into "B," but it is not without its problems.

On the assumption that marriage takes place during stage "C," a striking change takes place in every newlywed's way of life. Before marriage an individual ordinarily lived in his family of orientation (see page 450). Here he found himself forced to establish reciprocal ties of behavior with each of his parents and, if he had a brother and sister, with each of his siblings. Within his family of orientation *Ego* was subordinate to his father and mother, but more or less on a par with his brother and sister. At marriage, and particularly after he has begotten children, all this changes. Now a person finds himself occupying a different status in a *family of procreation*. Not only must he develop and maintain new bonds with his spouse, but he also finds himself dominant over his children.[4] Complications are likely to arise because a person is not expected to cancel all of the old ties in his family of orientation when he assumes different responsibilities in his family of procreation.

What has been said so far about "C" applies universally to all human societies. But in the United States additional strains may arise from our lack of firm standards of values regarding the change-over from one family system to the other (Fig. 25–2). Suppose, in the case of a son, that his father were elderly and sick. As long as a male *Ego* continued to live in his family of orientation he would be expected,

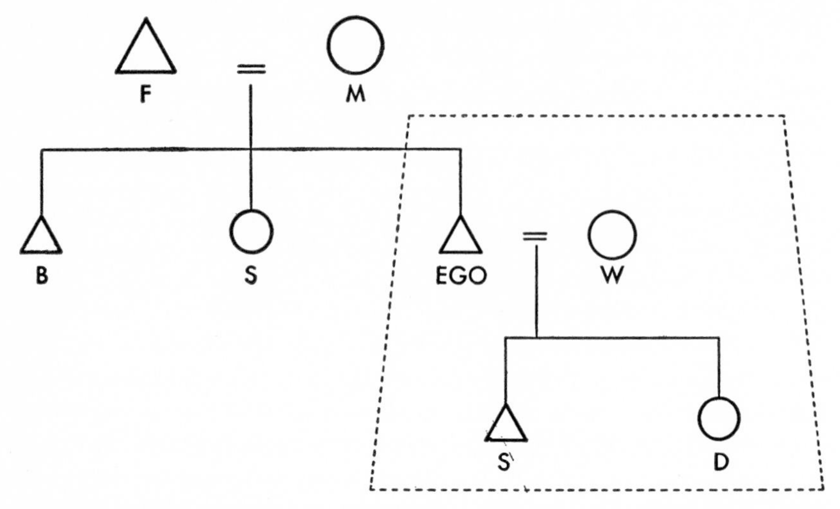

FIG. 25-2. *Ego* in his families of orientation and procreation. While *Ego* is unwed, he resides in his family of orientation (left), where he is equal to his siblings but subordinate to his parents. When, at marriage, he shifts to his family of procreation (right), he becomes dominant over his children.

from the time that he was old enough, to help his father. But if the father were still living when *Ego* married, what then? *Ego* is obligated to look after his wife and children, and he may not be in a position to help his father. Most Americans would agree that a man's first duty is toward his wife and children, but they would also insist that it is not right to neglect a sick and aged parent. Not all societies permit conflicts of this kind to arise. In old Japan, a man's obligations to his father were paramount and remained fixed. A filial son would neither feel upset nor would he arouse social criticism merely because he favored a parent

[4] W. L. Warner, *American Life: Dream and Reality,* Chicago, 1953, pp. 81–83.

over his wife and children. This is not to say that all Japanese cultural values were permanently fixed, but the values in this particular case were.

Last of the stages of the enculturational process is the one marked "D." It is entered in old age, as any society chooses to define senescence. Ordinarily, a person who crosses this point is assumed to have a fairly complete knowledge of his group's culture. Thus, as he approaches a greatly advanced age he is no longer expected to add still more cultural factors to his conduct. On the contrary, a very old person is permitted in all societies to revert somewhat to the biological behavior of a neonate. Our popular sayings about second childhood reflect an awareness of this reversion. If an extremely aged person soils himself or happens to expose his body, not much more is thought about it than if a small baby does the same things. Some of the behavior manifested in "D" may be rationalized or considered unavoidable because it is an outgrowth of physical change, but all cultures make allowances for such changes. Inevitably, death intervenes to halt the complete reversion from "D" to "A."

INTERIORIZING CULTURAL VALUES

As a baby grows up in any society it learns that much of what it was permitted to do as an infant is not allowed at a somewhat later date. Such teachings take the form of negative statements directed to a youngster by older people. "Don't do this," "Don't be naughty," "Don't do that," "You mustn't," is what a child hears repeatedly. Consciously or not, a baby finds itself recurrently in a hostility-fraught situation wherein it will arouse adult displeasure if it persists in following its own dictates; and adult displeasure, it soon learns from experience, leads to punishment in one form or another. Yet, an infant can never become emotionally content if it is constantly prevented from doing what it wishes. The commonest way out of this inescapable dilemma is for a child to bring itself to identify its own views with those of the more powerful grownups, until it gradually acquires the feeling of wanting to do what they think it ought to do. If, and when, such a point is reached the instances of open hostility diminish and the youngster may be said to have *interiorized* the cultural values of his society. Much of the earlier antagonism may persist in the subconscious levels of personality, but on the surface conformity without compulsion seems to prevail. Studies of personality formation, as well as analyses of the interplay between individuals and their cultures, must take into account the process of *value interiorization.* In reality, a child's formation of a *social conscience* may refer to the internalizing of its group's standards of values.

Interiorization is most successful and complete when a person comes to carry out the teachings of his culture without conscious thought. If the welfare of a society depends on promptness, for instance, it would never be enough for each individual to have to remind himself continuously that he must be on time. Only when everyone concerned has so completely interiorized the value of promptness that he no longer has to think about it can promptness be taken for granted by the society as a whole. This type of thoroughgoing interiorization provides the only guarantee that a pattern of culture will function properly.

Because the processes of enculturation and value interiorization go on simultaneously, or nearly so, they are sometimes regarded as one and the same. They are not, however, alike. During the earliest stages of enculturation, a baby has no option, at the outset, but to allow himself to become enwrapped, as it were, in its society's culture. On the other hand, interiorization is a completely active process, and a child has a small degree of choice with respect to the selection of the items it will interiorize as well as to the method, time, and order in which interiorizing will take place. A crude analogy may help to illustrate the essential difference between the two processes. A young child may be likened to a little customer with one cent in a candy store. The cent represents his limited facility for coping with a culture. When the storekeeper, who stands for parents or enculturators in a society, puts out a few bits of penny candy (cultural traits) it is *he* who makes the choice of what to offer. He may even go so far as to push one particular piece forward, which the little purchaser is very likely to choose. When the child makes the selection and actively absorbs the candy by sucking or chewing, it is as though he were interiorizing an item of culture.

To drop the analogy, we seem to have arrived at a pair of universal laws governing the interplay of an individual and his culture. Each society insists that its neonates adjust themselves to the pattern of culture that begins to enfold them as soon as they have been born; and value interiorization is one of the major mechanisms by which every baby makes the compulsory adjustment. Within the limits of even a single segment of a society and its particular subculture, the process of interiorization is complex and multidimensional. It appears to be compounded from at least three sets of variables, which probably differ for each infant. The first variable is biological, for it cannot be assumed that each neonate begins life with exactly the same genes and inborn equipment. This may help to account for the differing degrees of acceptance, or *thresholds of frustration,* that have been observed in babies. Experiments with very young children have proved that they react differently to stimuli that are precisely alike. The second variable is sociological, for every additional child that is born to a family occupies a different place in respect to its siblings and confronts its parents at a different stage of their age and experience. The third variable is cultural, inasmuch as patterns differ from one social unit to another and no design for group living remains static forever. Hence, something a child first learned to regard as wrong may later be considered acceptable. In 1900, for example, it was illegal and daring in New York City for women to smoke in public, but today such behavior is commonplace and perfectly legal.

This discussion may also serve to throw light on why a pattern of culture may, in theory, be treated as something that has an existence independent of the people who are its bearers. For one thing, patterns of culture are transmitted from one generation to another quite apart from the life and death of particular persons. They can also be more or less completely accepted and interiorized in different ways by different people. Moreover, the origins and changes of cultural patterns are not entirely controlled by the wishes or desires of the persons whose conduct they help to regulate. How subtly the forces of a culture can affect individual behavior is strikingly shown in the studies conducted by Gesell. The maturational sequences of an infant's physical development, which were carefully worked out in his clinic at Yale University[5] and which were assumed at first to be biologically universal for all of *Homo sapiens,* were later found to be partly cultural and to have their best application to children born into the subculture of middle-class parents in New Haven.

Early in the book the point was made that a human baby-to-be can exercise no choice over the genetic elements that it will receive from its parents at the moment of conception. This situation was contrasted with an infant's postnatal acquisition of culture with respect to which it could exercise a measure of selection. Theoretically, a growing child can decide to accept, modify, or reject any trait of culture whatsoever. Why, then, do people so seldom fail to accept and interiorize the values of their culture, even if many items are personally uncongenial or distasteful? The answer revolves around a few basic points. In the first place, enculturation begins at so early an age that a baby must be a passive recipient, without much capacity for active agreement or disagreement. In the second place, it is impossible during the early stages

[5] A. Gesell, *Embryology of Behavior,* New York, 1945.

of life to reject a culture without repudiating parents, kinfolk, and other enculturators—members of the society on whom one's welfare depends. In the third place, how is a baby to know what other ways of life there may be? Finally, it takes a long time and it is not easy for an individual to learn any pattern of culture thoroughly. We know full well that if we were asked to name an informant who could properly explain our culture to an outsider we would suggest neither a young child nor an adolescent, but a mature person 25 years of age or older. This is equivalent to saying implicitly that we think it takes at least a quarter of a century to learn thoroughly a single manner of living. Even though, admittedly, a second way of life might be learned more rapidly than a first, it would still be extremely time-consuming and difficult for an adult who had been brought up in one fashion to learn flawlessly the requirements of speaking a new language, to form new motor habits, to adopt new eating habits and preferences, and to accept a new set of outlooks on life, including new political allegiance and the practice of a new religion. The sheer hardship of learning another culture pattern thoroughly is enough to discourage all but a small number of people from voluntarily forsaking the way of life that they had learned as children. Immigrants, it is true, often make drastic changes of culture, but it generally takes an exceptionally strong expulsive force to get them to leave their home societies.

THE INTERACTION OF INDIVIDUAL TEMPERAMENTS AND PATTERNS OF CULTURE

In all investigations of enculturation and value interiorization there is one question that always stands forth prominently. What does each child bring into the world with which it must confront its society's culture? No matter what reply is made, one fact seems indisputable. Owing to the complexities of human reproduction, as has previously been noted, the likelihood is slim that any two offspring, excepting identical twins, will have inherited precisely the same genetic composition. To this extent it may be said that no two neonates face the world with exactly the same inborn equipment.[6] Even if they found themselves in absolutely identical societies and cultures, which is impossible in

[6] Much new light is being shed on this topic by the investigations of Roger J. Williams, who has published some of his findings in *Biochemical Individuality,* New York and London, 1956. Williams does not believe that any two people are exactly alike.

practice, they would still react in different ways. Yet, in spite of individual variability, each would resemble others of its kind in seeking air, food, warmth, dryness, and stability; each would respond to some stimuli by crying and to others by falling asleep; and each would digest food and excrete waste matter in fairly similar ways. In the most minimal and essential aspects of its bodily activities, therefore, every infant somehow reaches an equilibrium between its unique nature and the conformity of behavior that applies to its whole species. As it grows older another kind of balance has to be struck, this time between the child's inherited biological character and the culture pattern to which it must mold itself.[7] By the time it has reached maturity each youngster will have learned to conform reasonably well to the demands of its culture, but it should not be assumed that all children end up exactly alike. It is much more likely that each child will have retained a measure of individuality and that each will have paid a different price in terms of suppressions and repressions. Cultural conformity is a hard taskmaster, and it has also been known to exact high fees in the shape of warped personalities.

Individual personality is the product of an inherited biological character modified by the demands of culture. From this standpoint it becomes clear that variations in people may result either from the effects of a similar pattern of culture imposed on different organisms, or else from the impact of essentially dissimilar ways of life on reasonably similar biological entities. The possibilities inherent in these situations may be illustrated by combining some of William H. Sheldon's notions with some of the late Ruth Benedict's. According to Sheldon,[8] people of mesomorphic type, who are muscular and sturdily built, are somatotonic of temperament, and enjoy physical exercise, show a love of daring and boldness, seem indifferent to pain, and are assertive and aggressive, especially when under the influence of alcohol. These temperamental characteristics agree quite well with Benedict's portrayal of Dionysian patterns of culture, which honor aggression and reckless conduct in men.

Almost exactly opposite are the personality traits of those whom Sheldon calls ectomorphic. They are thin and fragile in anatomical structure and have cerebrotonic dispositions. Their actions are restrained, and they are inhibited in dealing with others. They are hypersensitive to pain, and they resist alcohol and other drugs. On the whole their

---

[7] A great deal of information on the biochemistry of child growth may be found in I. G. Macy and H. J. Kelly, *Chemical Anthropology*, Chicago, 1957.

[8] Sheldon is one of the pioneers in *constitutional anthropology*. He believes that a person's biological inheritance, as expressed by his body build, always conditions his reactions to culture.

temperaments are in accord with Benedict's account of Apollonian culture, which rewards self-restraint and sobriety.

If a male of mesomorphic build and somatotonic temperament should happen to be brought up in a Dionysian culture, it seems likely that he would conform easily, without conflict and with little cause for psychological maladjustment. Similarly, there seems to be little reason why an ectomorph who is cerebrotonic could not be expected to adjust smoothly to the requirements of an Apollonian way of life. But youngsters of all kinds are born into every sort of society, which suggests that somatotonics might find it hard to suit themselves to Apollonian patterns and that cerebrotonics would suffer where Dionysian standards prevailed.

The use of Sheldon's and Benedict's terminology does not mean that the author accepts their teachings without any reservation.[9] Some peoples and cultures can be found that conform reasonably well to their descriptions. At the same time, what Sheldon and Benedict have brought out applies best to extreme cases and has less application to the majority of individuals and patterns of culture, which tend to be mixed rather than purely of one type or the other. The extremes have been used here only to bring the main issues into sharp focus. Now we must ask: "What psychological price do individuals physically given to one kind of behavior actually pay when they force themselves to conform to a way of life that is uncongenial to their innate temperaments?" and "How many maladjusted and neurotic individuals in any society result from the unspoken insistence that everyone, regardless of his inborn disposition, must regulate his conduct in agreement with predetermined cultural norms?"

At this point the danger of biocultural unconformity (page 398) again looms large. Suppose an American father whose son was neither physically nor temperamentally suited for athletics insisted that the boy should become a football player. In such a dilemma, what is a poor child to do? If he disobeys his father, he runs the risk of losing his affection and support; but if he obeys, he is in danger of becoming internally upset. So it often is with the requirements of culture. From time to time every individual is placed in a situation where he offends his fellow men if he follows his own personal leanings, but where he must take a chance on personality maladjustment if he makes himself conform to the dictates of his society.

A program ought to be undertaken to discover exactly what hap-

[9] The Pueblo Indians are not at all ectomorphic in body build, yet their culture and behavior are largely Apollonian.

pens to a neonate's biological system as a child modifies it in keeping with the requirements of his culture. At the moment it is conventional to say that cultural restrictions induce feelings of frustration in babies, who cry when they are prevented from doing what they would like. Norman R. Maier, a psychologist, suggests a contrasting interpretation. He defines frustration as "behavior without a goal,"[10] and he asks whether infantile crying may not be a "problem-solving technique?" Perhaps Maier's theory is right. It is just as likely that infants cry

FIG. 25-3. Baby in a cradleboard. It is widely held that being tied in a cradleboard is a frustrating experience for an infant. However, cradleboards are very common in primitive societies, and their use seems to have no harmful effect on a child's later development.

deliberately for the express purpose of being taken out of an unpleasant situation (Fig. 25–3), as that they weep only to express resentment and helplessness. Answers to vital questions of this sort will never be found if students of personality and culture start with personality structures that are fully or reasonably well formed and then try to deduce the kind of childhood experience that a subject may have had. Such a deductive method puts students of personality on the level of medical researchers before the causes of most diseases were well known. In those days doctors could not recognize an ailment until it was well advanced, which made cures exceedingly difficult and preventive medicine impossible. Only when investigators begin to examine inductively the mechanisms by which newly born infants adjust their inherited natures to prescribed

[10] N. R. F. Maier, *Frustration: The Study of Behavior Without a Goal,* New York, 1949.

standards of culture will students of personality reach the scientific goal of knowing how personalities are formed. Then corrective measures could be applied where necessary.[11]

Personality formation and culture change

There is no reason to believe that very poor, neglected, or abnormal children, unwanted (rejected) offspring, or children from broken homes are the only ones to encounter difficulties in moving from one enculturational stage to another. Normal youngsters, too, find it no trifling matter to grow up properly in any society and culture. Enculturation is a difficult process, and it is high time that we stopped regarding as abnormal every person who stumbles and requires help somewhere along the line. Occasionally, in a perfectly sound home, a boy may come to resent his enculturating father in a way that has little to do with sexual jealousy. A son may regard a very successful parent as an unfair rival who started long ahead of him in the race of life and who has reached a position of prominence that the son feels he can never attain. In such cases a good boy from an unbroken home sometimes "goes to pieces."

Enculturation is harder than ever when socially sanctioned values are indistinct or subject to rapid change. Theoretically, every individual should be prepared to accept different standards of values whenever necessary. But it is not easy to make such shifts, especially if the new values run counter to the old and little time is provided for making the transition. A child who has thoroughly interiorized the belief that a particular way of life is right cannot quickly accept the opposite premise. Not enough attention has heretofore been given to the problems created by pressures to accept new, and sometimes contradictory, standards of values on short notice.

American marriage counselors are all familiar with the phenomenon of *marital frigidity* on the part of numerous wives. Many advisers have long realized that the problem is more often cultural than biological, yet they do not seem to have given enough weight to the difficulties

---

[11] Claims have recently been put forward for psychological tests that enable investigators of youngsters to detect future alcoholics. Proponents believe that if these tests are given early enough, proper diets can keep susceptible children from becoming chronic alcoholics later on. These claims have not yet been substantiated, but such tests are indicative of a trend toward discovering and correcting defects of personality before they are fully formed.

of making quick shifts of culture values. We are naïve if we think that every girl who has been taught to cherish her virginity and has resisted masculine advances for twenty years or so can without uneasiness give herself to her husband one night later, simply because she has been officially married to him earlier that day. No wonder a number of wives find it hard to make such a rapid changeover and no wonder that feelings of shame or guilt regarding sexual relations often arise even in the legally married.

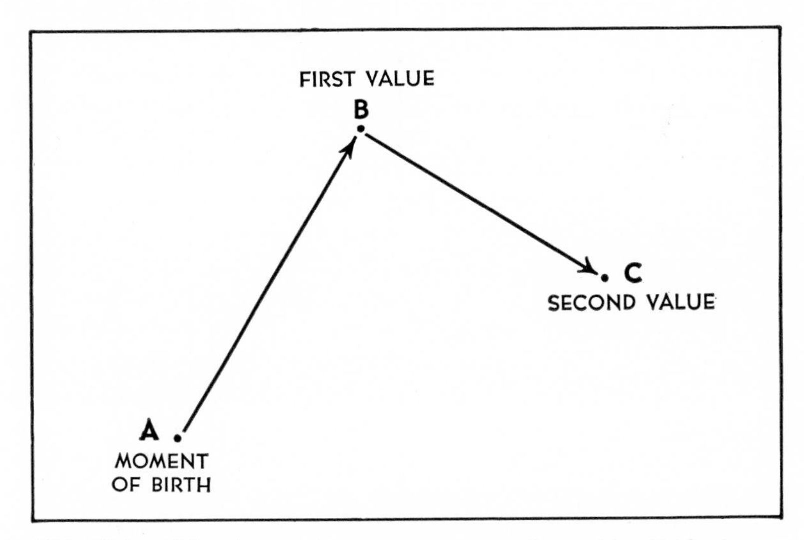

FIG. 25-4. Value changes. As a person grows up, he must inevitably change some of his values. Adjustments become harder in proportion to the length of time that a first value has been held, in regard to the thoroughness with which a first value has been interiorized, in relation to the degree of contradiction or opposition between "B" and "C," and in accord with the preparation and length of time allowed for a change.

Up to the present it has been customary for psychoanalysts and others who try to correct such difficulties as marital frigidity to seek the causes along the line *AB*, as shown in Figure 25–4. "Perhaps," it is said or implied, "the patient once experienced an emotional block in her premarital upbringing and has transferred her hostility from the man who caused the block to her husband." Theoretically, it is just as possible that the source of trouble lies along the line *BC* instead of *AB*, and is caused by sociocultural insistence on an overnight reversal of what had previously been considered wrong. The causes of personality maladjustments need not be sought exclusively in one direction or the other.

Modal personalities and national character

Despite the feeling that studies of "persons-in-a-culture" should be conducted on specific individuals, some scholars have tried, in a manner of speaking, to combine the results of the investigations of numerous individuals into a kind of average, usually known as a *modal*, or *basic*, *personality type*. In addition to the convenience of grouping a large number of discrete studies under a single head, efforts to establish modal personality types have some scientific justification. Supporters argue that it is to be expected that people who are brought up in the same patterns of culture and who are subjected to the same systems of values will show, at least on the surface, a number of common personality characteristics. These are what descriptions of modal personality types attempt to depict.

Following along similar lines, there has recently arisen an interest in what is often called *national character*. Such studies do not restrict themselves to culturally homogeneous tribal groups, but undertake to deal with large, literate, heavily industrialized and heterogeneous social units on the scale of the United States or the Soviet Union. They are based on the assumption that all citizens of a modern nation are exposed to so many uniform cultural institutions—such as public schools, widely distributed newspaper features, economic regulations, and dealings with federal government—that they develop similar characteristics of personality and behavior. Efforts are made to delineate national character in terms of regularities of behavior that can be predicted.

Proponents of national character studies, led in the United States by Margaret Mead, are confident that this is a legitimate branch of cultural anthropology. They recognize that big societies tend to divide into subgroups with distinctive subcultures, but they claim that it is possible to reconcile the customs of the smaller divisions with the established ways of life of the larger units. One American, they insist, especially in the case of conformists, is more like another American than he is like a Balinese, whether the American is a New England textile worker or a Texas rancher.

As for the use of cultural anthropologists in this type of research, it is felt that they have much that is valuable to contribute. They are supposed to be able to make disciplined studies of primitive societies, which may serve as models for analyzing large nations; their research tools and techniques should prove applicable to social units of any kind irrespective of location; they are accustomed to integrating the various aspects of culture into one whole structure; they have been schooled to discount their personal biases and prejudices; and they are so intimately acquainted with many diversified ways of life as to make possible valid intercultural comparisons.[12] At the same time it is realized that whereas one observer might be competent to make a singlehanded study of a small community, he might not be able singlehandedly to note and understand all the complexities of a large nation-state. For this reason teams of investigators are recommended, at least one of whom should be thoroughly acquainted with anthropological concepts and methods.

As in the case of all personality and culture studies, it is suggested that a thorough knowledge of culture patterns should be acquired before research on basic personality formation is begun. Child-training practices, especially, the effects of which are thought to be essential to the development of each individual's adult personality, are supposed to be carefully studied, not only for their own sakes and the understanding of personality formation that they may yield, but also because they may be expected to provide clues to a society's system of values. Plots of popular films and novels, autobiographical accounts, and large-scale projective tests may likewise throw much light on national outlooks, values, and emphases. Ultimately, it will probably be found that although all cultures and subcultures appear to be unique when studied one at a time, they are likely to reveal many similarities when examined on a comparative basis. Investigators of national character feel that if we acquire an understanding of the universal elements that exist in all patterns of culture, we shall have in our hands the potential for a better control of the biocultural behavior of all mankind.

Selected References

Benedict, Ruth F., "Psychological Types in the Cultures of the Southwest," *Proceedings, Twenty-third International Congress of Americanists,* 1928, pp. 572–81.

———, *Patterns of Culture,* Boston, 1934.

Gorer, Geoffrey, "Themes in Japanese Culture," *Transactions, New York Academy of Sciences,* Series 2, Vol. 5, 1943, pp. 106–24.

---

[12] For many years a number of scholars have been assembling data from all over the world for the *Human Relations Area File* at Yale University. These data are arranged by topics, tribes, and regions. They are so cross-indexed as to make possible a large number of cross-cultural comparisons.

Hallowell, A. Irving, "Culture, Personality, and Society," in A. L. Kroeber, ed., *Anthropology Today,* Chicago, 1953, pp. 597–620.

Herskovits, Melville J., *Man and His Works,* New York, 1948. (Look up references to enculturation in the index.)

Hilgard, E. R., *Theories of Learning,* rev. ed., New York, 1956.

Honigmann, John J., *Culture and Personality,* New York, 1954.

Hutt, Max L., *et al.,* "Social Values and Personality Development," *Journal of Social Issues,* Vol. 5, No. 4, 1949.

Kardiner, Abraham, *The Individual and His Society,* New York, 1939.

———, *Psychological Frontiers of Society,* New York, 1945.

Kluckhohn, Clyde, and Murray, H. A., eds., *Personality in Nature, Society and Culture,* New York, 1948.

Linton, Ralph, *The Cultural Background of Personality,* New York, 1945.

Mead, Margaret, "National Character," in A. L. Kroeber, ed., *Anthropology Today,* Chicago, 1953, pp. 642–67.

———, "The Implications of Culture Change for Personality Development," *American Journal of Orthopsychiatry,* Vol. 17, 1947, pp. 633–46.

Sapir, Edward, "The Contribution of Psychiatry to an Understanding of Behavior in Society," *American Journal of Sociology,* Vol. 42, 1937, pp. 862–70.

Wallace, Anthony F. C., *Personality and Culture,* New York, 1962.

Man and the Supernatural

CHAPTER 26

PRIMITIVE RELIGION AS A SOCIOCULTURAL FORCE[1]

The very existence of symbolic cultural values creates difficulties, unknown to subhumans, with which every humanly devised pattern of group living must successfully deal lest it be torn apart. These difficulties, which invariably arouse tension and anxiety, may be of various kinds, but some of the most important ones always concern shortages and their consequences.

With respect to man's interactions with his environment, it will always be the case that cultural values, expressed chiefly as preferences or taboos, must diminish the impartial use of all that nature provides. Similarly, in the matter of interpersonal relations, cultural values, often in the form of moral or ethical rules, serve to lessen at least the number of potential outlets for sexual relations. When the situation is thus viewed, *Homo sapiens* is seen to be faced with the threat of two kinds of shortages, those originating from environmental or natural deficiencies, and those arising from cultural restrictions. Primitive people know pitifully little about overcoming the one or changing the other.

[1] Religion is a broad subject to which many volumes have been devoted and on which numerous books are sure to be published in the future. Since the space for treating the topic in this text is limited, and since the author does not feel competent to discuss all aspects, it is only fair to the reader to explain the viewpoint that is to be followed. Every effort has been made to bring out the sociocultural implications of the subject and to analyze religion as a powerful force in society. Entirely omitted from consideration are such important features as individual motivations and the feelings of pleasure or comfort that worshipers may derive from religious practices.

No matter what their origin, shortages invariably cause unhappiness to some members of a society. Accordingly, in terms of biocultural dynamics, shortages may be said to give rise to disruptive forces that endanger the continued existence of every pattern of culture.[2] To prevent dissolution each configuration must, therefore, have adequate safety valves. In addition, as an extra guarantee, each society has one or more cohesive elements (sides) strong enough to outweigh the forces of disintegration. Perhaps that is why religion is a universal feature of all societies whose cultures have been studied. How it works is most clearly seen when dissatisfactions arise that are likely to be blamed on individuals, particularly chiefs. The dangers of rebellion against leaders, or of withdrawal from a society, are greatly diminished if dissatisfied persons are taught to believe that whatever evils befall are the will not of their rulers, but of supernatural powers. All social units are internally strengthened if their members are convinced that whatever happens is the will of God. In certain cases, threat of punishment by such secular agencies as a police force may be enough to make people adhere to their society's dictates. In other instances, patriotism or the overriding loyalty of each individual to his social unit is enough to supply the needed cohesion. But in most primitive communities the bond of patriotism is reinforced so closely by supernatural sanctions that in many instances patriotism and religion cannot be told apart, and both bonds are used to hold together the same group of people.[3]

Even in the United States, where the separation of "church" and "state" has long been a cardinal operating principle, we still hear phrases like "the flag is sacred"; and children pledge their allegiance to "one nation, under God." Yet, Americans are forbidden by their Constitution to have a national religion. They cannot, as a result, utilize the doubly cohesive bonds of patriotic and religious loyalty that are so common in primitive societies (see Fig. 26–1). Interestingly enough, the modern totalitarian nations featuring nazism, fascism, or communism, have tried to bind their citizens closely together by simulating the twice-bound sociocultural structures of primitive societies. This they have attempted to do by merging political loyalty with worship of the state and by seeking to deify the head of the state. The United States has tried to achieve much the same effect by doubling the ties of loyalty. That is why in times of crisis, when the threats of internal separatism

[2] Shortages are not necessarily the only things that give rise to religious beliefs and activities.

[3] The notion that a particular religion may be used to back up a particular social order is clearly expressed in C. C. Gillespie, *Genesis and Geology,* Cambridge, Mass., 1951, p. 31.

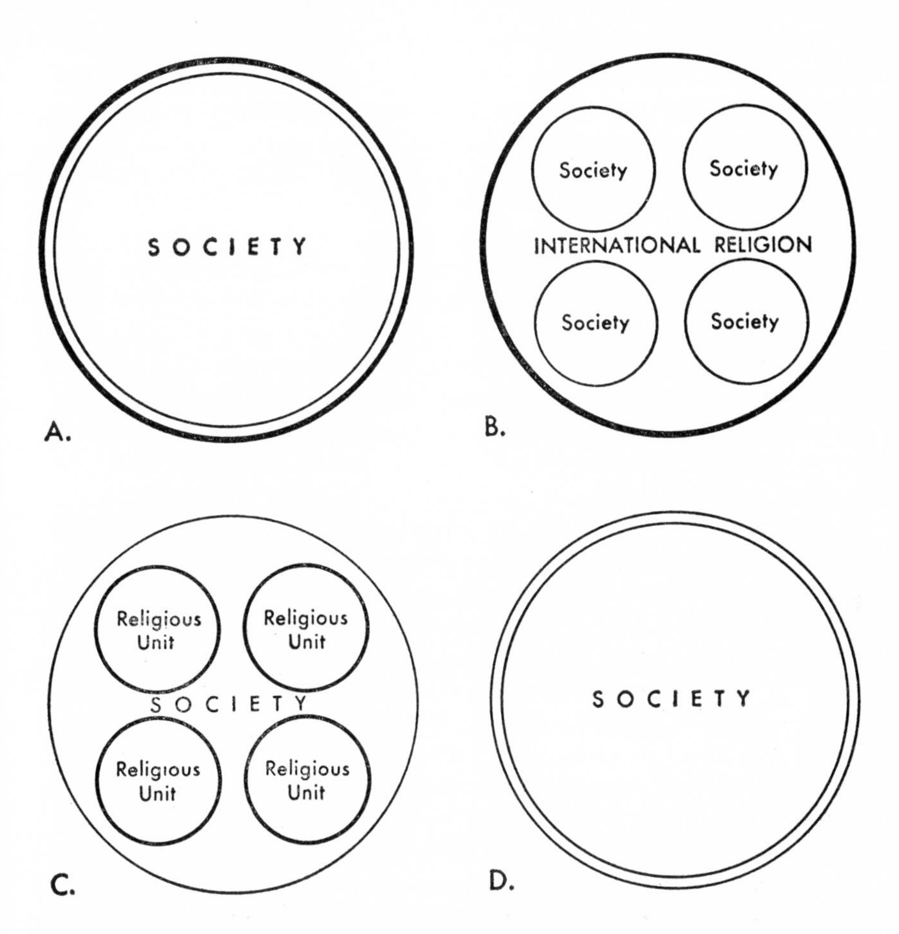

FIG. 26-1. Social (patriotic) and religious bonds. The light lines stand for the limits of social, national, or loyalty bonds; the dark ones for adherence to a common religion. A. The primitive condition. In homogeneous societies ties of religion tend to coincide with and reinforce the social bonds that hold members of a society together. The pattern so formed is structurally firmer than (B) or (C). B. Varying social units within a single, international religion. This represents the situation of those who adhere to a common faith but have differing political loyalties, as is true of French Catholics, American Catholics, Italian Catholics, Irish Catholics, and many others. C. Differing religions within a single social structure. A good example would include American Catholics, American Protestants, American Jews, and American Moslems. D. Double ties of loyalty. At present the Constitution prevents the United States from establishing a national religion. In times of crisis efforts are made to achieve the solidarity of (A) by doubling the patriotic bonds of loyalty that hold a national group together.

or social disintegration loom large, Americans double their efforts to secure effective patriotism by calling for more and more tokens of loyalty; increased expressions of sentiments of attachment to the social unit, in terms of enforced oaths and pledges of allegiance; more stringent investigations of the potentially disloyal; and heightened demands for the exclusion of foreigners.

Since no social unit can exist without people, the withdrawal of any individual is a threat to the society as a whole. On this basis death represents the greatest of all forces of disintegration. No society remains indifferent to the consequences of death, but inasmuch as there is no physical means of preventing death's inroads, recourse to something supernatural is the only possible way to cushion or neutralize its impact. This helps to explain why the notion of another world in the hereafter, where the souls of the dead live on after the fashion of life on earth, is so very common. It amounts to saying that a deceased person, even when his body is no longer present, is still a spiritual member of his former society. There are tribes that go even further, by developing beliefs that at some future time the dead will be reunited with the living. Such beliefs function to guarantee that a society, like a perpetual belt, will never come to an end. By the extension of the continuity of a social group into the indefinite future, death is "eliminated" as a threat to any society's perpetuation.

Social scientists of the future will have to deal with the problems involved in the growth of widespread international religions. It is obvious that they do not have the same functions as do religious beliefs in the world of primitive man. Apart from whatever other purposes they may serve, the supernatural practices of many tribes can be shown to be tailored to the needs of particular societies. Yet, except in a figurative sense, there is no single Christian, or Jewish, or Buddhist, or Moslem society. Members of each of these faiths reside in a large number of widely separated nations, with vastly different patterns of culture. Perhaps that is one reason why international religions put so much stress not on societal structures but on universal moral or ethical principles that are supposedly applicable to all of mankind, regardless of nationality or social groupings.

Religion may well be disruptive in a heterogeneous society that contains adherents to several rival faiths, but in primitive communities it acts as a strong, cohesive force. It intensifies the allegiance of individuals to their social unit, functions to overcome dissatisfactions arising in the realm of man's relations to his environment, relieves anxieties, smooths over many rough spots in man's dealings with his fellows, and helps to negate the unsettling effects of death. It is with the help of deeply ingrained religious beliefs that societies everywhere try to hold in line the hungry, poorly housed, badly clad, and sexually dissatisfied. No matter where ethnologists may look, they always find religious convictions employed in primitive societies to bolster weak points in patterns of culture.

A minimum definition

Religion is such a vast and emotionally laden subject that it may mean all sorts of different things to different people. Ethnologists have found it so difficult to establish a satisfactory all-embracing definition that they have gone to the other extreme. In keeping with a suggestion originally proposed by E. B. Tylor, they have tended to work with a *minimum definition* that provides the least common denominator of elements to be found in all manifestations of religion. By reducing Tylor's proposal to its barest essentials, we arrive at a minimum definition of religion as a "belief in the supernatural." Of itself the word "belief" implies an element of faith, a willingness to accept something without tangible demonstration or proof. To borrow an idea and a phrase from Wordsworth, religious, like "poetic faith," calls for "a willing suspension of disbelief." It should be realized that faith has strong emotional connotations, based on a sense of wonder or awe aroused by something mysterious. Earlier writers, not infrequently, referred to this aspect of emotionalism as a *religious thrill.*

When belief is applied to the supernatural, it signifies the willing acceptance of an order of things that cannot, so far as is known, be proved by logic nor grasped by man's senses or any extension thereof. When we describe something as supernatural, then, we mean that it lies beyond the reach of the sense organs and that it can never be made manifest to human taste, touch, smell, sight, or hearing, even with the aid of such devices as powerful telescopes or sound amplifiers. To believe wholeheartedly in the existence of something that cannot and may never be grasped by one's senses forms the very core of religion and furnishes the foundation on which all religious systems are reared. Beliefs of this kind comprise the quintessence of algebraic mentality, which can deal with abstract or symbolic concepts as readily as if they had objective reality. Emily Dickinson has accurately expressed this idea in her famous lines:

> "I never spoke with God,
>   Nor visited in Heaven;
> Yet certain am I of the spot
>   As if the chart were given."

In practice, no religion fails to go far beyond the two elements in the minimum definition, but every society builds its religious superstructure on the same least common denominators. Since supernatural constructs have no material existence and may differ widely from culture to culture, there is no way that an ethnologist in the field can recognize, before they are pointed out to him, the objects to which a tribe ascribes religious significance. It may take a long time before people confide their beliefs to an investigator, and meanwhile he must be very circumspect lest he unintentionally damage or pollute something that may turn out to be holy in the minds of the natives.

THE CONCEPT OF MANA[4]

As an ethnologist gains the confidence of tribespeople and begins to learn their innermost system of symbolic values, he comes to realize that they divide their world into *sacred* and *profane* categories. Certain objects, places, words, and people will be classed as sacred, whereas other externally identical items will be treated as secular or profane. The only difference will be one of native belief. An example from the Christian religion might deal with the distinction between a font of holy water and a similar basin of plain water. Through the use of none of his senses or scientific apparatus could an outsider, even if he were a specialist in qualitative chemistry, detect any difference in the two liquids, yet no true Christian would dream of using them indiscriminately.

The particular component of supernaturalism that distinguishes the sacred from the profane may be described as mana. Mana can best be understood as a powerful force, beyond the understanding, direct observation, or full control of ordinary folk, that has an unlimited capacity for getting things done. Within itself mana is amoral and neutral in the sense that it is neither automatically good nor bad, and that it is indifferent as to whether its accomplishments are considered beneficial or harmful to individuals or societies. In this respect it is exactly like electricity,

---

[4] The term *mana* was originally reported from the islands of the south Pacific that run from New Guinea to Fiji and was first employed, with very little variation from the way it is used here, in R. H. Codrington, *The Melanesians,* Oxford, 1891, Chap. 12. Cultural anthropologists have found that in other primitive societies there are usually words that correspond more or less exactly to mana. Among those which are most commonly cited are: *manitou,* as rendered by American Indian speakers of Algonkian languages; *wakan* or *wakonda,* as it occurs in Siouan tongues; *baraka,* which is sometimes equated with holiness, as it is used by several Moslem groups in north Africa; and *orenda,* as used by speakers of Iroquois in North America.

which cares not at all if it is used to kill a person or to run a refrigerator. Because of the belief that it can with equal facility do good or harm in the eyes of man, mana is always regarded as potentially dangerous. However, again like electricity, it is subject to a measure of control, and some people in every society learn to handle it safely, usually through training but sometimes by inspiration. All others must avoid unauthorized contacts with mana in any form.

A splendid example of how the power of mana may work is to be found in the Old Testament.[5] Uzzah, a cart driver, was transporting the sacred Ark of the Covenant from one place to another. The road was rough, and at one point Uzzah reached out to steady the Ark with his hand, whereupon he was stricken dead. No matter how good his intentions may have been, Uzzah was not authorized to touch so mana-charged an object, and his impulsive action cost him his life. Since the power of mana can destroy as well as aid mankind, efforts must be made to keep it under control. In order to safeguard the lay public, sacred things may be plainly marked with symbols that serve to identify them and to act as warnings, they may be kept hidden in secret places, or they may be subjected to *taboo,* which has the effect of keeping unqualified people at a safe distance. A taboo here serves as a restraining order, a prohibition generally backed up by the threat of supernatural punishment for any violation.

A society may ascribe supernatural value to anything that seems to have an inexplicable capacity for getting successful results. This capacity is attributed to the mysterious power of mana and may be variously assigned to a weapon with which a warrior has dispatched many enemies, to a stone that is believed to have brought rain, to an individual with a powerful personality, to one who has been outstandingly successful, to a person of high rank whose commands win obedience, to anything worn by a mighty personage, or to whatever has been in contact with something already thought to have been endowed with mana. For mana is transferable by contact or *contagion* and can be handed on by touch, association, or inheritance. The best-known illustration of the transfer of mana by contagion is the *laying on of hands.* In all such cases it is believed that the mana of a superior person flows on contact into an inferior individual (Fig. 26–2). In England in times past the ailment known as scrofula was called "the king's evil," and it was believed that a cure could be brought about if the ruler touched a sufferer. The concept of a national leader as a healer should be kept in mind when the reader comes to the section that follows. As a rule of

---

[5] II Samuel 6:3–8.

thumb, it may be said that everything that is endowed with mana is sacred, all else is profane.

Many years ago scholars believed that the power of mana was virtually identical with the life force—that is, with whatever it is that gives an organic thing its quality of being alive. Life force was said to animate an organism and to depart temporarily when a person dreamed or swooned, and to leave permanently whenever an organism died. Under the influence of E. B. Tylor, the animating life force was in most cases described in English as a *soul* or *spirit*, and it was said that this was what

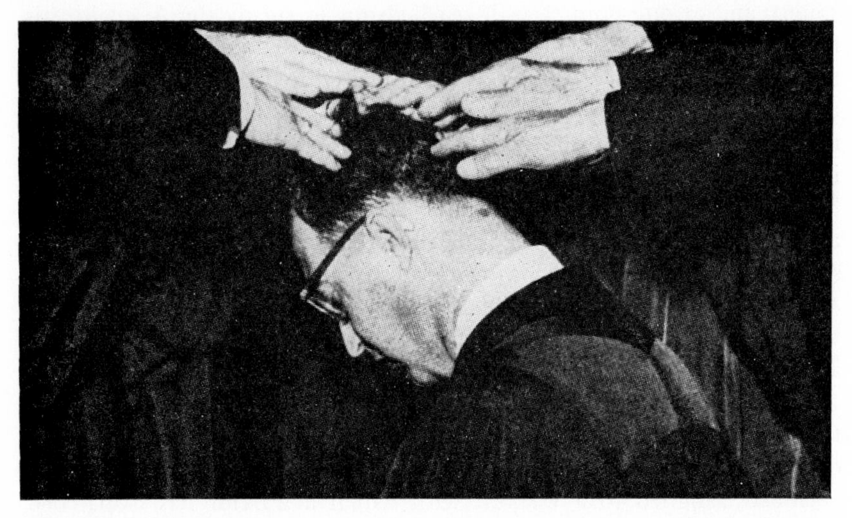

FIG. 26-2. The laying on of hands. Part of the consecration ceremonies for new ministers in many Christian sects includes the laying on of hands by officers who are already ordained. By this act mana is supposed to flow, by contagion, from his superiors into the novice.

lived on, after the death of a once-alive organism, in a shadowy kind of hereafter. Beliefs of this sort were grouped together under the heading of *animism*; and since living things were known to be either plants or animals, the term "animism" came to be subdivided into *botanical* and *zoological animism*.

Some time later, when field studies revealed countless examples of beliefs in supernatural power that was lodged in nonliving objects such as those made of stone or metal, a new word was coined. For this entire category of belief R. R. Marett used the term *animatism*. For a while, there were some anthropologists who thought that animatism always preceded animism, but modern students have found so many examples of the two sets of beliefs existing side by side that they no longer regard the one as being prior or ancestral to the other.

Priests, Shamans, chiefs, and gods[6]

If the power of mana is too dangerous to be left uncontrolled, ways must be found of directing it into beneficial channels. This can be done only if some persons become qualified to deal with the supernatural and succeed in setting up techniques for getting it to work favorably. Individuals who specialize in dealing with the world of the sacred are to be found in all societies and may be described, in general, as *priests* or *shamans.* It is not easy, especially when dealing with primitive religions, to make a precise distinction between a priest and a shaman. Priests generally go through a recognized period of formal training, and they usually serve entire communities. They are, in consequence, socially sanctioned. Some shamans may also serve apprenticeships, but they are more likely than priests to start functioning as the result of a sudden inspiration or in the wake of an unusual experience. Then, again, shamans are more likely to serve particular individuals than entire societies.

Except in a limited number of tribes, priests (and, sometimes, shamans) are distinguished from laymen not only by their ability to deal with mana properly, but also by the clothes they wear, the tasks they perform, the objects they handle, the taboos they observe, and the codes of conduct that they follow, with particular emphasis on food and sex habits. As their duties must bring them into close touch with things supernatural, they acquire an aura of sanctity and are themselves usually held to be charged with mana, as are their costumes and whatever things they may use in the performance of their sacerdotal duties.

Members of nonliterate societies do not, as a rule, differentiate one kind of extremely great power from another. Tribal leaders or chiefs, with the exception of those who exert little or no authority, are regularly thought to have as much mana as priests. Their persons, garments, and accessories, together with their habitations and all their furnishings and belongings, are equally likely to be thought sacred and to be subject to taboo. To a commoner it makes little difference if the power to regulate,

[6] Primitive societies often exhibit a great deal of overlap between priests, chiefs, and gods. It seems hardly necessary to point out that "priest" is being used to denote any personage who is qualified to deal with the supernatural, and not with reference to a particular kind of Christian clergyman.

disrupt, or terminate his life is derived from a supernatural or a political source. Anyone who wields great authority over others will be looked upon with much the same awe and respect as a supernatural personage. The tendency to equate sacred and political power is particularly strong in societies where a chief really has priestly functions. Instances of this kind are far from rare. At Old Oraibi the village chief is automatically leader of the town's most important religious observance, the Soyal. Numerous chiefs throughout the Pacific islands of Polynesia serve as priests, and similar examples can be cited from any large area of the globe. Speaking broadly, it is only in recent times and in those restricted

FIG. 26-3. Emperor, high priest, and living god. Japan is far from a primitive nation, and it has one of the world's highest rates of literacy. Yet, before World War II, the Japanese were taught to reverence their emperor as a high priest and a living god. (International News Photos.)

portions of the Euro-American world where a sharp distinction has been drawn between church and state that priests and chiefs have been entirely separated. Odd as it may seem to modern Americans, there are many people alive today who would find it difficult to understand how anyone could doubt the overlap of politics and religion.[7] In this connec-

[7] Even as late as the seventeenth century A.D., many *religious* sects in America functioned as *political* entities. For supporting facts see Chapter 4, "Diversity of Religions," in L. B. Wright, *The Cultural Life of the American Colonies,* New York, 1957, pp. 72–97.

Americans traveling in the Near East are often puzzled when officials ask them about their nationalities, meaning their religions. See E. Wilson, *The Scrolls from the Dead Sea,* New York, 1955, p. 12.

tion Horace M. Miner has written that the Koran, the sacred text of the Moslems, explicitly aims to achieve political unity through a common religion.[8]

Not only are chiefs frequently equated with priests, but they are sometimes, as has already been said, identified with *gods*. In minimum but basic terms, a god, in primitive society, may be defined as a local, supernatural personage, heavily endowed with mana. The tie between chiefs and gods seems to rest on the assumption that the soul of a person who once exerted great power while alive will still retain his mana after he dies and becomes a spirit in the other world. As it is to the advantage of the surviving members of the society to have their late chief's power exerted on their behalf, his soul is often called upon for help by his former subjects. The dead chief's successor is commonly thought to be the best suited for this important task. Wherever such customs are practiced, a succession is likely to be set up whereby a chief acts as a priest while alive and becomes converted to a god when he has died. These customs also help to explain why chiefs are so likely to be regarded as future gods that they may be reverenced as divine even while they are still alive (Fig. 26–3).

Getting in touch with the world of the supernatural

Primitive man seldom regards his beliefs in the supernatural as luxury items, but is more likely to give them a practical value as something that can help his society to maintain itself. Hence, the mysterious world of the supernatural is not permitted to lie outside the sphere of ordinary existence, but is brought into the framework of life on earth. This is accomplished by the belief that some people, usually those who have been designated as priests or shamans, know how to get in touch with the other world. Communication may be established in either direction. Messages are sometimes sent from a social unit to the realm of the supernatural, but at other times the other world sends directives to the members of a living society. In either case it usually happens that priests, or other individuals endowed with mana, act as intermediaries or interpreters between ordinary people and supernatural agencies.

Plain speech, often set in prescribed form to make a *prayer,* is the simplest and commonest way to send a message to the other world.

[8] H. M. Miner, *The Primitive City of Timbuctoo,* Princeton, N.J., 1953, p. 72.

Prayers are generally addressed to a particular object or place where supernatural beings are thought to reside; they may be accompanied by required gestures or stances; and they may be uttered together with some device, such as striking a gong or bell, to attract the attention of the power for whom the message is intended. Songs may be substituted for spoken prayers, and they may be integrated with dances. Processions and religious dramas, too, are sometimes little more than complex ways of sending messages to the other world.

Most prayers contain requests for guidance or help. There is implied a belief that supernatural agencies can, if they will, help living men and women to achieve what they most desire. So strong are such beliefs that it is frequently felt that people can get what they want if they act in conformity with the wishes of the supernatural. It thus becomes of the utmost necessity to interpret correctly whatever messages the other world may care to send to this one. Only by acting in accordance with expressed supernatural wishes can living people feel assured of getting supernatural backing for their enterprises.

Once again do we see the importance of mana. It is mana that serves as the means of communication between the two worlds. Things that have mana are the most likely to convey messages from the supernatural, and people who have mana are best suited to act as interpreters.

All primitive efforts to determine the will of the supernatural are generally grouped together as *mantic "sciences,"*[9] that is, as "sciences" of prophecy, or efforts to find out in advance what kinds of behavior the gods expect of man and are willing to support. Such efforts may be grouped into two categories. In one case, which may be called *spontaneous,* the other world takes the initiative, and man needs only to know how to interpret aright whatever signs are sent; but at other times what may be called *directed messages* are sought, as when human beings deliberately set up test conditions and request the other world to make known its wishes in some way. Spontaneous messages may take such forms as sudden claps of thunder, volcanic eruptions, unexpected dreams, uncontrolled body twitches, hiccoughs or sneezes, strange behavior on the part of an animal, or the pattern of leaves left in the bottom of a cup of tea. Directed messages may be received when people deliberately seek visions, or when the organs or death throes of purposely slain animals are carefully observed, or if bones, twigs, or stones are tossed with the intent that the patterns into which the supernatural causes them to fall may determine what should be done (see Fig. 26–4).

[9] Closely related to the mantic "sciences" is *divination.* A *diviner* may try to discover the supernatural will, or else he may merely seek information, such as the whereabouts of a lost object, from the supernatural world.

Many children's games in our culture, such as *counting-out rhymes* or "*London Bridge*," are thought to be relics of former primitive efforts to get directed messages from the supernatural world. Possibly, the tossing of coins or the cutting of cards, to which many people resort when faced with the need for making difficult decisions, are likewise "superstitions" or carry-overs of the primitive notion of getting a directed message from the supernatural world. In all such cases the underlying idea seems to be that man himself is not responsible for making a

FIG. 26-4. An African diviner. The individual shown is a member of the Bavenda tribe in Africa. He is believed to have the power of determining supernatural wishes by studying the patterns into which his divining bones fall when they are tossed. (Courtesy of the Museum of Anthropology, University of Michigan).

decision, but that he is acting in accordance with the expressed will of supernatural powers. We shall encounter other possible elements of primitive religion when we discuss games and the fine arts.

Shamans and curing rituals; witches and witchcraft

No society can possibly endure on earth if all its constituent members are suddenly removed by death or any other cause. True, deeply held beliefs in the continued existence of souls in another world may soften the impact of death, but never are convictions of this sort sufficient to make people completely indifferent to the effects of death. All societies, without exception, make an effort to keep death away from individuals as long as possible. In the primitive world these efforts are customarily made by *medicine men* or, as they are often but somewhat inaccurately called, shamans.

With the growth of scientific medicine in our country, we are taught to ascribe all diseases to known or knowable causes. Primitive men and women, knowing little or nothing of science, are very likely to attribute sickness to supernatural agencies. So it is that their shamans are closely equated with priests and are supposed to know how to deal with mana-caused ailments.[10] Seldom, indeed, is any illness that befalls primitive man regarded as "natural." Most often, with the exceptions of ailments resulting from battle injuries or old age, the things that bring about death are thought to be of supernatural origin. Once in a while an act of indiscretion, such as the violation of a taboo, is regarded as the source of a sickness, but much more commonly a person is supposed to become ill because of *witchcraft.* Even accidental injuries are attributed in some societies to witchcraft. Either the accident was caused by a *witch,* or else the victim is himself a witch who suffered an accident as punishment for having previously engaged in antisocial activities.

A witch may be defined as an individual of any age and of either sex who uses the power of mana for antisocial purposes or for opposing a society's values. Hence he causes sickness and death, makes crops fail, diminishes a game supply, or brings on foul weather. To appreciate why witchcraft is sometimes successful we must recall that in and of itself mana is neutral. The same power, as in an automobile engine, can be utilized for going forward or backward.[11] In medieval Europe where Christianity was the dominant religion, it was widely believed that recital of the Lord's Prayer was beneficial, but that evil would result when the Lord's Prayer was recited backward. This illustrates the concept that mana can be manipulated either to strengthen a society or to weaken it. Whatever a witch does to harm a social unit, therefore, must be neutralized or overcome by one who uses mana for prosocial purposes.[12] This is frequently the role of the shaman or priest.

When it comes to causing sickness and death, witches are in many

---

[10] The tie-in between priests and curers is still evident even in Christianity. A passage in the New Testament, James 5:14, makes the connection perfectly clear. "Is any sick among you? Let him call for the elders of the church; and let them pray over him, anointing him with oil in the name of the Lord." The Bible is full of references to healing and healers.

[11] Some religious people in our culture are inclined to believe that not all supernatural power is of the same sort. They prefer to think that forces of good emanate from such a source as the Christian God, whereas forces of evil come from the devil.

[12] Former writers on primitive religion were frequently in the habit of calling good or prosocial supernaturalistic activities *white magic,* whereas antisocial or bad activities were called *black magic.*

cases thought to have the power to send foreign, disease-causing substances into the body of a prospective victim. Where beliefs of this kind prevail, a shaman is often summoned to remove the offending objects from a patient. There then follows a contest between the witch and the medicine man, and if the latter can mobilize more mana the patient recovers. Failures are blamed on the fact that the force of evil was too strong to have been overcome by the power of good.

It is always dangerous in ethnology to derive a broad principle from an instance noted in a single tribe, but some light may be shed on the topic under discussion by an episode that the writer witnessed among the Hopi Indians. On one occasion a man who was suffering stomach-aches summoned a shaman. In the author's presence the medicine man "extracted" from the patient's stomach a number of "poison arrows," after which the pains subsided. Some time later, attention was diplomatically called to the facts that the "poison arrows" had emerged dry and bloodless and that at no time had the skin of the stomach been broken. Far from arousing disbelief, these facts had the opposite effect. "Aren't those medicine men wonderful?" asked the ex-patient. "Who else could take things out of a person's stomach without getting them wet and bloody and without breaking the skin?"

Questions are often asked about the sincerity of shamans who know it is sleight of hand that makes it look as though they were extracting substances from a victim's body. Quite often, when they are asked about such matters point-blank, medicine men reply in effect: "I don't know how it works, but you noticed that after I treated the sick person he got better." Since many of their patients do get better, it is not at all certain that every shaman is insincere.

Another favorite act of witchcraft, usually done at one person's request, is based on the principle that ethnologists call *mimetic magic.* Mimetic magic causes like to produce like, and refers to any activity that provokes similar behavior from the supernatural world. Very commonly a witch will shape an image, crudely or carefully made in the likeness of an intended victim. Then, if the effigy is made to disintegrate the victim is expected likewise to waste away; and if the image is stuck with pins, the victim is supposed to suffer sharp pains from a disease, like rheumatism. Figures used in this way are supposed to be most effective if their manufacture also incorporates the principle of contagion, that is, they are supposed to work best when their maker includes some part of a victim's body, such as his nail parings or hair clippings.

Beliefs of this kind help us to understand why so many primitive people conceal or destroy discarded body parts, including bodily wastes and excretions. Even urine or feces may be carefully hidden to keep them safe out of the hands of witches. This suggests the possibility of a link between religion and medicine, for toilets may result from beliefs in the supernatural as well as from regard for sanitation and hygiene.

Concerning the prevalence of witchcraft beliefs, there are at least two ways in which they may aid the cohesion of a society. Sometimes, when a group's culture forbids any show of aggression, hatred of witches provides a socially sanctioned outlet for aggressive tendencies. At other times, when disaster strikes, people do not blame their chiefs, their gods, or one another, but place the entire fault on witches. Thanks to such beliefs, even witchcraft notions may help to hold a society firmly together. Nor are suspected witches invariably punished. There is often a widespread fear that witches will make things far worse if their victims show overt hostility toward them.

SCIENCE AND THE LAW OF CONTROLLED CAUSATION

Cultural progress is inevitably associated with an increase in a group's fund of knowledge. Primitive or nonliterate folk, by and large, have far less knowledge at their collective disposal than do the members of literate societies. This amounts to saying that primitive people are more ignorant than others. One must hasten to add, though, that ignorance is not to be confused with stupidity. Some men and women who are basically smart and quick to learn and apply new bits of information may be ignorant of many reputed facts, and others who are dull and slow to learn may have a great deal of factual knowledge.

Much of what literate folk know is organized under the heading of science. As it is to be interpreted in the present context, the essence of science is an understanding of tangible causes and their effects. A sophisticated society that has a great deal of knowledge in this respect has a choice of two ways of explaining phenomena, whereas a primitive group has only one. As an example, suppose a plot of ground that has yielded good crops year in and year out suddenly fails to grow anything even though external conditions appear to be unchanged. Primitive farmers, if it is correct to assume that they lack all scientific knowledge of plant and soil diseases (yet wish to continue using the same spot), would have no choice but to regard the event as supernaturally caused and to resort for help to religious practices. A modern farmer, under the same circumstances, would have two courses of action. He might call on an agricultural specialist, or he might resort to religion. The difference is usually a matter of degree or proportion. Neither farmer is pledged to use one technique to the complete exclusion of the other. No primitive agriculturalist would expect to grow things, even if he relied heavily on supernatural assistance, without planting seeds at the right time, clearing the ground of weeds, and so forth. Nor would it be surprising for a modern farmer to resort to prayer or some other supernatural activity in addition to calling for the help of an agronomist.

Within the limits of their knowledge and resources, people always try to gain their ends by using all the tangible means at their disposal, but if these prove to be inadequate, calls may be made for supernatural help. Rarely is one method used without a speck of the other. The more uncertain may be the satisfactory outcome of a difficult or dangerous situation, the more is it likely that a high proportion of religious elements will be combined with other efforts to get a happy solution.[13]

Simple knowledge of cause-and-effect relationships may not in itself lead to greater reliance on science than on supernaturalism. What is much more likely to prove effective is based on *the law of controlled causation.* Whenever men are able to demonstrate that they can produce stated effects by manipulating their causes, the phenomena with which they deal move from the realm of religion to the realm of science. Thus, as more facts become scientifically known, the law of controlled causation covers ever more cases, and man's *reliance* on the supernatural shrinks. This is merely another way of saying that as the amount of knowledge in a society goes up, there is a proportionate decrease of its *dependence* on supernaturalism (Fig. 26–5). To test the validity of this hypothesis one has only to note that genuine *reliance* on the supernatural remains strongest in sophisticated societies in precisely those areas, such as the fate of the soul, where the law of controlled causation cannot be said to operate.

Nor should an increase of church attendance be automatically equated with an increase of *reliance* on the supernatural. People may attend religious services for a variety of reasons. Within the last few years the United States has seen a great upswing of church memberships, but many professional religionists openly admit that they do not know the meaning of this trend. Of one thing, though, we may be certain.

---

[13] For an expansion of this idea see B. Malinowski's article, "Culture," in *Encyclopaedia of the Social Sciences,* Vol. 4, 1931, pp. 621–46. While reading this essay, one should temporarily disregard Malinowski's efforts to distinguish between magic and religion.

Malinowski has presented his views in full in "Magic, Science, and Religion," in J. Needham, ed., *Science, Religion, and Reality,* New York, 1925.

The great increase of worship in churches does not mean that Americans are going to abandon their faith in science for increased *reliance* on the supernatural to solve their problems.

Religion does not remain static, but rather stands in a dynamic relationship to the amount of a society's knowledge. Hence, the explanation of a phenomenon might belong in the field of religion at one stage of a society's history, but might be classified under science at a later date. Many a tribe that used to dance for rain when water was

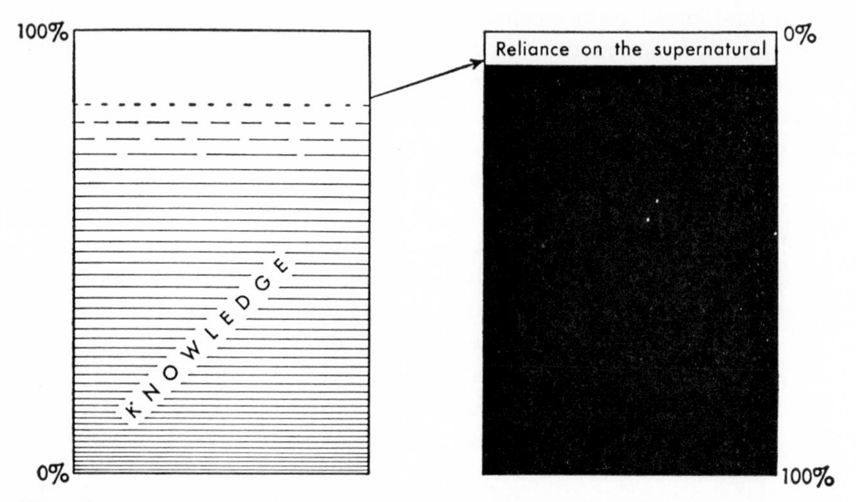

FIG. 26-5. Knowledge, and reliance on the supernatural. As the percentage of a society's knowledge increases, a greater degree of controlled causation becomes possible and the group's reliance on the supernatural for the solution of problems decreases.

scarce and depended only on uncontrollable forces of nature gave up dancing for rain when ample water could be obtained by turning a faucet.

There are more than a few instances in which scientists and religionists, operating from different premises, have reached surprisingly similar conclusions. A number of drugs, used by primitive medicine men because they were supposed to contain powerful spirits, have been used for nearly identical purposes by modern doctors because of their chemical properties.[14] Long before the germ theory of disease came to

[14] A belief prevails in some primitive societies that plants or other things in nature occasionally reveal their usefulness to man by something in their shape or color. Thus bloodroot, whose sap is red, is supposedly a good remedy for blood diseases. Beliefs of this type have been categorized as *the doctrine of signatures.*

be widely accepted, shamans believed that sickness could be spread by contagion from one center of evil mana to others.

For all their near approach to one another in certain contexts, scientists and religionists differ fundamentally on one important score at least. Each starts out on a basis of faith, at least in so far as willingness to believe in some thing without immediate tangible proof is concerned. But that is as far as the resemblance goes. A religionist may have unwavering faith in the supernatural and may not feel impelled to provide sensory proof or to change his position under any circumstances whatsoever. A scientist, on the contrary, feels that he must go on testing all hypotheses and must always take another position if his hypotheses are wrong. He has faith that pursuit of his methods will lead to an ever greater accumulation of knowledge, that all phenomena presently unknown to humans will some day be brought into the sphere of the known, and that when this happens more and more things will be made subject to the law of controlled causation.

Yet, one should not jump to the conclusion that science and religion must forever be in conflict. As was pointed out on page 370, biocultural trends cannot be assumed to move unfailingly in one direction. Moreover, human beings have an amazing ability to adjust to a diversity of ideas. Many an American citizen keeps varying and conflicting concepts so thoroughly compartmentalized that he can at the same time be a devout worshiper and a fine scientist.

Selected References

Codrington, Robert H., *The Melanesians: Studies in their Anthropology and Folklore,* Oxford, 1891.

Durkheim, Emile, *The Elementary Forms of the Religious Life,* rev. ed., Glencoe, Ill., 1947.

Frazer, James G., *The Golden Bough,* one-volume edition, New York, 1941.

Howells, William W., *The Heathens,* New York, 1948.

Lessa, William A., and Vogt, Evon Z., *Reader in Comparative Religion: An Anthropological Approach,* Evanston, Ill., 1958.

Lowie, Robert H., *Primitive Religion,* New York, 1924.

Malinowski, Bronislaw, *Magic, Science, and Religion,* rev. ed., Glencoe, Ill., 1948.

Mandelbaum, David G., "Form, Variation, and Meaning of a Ceremony," in R. F. Spencer, ed., *Method and Perspective in Anthropology,* Minneapolis, 1954, pp. 60–102.

Marett, Robert R., *The Threshold of Religion,* rev. ed., New York, 1914.
Norbeck, Edward, *Religion in Primitive Society,* New York, 1961.
Radin, Paul, *Primitive Man as a Philosopher,* New York, 1927.
Titiev, Mischa, "A Fresh Approach to the Problem of Magic and Religion," *Southwestern Journal of Anthropology,* Vol. 16, 1960, pp. 292–98.
———, "Notes on Hopi Witchcraft," *Papers of the Michigan Academy of Science, Arts, and Letters,* Vol. 28, 1943, pp. 549–57.
———, "Shamans, Witches, and Chiefs among the Hopi," *Tomorrow,* Vol. 4, No. 3, 1956, pp. 51–56.

Religion and Magic

CHAPTER 27

THE SEARCH FOR A DISTINCTION

Many years ago ethnologists became convinced that not all practices involving a belief in the supernatural were identical in character. To express the difference, some activities were called *religious* and others were termed *magical.* Soon, however, it became clear that no hard and fast distinction could be drawn between *religion* and *magic,* and at present a number of students of culture have become so convinced that no dividing line can be established that they have given up the quest for one altogether.

One of the first bases of difference to have attracted notice was the greater degree of compulsion that seemed to be involved in certain rituals. Religion, some scholars argued, leaves the ultimate decision for any action in the hands of a divinity, who may act or not as he sees fit. Truly religious behavior, in keeping with such arguments, never goes beyond supplication or the expression of a hope which a deity may or may not fulfill. Magic, so these same scholars used to say, compels supernatural agents to do man's bidding, provided only that magical formulas and practices are properly executed. Today it is realized that many *religionists* are as confident of getting results as are *magicians.* Still, it would be hard to deny that many magicians give the impression of being able to command supernatural forces, whereas most religionists express dependence on or submission to supernatural powers.

Ever since publication of *The Golden Bough* by Sir James G.

Frazer, there has been a tendency to equate science with magic, on the ground that both rest on the firm conviction of order and regularity in nature. However, the magician may try to impose his own will on nature's regularity, whereas a scientist feels that he can get results only when he knows and does not oppose the orderly forces of nature.

Efforts were also made in times past to separate religion from magic on the grounds that magic had no "church." The implication was that individual or private appeals to the supernatural were magical, whereas only group or social communications with the supernatural were truly religious. Before long it was pointed out that it was silly to call private prayer in one's own study or closet "magic," and similar prayer, publicly expressed, "religion." Examples of this kind tended to diminish the distinction between magic and religion.

Yet, as one studies the range of supernatural beliefs and practices that exist throughout the world the need for a distinction of some sort remains evident. As a fresh start, it may be fruitful to divide all religious phenomena into two different categories—those that are *calendrical* and can be scheduled ahead, and those of an emergency nature that cannot be anticipated and must, accordingly, be *unscheduled* and *critical.* By "calendrical" are meant all practices based on a belief in the supernatural that are regularly performed at stated intervals, regardless of whether any need for supernatural help is felt at the moment of performance. Calendrical rituals, which are scheduled recurrently long in advance, give the members of a society time to develop a communal sense of anticipation. They thus help to intensify group feelings of belonging together and come to be regarded as holidays. They are likely to be entrusted to socially sanctioned priests and to be looked upon as providing some generalized benefit for everybody in a society. To an extent, therefore, calendrical performances always have a "church" and so come closer to long-established concepts of religion than they do to those of magic.

Unscheduled, critical rites differ because they involve appeals for supernatural assistance to overcome a present difficulty or an immediate emergency. They cannot, because of their very nature, be regularly held at stated intervals that may lie far in the future. Moreover, since it is unlikely, although not altogether impossible, that all the members of a society will be confronted with emergencies at one and the same moment of time, critical rites are very likely to be performed by or for individuals, and are, accordingly, less certain to have a "church." To a limited extent, therefore, they conform to earlier definitions of magic. On some occasions, though, as in the event of a widespread drought, critical rites may be performed for the benefit of an entire group.

Lest this discussion should seem far-fetched to certain readers, illustrations will be given from Christianity. Christmas is a prime example of a calendrical rite. In the Euro-American world it always falls on December 25, and it is scheduled to be held whether or not any individual Christian feels the need that particular day for divine assistance. Personal prayer for the recovery of a sick child, however, seems to belong in another category and may well be called an unscheduled or critical rite. And when all Christians are asked to pray for peace if war threatens, we have an example of a noncalendrical but critical ritual performed by an entire society of believers.

Ceremonial calendars

Never should it be thought that calendrical rituals, because they are held without reference to the needs of the moment, are only of minor or secondary importance. Far from it. Customarily they are looked upon as rituals of intensification that strengthen the bonds of cohesion that unite all a society's members; that help all the people of a group to get along with each other; or that aid an entire society to adjust to its surroundings. Ceremonies for increasing the food supply, augmenting raw materials, controlling the weather, and warding off natural catastrophes are universal and commonplace. It is in this sense that supernatural activities are most clearly seen as nonempirical means of attaining empirical ends.

No society waits until a serious crisis has actually arisen before it performs whatever rituals it considers beneficial to the whole social unit. In such cases the religious activities are always regulated by a *ceremonial calendar*. Even nonliterate people may have ways of keeping track of the year's progress. Simplest of all are means of observing shadows, or of watching each day's sunrise from one spot, following the sun's apparent north-south movements, and noting the solstices or turning points that occur annually around June 21 and December 21 in northern latitudes.[1] For about six months of each year, north of the equator, the sun seems to rise a bit farther south every morning, and for the remaining six months each sunrise appears to move to the north.

[1] In the Southern Hemisphere, as well as in other parts of the world, different calendrical points may be important. Onsets of rainy or dry seasons, equinoxes, seasonal floods, or other phenomena may be more crucial than the solstices. As it happens, cultural anthropologists know more about religions of the Northern Hemisphere, and few doubt that Judaism and Christianity arose among farming and herding folk who lived north of the equator.

Where the eastern horizon is irregular, it appears to sunrise observers watching from a fixed spot that the sun rises now from a bit of forest, now from a mountain peak, and so on (Fig. 27–1). In this way the coincidence of a sunrise with a particular landmark is used as a seasonal checkpoint and may serve to indicate the time when a given calendrical rite is supposed to be held.

Religious calendars are never limited solely to the recognition and celebration of the solstices. Observances that are celebrated at fixed times each year may be performed at any season, particularly when economic duties are slack, but only in well-integrated, actively functioning societies are annual ceremonies systematically held. Time and

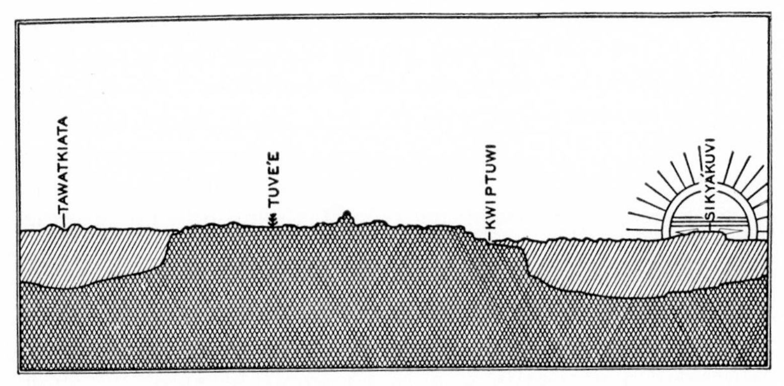

FIG. 27-1. Sunrise calendar at Oraibi. Sun watchers at Oraibi used to watch, from a given place, where the sun rose each day. In this way they kept track of the sun's seeming movements from north to south and south to north. Calendrical rituals were announced whenever the sun reached a designated spot on the eastern skyline.

again have ethnologists found it to be true that when a tribe is neglecting its ceremonial calendar it is also giving up its old way of life. Whether or not people are aware of it, it is apparently their system of supernatural beliefs that gives their society much of its continuity, cohesion, and stability. When a society is disintegrating, or undergoing rapid change, its members sometimes eagerly subscribe to a *nativistic* or *Messianic Cult* and look forward to the coming of a Messiah who holds forth the promise of better days to come, or of a return to some golden age of the past.[2]

[2] This point is amplified in R. Linton, "Nativistic Movements," *American Anthropologist,* Vol. 45, 1943, pp. 230–40. A more recent treatment may be found in A. F. C. Wallace, "Revitalization Movements," *American Anthropologist,* Vol. 58, 1956, pp. 264–81.

THE OLD AND THE NEW

Primitive farmers, realizing that the movements of the sun lie beyond their sphere of controlled causation, are greatly concerned lest a winter season should be so indefinitely extended that they would be unable to grow crops. Those who live north of the equator are most worried at the time of the winter solstice, when the rising sun reaches the southernmost point of its annual journey. Suppose the sun failed to reverse its course and start northward? That indeed would be a calamity. It would lead to perpetual winter with the sun so feeble that days would be short, dark, and cold. There would be no spring and summer, vegetation would fail to revive, and plant foods could not be grown. This would imperil alike the lives of grazing animals and of human beings.

Even today no scientific method of controlling the sun is known, so it is not surprising that primitive man had to resort to the supernatural. Noting that after the winter solstice the days got gradually longer and warmer as the power of the sun increased, he devised rituals to express his desires. Sometimes he twirled a disk-shaped object at midnight of December 21 to convey the idea that the sun ought to round the southernmost point of its yearly path and start northward, and sometimes he kindled fresh fires to indicate that the sun was to increase its light and heat. Each of these activities is based on the notion of mimetic magic.

Best known of all calendrical observances involving the concept of mimetic magic are *New Fire Rites.* They generally occur at the time of the winter solstice, and, as the name implies, their central act consists of the kindling of a fresh blaze in the hope of persuading the sun to grow brighter and warmer. Rituals of this kind benefit an entire society, and provide an answer to Shelley's poetic question, "O, Wind, if Winter comes, can Spring be far behind?" It is significant that both the Jewish festival of Hanukkah and the Christian celebration of Christmas, each of which falls in late December, involve symbolism suggestive of increased light and heat. At the same time, the implication that "dead" vegetation will soon "return to life" emphasizes the motive of death and rebirth.

When solstice rituals call for the lighting of new fires, old fires may be extinguished and fire hearths cleaned out before a fresh blaze is kindled. Sometimes a priest performs the office on behalf of an entire community, whereupon brands from the communal fire are carried home to ignite fires in individual houses.

Throughout the activities of the New Fire Rites there runs the idea that something old has ended and something new has begun. It is no accident that our New Year begins shortly after the winter season has reached its turning point. Various means may be used to express the same idea. They may range all the way from the making of new resolutions and the cancellation of old debts to thoroughgoing housecleaning, and even enactments of death followed by birth. The one concept that seems to be common to all these activities is the notion of starting afresh, of "turning over a new leaf."

Nearly as common as winter solstice ceremonies are *first-fruit rites*, which occur when a new crop is ripening or ready for harvesting. The central theme is always the same—man must express his obligation to the supernatural powers that have sent him food, although the words "crop" and "fruit" may be used in such a figurative sense as to apply to fish, game, or edible insects, as well as to all manner of agricultural products. In fact, one well-known interpretation of what is clearly a first-fruit rite deals with the first seasonal run of salmon.[3] First-fruit rites have been described as thank offerings, sacrifices to the gods, and ways of lifting taboos from the remainder of a crop, but no matter how they are interpreted they always conform to rituals that are designed for the good of a total society.

The journey of life

Various primitive societies perform a series of critical rites almost with the same regularity as calendrical rituals. These are concerned with the welfare of individuals and with their relationships to their social units. More than fifty years ago a student of human affairs, Van Gennep, made the astute observation that primitive peoples frequently regarded the life cycle as a journey from one stage of existence to another. He noted that each individual normally passes through the phases of birth, puberty, marriage, and death. These represent critical points that require supernatural help if a person is to make a safe and proper transition from one stage to the next. Van Gennep termed the appropriate religious practices *rites of passage*,[4] and in one guise or another they are likely to be found in any society.

In the light of information that has become available since Van

[3] E. Gunther, "An Analysis of the First Salmon Ceremony," *American Anthropologist*, Vol. 28, 1926.

[4] A. Van Gennep, *Les Rites de Passage*, Paris, 1909. A fresh translation has recently been published. See A. Van Gennep, *The Rites of Passage*, M. B. Vizedom and G. L. Caffee, trans., Chicago, 1960.

Gennep's day, it is necessary to elaborate his stages. We shall keep his basic ground plan, but in our treatment the four stages will represent birth and infancy, puberty and adolescence, maturity and marriage, old age and death. These cover the full life cycle of every normal individual, and since each new stage demands a change in a person's social relations, helpful religious rites are likely to be performed whenever a person is about to enter a new phase (Fig. 27–2).

Birth and infancy are universally believed to be full of hazards for

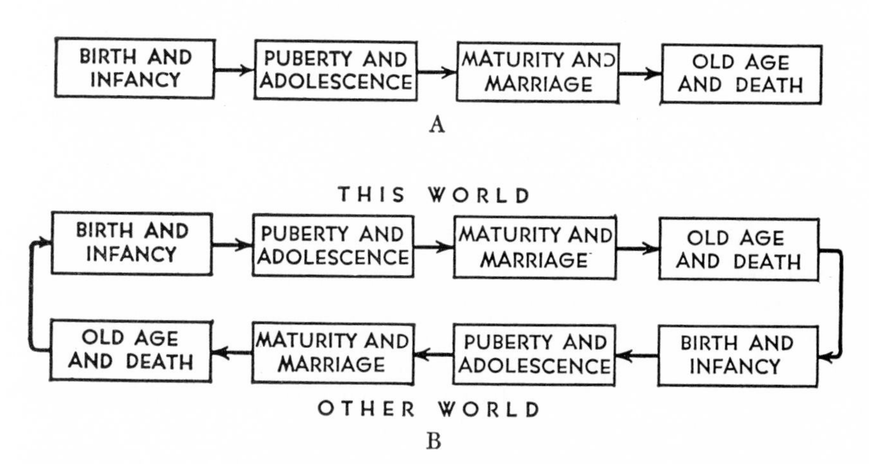

FIG. 27-2. The rites of passage. A. According to Van Gennep, every individual passes through four critical stages in his life cycle. To assure a safe passage, members of primitive societies customarily felt it necessary to hold rites whenever entrance to the next state, indicated by arrows, was being made. B. By combining existence on earth with life in the other world, death is "eliminated" as a final stage in this world. Not all primitive peoples believe that a disembodied soul passes through all of the four stages of life on earth, but there is wide acceptance of the idea that earthly death is followed by birth in the hereafter and that death in the other world is followed by birth on earth. Wherever such concepts prevail, the stages in the other world are the exact opposite of the stages in the world of the living.

a mother and babe, and to some extent for other relatives and for the community at large. Fears of death in childbirth, of bloodshedding, of infant mortality, and of evil supernatural forces that may prey on weak or immature bodies are variously expressed. Protective countermeasures, designed to keep mother and child safely in the world of the living, are everywhere to be found. These devices may exhibit more concern over physical than supernatural dangers, or the other way around, but in most cases the means of protection will exhibit a blend of natural and religious elements. It is sometimes stated that primitive women give birth without much physical difficulty, but it cannot be proved that they bear children any more easily than do women in nonprimitive societies. Cultural conventions may encourage loud outcries during labor or may insist on stoic silence, but the biological mechanisms of parturition are everywhere much alike.[5]

Only a few exceptional societies attempt to treat the delivery and care of infants as natural phenomena that do not require any supernatural help. Even so, the most scientific of obstetricians and pediatricians have something in common with primitive midwives and shamans, for all seek to make childbirth safe and to help a baby get through the dangerous period of infancy.

Efforts to assist an infant do not stop when a successful confinement has been achieved. Many a youngster in the primitive world goes about wearing inanimate objects that are supposedly endowed with mana for attracting supernatural aid (*charms* or *talismans*), or for warding off supernatural powers of evil (*amulets*). It is felt that these objects will help a child even when it is out of the sight of its parents or guardians (see Fig. 27–3).

Of course, it is not always possible to draw clear lines between charms, talismans, and amulets, or between the attraction of good supernatural power and the repulsion of evil. Despite the dangers of overlap, it may be said that charms are somewhat more commonly used to bring assistance, whereas amulets have more of a defensive connotation. Talismans partake of the nature of charms, but since they often include bits of sacred writing they do not occur technically in nonliterate societies. *Idols* are often included with other inanimate objects that are supposed to have mana. They are usually carved in three-dimensional form, and some of them are supposed to depict the appearance of the souls or spirits that they are thought to contain. All of these are sometimes lumped together as *fetishes,* and all may be regarded as examples of animatism.

Psychologists and psychiatrists are agreed that the transition from infancy to the period of puberty and adolescence is critical and full of exceedingly hard problems. Primitive peoples long ago recognized the difficulties involved, and in countless ways they tried to get supernatural assistance. Formal rites of passage at this stage are more likely to be designed for boys than for girls, who may simply be taught to resort periodically to menstrual lodges, out of the way of the rest of the community.[6] Quite often the masculine observances incorporate a *tribal*

---

[5] A study that throws much doubt on easy childbirth among primitive women, is L. Z. Freedman, and V. M. Ferguson, "The Question of 'Painless Childbirth' in Primitive Cultures," *American Journal of Orthopsychiatry,* Vol. 20, 1950, pp. 363–72.

[6] Fear of menstrual blood is one of the most frequently encountered phenomena in primitive cultures.

initiation. This is intended to teach a youth the lore of his group and to make him recognize the authority of elders and chiefs, so that he may be the better qualified to take his place as an adult member of his tribe. Sometimes the aspect of transition is dramatized in tribal initiation ceremonies by "killing" the initiate as a child and having him "reborn" as a man. Thus is symbolized the termination of one stage of an individual's existence and the start of a new one.

FIG. 27-3. An Eskimo boy, wearing amulets. This youngster is supposed to be protected from evil forces by the amulets that he is wearing. (Courtesy of the Museum of Anthropology, University of Michigan.)

Tribal initiation ceremonies may take place at calendrically fixed times of the year. In such cases they apply to all who are eligible when the rites are scheduled to be held. On this score, tribal initiation rituals are unlike the ceremonies accompanying birth, marriage, and death, which apply to the social adjustment of single individuals and to events that cannot be predicted in advance.

Maturity and marriage represent a different set of problems. Foremost of these are the dangers, wherever virginity is demanded of a bride, of bloodletting, the needs of newlyweds to adjust to each other and their in-laws, reluctance to admit an outsider to intimacy with a group of consanguineous kin, fear that the married couple may fail to have offspring, and concern over a young pair's fitness to rear properly whatever children may be born to them. No sure method of guaranteeing the soundness of marriages is known anywhere, nor is there any assured solution to the many problems that are so likely to follow in the wake of a marriage. It is a realistic awareness of the difficulties involved that leads practically all societies to look upon weddings as critical transition points. There is a widespread feeling that the principals might make the passage more safely if they had the benefit of supernatural help. Only once in a while does a group completely dispense with religious activities at marriage,[7] and rare are the societies that fail to permit divorce to serve as a safety valve for allowing the escape of tensions arising from marriages that have failed.

Not all peoples recognize old age as a distinct stage of existence,[8] but rites of passage that are concerned with death are among those that occur most regularly. Here is an inevitable source of recurring crises, for no social unit is complacent about losing members, yet none can prevent their loss. Some actions, such as the pinching of a patient's nostrils to keep his life force (soul) from departing, strike us as irrational; but others, including treatment with herbs, appear perfectly logical. If, despite all efforts, death takes place, religious rites may be performed to encourage the soul of the deceased to depart, without undue delay, for the other world. Often, too, steps involving supernatural practices are taken to make sure that the soul of the departed enjoys its existence in the afterlife so much that it will not come back to haunt the living.

Many people believe that the soul of a dead person can utilize its mana more effectively because it is no longer confined to a material body. Since a society's dead, in broad terms, are the forebears of the living, a form of *generalized ancestor worship* comes into play. This is not the same thing as the particularized veneration of specific ancestors

---

[7] Only a minority of the world's societies recognizes the validity of civil marriages. In the United States, even people who are not deeply religious are likely to have church weddings or their equivalents.

[8] Sometimes societies that do not necessarily invoke the supernatural when old age is reached may recognize this phase politically, as is the case with groups that assign political power to a *council of elders*. Government conducted by older people is not uncommon in the primitive world, and is known as *gerontocracy*.

In a few instances there is a general sociocultural rather than a strictly political recognition of old age. In times past, a Japanese elder, particularly in rural areas, was expected to retire in his mid-fifties and to turn over the active management of his household affairs to his eldest son.

that used to prevail in China and other Far Eastern countries but, different though they are, the two systems of belief have a common base. In each case the dead are somehow kept within a society instead of being expelled from it.

Nevertheless, social groups incline strongly to hold an ambivalent attitude toward their dead. On the one hand, they may love a dying individual and sincerely mourn his departure if he expires. On the other hand, they may also fear the spirit of a deceased person and may do all they can to speed its departure to the other world.

Fear of a dead person's soul is one of the most recurrent themes of *mourning customs* in primitive societies. Corpses may be removed through a specially made opening, other than the usual doors or windows, that is later sealed; returns from a burial may be made by circuitous paths in the hope that a spirit will be unable to follow the living; and the bereaved may adopt various disguises, such as painting black skins white, in order to conceal their identities (Fig. 27–4).

Throughout parts of Asia, particularly from India to the east and

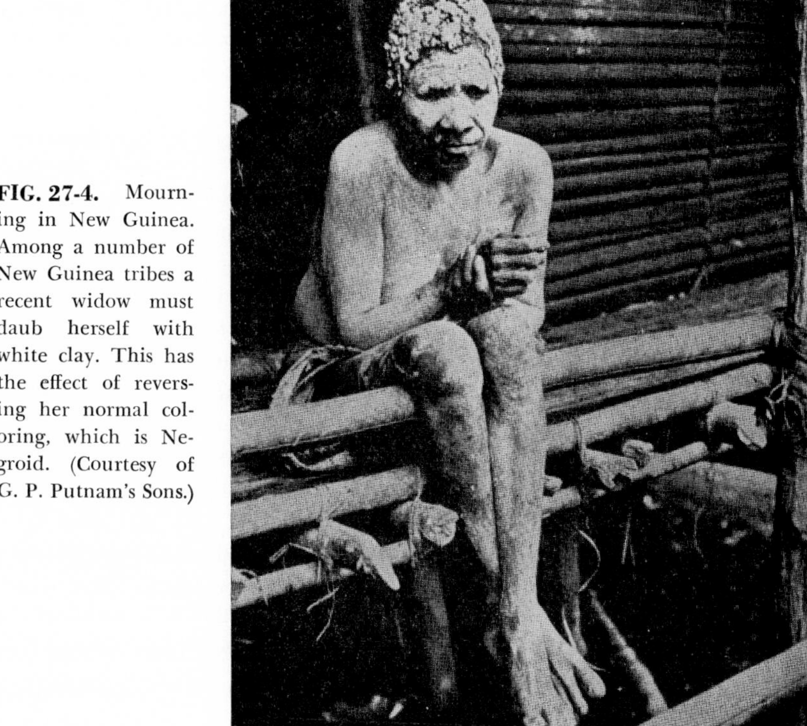

FIG. 27-4. Mourning in New Guinea. Among a number of New Guinea tribes a recent widow must daub herself with white clay. This has the effect of reversing her normal coloring, which is Negroid. (Courtesy of G. P. Putnam's Sons.)

south, many communities are subject to *genna taboos*. There may be a variety of motives for the imposition of a genna taboo, but whenever one is proclaimed it has the effect of stopping all but the most vital of activities. Genna is most likely to be proclaimed whenever a mighty personage has died. The thinking behind it seems to run somewhat as follows: "If the powerful antisocial forces that caused the death of so great a person are still around, think of what they could do to an ordinary individual like you. Therefore, the more inconspicuous and inactive you are, the better." It is tempting to think that gennalike ideas are somehow at the bottom of the restrictions on activities that play so prominent a part in the Sabbath "blue laws" of Judeo-Christian societies.

Another prominent feature of mourning customs is an effort to show that death has not seriously weakened the cohesion of a social group. Survivors are frequently called upon to make a show of great solidarity following a death. This practice is most readily accomplished by having the kin of the deceased gather or feast together. It is a commonplace observation among us that one meets more of his remote relatives at a funeral than on any other occasion. So highly regarded are the supernatural practices associated with death that they are likely to be carried out even by persons who claim to be agnostic or atheistic.

O DEATH, WHERE IS THY STING?

All societies try to minimize the inroads of death. One course is followed almost universally to help accomplish this end. It consists of developing myths that explain away death as something trivial and quite unimportant. The effect that is sought is to assure people that death doesn't really matter. Among some tribes the origin of death is attributed to a lapse of memory; among others it is said to be the result of a trifling error of conduct. In all cases it raises the possibility that death might have been avoided if only. . . . In terms of Christian beliefs, it amounts to saying: "If only Adam and Eve hadn't eaten the fruit of the forbidden tree."

Even more effective is the notion that life and death on earth are no more than parts of a continuous chain of existences. Thus, death can be "eliminated" if the idea gains acceptance that it is followed by birth in the other world, and that death in the afterlife is followed by birth in this world. Where such beliefs are held, death is robbed of much of its sting. Instead of meaning that a deceased person is forever lost to his relatives and society in general, it means only that the departed has moved temporarily to another sphere and will ultimately be reborn in this world. Something of the same idea may be found in the words attributed to Christ: "I am the resurrection and the life. He that believeth in Me, though he were dead, yet shall he live."

As can be seen in Figure 27–2, the stages of life in the other world are the opposite or reverse of life on earth. This notion of reversal may be found in any body of supernatural practices, whether they are scheduled in advance (calendrical) or not. For example, some tribes believe when it is daytime on earth, it is night in the other world; and that when it is summer here, it is winter there (Fig. 27–5). Consequently, those who represent the dead often act in reverse fashion from the living. Many instances are known to ethnologists of *clowns,* who speak or act backward or by opposites. When they are hot, they complain of being cold; and where sacred dancers stamp with the right foot, they may stamp with the left. Unfortunately, it cannot always be proved that clowns who act by opposites are representatives of the dead, but a few cases are known in which clowns and the dead are equated.

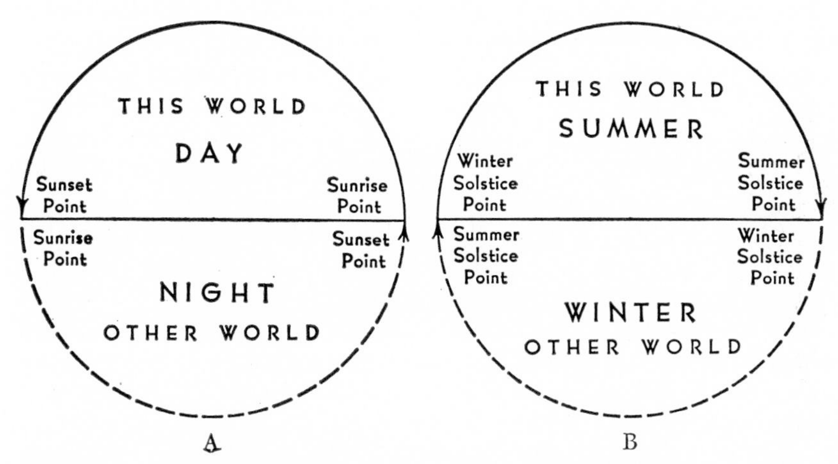

FIG. 27-5. The opposition of this world and the other world. A. The sun's daily journey. Primitive people have observed that the sun rises daily in the east and sets in the west. Many believe this to mean that during the night it travels elsewhere from west to east. Thus daytime on earth corresponds to nighttime in the other world. B. The sun's seasonal journey. By analogy with (A), the seasons are often reversed between the world of the living and the world of the dead.

Members of some *military societies* occasionally act like clowns. They, too, may do things in reverse or talk backward. The connection of military societies with death is perfectly obvious.[9]

Summary

No society looks forward to early extinction; thus, it takes whatever practical measures it can to preserve its existence. But whenever these give evidence of being insufficient they may be buttressed by resort to religious beliefs. Methods usually are devised that call for the setting up of a system of communication by means of which people on earth may send or receive messages dealing with help or guidance from the supernatural world. Quite often the messages involve mana-laden objects, and their meanings are interpreted by priests or shamans, who serve as intermediaries between the lay members of a society and their gods.

A social unit may also seek supernatural help by the performance of ceremonies. These are of two kinds. Some occur at regular times, in conformity with a ceremonial calendar, regardless of whether or not any worshiper has a pressing problem when the time comes. Most common of the calendrical observances in primitive societies are New Fire Rites, which, in northern latitudes, customarily fall at the season of the winter solstice, around December 21. When the sun is observed at daybreak to have reversed its course and started northward, a feeling of relief and starting afresh prevails, and there is likely to be either a dramatization of the end (death) of one era and the start (birth) of another, or the celebration of a new year. First-fruit rites make up another common category of calendrical observances.

Noncalendrical, critical rituals, which represent the second type, are performed primarily in times of need. They can, accordingly, seldom be scheduled far in advance. Those which are most widely found in primitive societies are the rites of passage. They are based on the notions that life is a journey from birth to death and that each stage of the trip creates a crisis for the individual and his society, a crisis that has a better chance for a socially desirable outcome if supernatural help is obtained. Rituals that are designed to assist boys, usually at puberty or early adolescence, to enter into manhood, frequently take the form of

[9] In some African tribes, hunters of dangerous animals may express the fact that they differ from ordinary people by deliberately committing incest with their daughters.

tribal initiations, during which the initiate learns the sacred lore of his tribe. It is not unusual to find that in the course of the proceedings the candidate's childhood is "killed" or brought to an end in one way or another and that he is "reborn" as a man. Of all the rites of passage, only those pertaining to adolescence can be regularly planned ahead, for no one can predict, before a conception has taken place, when a child will be born; nor does anyone know far ahead of time when a person will get married or die.

When religion is analyzed in terms of cultural dynamics, it becomes clear that one of its principal purposes—the major one discussed here—is to intensify or strengthen the cohesion that binds the people of a social unit to their group. Judged from this point of view, death is the greatest of all threats to the continuation of any society, for it constantly takes individual members away from a group. Several supernatural factors combine to negate the social consequences of death. Myths frequently dismiss death as a mere trifle, concepts of an afterlife teach that souls or spirits of the dead continue to live on in another world, and beliefs in rebirths, days of judgment, or reincarnation make people feel that death is not final, that it may be followed by a reappearance on earth, and that it is no more than a passing phase in a never-ending round of existences.

Beliefs in the supernatural, on which all religious systems depend, are possible only to creatures in possession of complete algebraic mentalities. Except in this indirect way, religion, unlike man's interrelations with his environment or with his fellow men, does not appear to be an outgrowth of any aspect of biology. Nevertheless, religious ideas are exceedingly important for the maintenance of any biocultural configuration. Perhaps that is why cultural anthropologists have never found a society that had failed to develop a belief in the supernatural.

Selected References

Boas, Franz, "Ethnology of the Kwakiutl," *Bulletin, Bureau of American Ethnology,* Vol. 35, 1921.

Evans-Pritchard, Edward E., *Nuer Religion,* London, 1956.

———, *Witchcraft, Oracles, and Magic among the Azande,* Oxford, 1937.

Fewkes, Jesse W., "The New-Fire Ceremony at Walpi," *American Anthropologist,* Vol. 2, No. 1, 1900.

Gunther, Erna, "An Analysis of the First Salmon Ceremony," *American Anthropologist,* Vol. 28, 1926.

Herskovits, Melville J., and Frances S., "An Outline of Dahomean Religious Belief," *Memoir, American Anthropological Association,* No. 41, 1933.

Mead, Margaret, "The Mountain Arapesh," Vol. 2, "Supernaturalism," *Anthropological Papers, American Museum of Natural History,* Vol. 37, Part III, 1940.

Nadel, S. Frederick, *Nupe Religion,* London, 1954.

Powdermaker, Hortense, *Life in Lesu,* London, 1933.

Titiev, Mischa, "Old Oraibi," *Papers of the Peabody Museum of American Archaeology and Ethnology,* Cambridge, Mass., Vol. 22, No. 1, Part Two, 1944.

Tschopik, Harry, Jr., "The Aymara of Chucuito, Peru," *Anthropological Papers, American Museum of Natural History,* Vol. 44, Part II, 1951.

Van Gennep, Arnold, *Les Rites de Passage,* Paris, 1909.

Whiting, John W. M., *Becoming a Kwoma,* New Haven, Conn., 1941.

Language and the Verbal Arts[1]

CHAPTER 28

LANGUAGE AND CULTURE

Among other things, this chapter is meant to drive home the lesson that a biocultural model in the shape of a triangle does not encompass all the essential aspects of a society's way of living together. Foremost of the facets omitted is language. Although it is widely held that each language consists of patterned and repetitive forms of behavior that are part and parcel of every society's way of life, linguistics has long been studied by itself and has developed many specialized and traditional approaches, some of which are far removed from the customary concerns of anthropologists. Consequently, although anthropologically trained linguists are generally well aware of the cultural implications of their work, many other students of language have but little interest in things cultural.

The basic importance of human speech for the development and continuation of any pattern of culture need not be questioned. Symbolic values can best be expressed through linguistic utterances, and no better medium is known for teaching children to accept and follow a particular form of culture. Moreover, it is only when they are put into words that abstractions and imaginary or non-sensory concepts of any kind acquire reality. Without the use of language, therefore, it would be practically impossible to teach the essentials of any system of supernatural beliefs. Neither Judaism nor Christianity could be taught with-

[1] The material presented in this chapter has benefited greatly from a detailed and thoughtful criticism provided by my colleague, Kenneth L. Pike, the linguist. Pike is not, of course, responsible for any flaws.

out the use of such words as faith, soul, God, and heaven. Then, too, language is the most effective device known for getting people to co-operate or to coordinate their activities.

Every human society, it is worth repeating, has a language and a culture. The two are completely interdependent. For this reason some scholars would go so far as to say that language and culture are one and the same, but for analytical purposes it is better to admit their close ties but to treat them as separate. By definition, language deals only with forms of behavior that are vocalized, but culture is also concerned with numerous activities, such as motor habits, that may never be expressed in words or accompanied by speech. There need be nothing verbal about tipping one's hat, yet it may be an important act of culture and may convey as subtle a symbolic meaning as a word.

It has already been pointed out that human beings who possess algebraic mentalities are the only animals capable of assigning symbolic and even arbitrary values to vocal utterances. But once man had acquired the necessary capacity he seems never to have improved on it.[2] On the basis of their experiences with many societies and cultures, ethnologists find it impossible to rate entire languages as better or worse, or more or less effective. It does not follow that all vocabularies are at present equally serviceable for dealing with anything whatsoever. Specialized vocabularies, such as our own lists of words for scientific and technological matters, are very well known. All that is meant is that each language is adjusted to the culture in which it is used and that new forms of speech can be borrowed or invented to keep pace with any changes of culture that may occur.

As far as is known, all languages serve equally well as systems of communication among the members of a society who have learned to associate the same meanings with the same sounds. Never should it be overlooked that as a method of communication a language is of inestimable value only in the society where it is habitually used. Across cultural lines it may be quite worthless. So it is that a craftsman such as a potter may watch and understand the work of a maker of pottery from any part of the world, but he would not necessarily understand a word of the other artisan's speech.[3]

[2] It is interesting to note that all prespeech babies, while they are expressing themselves more or less biologically by crying, sound alike; but as they become enculturated in different societies and learn to speak different languages, they no longer sound alike.

[3] In Bertold Brecht's moving play, *The Killer,* an abnormal murderer advances with a knife on an innocent man. The victim pleads for his life with conviction and feeling, but to each of his remarks the killer responds with a strange laugh. In this case, it is clear, words cannot cross psychological barriers.

Like anthropologists in general, anthropologically trained linguists most often deal with primitive peoples, but it should not be thought that primitive languages are simple and inefficient. This fact was not always understood. Before modern methods of investigation were developed, the analysis and interpretation of nonliterate tongues were attempted by scholars who had been trained to deal with the written languages that make up the great Indo-European family. Some of these scholars engaged in field work, but they usually took along grammatical tables of declensions and conjugations based on their knowledge of Indo-European forms. Into these previously prepared grammatical diagrams they tried to force whatever native language they were studying, and in keeping with the practice of their day, they marked as missing or deficient everything that seemed to be absent or which failed to conform to Indo-European models. None of the pioneer students of primitive speech was particularly interested in the fact that each culture has its own distinctive vocabulary and grammar and that its ways of expression might differ completely from the methods commonly found in Indo-European tongues. In the footsteps of such men as Boas, Sapir, and Bloomfield, anthropologically trained linguists in the United States began to go into the field without preconceived ideas, and they were among the first who tried to understand and analyze native languages not in preconceived terms, but only in regard to what they actually heard and saw.

LINGUISTIC ANALYSES AND CLASSIFICATION[4]

Vocal utterances to which a social group may assign symbolic meanings cover a wide range of possibilities. Sounds that strike speakers of English as clicks, hisses, snorts, gulps, or whines may be just as conventional for speaking other languages as are the consonants and vowels familiar to us. The only requirements for what is called *articulate speech* are that each unit of sound to which values are to be attached must be distinct enough to be set apart from other sounds, that it must have a beginning and an end that can be reasonably well recognized, and that the meaningful sounds should be capable of a marked degree of repetition by all who speak the same language.

All languages consist of sounds whose production, orderly arrangement, and combination serve to communicate definite meanings

[4] This section owes much to the treatment of language in Beals and Hoijer, *op. cit.*, Chap. 17.

from a speaker to his listeners. Every tongue that is spoken uses only a fraction of all the vocal utterances that men can make. Each language, then, has a finite number of distinctive sounds to which its speakers attach meaning. The smallest identifiable unit of significant or contrastive sound is called a *phoneme*. The entire English language, for instance, is built on only 45 phonemes, such as the *th* in *something*, or the *b* in *banker*. Phonemes rarely stand alone, but are combined with other minimum units of sound in fixed patterns, of which the smallest element that has meaning is called a *morpheme*. When an indivisible morpheme can stand by itself and carry the significance of a word, it is called *free*. Monosyllables in English are usually *free morphemes*, as in the case of words like *fish* or *book*. When a morpheme conveys no meaning by itself, but gains meaning when it is combined with other sounds, it is called *bound*. Examples of *bound morphemes* include the *ly* of *lovely*, and the *er* of *driver*.

Sounds that frequently recur in a language fall into characteristic sequences or patterns that may be quite rigid. Thus, in English, the *ng* of *clang* never begins a word, the *h* of *hollow* never ends one, and the sound *r* may follow initial *p* as in *pray*, but *p* can never follow initial *r*. Such speech arrangements are learned early in life, and adult speakers adjusted to one language find it very difficult to learn a different one. Both the production of sounds and their position in words or morphemes are equally fixed in each culture. This explains why people who habitually use a sound in one place, let us say initially, may have trouble in using virtually the same sound in a different position, let us say finally.

Sometimes different sounds or pronunciations have exactly the same meaning in a given language. Such cases are known as *allophones*. Thus, *been* means exactly the same thing in English, whether it is pronounced *bin, ben,* or *bean*. In this case *bin, ben,* and *bean* are allophones.

Besides studying sounds and their order of occurrence in morphemes or words, linguists are also concerned with their arrangement into meaningful phrases and sentences. Syntax or grammar is now the goal. Rules of grammar bring out the interdependence of words and arouse certain expectations on the part of a hearer. We feel satisfied with the complete sentence, "John is walking home"; but we feel dissatisfied if someone says only "John is."

Each language has a set of fixed rules. If word order is an important grammatical device it means one thing to say "dog bites man," and quite another to say "man bites dog." Pitch or intonation changes are equally effective for conveying different meanings, as we realize when we say, in level tones, "Oh, yes," or, with rising pitch, "Oh, yes?" Differences of accent also produce a variety of meanings. School children in recent years have teased their parents to say "What am I doing?" with the stress on a different word each time. When the unwary adult obliges with "*What* am I doing? What *am* I doing? What am *I* doing?" and "What am I *doing*?" the child retorts, "Making a fool of yourself!"

There are times when a simple pause brings about a complete difference of meaning. Any speaker of English recognizes this when he says aloud, "nitrate" and "night rate."

Another example of the way in which meanings may be changed without any change of vocabulary or grammatical arrangement may be found in the old saying:

> The devil was ill,
> The devil a monk would be;
> The devil got well,
> The de′vil a monk he'd be.

Here the entire meaning depends on matters of stress, pitch, intonation, rhythm, pauses, and the like. This bears out what cultural anthropologists have long known about speaking foreign languages. Again and again has it been found that one can make himself better understood by imitating the cadence or rhythmic flow of a linguistic utterance, even if one's enunciation continues to be poor and knowledge of vocabulary and grammar is limited.

There are many ways of changing the meanings of words and sentences. Well known is *phonetic modification*, whereby, in English, *woman* is singular and *women* is plural. Also widely used is *reduplication*, so that when the Saramacca Bush-Negroes of Dutch Guiana say "*hesi*," it means "to go fast," but when they say "*hesi hesi*," it means "speed."[5] Frequently employed, too, are the devices of adding prefixes, infixes (the addition of an element into the middle of a word), and suffixes. No language uses one method only, and linguists are alert to describe all the ways in which speakers of a specific tongue achieve variations of meaning.

A number of goals are sought by anthropologically trained linguists. They are anxious to record accurately as many primitive languages as possible; they try to analyze the sounds, arrangements, and grammatical rules by which a variety of meanings may be communicated; they seek to show in how many details a language may reflect the environmental or cultural setting of its speakers; they attempt to demonstrate the historic changes that may have been brought about by internal factors or external processes such as borrowing; and they are interested

---

[5] This example is taken from M. J. Herskovits, *op. cit.*, p. 449.

in fitting single tongues into larger and larger relationship units, such as speech families, on the basis of shared similarities. This last approach is reminiscent of the efforts of taxonomists to group biological specimens into species, genera, families, and so on. *Descriptive linguistics* deals with sounds, vocabularies and grammars; *historical linguistics* attempts to group together related tongues; and *metalinguistics* is concerned with various philosophical, psychological and cultural implications of language.

Students of oral languages require first of all a means of noting down whatever sounds they hear in articulate speech. Only after a language has been recorded in writing can its component parts later be systematically analyzed and compared with the components of other tongues. Obviously, the English alphabet is not equipped to render accurately the many sounds that human beings can make with their vocal apparatus. No method of writing or spelling is either perfect or universal. Before linguistic analysis could proceed, therefore, it was necessary to develop an all-embracing system of notation by means of which any articulate utterance could be transcribed. Although present-day linguists can write down for later review and analysis just about every sound they hear, including all shades of inflexion and pronunciation, they are most interested in recording the elements that are classed as phonemes. A method of phonemic transcription was worked out several decades ago and, with some variations, it is still widely used by linguists.[6]

Those who habitually converse with one another form a *speech community*, but within the same speech community different usages may exist for infants and adults, men and women, occupational groups, residents of different parts of a large area, or those who are differently trained and educated. If these variations of speech, sometimes known as *dialects,* do not prevent all or most of the members of a society from understanding each other, the speakers of the various dialects may still be said to form a single speech community, and this is usually the case with primitive tribes. Only within very large social units is one likely to find speakers of dialects or languages that are not mutually intelligible.

When linguists find certain combinations of sounds always repeated under similar circumstances they may describe the phenomenon as a law. One of these laws pertains to the making of the most common plurals in English. Many of the sounds we use, as is true throughout the

[6] The system of phonetic or phonemic transcription most widely used was devised by the International Phonetic Association, and is reproduced in K. L. Pike, "Phonemics," *University of Michigan Publications in Linguistics,* Vol. III, Ann Arbor, Mich., 1947, p. 232. In this book the techniques for rendering oral languages in writing are thoroughly discussed.

world, come in two forms. If we strongly vibrate the vocal cords, the resulting sound is known as *voiced.* If we make a similar sound without much vibration of the vocal cords, it is called *unvoiced.* A partial list of pairs follows:

Unvoiced	*Voiced*
p	b
t	d
k	g
s	z

Whenever a word ends in an unvoiced consonant we form the plural with an unvoiced *s.* Whenever a word ends in a voiced consonant, we make the plural with a voiced *z.* Thus, we say lap–laps, bet–bets, and rack–racks; but tab–tabz, bed–bedz, and rag–ragz. In fact, if a foreigner or a nonhabitual speaker of English breaks this law, we tend not to understand. Thus, if someone says betz, we are inclined to think he is trying to say bedz, and so we may misunderstand.

A complete language, including its patterned use of phonemes, its ways of producing and combining sounds, its vocabulary and grammar, is so complex that it is unlikely to have been independently invented in its entirety more than once. Accordingly, when contemporary linguists find two separated peoples speaking closely similar or identical tongues, they feel justified in assuming that at some earlier period of their history the two were together, in actual touch or in proximity. On the primitive level this kind of analysis has served to demonstrate that the Navaho and Apache, who now live in the southwestern United States, once resided close to the speakers of northern Athabaskan tongues, who still live in northern Canada and Alaska. Similarly, even if every other fact about the Anglo-Saxon settlement of the United States were to be lost, linguists could infer from their speech resemblances that the American colonists had once been in contact with other speakers of English. Simple linguistic analysis might or might not reveal which group had remained in its homeland and which had migrated to other regions, but an earlier connection between the two social units speaking much the same language could be postulated beyond reasonable dispute. One complicating factor that makes all such hypotheses open to doubt is the possibility of diffusion. It is not inconceivable that a language could be spread from one group to another by travelers, traders, or military conquerors. The result would be two widely separated societies, who might never have lived near one another, using closely similar forms of speech.

A more refined approach to this sort of interpretation, staunchly recommended and defended in this country by Swadesh, goes by the name of *glottochronology*, or *lexicostatistics*.[7] Among other objectives this method attempts to provide the date when two related languages became separated. Essential to the technique is the preparation of word lists in the languages to be compared. Lists of about one hundred items are recommended.[8] Glottochronological analysis rests on a number of assumptions, not all of which have been tested and accepted. It is assumed that some portions of a vocabulary, such as pronouns and words relating to numbers or to parts of the body, form a basic core and are slow or resistant to change. It is further assumed that whatever changes take place in the basic core will occur at a regular or constant speed through time, and that basic cores will be modified at a similar rate in all languages. Hence, proponents of the method claim that if one knows the percentage of true cognates within the core vocabularies of any pair of related tongues, one can figure out the length of time that has elapsed since the two languages began to part company. At present, a loss of roughly 15 or 20 percent of cognate forms is supposed to take place every thousand years. Simply stated, this means that the number of changes that can be shown to have taken place in a core vocabulary may be used as a measure of time. Even some of those who have faith in the validity of glottochronology are likely to recognize that such historic factors as migrations or conquests, which are agencies of diffusion, may wreak havoc with the satisfactory use of this technique. Just the same, they feel that lexicostatistics yields dates that can be linked with those of archeology and history, and they are of the opinion that this method may provide a means for connecting some peoples and cultures, hitherto unidentified but known from archeological remains, with certain groups that have actually been identified in history. As for its linguistic values, supporters of the glottochronological approach believe that this technique yields information about the time order in which various dialects were formed, and they think that such data can be correlated with known or suspected prehistoric migrations as well as with various aspects of cultural growth and change.

Not so very long ago it was completely believed that a person's thoughts dictated his choice of words. Now this sequence is being chal-

[7] S. C. Gudschinsky, "The ABC's of Lexicostatistics (Glottochronology)," *Word*, Vol. 12, No. 2, 1956. This article gives an account, in simple language, of glottochronological techniques.

[8] M. Swadesh, "Towards Greater Accuracy in Lexicostatistical Dating," *International Journal of American Linguists*, Vol. 21, 1955, pp. 121–37.

For a summary of what glottochronology has so far accomplished, see A. L. Kroeber, "Linguistic Time Depth Results So Far, and Their Meaning," *International Journal of American Linguistics*, Vol. 21, 1955, pp. 91–104, and D. H. Hymes, "Lexicostatistics So Far," *Current Anthropology*, Vol. 1, 1960, pp. 3–44.

lenged. Some modern linguists are of the opinion that the opposite is true and that the words an individual customarily uses may direct his thoughts. The late Benjamin Whorf once stated flatly that a socially accepted pattern of word usage is often prior to certain culturally sanctioned forms of thinking and behavior.[9] Whorf's hypothesis was supported by Sapir, and it should be taken in conjunction with Clyde Kluckhohn's assertion that the underlying conceptual images of each language make up a coherent though unconscious philosophy.[10] Stated somewhat differently, the idea has been proposed that our very vocabularies and grammars may influence our outlooks on life, on our fellow men, and on the world about us. Paradoxically, we render our thoughts in words, but our words may help to shape our thoughts.

Wonder is sometimes expressed that no international language, such as Esperanto, has ever been a great success. The failure is not the result of any lack of knowledge or technical skill on the part of linguists. What is often overlooked is the patent fact that no language exists apart from some society and its culture. Every tongue, to a marked degree, reflects the cultural background of its speakers and gives an indication both of their universe and of how they interpret it. Thus, Eskimos are said to have a great number of words describing snow under varying conditions, and Arabian vocabularies deal much with camels and their equipment. Not until there is a universal culture by which all the world lives is there much chance for a global language to succeed.

On the basis of recent estimates by Harry Hoijer,[11] the most widespread family of languages is the Indo-European. It includes Germanic, Slavic, Romance, Greek, Indo-Iranian, and other languages and, taking all its branches together, it is spoken by well over one billion inhabitants of Europe and Asia. Within these continents another 50 million or so speak languages of the Turkic, Mongolian, and Tungus families. Southern India has about 60 million speakers of Dravidian and other native tongues; and East Asia has over 600 million Sino-Tibetan speakers, most of whom use Chinese tongues. East Asia also includes approximately 27 million users of Korean and about 90 million speakers of Japanese.

Africa has relatively small numbers who speak historically important Semitic and Hamitic tongues, but there are about 57 million

---

[9] B. L. Whorf, "The Relation of Habitual Thought and Behavior to Language," in L. Spier, *et al.*, eds., *Language, Culture, and Personality*, Menasha, Wis., 1941, p. 75.

[10] C. Kluckhohn, *Mirror for Man*, New York, 1949, p. 111.

[11] Beals and Hoijer, *op. cit.*, pp. 511–14. The figures cited are from the first edition, and have been multiplied by 0.15 as a rough correction for recent increases of population. All figures are rounded and approximate.

people each who speak Sudanic, just south of the Sahara, and Bantu, further south. The islands of the southern basin of the Pacific Ocean (Oceania) are dominated by tribes belonging to one large linguistic family called Malayo-Polynesian. These languages are used by nearly 65 million natives and include all the tongues of aborigines in this vast area, except those of the inhabitants of Australia and of New Guinea, whose languages are extremely varied. In sharp contrast to the uniformity of the greater part of Oceania is the situation in the New World, which seems to show the greatest linguistic diversity on earth. Many linguistic scholars in the past, with the noteworthy exception of Edward Sapir and his followers, believed that a few million pre-Columbian American Indians spoke tongues pertaining to well over 80 distinct families, each of which was unrelated in any manner to the others, and none of which had any connection with the languages of the Old World. Modern scholars are somewhat more conservative, and link together numerous American languages that were once thought to be unrelated.[12] Nonetheless, in view of the probable diversity of American Indian languages, ethnologists may be forgiven if they smile a bit knowingly when people ask, "What is *the* Indian word for . . . ?"

Much has been made, in some quarters, of American Indian *sign language*. It is true that in a few areas, notably in the Plains,[13] some two dozen tribes that spoke different tongues could communicate with each other through a set of common gestures. However, it must be realized that very few abstractions and ideas can be expressed by bodily movements. Hence, sign language, at best, was only a very limited means of communication.[14]

Folklore

Speech forms are widely used for communicating facts and ideas from a speaker to his auditors, but they may also be used for arousing particular kinds of behavior or reaction on the part of listeners. It is perfectly possible to employ language for self-expression or else to convey or heighten emotions, but most utterances in daily life are directed to some practical end. Storytelling combines practical and emotional purposes,

---

12 The view has been expressed that some day it may be found that not only are all the American Indian tongues related, but that all the languages of the world have a common ancestry.

13 W. Tomkins, *Universal Indian Sign Language of the Plains Indians . . .*, San Diego, 1929.

14 R. L. Birdwhistle, *Introduction to Kinesics: An Annotation System for Analysis of Body Motion and Gesture,* Louisville, 1952.

for it may be used to impart lessons at the same time that it arouses pleasure. Few primitive peoples look lightly upon storytelling. There may be restrictions on who is permitted to tell tales, as well as on the time, place, subject matter, and listeners. Simple stories are told in what we would describe as prose and are subject to a minimum of restrictions. Anonymous tales that are well known and often repeated throughout a speech community make up its *folklore*.[15] Attempts have been made to distinguish various kinds of tales on the basis of their subject matter, but it is impossible to make clear-cut distinctions. As a general rule, stories may be classified as *myths*, if they deal primarily with supernatural characters or events, and as *legends* when they are devoted to historic or supposedly historic persons or happenings. There are so many narratives that combine the two characteristics that anthropologists have practically given up the effort to separate myths from legends.

Folklore is not without practical significance. It often mirrors a tribe's culture, past or present, and affords clues to migrations and contacts with other peoples. Many stories reassert the moral values of a society, and some tales are specifically used to provide instruction. Of world-wide distribution are narratives that seek to describe the origin and nature of the universe (*cosmogony* and *cosmology*), to account for the characteristics of familiar animals and other aspects of the environment, to tell how a *culture hero* inaugurated a particular pattern of culture, to explain the beginnings of life and death, and to picture the other world and what goes on there. Two common features of folklore help to strengthen the solidarity of a society. Death, as has been previously noted, is dismissed as unimportant, arising from some trivial error; and the less favored are given opportunities to blow off steam by laughing at stories in which the high and mighty suffer failure or discomfiture. People who find themselves occupying low statuses and those who believe that they have, through no fault of their own, been forced to undergo hardships or tribulations, are much less likely to rebel against their society and its leaders if they discover that even the mightiest of personages sometimes suffer identical misfortunes.

POETRY, PRAYER, AND SONG

Because each language imposes a rigid limitation on the number of vocal sounds to which meanings are attached, because each tongue

---

[15] Further information on this subject may be found in S. Thompson, *The Folktale*, New York, 1946.

likewise delimits the way in which meaningful sounds are to be produced and combined, and because a language also stipulates the stress and intonation with which vocalizations are to be expressed, every prose utterance cannot help but repeat some of its elements over and over again. Repetition of sounds provides a potential basis for alliteration, vowel harmony, and rhyme; and orderly recurrences of stress can be used to make rhythmic patterns. When these aspects of speech, singly or together, are deliberately emphasized, *poetry* results. Its use is found in all cultures, and it has been noted that it always increases the emotional impact of a statement on its hearers. Furthermore, both rhyme and rhythm, as they are employed in poetry, make remembrance and memorization easier because of their repetitive qualities. All of these factors are basic to an understanding of why prayer so frequently resembles poetry. In addition, investigators have found that people commonly have a covert belief that a prayer formula, which is supposed to have gained supernatural help in the past, will lose its effectiveness if it is changed in any way at all. That is why the language of prayer is often archaic and so much more conservative than everyday talk.

Very closely allied to poetry is vocal music, or *song*. In each instance the same anatomical mechanisms are employed. It is easy enough to say that song is poetry with the addition of melody, but it is extremely hard to explain what melody is. Cultural conditioning, which may at times incorporate some seemingly arbitrary values, plays so great a part in this context that what strikes some people as a pleasant succession of sounds may appear to others as harsh and disturbing. Nevertheless, the intimate relation of song to poetry has been recognized at least for many centuries, and it has been firmly established that in ancient times much poetry, both secular and sacred, was meant to be sung.

Sacred singing as a means of putting human beings in touch with supernatural powers, or of acquiring extra power, is an accepted habit in many primitive societies.[16] Cultural anthropologists know of numerous religious practices wherein singing plays a fundamental part, and even in modern services chanting and singing are outstanding features. As any English dictionary shows, the word "charm," in a supernatural context, is derived from "carmen," which was originally a sacred incantation; and cantors, who sing holy songs in synagogues, are important religious officers among persons of Jewish faith.

The effectiveness of poetry and song as ways of communicating ideas or information has been given prominence of late by those who advertise their wares over the radio and television. Many a "blurb" nowadays is delivered in rhyme or in the form of a song. Esthetically,

[16] For an example see R. Underhill, *Singing for Power*, Berkeley, Calif., 1938.

such renditions may leave much to be desired, but their practical value for making people remember advertised products can scarcely be doubted.

Singing does not always have pleasant connotations in primitive societies. It can be a very grim affair, packed with "social significance." This was the case among the Eskimo, who used to settle disputes, often very serious ones, by resort to the custom of *song-tying*. An aggrieved Eskimo might challenge an opponent to a song contest. In the presence of their fellows each contestant sang as bitterly and satirically as he could about the other. He who received the greater acclaim and applause from the audience became the winner, and the loser was temporarily disgraced.[17]

Song contests as substitutes for other forms of aggressive conduct are known in many societies. They may not conform exactly to Eskimo song-tying, but their general resemblance is usually easy to detect. In all cases they serve to release sociocultural tensions without resort to physical violence.

Somewhat related to the foregoing, but quite different in numerous ways, is the custom of social singing among the Araucanians or Mapuche. It used to be the habit of these Indians to visit friendly chiefs from time to time. On these occasions young women, who usually held low status in Araucanian society, were permitted to express their pent-up grievances. Brides were particularly likely to be unhappy because of the strict enforcement of patrilocal residence in a tribe where several brothers might be living under the same roof as their father. Many a young wife revealed her unhappiness under these conditions in her songs, and although she might be answered and even be told euphemistically to keep quiet, she was not subject to punishment for anything she sang about. On the contrary, if some of her auditors felt that they could remedy her situation, they might take steps to make things better for her in the future.[18]

Drama

There is always a close connection among language, poetry, song, and *drama*. Regardless of specific forms and aims, which vary in every con-

---

[17] For further information on this topic consult K. Rasmussen, *Across Arctic America*, New York, 1927.

[18] More details, and a number of typical songs, are given in M. Titiev, "Social Singing among the Mapuche," *Anthropological Papers, Museum of Anthropology, University of Michigan*, No. 2, Ann Arbor, Mich., 1949.

ceivable way, all dramas contain characters who usually wear costumes or carry symbolic accessories, and who take turns in a fixed order in saying, reciting, or singing something to be heard by an audience. The vocal utterances are generally accompanied by gestures or other movements of the body. Like all of the verbal arts, drama serves to arouse and heighten the emotions of those who watch and listen. Again, like folklore, it may be used effectively to drive home lessons that reflect a social unit's cultural beliefs and values. Drama has an added advantage in that it can also be used to give concrete expression to intangible abstractions. This can be done by having players act as representatives of such abstract ideas as lust or greed.

Religionists early realized the power of dramatic devices for instilling supernatural concepts. Virtually all societies use dramatic performances in conjunction with the practice of religion, and some primitive rituals may be shown to be clever dramatizations of myths dealing with supernatural personages and events.

Accordingly, it is not surprising that one of the main streams of the modern English drama flowed out of sacred theatrical performances. As every student of the subject knows, parts of Christian services were often dramatized in the early medieval period. Some of these small dramas were called *tropes* and were associated with Gregorian chants. They were extremely popular, a fact that is readily understood when one considers that in those days the vast majority of the worshipers were nonliterate or illiterate and that laymen who were literate were generally forbidden to read the Bible for themselves. As a consequence, the tropes or dramatized portions of the liturgy, during which the faithful could personally see enacted many of the things that they had been told, drew great throngs into the churches.

A number of scholars believe that the very popularity of the tropes so badly overcrowded the churches and so threatened to unbalance the remainder of the service that the authorities finally felt it necessary to ban the dramas from within the church. In this way an important segment of the English drama moved outdoors and step by step became altered from a religious performance to a popular form of secular entertainment.

The power of words and names

Because we have readily available so many forms of activity and entertainment, we do not always grasp the full import of words and speech in primitive societies. To many peoples even an ordinary conversation may be of prime significance, and it is most unusual to find that words are taken lightly. Statements that we would classify as empty gossip or mere yarning may be highly regarded and carefully analyzed. Unlike ourselves, many primitives pay considerable attention even to the remarks of known liars. If a bewildered anthropologist protests against such an attitude, he is likely to be told: "But he (or she) *said* it!"

Some observers feel that the value which many primitive men and women assign to words stems from their confusion of a word and the actual thing for which it stands.[19] Thus, if a thing is important, so too is its associated word. A number of students believe that in the primitive attitude toward speech we may have a covert forerunner of something known to all clinical psychologists and psychiatrists. They know very well how much a person may reveal about himself when he is encouraged to talk without restraint. Even downright lies may have deep significance.

Once we learn to appreciate how much words mean to primitive people we can readily grasp why *orators* and *oratory* are so highly regarded. Not everyone can sway an audience, and in many societies no man could hope to exert powerful leadership unless he were a good orator. A speaker who can bend the thoughts and actions of his hearers to his will is seldom regarded as an ordinary mortal.

More important than commonplace words are *names.* In this connection it can be shown that names, too, are frequently regarded as much the same as the personages or things for which they stand. Accordingly, it follows that to get hold of a person's name is equivalent to getting hold of the person himself. That is why names are most unlikely to be freely bandied about, and that explains why married couples, in some primitive societies, may wait for years before getting up the courage to reveal their true names to one another. In the meantime, for purposes of convenience and identification, *nicknames* may serve very well. Nicknames may be employed for a wide variety of purposes, but in a large number of cases they are used to conceal a true name.

Names may also be used interchangeably with or else to stand for abstract or non-sensory concepts. Names of supernatural powers, especially gods, are carefully concealed lest they fall into unauthorized hands.

---

[19] A fuller discussion of this topic may be found in B. Malinowski, "The Problem of Meaning in Primitive Languages," in C. K. Ogden and I. A. Richards, *The Meaning of Meaning,* New York, 1923, pp. 451–510.

For a penetrating analysis of some of Malinowski's linguistic material, see D. Lee, "Being and Value in Primitive Culture," *Journal of Philosophy,* Vol. 46, No. 13, 1949, pp. 401–15.

"Thou shalt not take the name of the Lord, thy God, in vain" is a commandment of very wide distribution. To make the names of one's gods known to an enemy is a treacherous act of the greatest magnitude. It is equivalent to turning one's deities over to an opponent.

Supernatural ideas are not the only abstractions that can be made more concrete by being named. We sometimes overlook the fact that this same principle is operating among us whenever an officer says: "In the *name* of the law." Belief in the great power of words and names is not limited to primitive societies.

Selected References

Bloomfield, Leonard, *Language,* New York, 1933.

Greenberg, Joseph H., "Essays in Linguistics," *Viking Fund Publications,* No. 24, New York, 1957.

Gudschinsky, Sarah C., "The ABC's of Lexicostatistics (Glottochronology)," *Word,* Vol. 12, No. 2, 1956.

Harris, Zellig S., *Methods in Structural Linguistics,* Chicago, 1951.

Hoijer, Harry, ed., "Language in Culture," *Memoir, American Anthropological Association,* No. 79, 1954.

Kluckhohn, Clyde, "Myths and Rituals: A General Theory," *Harvard Theological Review,* Vol. 35, 1942.

Pike, Kenneth L., "Phonemics," *University of Michigan Publications in Linguistics,* Vol. 3, Ann Arbor, Mich., 1947.

Sapir, Edward, *Language,* New York, 1921.

Swadesh, Morris, "Towards Greater Accuracy in Lexicostatistical Dating," *International Journal of American Linguistics,* Vol. 21, 1955, pp. 121–37.

Thompson, Stith, "Advances in Folklore Studies," in A. L. Kroeber, ed., *Anthropology Today,* Chicago, 1953, pp. 587–96.

———, *The Folk Tale,* New York, 1946.

Titiev, Mischa, "Social Singing among the Mapuche," *Anthropological Papers, Museum of Anthropology, University of Michigan,* No. 2, Ann Arbor, Mich., 1949.

Voegelin, Carl F., and Harris, Zellig S., "Linguistics in Ethnology," *Southwestern Journal of Anthropology,* Vol. 1, 1945, pp. 455–65.

Whorf, Benjamin L., "Four Articles on Metalinguistics," *Foreign Service Institute, Department of State,* Washington, D.C., 1949.

———, "The Relation of Habitual Thought and Behavior to Language," in L. Spier, *et al.,* eds., *Language, Culture, and Personality,* Menasha, Wis., 1941, pp. 75–93.

Nonverbal Arts and Games

CHAPTER 29

As far back as the Old Stone Age, craftsmen sometimes took pains to perfect or beautify an implement in ways that could not possibly improve its practical effectiveness. This tendency has continued into our own day, and modern examples would include decorated chairs that are no more comfortable for sitting than plain ones, ornamental garments that add nothing to the wearer's "creature comforts," carved musical instruments that may not sound as well as their uncarved parallels, and pearl-handled revolvers that may or may not shoot straight. For want of a better way of explaining this phenomenon, originally expressed as no more than evenness or symmetry, there are some scholars who refer to an esthetic urge or drive. Whether or not human beings actually possess such an esthetic drive is still unsettled, but the fact remains that great numbers of people go to considerable lengths to embellish things for nonpractical purposes, or to look upon or to purchase artistic products. Whatever people's basic motives may turn out to be, such activities are customarily related to a pleasurable emotion. Either the workman takes delight in what he is doing, or the user enjoys the nonessential elements, or spectators find pleasure in the contemplation of something artistic. It is also possible, as our expression "art for art's sake" implies, to make esthetic objects that have no reference whatsoever to practical considerations. On the whole, though, primitive peoples are unlikely to separate art from utility. Anything capable of arousing emotion can be put to use, without exception, in the exercise of religion. If we bear this in mind, we do not wonder at finding so much painting, sculpture, music, rich ornamentation, and other expressions of the fine arts intimately associated with religious structures and services. In addition, various artistic objects are believed to contain within themselves the mysterious power that is best described as mana.

Many anthropologists believe that art arose out of man's handling of various substances in the course of toolmaking and during the development of technology in general. Sometimes craftsmen liked to display their mastery of techniques by going beyond the boundaries of plain efficiency; at other times, it can be shown, pleasing patterns emerged simply as offshoots of methods of manufacturing or through the use of differing kinds of materials. Considerations of this sort form the essence of an entire book on the subject by Gene Weltfish, who believes that art, especially elements of design, was born from industry.[1]

Be that as it may, students of man have long been intrigued by the place of fine arts in culture, and in recent years a great deal of attention has been focused on the relation of the artist to his society and culture. Answers are being sought to such questions as: Is artistic ability inevitably inherited or can it be brought into being, stimulated, and developed through cultural training? Does the impulse to make a work of art arise spontaneously, or does it have to be acquired? Is there an unlimited freedom of scope to artistic formulations, or is each artist forced to work within broad limits set by the nature of his medium and by the cultural concepts of his society?

None of these questions can be settled fully, and some cannot even be partially answered. This much is known. Art styles, like objects of material culture, can be diffused from one tribe or region to another; sexual dichotomy may allot art work to men or to women; some societies have groups of artistic specialists; and primitives can and do distinguish what they consider good art from bad. They also recognize great differences in individual ability, and the vast bulk of their artistic output conforms in general to the established forms and techniques that prevail in their culture. Rare, indeed, is the individual genius who ranges far beyond the cultural boundaries of his group. For instance, it is well known that pottery designs from a given time and place are usually so standardized that they can be readily assigned to their proper cultures, yet the pots often show individual characteristics. How a potter can introduce personal elements while staying within the limits of his society's conventions is a problem of the fine arts that has not yet been conclusively solved.

One of the most striking characteristics of primitive art is its ingenious simplicity. Many an artist used only the plainest of ingredients drawn from his immediate environment. Yet, though they worked with crude tools on everyday materials, primitive artists frequently

[1] G. Weltfish, *The Origins of Art,* Indianapolis and New York, 1953.

managed to be charming at the same time that they were direct and simple. This is the secret of primitive and "folk" art.

Instrumental music

The productions of *instrumental music* come very close to the structured patterns of the verbal arts. They are widespread among all groups of human beings, but are never found among other animals. Their aim is to produce particular sounds in a definite order and in accordance with a fixed arrangement of stresses, pitches, intonations, and rhythms. The conventional pattern may vary in each of these characteristics from group to group. Moreover, there is little to prevent a society from attributing to musical utterances, as it does to words, whatever emotional or other symbolic meanings it wishes, although one must not overlook the possibility that some kinds of music may arouse physiological responses that affect all of mankind rather than the members of one particular community.

As a rule, the meanings that are associated with musical compositions are likely to be culturally determined. Euro-American listeners learn to consider some forms of instrumental music as jolly and others as sad. We are inclined to think of marching soldiers when we hear what we regard as a martial air, and of brides when we listen to the strains of what we have learned to recognize as a wedding march. As with vocal utterances, however, no two social units need necessarily ascribe the same meanings to the same sounds. Hence, what one group regards as mournful another may interpret as gay.

The cultural implications of music are of particular concern to those anthropologists who have come to be known as *ethnomusicologists*. They are, at present, few in number, largely because their specialty calls for a great deal of training in music as well as in anthropology. Their broad aims are to acquire an understanding and to present an interpretation of the totality of human music, without limitations of race, time, or geography. As anthropologists, too, they tend to look upon a musical production as only a single segment of a culture, linked to other manifestations of a society's way of life.[2]

Conventionally, musical instruments have been classified according to whether they are intended to emphasize melody or rhythm, but it is also possible to describe and discuss them in terms of their construction, the ways they are played, or the materials of which they are

---

[2] W. Rhodes, "Toward a Definition of Ethnomusicology," *American Anthropologist,* Vol. 58, 1956, pp. 457–63.

made. A recent classification, based on methods of sound production, divides musical instruments into four groups: *idiophones,* such as bells and rattles, which make sounds by the vibration of the entire instrument; *aerophones,* like flutes, clarinets, trumpets, and pan pipes that depend on a closed column of vibrating air; *membraphones,* referring to all manner of drums, that utilize a vibrating membrane; and *chordophones,* including violins and guitars, that get their effects from the vibrations of strings.[3] Regardless of which methods of classification are used, data on instrumental music can always be employed to round out descriptions of culture patterns, to help delineate culture areas, to aid in studies of invention and diffusion, and to provide factual materials that are useful in the consideration of topics like migration, culture history, and culture change.

People in primitive societies, unlike ourselves, seldom play instrumental music for its own sake. They are much more given to use it as an accompaniment for singing, processions, dances, or some other activity. Experience has shown that the emotional impact of many activities is greatly increased when they are accompanied by music played on an assortment of instruments.

Processions and dances

Processions, except in the form of parades, or at funerals in some countries, play so trivial a part in our way of life today that we are apt to overlook the importance that they once had in Euro-American culture, or that they still have in a number of primitive societies. In its simplest terms, a procession need be no more than a movement of people along a predetermined route, but it is very seldom as prosaic as that. It is unusual to find a procession that fails to have a specific purpose or that does not combine a number of fine arts, such as painting, masking, costuming, or the making of music. To appreciate its significance as an artistic outlet, we must try to picture the contrasting effect of a highly colorful procession on a folk whose daily lives unfold in rather colorless and even drab surroundings.

Like other renderings of the fine arts, processions are seldom regarded as ends in themselves. They may be held for a variety of purposes. It would be extremely difficult to try to enumerate all the kinds of processions, but a partial list would include those that take place in conjunction with economic activities, for political purposes, in carrying

[3] B. Nettl, *Music in Primitive Culture,* Cambridge, Mass., 1956, p. 90.

out rites of passage, especially when death strikes, and as prayers or other ways of communicating with the supernatural world.

Processions that are somehow connected with religious observances are among those that are best known to ethnologists. Usually the marchers carry an idol or a supernatural image of some sort, and their route generally takes a circular or squarish form. These customs imply that such processions are designed to spread about mana, especially among those enclosed within the line of march, at the same time that they prevent evil supernatural forces from penetrating the charmed circle.

Processions of a religious nature are everyday features of primitive ceremonialism and were once exceedingly important to the practice of Christianity. Even the parochial Mass, so the Catholic Encyclopedia tells us, formerly opened with a procession;[4] and from the same source we learn that in times of crisis or emergency extraordinary processions may be held to ask for rain or fine weather, or else to avert storms, famine, plague, or war.

Closely allied to processions, instrumental music, religious practices, and esthetics in general is the art of *dancing*. In truth, it is not always easy to tell a procession from a dance. For instance, in some African tribes it used to be customary to render special treatment to a girl when she attained puberty. Her head was shaved, her body was anointed with medicinal oil, she was dressed in bark cloth, and she walked along carrying a model of a house as a sign that she was ready to become a housekeeper. From the nature of the performance most of us would call it a procession, but the natives described the rites as "dancing a girl into womanhood."[5]

In primitive societies, especially, there is very often a close connection also between dancing and the verbal arts. Dancing has been aptly described as "poetry in motion," and, as is the case with speech production, its essence consists of rhythmically controlled movements of the body or some of its parts. Furthermore, as modern choreographers know so well, dancing can also be used to tell a story. When combined with instrumental music, dancing has a powerful emotional effect on performers and spectators alike. It can induce trance, mass hypnotism, ecstasy, or frenzy (Fig. 29–1). Primitive religions make such great use of dancing that the terms *dance* and *rite* are often used interchangeably. Although early Christianity relied much on dancing, a number of sects in recent times have frowned on the use of either instrumental music or dancing.

[4] *Catholic Encyclopedia,* Vol. II, p. 446.

[5] W. D. Hambly, *Tribal Dancing and Social Developments,* New York, 1927, p. 125.

Dances may be performed as social festivities, to honor a deity or some other abstract supernatural power, to win the pity of the other world, sometimes through hard work or torture, or to ask for supernatural help. It is in the latter context that the renowned *kachina dances*

FIG. 29-1. Dancing in a trance. On the islands of Malaya or Indonesia, as well as in other parts of the world, native dancers regularly become entranced. Here an entranced dancer on Bali is about to wound himself with a kris. Spectators often have to interfere to prevent a dancer from seriously injuring himself. (Courtesy Museum of Anthropology, University of Michigan.)

of the Pueblo Indians can best be understood. They are essentially religious performances, but they incorporate a great many esthetic and social elements. A *kachina* is a friendly spirit, capable of bringing rain and other benefits. Long ago, as several myths have it, the *kachinas* were supposed to have lived on earth, but enemies later killed them off.

To gain their spiritual aid, men learned to impersonate the *kachinas* and to represent these spirits by dressing in elaborate, gaily-painted costumes, including large, colorful masks that completely hide the face and head of the wearer and come to rest on his shoulders (Fig. 29–2). Males only can perform as *kachinas,* and, according to the Hopi, a man becomes a living god as soon as he dons a mask. Thereafter he is forbidden to speak naturally, lest his voice reveal his identity. In advance of a public performance, popularly known as a "rain dance," the dancers retire to kivas to prepare their costumes, learn a newly composed cycle of songs, and practice the appropriate steps and gestures. On the scheduled day they appear in the village plaza to sing and dance, with intervals of rest interspersed, from daybreak to sunset. Throughout their afternoon appearances they bring gifts, usually prepared in advance by the kin of the recipients. Most often these consist of toy bows and arrows or of carved and painted wooden *kachina dolls,* which help youngsters to learn the proper markings of an untold number of beneficial spirits. Occasionally, *kachina* dancers are accompanied by a drummer, and in other cases some of the performers scrape an animal shoulder blade (scapula) rhythmically against a notched stick that rests on an inverted gourd. *Kachina* dances are highly esteemed by participants and observers alike, both for their religious values and their artistic appeal. On these occasions women dress themselves and their children in their best clothes, fix elaborate meals, and keep open house throughout the day.

Kachina dances, among the Hopi, are regulated by the ceremonial calendar. In native theory there is an open season, running approximately from the first of January to the end of June, whereas the rest of the year makes up a closed season during which no masked (*kachina*) dances may be held. All the *kachinas* except one, *Masau,* who stands for the god of death and therefore does things by opposites, are supposed to be sleeping or resting throughout the closed season.

Graphic and Plastic Arts

Under the heading of *graphic* and *plastic arts* are generally included all manner of painting, engraving, carving, and sculpturing. They may follow realistic and representational styles, or else abstract or conventionalized ones. Many years ago, under the stimulus of work by A. C. Haddon,[6] it was thought that realism always preceded conventionalization. Since Haddon's day, Boas and others have shown that art styles

[6] A. C. Haddon, *Evolution in Art,* London, 1895.

FIG. 29-2. Hopi *Kachinas*. Left: A dancer in costume. The Jemez (Hümis) *Kachina* costume pictured is a favorite type for the Homegoing (Niman) dance, which ends the open season for *Kachina* performances in midsummer. However, this costume is not obligatory for the Homegoing dance. It may be worn, in addition to many other styles, on other occasions. (Courtesy of Frederick J. Dockstader.) Above: Hopi dancers at Walpi. They are impersonating the Angya (Longhaired) *kachina*. Males in masculine costume are at the right, and two men in feminine garb are at the left. *Kachina* performers sing as they dance. They are pictured in the act of executing an about-face, one man at a time. (Courtesy of the Bureau of American Ethnology.)

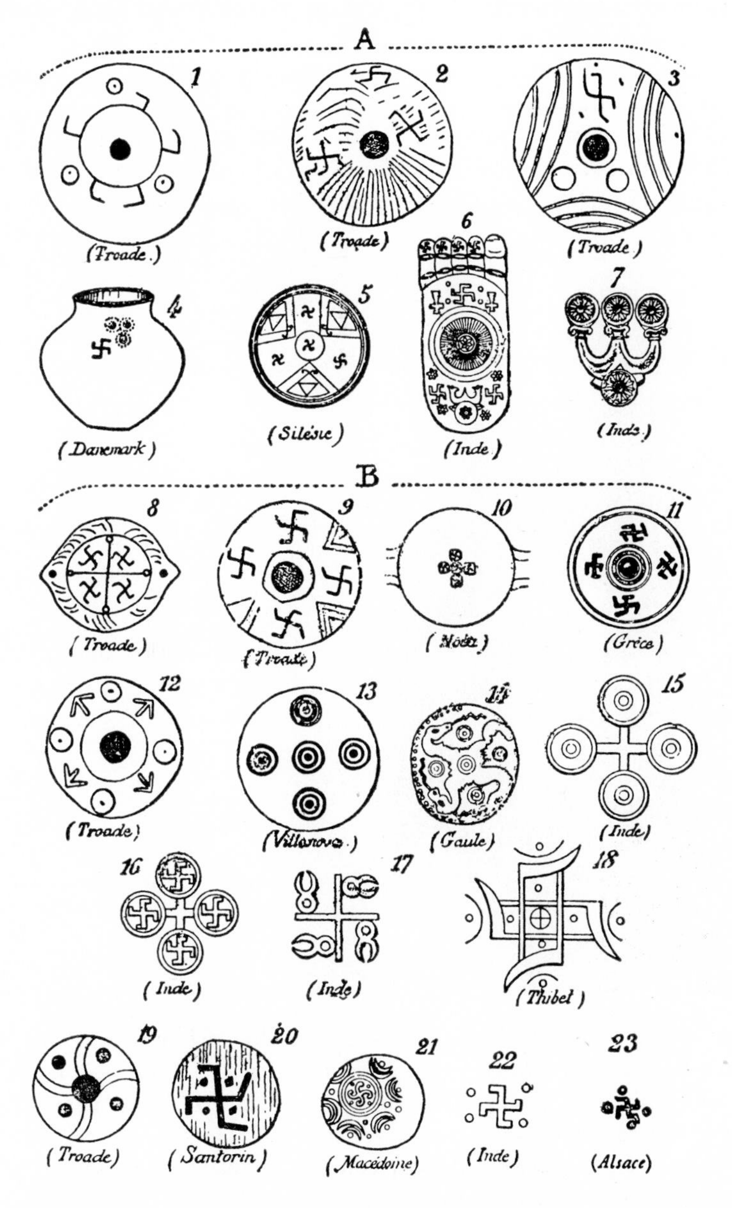

FIG. 29-3. Distribution of the swastika. The swastika is a very old and widely distributed element of design. It occurs in a great profusion of forms and is variously interpreted in different societies. (From Count d'Alviella, *The Migration of Symbols*. New York, 1956. Courtesy of University Books, Inc.)

seem on occasion to move in the reverse direction, and today matters of priority excite but little interest.

Whether it be a realistic portrayal or a geometric figure, a work of art is presently thought of in terms of its meaning, and this, in turn, is looked upon as a matter of cultural interpretation. In some cases a realistic work "freezes" a particular aspect of culture at a given moment of time. Thus, Brueghel's highly realistic sixteenth-century paintings

FIG. 29-4. Stone figures from Easter Island. These monumental carvings have aroused much speculation among anthropologists. (Courtesy of W. Mulloy.)

show games being played, several of which, such as wrestling, blind man's buff, stilt walking, and hoop rolling, are still popular today.

Occasionally works of art have significance only for their creators or for the restricted membership of a particular subculture, but more commonly an artistic expression conveys a similar meaning to all the people who make up a particular society. On the other hand, it is doubtful whether any esthetic product has ever been created that has an identical meaning in all the cultures known to anthropologists. The swastika, for example, is very widely distributed throughout the world, but it is variously portrayed and interpreted in different places (see Fig. 29–3).

Much has been written about the supposed resemblance of primitive art to the art of children. Anthropologists are agreed that such analogies are misleading. Many a work of primitive art shows a mastery of techniques and an understanding of materials that are far from childish. Nor should we forget, if we are judging a piece of primitive art which was produced in a school or other institution, that a work from any culture may appear crude if the artist uses unfamiliar tools and materials. Then, too, we must beware of criticizing something that the artist might neither have tried nor wanted to do in the first place. For example, observers were quick to note that Upper Paleolithic cave paintings have many splendid portrayals of animals but no realistic representations of human beings. No contemporary critic knows whether the lack is due to the inability of Upper Paleolithic artists to picture the human figure or to a complete lack of desire to depict human beings accurately.

The products of the graphic and plastic arts, like other expressions of esthetics, are seldom created for their own sakes in primitive societies. Sometimes they double as house posts, graveyard markers, headrests, cooking utensils, or containers.[7] These instances represent but a sprinkling of the practical purposes that works of art may serve. It should also be kept in mind that many students of culture feel that writing is somehow an outgrowth of pictorial art.

To cite only a few of the best-known examples of primitive art we can mention the splendid ritual bronzes of the Shang period in ancient China, the subtle metal figures created by African dwellers in the neighborhood of the Bay of Benin, the carefully sculptured and painted wooden totem poles of the Indians who used to dwell along the northern Pacific coast of the Americas, the awe-inspiring masks and shields of countless aboriginal tribes, the highly symbolic sand paintings of the Navaho Indians, the astounding stone figures on Easter Island (Fig. 29–4), the exquisite textiles of aboriginal Peru, and the amazing religious architecture of the Mayas and Aztecs, to say nothing of the splendor of the buildings and stone sculptures at Angkor Wat in Cambodia or the remarkable Borobodur monument in Java (Fig. 29–5). Such a list is really unfair as well as incomplete, for it leaves out a host of equally important artistic creations in an incredibly wide assortment of media. For all

---

[7] Much additional information on this topic may be secured from M. J. Herskovits, *Man and His Works,* New York, 1948, pp. 378–413.

their diversity these artistic products are alike in that they gave pleasure to their creators as well as to their users and countless observers.

Playing games[8]

Kroeber has defined play as wasteful but pleasurable bodily activity.[9] By "wasteful" he means presumably that play is not directed to the satisfaction of any of the biological imperatives or other essential needs of mankind. He finds playfulness most fully developed among mammals and he attributes to the rechanneling of play impulses a great many human actions that culminate in esthetic and intellectual pursuits. Kroeber's viewpoint is very interesting and may explain why games and amusements are universal features of all societies. Without exception, though, play among human beings is inevitably a biocultural rather than a biological activity. Bodies may perform all the requisite actions, but cultures determine how the body shall be used and what the rules of any game shall be.

Nor is play invariably wasteful. Youngsters everywhere like to mimic their elders' behavior, and many children's games serve to train them for adult tasks. Such games may be said to have important educational functions and to be practical rather than wasteful. A valuable research program that is designed to determine the relationship of game involvement to child training is now being conducted at Cornell.[10]

Anthropologists distinguish between *games of chance* and *games*

[8] A modern treatment of games may be found in J. M. Roberts, M. J. Arth, and R. R. Bush, "Games in Culture," *American Anthropologist,* Vol. 61, 1959, pp. 597–605.
[9] A. L. Kroeber, *Anthropology,* New York, rev. ed., 1948, pp. 28–29.
[10] For an account of this project, see J. M. Roberts and B. Sutton-Smith, "Child Training and Game Involvement," *Ethnology,* Vol. I, 1962, pp. 166–85.

FIG. 29-5. Examples of primitive arts. A. Navaho sand painting. A medicine man is teaching an apprentice how to make a sand painting by sprinkling grains of colored sand on a neutral background. Figures so constructed represent gods and cosmic symbols, part of the elaborate curing rites that comprise the essence of Navaho religion. B. Brazilian pottery vessel. This type of jar was used as a burial urn by Indians living at the mouth of the Amazon. In the original, the painted design is in several colors. C. Bronze head from Benin. West African tribes in the vicinity of Benin are famous for their skillful work in bronze. D. The Borobodur in Java. This splendid architectural monument is dedicated to Buddha, but it is highly respected by the Moslems of Java. [(A) Courtesy of D. Clifford Bond. (B) Courtesy of Clifford Evans and the Smithsonian Institution. (C) and (D) Courtesy of the Museum of Anthropology, University of Michigan.]

A

B

C

D

of skill.[11] Games of chance, since their outcome is always a matter of uncertainty, offer opportunities for wagering and gambling. As with the question of his supposed esthetic urge, the nature of man's interest in gambling has never been settled. A novice in the study of cultural anthropology is usually amazed to discover how varied and widespread games of chance are in primitive societies. Card games, dice games, guessing games, and lotteries occur in a tremendous profusion of forms, and the stakes may be exceedingly high. In many tribes an excited player may gamble away not only valuable property, but even a beloved wife or child. Men have gambled themselves and their families into destitution and even slavery; yet no society seems to have profited from their misery, and games of chance continue to be played throughout the world.[12]

Various motives may exist for the playing of games of skill. A few such games are played for gambling, sheer amusement, or intellectual pleasure; others are little more than physical pastimes; many involve difficult competition and a determined effort to outdo one's rivals; not a few have religious motivations; and some serve the avowed purposes of training exercises for war. It is rather firmly held, on the basis of convincing proof, that many of the implements that are used in games of skill, particularly sticks and clubs, were originally weapons.

Games of skill, which test intellectual prowess, fall into classes closely resembling checkers or chess. These are allied to others, such as backgammon, which combine skill with chance. In such games counters are moved across a board not according to individual decisions but as determined by throws of dice (Fig. 29–6). E. B. Tylor, late in the last century, found that such games had world-wide distribution, and his studies of *patolli* led him to conclude that their presence in America gave evidence of diffusion from Asia,[13] but Kroeber later cast doubt on Tylor's conclusion.[14]

Many games, particularly those that we identify as *sports,* depend on the strenuous yet well-controlled use of the body. Essentially, the acquisition of what athletes usually call "good form" is required. Once

---

[11] Roberts and Sutton-Smith, *op. cit.,* p. 166, suggest games of strategy as a third category. They also recognize various combinations of physical skill, chance, and strategy.

[12] A study of this subject has been made by E. Bergler, *The Psychology of Gambling,* New York, 1957.

[13] Tylor's studies are conveniently summarized in A. L. Kroeber and T. T. Waterman, *Source Book in Anthropology,* New York, 1931, pp. 388–97.

[14] A. L. Kroeber, *Anthropology,* New York, rev. ed., 1948, p. 551.

more we come across the advantages of man's ability to look ahead and to be content with the hope of future rewards for difficult actions that yield no compensation at the moment. All athletes are aware of the drudgery of practice periods during which good form is acquired, but few players dare rely on inherited talents to the extent of foregoing training sessions. As sports become more highly organized, the amount of effort devoted to coaching and preliminary training increases.

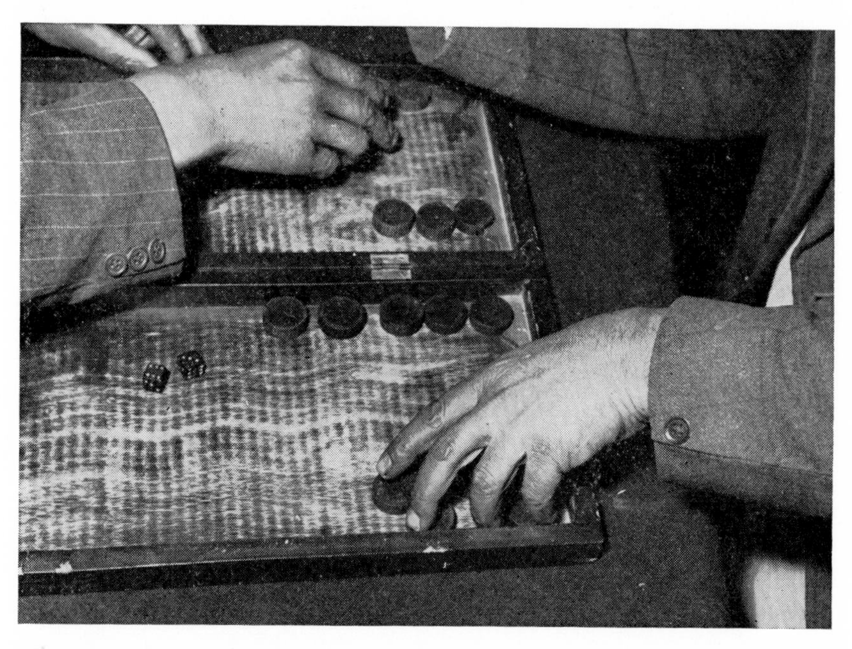

FIG. 29-6. Iranian (Persian) men playing backgammon. Known as *tric-trac,* this form of backgammon is very popular in Iran. It is usually played by men in coffee shops. (Courtesy of Three Lions.)

Wrestling, which depends on strength and the skillful use of the body, is practically universal. So important an aspect of culture was it once considered to be that, according to a story which is still current, the Olympic games originated from a divine wrestling match in which Zeus, the chief deity of the ancient Greeks, overcame Chronos, the god of time. Races of all kinds are also very common. Many of them are simple running races, but among several tribes of Indians the contestants also kick a stone or a stick as they run.

Archeologists have uncovered a vast number of ball courts (Fig. 29–7). Their evidence makes it clear that ball games of many kinds had a wide distribution in times past,[15] and many contemporary people continue to hold such contests regularly. Among these one of the best-known examples is hockey (*chueca*), as played by the Araucanian Indians of Chile. This tribe was among the last big ones in the New World to be pacified by Caucasoids, and until a few decades ago its entire culture was geared to war. As long as active fighting prevailed the Araucanians frankly looked upon hockey as a training exercise for war and the terms for hockey player and warrior were used interchangeably, but since their

FIG. 29-7. A Maya ball court. The ancient Maya Indians played an important game on a court. Not all the details are known, but it is thought that scores were made by passing a ball through a loop such as the one shown on the wall at the right. (Courtesy of Southwest Museum.)

pacification the natives play chiefly for sport and wagering. The game resembles field hockey as played by teams of women in Euro-American countries, but it is a rough-and-tumble masculine sport among the Araucanians. It calls for speed, stamina, daring, and good coordination, qualities whose usefulness in war is self-evident.[16]

In trying to understand the world-wide prevalence of games, it is possible to analyze some of their functions in terms of biocultural dynamics. Team games intensify the solidarity of a society by offering socially sanctioned outlets for aggression. We must remember that those who indulge in games of chance are forever trying to win over others,

---

[15] C. S. Chard, "Distribution and Significance of Ball-Courts in the Southwest," *Papers of the Excavators' Club,* Vol. 1, No. 2, 1940.

[16] M. Titiev, "Araucanian Culture in Transition," *Occasional Contributions from the Museum of Anthropology,* No. 15, Ann Arbor, Mich., 1951.

and even when intellectual games like checkers or chess are played, we speak of trying to beat an opponent. Moreover, whether we watch or play team games, we identify ourselves with one social unit, usually our own, and do our best to make it triumph over another group.

SUPERNATURALISM IN GAMES

Stewart Culin, an early but outstanding specialist in the study of games, has unequivocally stated that many games that appear on the surface to be played only for gain, exercise, or amusement are also performed as sacred rites for pleasing the gods. They may be played in the hope of winning general approval from the supernatural world or else for such specific purposes as driving away evil, averting sickness, bringing rain, and aiding the reproduction of plants, animals, and human beings.[17] Games have undergone so many changes and reinterpretations in historic times that a modern reader may question the truth of Culin's analysis. Many factors make the proper classification of games difficult if not impossible. It is very hard to know, for instance, when rowing ceases to be a game and becomes work. Similarly, many of us find it far from easy to differentiate between an amateur with a generous expense account and a professional athlete. Yet, societies may set great store on such distinctions. Differing kinds of spectators watch amateur (collegiate) and professional football; and in the United States amateur track meets are well attended, but virtually no one goes to a professional track meet.

Returning to the theme of supernaturalism and games, everyone in America rather vaguely associates superstition with gamblers and athletes; but it is much harder to believe that innocent-looking games involving hoops and poles may often be traced back to practices of mimetic magic, when these objects stood for the female and male sex organs, respectively, and when their use symbolized sexual relations as a request for fertility.

The clearest links between the playing of games and religious practices seem to depend on the element of the unknown or uncontrollable. When we are at a loss to understand why something unexpected happens in sports or gambling, we are apt to attribute it to "luck," but primitive peoples more often assign such events to supernatural forces.

---

[17] S. Culin, "Games of the North American Indians," *Annual Report, Bureau of American Ethnology,* No. 24, Washington, D.C., 1907. For wider and more up-to-date treatment, see F. Barth, "Segmentary Opposition and the Theory of Games," *Journal of the Royal Anthropological Institute,* Vol. 89, Part 1, 1959, pp. 5–21.

From this standpoint it is simple to see why all games of chance should have religious implications. The connection with games of skill may be less clear until we realize that in them, too, unless there is cheating, the outcome is never known in advance, and wherever controlled causation is missing, recourse may be had to the supernatural.

Games of chance are closely related to ordeals in that the winner is supposedly determined by some extrahuman or supernatural agency. That is why difficult decisions may be left to the throw of dice, the cutting of cards, the toss of a coin, or a similar activity. Counting-out procedures, if truly left to chance, belong in the same category. It seems unnecessary to repeat that sophisticated individuals who indulge in such practices may have no awareness of the supernatural implications of what they are doing and may even resent any interpretation along religious lines. Not everyone in our culture is willing to consider belief in "luck" to be even partially equivalent to faith in the supernatural.

In the primitive world, games of chance are more likely to be directly connected with religion. Many a player prays long and earnestly for supernatural guidance before he draws lots or makes a decision in what looks to us like a childish game of "Button, button, who's got the button?" Also, it is reported that some of the Sioux-speaking tribes long ago had a *ghost gamble*, the purpose of which was to play for the effects of a recently deceased individual. The goods were placed into a number of piles, marked peach stones were used as counters, and the living pitted their luck against a player who impersonated the deceased. If a man were fortunate he might thus win cheaply some of the dead person's belongings. All proceeds went to the heirs of the deceased.

Games of skill likewise show frequent religious motivations. A swift runner who carries water may not only triumph over others but may also, on the basis of mimetic magic, represent an automatic prayer for rain to come quickly. Similarly, several North American Indian tribes used to play a type of hockey or shinny in which the ball was stuffed with seeds. The idea was that if the ball were quickly burst and the seeds widely scattered, the gods would send early and bountiful harvests. Throughout many parts of the world, too, games organized like a tug of war are used to induce supernatural powers to send favors, such as sunshine, in the direction indicated by the winners.

Some games associated with religion may be calendrical, whereas others may be critical and not scheduled long in advance. The most widely distributed of the calendrical games consists of assorted ways of making *string figures*, or what we call "cat's cradle." Not all peoples who fashion elaborate designs with string limit themselves to playing at the same seasons of the year, nor do they all offer identical explanations for similar designs or for the game itself, but it is not uncommon to find a calendrical or seasonal implication. Some Eskimo groups make string figures primarily late in the summer, in order to enmesh and detain the sun; but certain New Guinea tribes play "cat's cradle" in the growing season, in order to make their yams grow (Fig. 29–8).

Funeral games, on the other hand, must always, from their very nature, be played only in times of crisis. They need not, however, always

FIG. 29-8. Cat's cradle in New Guinea. Cat's cradle is played almost universally. While it may have had religious connotations in the past, it has often degenerated into a simple game for children. (From H. I. Hogbin, *Peoples of the Southwest Pacific.* New York, 1945–1946. Courtesy Asia Press, Inc.)

be limited to a single purpose. In some cases their main intent apparently is to speed the spirit of the deceased to the other world, where he belongs. In other cases, the chief purpose appears to be the freeing of the survivors from the fear that they might be stricken by the same evil power that caused one of their members to die. Feelings of relief, joy, or pleasure may thus enter into the performance of funeral games.

Those who strive for victory in games very commonly seek supernatural additions to their skill. Everything from a favorite garment to a lucky coin or a rabbit's foot may be used to supplement one's own ability. Paraphernalia that are thought to be full of mana because they were used with success in the past may be used to the exclusion of all similar items. Sporting circles are full of talk about "lucky bats," "lucky shoes," "lucky tennis rackets," "lucky fishing rods," and so forth. Many players also resort to bits of private ritual, such as always repeating a set formula in a crisis, or always touching second base with the left foot on the way in from the field.[18]

It is difficult for us to realize how seriously many primitive groups

FIG. 29-9. Cherokee ball game. The players are shown around the fire at the right. Their rackets are being blessed by the drummer, priest, and women. The game was a very serious affair, and it was felt that supernatural support was needed for victory. (Courtesy of the Bureau of American Ethnology.)

take their games. The Cherokee Indians of North Carolina and elsewhere used to play a tough lacrosse game in which teams from various towns competed.[19] Contrary to our practice of resting players in seclusion on the eve of an important contest, the Cherokee players remained awake all night. They were subjected to painful ordeals, and they participated in highly important rituals (Fig. 29–9), designed to gain supernatural support that would help them to victory on the morrow.

[18] A number of the "superstitious" practices of professional baseball players and their wives are described in the Women's Section of the *Detroit News*, Sunday, Sept. 17, 1950. Many of them correspond to items mentioned here.

[19] J. Mooney, "The Cherokee Ball Play," *American Anthropologist*, Vol. 3, No. 2, 1890.

The wholehearted reliance that primitive peoples may put on supernatural decisions as expressed in the results of games should not be minimized. Early in September of 1906, the Hopi pueblo of Old Oraibi found itself so badly divided over many questions, including the acceptance of "white" schooling, that it was agreed to separate the two factions permanently. To decide which faction should leave its traditional home, the Indians traced a line on the ground and the sides faced each other, with the understanding that those who were pushed across would be the losers and would have to leave. In the ensuing "push fest," the conservatives who opposed the new schools lost, whereupon their leader yielded to his fate and led his followers to a vacant site where they founded the village of Hotevilla.[20] Here were about 400 individuals who, with their ancestors, had lived at Oraibi for centuries, but who left their old homes without further argument because their gods had made known their wills through the outcome of a game.

Selected References

Adam, Leonhard, *Primitive Art,* rev. ed., London and Baltimore, 1954.

Boas, Franz, *Primitive Art,* Oslo, 1929.

Chard, Chester S., "Distribution and Significance of Ball Courts in the Southwest," *Papers of the Excavators' Club,* Vol. I, No. 2, 1940.

Culin, Stewart, "Games of the North American Indians," *Bureau of American Ethnology, Annual Report,* No. 24, Washington, D. C., 1907.

Derringer, D., *The Alphabet,* New York, 1948.

Dockstader, Frederick J., *Indian Art in America,* Greenwich, Conn., 1961.

Haddon, K., *Artists in String: Their Regional Distribution and Social Significance,* New York, 1930.

Hambly, W. D., *Tribal Dancing and Social Developments,* New York, 1927.

Herzog, George, "Research in Primitive and Folk Music in the United States," *American Council of Learned Societies,* Bulletin, No. 24, 1936, pp. 1–97.

Kurath, Gertrude P., "A New Method of Choreographic Notation," *American Anthropologist,* Vol. 52, No. 1, 1950, pp. 120–23.

[20] M. Titiev, "Old Oraibi: A Study of the Hopi Indians of Third Mesa," *Papers of the Peabody Museum of American Archaeology and Ethnology,* Cambridge, Mass., Vol. 22, No. 1, 1944, pp. 86 ff.

Linton, Ralph, and Wingert, Paul S., *Arts of the South Seas,* New York, 1946.

Mooney, James, "The Cherokee Ball Play," *American Anthropologist,* Vol. 3, No. 2, 1890.

Nettl, Bruno, *Music in Primitive Culture,* Cambridge, Mass., 1956.

Newcomb, F. J., *et al.,* "A Study of Navajo Symbolism," *Papers of the Peabody Museum of American Archaeology and Ethnology,* Cambridge, Mass., Vol. 32, No. 3, 1956.

Rhodes, W., "Toward a Definition of Ethnomusicology," *American Anthropologist,* Vol. 58, 1956.

Roberts, John M., Arth, M. M., and Bush, R. R., "Games in Culture," *American Anthropologist,* Vol. 61, 1959, pp. 597–605.

Smith, Marian W., ed., *The Artist in Tribal Society,* London, 1961.

Four Patterns of Culture

CHAPTER 30

Up to this point, in this part of the text, we have been primarily concerned with setting forth the principles, methods, and objectives of American cultural anthropology. Only occasionally, and usually for the sake of providing examples, have allusions been made to specific customs in particular societies. It seems highly appropriate, therefore, that we should now depict in reasonably complete, though in thumbnail fashion, the ways of life that exist in a number of representative societies.

As the study of *human ecology* makes clear, all groups of people must develop successful mechanisms for dealing with their physical settings.[1] This requirement provides a measure of similarity among all the societies to be discussed below. The Owens Valley Paiute are Amerinds, living in an arid environment; the Tikopians are Oceanic Negroids, who dwell on an island in the South Pacific; the Hopi are American Indian Mongoloids, who inhabit a semidesert portion of Arizona; and the people of the United States are primarily Caucasoids, who occupy a vast extent of variable territory, and are, in general, highly industrialized.

Racially, geographically, linguistically, and culturally these people are vastly different from one another; yet, each is equally repre-

[1] This important topic is discussed in a comprehensive article by June Helm, "The Ecological Approach in Anthropology," *The American Journal of Sociology,* Vol. 67, 1962, pp. 630-39. Her notes provide a fine bibliography. See, too, R. J. Braidwood and G. R. Willey, eds., *op. cit.*

sentative of *Homo sapiens,* and some of their ways are surprisingly alike. These similarities help to make the study of anthropology such a fascinating pursuit. In the exercise of our profession we are always on the watch for the universal uniformities of human behavior that so often underlie the external diversities of men's conduct. Our task is not merely to ferret out whatever universal principles we can find, but also to interpret them as well as we can.

The four groups to be considered here were chosen because they represent such greatly varied responses to their environment. These responses constantly interact with, and influence, all other features of a society's way of life. The Paiute are principally hunters and gatherers; the Tikopians are farmers, gatherers, and fishermen; the Hopi are farmers, primarily; and the people of the United States, for the most part, are somehow connected with industrial pursuits. In each case, too, the social organization and religion vary with the manner in which the environment is manipulated. It is because these variations are so strikingly different in their complexity and efficiency that some scholars seek to arrange them on a chronological, developmental, or evolutionary scale.

It will be noted that the present tense is widely used throughout our thumbnail descriptions, even though the works on which they are based were published years ago. This usage is known as the *ethnographic present.* It is employed for convenience and as a way of achieving uniformity in presenting the sketches. Use of the present tense is not intended to give the impression that the cultures involved have remained unchanged. Anthropologists know full well that processes of change operate constantly on all patterns of culture, sometimes without being apparent and sometimes in clear view. Since our major purpose in this chapter is not to trace or discuss culture change but only to summarize ways of life as they appeared at one moment of time, we shall write in the present without further apology.

One additional point. Studies of primitive customs would have only limited value if they failed to provide clues for a better understanding of our own mores. The examples from American culture that have occasionally been given were, on the whole, introduced to show that many basic principles of human conduct apply to Euro-American society just as well as to the world of primitive man. It is in the belief that we can gain a wider and better understanding of ourselves through a study of primitive cultures that a sketch of life in the United States is included in this chapter.

SUBSISTENCE AND MATERIAL CULTURE IN OWENS VALLEY[2]

Owens Valley lies in east central California, not far from the Nevada line. It is inhabited by Paiute Indians, who speak a Shoshonean language—a tongue that belongs to the Uto-Aztecan family and that was spoken here and there from Utah to the Valley of Mexico.

Owens Valley lies within the geographical region of the Great Basin, which means that much of it is arid, subject to hot summers and moderate winters, and has only a few streams, which generally end up in salt lakes. However, the snow-capped Sierra Nevada mountains are nearby, and afford many resources, including piñon trees, whose nuts these people gather as their main staple.

Nearly a thousand Indians live in Owens Valley, in a series of camps. Aboriginally, winter houses had dirt floors, entrances that faced east, and a smokehole in the center. They were constructed around a cone of poles that stood about 9 feet high and covered a space of 15 to 20 feet. The walls consisted of overlapping mats or "shingles," most often made of tule rushes and bound with willow withes (Fig. 30–1C). In the summer people lived under dome-shaped willow shades.

Different houses were used in the mountains, and there were a number of other variants, but the most important nondwelling structure was a large, earth-covered sweat house. Not only was this used as a sudatory, but it also served as a dormitory for unmarried males, a men's clubhouse, a community center, and a church.

The Owens Valley Paiute have a marked dichotomy between the sexes. Although pine nuts and edible roots are extremely important for all, they are gathered by women. Seeds or nuts are knocked into conical carrying baskets, and tubers are dug with pointed sticks. Piñon nuts are collected in the mountains, and when a fall "crop" is abundant it may last into the following summer. Nuts are roasted, or ground on a metate and winnowed to get rid of the shells. They may be eaten dry or made into a mush or soup.

Many other plants, including some acorns, are also used for food; and some plants, such as jimson weed and tobacco, get special emphasis. Although the Owens Valley Paiute have no agriculture, they do practice irrigation to increase natural yields; men build the dams and ditches.

---

[2] The material on these Indians is summarized, by permission, from J. H. Steward, "Ethnography of the Owens Valley Paiute," *University of California Publications in American Archaeology and Ethnology,* Vol. 33, No. 3, Berkeley, Calif., 1933.

FIG. 30-1. Scenes at Owens Valley. Top, left: Paiute man working a fire drill. Top, right: Man with a bow and arrow. Bottom: A Paiute house. The "shingles" are made of tule reeds. A baby is shown securely tied in its cradle board, to the right of the doorway. (Courtesy of Julian H. Steward.)

Besides their household and gathering duties, women make willow-splint pitch-lined water jars or ollas, and twined cradle boards of willow. A few women make pottery, usually with coils of clay; and, on occasion, females help with the fashioning of blankets made from strips of rabbit fur. As a rule, women make their buckskin skirts and wear nothing above the waist.

Men, too, have many duties at Owens Valley. They are expected to rise early, and their main occupation is hunting. The principal quarry consists of deer and rabbits. Deer are hunted individually, and killed with sinew-backed bows and obsidian-tipped arrows. Rabbits are generally hunted in communal drives, driven into nets, and slain with straight clubs. Other animals are also hunted on occasion.

Once in a while the men engage in trade. They also make weapons, fashion their own clothes, build houses, weave rabbitskin blankets, and make moccasins.

SUPERNATURALISM AND GAMES AMONG THE OWENS VALLEY PAIUTE

The Paiute in Owens Valley believe that the universe consists of a dome-shaped sky stretched over a flat earth. The earth is held in the hands of an unknown creature, and shakes when he moves. It was created by Wolf, a beneficent culture hero; Coyote, on the other hand, is responsible for evil. There are no formal rituals for these beings, and there are no full-time priests; but good thoughts are supposed to make nature benevolent, whereas bad thoughts bring on natural calamities.

Supernatural power, derived from most things in nature, comes to individuals unsought, as in unexpected dreams. Such power can be used for success in doctoring, gambling, warfare, plant gathering, etc. It is not limited to either sex.

Many "doctors" or shamans get their power from the Bear. Shamans may be men or women, and the ability to cure seems to run in families. Shamanistic power is supposed to come early in life—as early as the ages of 5 or 6—and to manifest itself primarily through the knowledge and possession of sacred songs.

Among the commonest ceremonies found among the Paiute at Owens Valley, are the rites of passage. A pregnant woman abstains from meat, and gives birth in a heated pit. A variety of taboos apply separately to the father and mother. A boy is named by his paternal grandfather and a girl by her paternal grandmother. Any name might be used except that of someone who was recently deceased.

Puberty rituals for a girl are connected with her first menses, and are designed to make her industrious, healthy, and suited for childbearing. She is expected to run westward, bathe in cold water, abstain from meat, and avoid all contact with males. Behavior at subsequent periods is a modification of the puberty rites.

A boy, at adolescence, is awakened early one day, listens to a variety of morning songs, bathes in a nearby stream, runs several miles uphill, learns the masculine virtues of his people, and asks the unknown for guidance, blessing, and power. There is no secret society for him to join.

Marriage is forbidden to "blood" relatives, and village exogamy prevails. It is also considered improper to take a spouse from the village of either parent. Marriages take place soon after puberty, and involve gift exchanges between the families of the principals. Polygyny is permitted, but is limited by a man's wealth.

When death strikes, relatives of the deceased are supposed to talk across a corpse to please its soul. The body, wrapped in an animal skin, is later buried, and relatives are supposed to sprinkle food on the ground, for the benefit of the "ghost." There is a funeral dance and a eulogy before the mourners disperse. There is no agreement on the nature of the other world.

The favorite amusements at Owens Valley always involve gambling, preferably for high stakes. There is also a popular hand game, during which opposing sides sing for guidance before guessing which of an opponent's hands conceals a number of small sticks. Women play with stick dice; and men shoot arrows competitively, play football and shinny, roll hoops, wrestle, and run races. Boys play quoits and a number of other games, but there are no games particularly designed for girls.

The Owens Valley Paiute usually scatter throughout most of the year, but they like to assemble in the fall, after seed harvest, for a round of gambling and dancing festivities. The favorite dance is a form of circle dance. It begins with a leader and six half-bent men carrying bows and arrows, but it soon expands to include all the men and women who want to join. There are also special dances—such as the Bear dance—in which half a dozen shamans dress in the skins and heads of grizzly bears.

As is to be expected at the hunting-gathering level of culture, the Owens Valley Paiute do not have formal, full-time priests, nor do they have outstanding specialists or powerful political leaders.

FIG. 30-2. A kava ritual. This scene is from New Zealand in Polynesia, where kava is more widely used than in Melanesia, wherein Tikopia is located. It may simply be drunk like coffee, or it may be consumed as a rite, with highly standardized procedures. (Courtesy New Zealand Embassy.)

LAND, LABOR, AND DAILY LIFE ON TIKOPIA[3]

Tikopia is a small island, roughly elliptical in shape, running about three miles from northeast to southwest and approximately one and a half miles in the other direction. Spatially, it lies within the area of Melanesia, although the customs of its 1281 inhabitants mark them as part of a Polynesian fringe.[4] For a small island, Tikopia has a varied

[3] This section and the next are based on Raymond Firth, *We, the Tikopia,* American Book Company, New York, 1936. Permission to summarize Firth's volume was graciously given by the author and publisher.

Firth lived on Tikopia as a participant-observer for a full year beginning in July, 1928. He quickly learned to speak the native language and thereafter worked directly, without using an interpreter.

[4] Melanesia conventionally refers to the islands that range from New Guinea to Fiji. Polynesia lies further east in the South Pacific and includes the territory within the approximate triangle formed by Hawaii in the north, New Zealand in the southwest, and Easter Island to the southeast.

terrain, including a reef but no lagoon, coastal beaches, woodlands, plains, a swamp, a fresh-water lake, and fairly rugged cliffs. At first impression it appears heavily wooded, with small and infrequent patches of cultivated land in the vicinity of scattered villages, but closer familiarity reveals that much of what seems to be wasteland is privately owned and carefully utilized. Very few of the island's resources are wasted, and the inhabitants pride themselves on the beauty and bounty of their homeland.

The people of Tikopia live primarily on vegetable foods, some of which grow wild and some of which are deliberately cultivated. Taro makes up the principal crop, but coconuts, breadfruit, yams, and bananas are also grown or gathered. *Betel nut,* a mild narcotic that stains the saliva red, is universally chewed by adults, and *kava* is drunk or offered to the gods during religious observances (Fig. 30–2). Vegetal products are supplemented with fish, and fresh water is obtained from springs.

Theoretically, all land and drinking water are owned by four chiefs, each of whom dwells near a spring and represents or controls the ancestral spirits who are thought to be the true owners of the island. In practice, there is a close link between land holdings and places of residence. Every cluster of huts is recognized as a village entity and with each there goes a name and fixed boundaries. Food-bearing lands are privately owned, but not much fuss is made over trespass if permission is sought beforehand or if a transgressor later tells a proprietor what he has done. Should an owner desire to prevent intrusions on his property he may declare his land taboo to all others. Customarily, a man's holdings are inherited by his sons. A female eats from her father's land before marriage, but from her husband's land thereafter.

Foods are by no means the only products that the natives get by interacting with their environment. Some fields are regularly set aside for the growing of first-fruit offerings. Houses, built low to minimize the effects of gales, are made principally of local woods and sago palm. Furnishings are scant, consisting primarily of mats made of plaited coconut leaves, and people sleep under bark-cloth covers on pandanus bed mats. Although the temperature is fairly equable and quite high, averaging between 80 and 85 degrees Fahrenheit, the humidity is great and some periods of coolness are known. Everyday garments consist of waistbands or kilts of bark cloth for men and skirts of the same material for women. Adults of both sexes like to wear as much calico, which has been given religious significance, as they can get. Youngsters run about naked.

A

B

FIG. 30-3. Tikopians dancing. Dancing is an important activity in Tikopia. Women dance in one style (A), and men in another (B). (Courtesy of R. Firth and American Book Company.)

Tikopians awaken soon after sunrise every morning and straggle to the beach, where they bathe and make their toilets. Each sex goes to a different spot, but men and women remain in full view of one another and trust to cultural blindness to preserve their modesty. Within each house a smoldering fire is blown into flame, but breakfast is eaten informally and usually consists of cold leftovers. People then go to work, farming, gardening, gathering food, fishing, beating out bark cloth, or caring for infants. Tasks are often combined with a bit of fun, and in the afternoon everyone returns to prepare for the big meal of the day. For this, both sexes share the responsibility. Normally, the inhabitants of each household fix and eat their food by themselves. Cooking is done in ovens, which are generally located in separate structures close by each dwelling. After eating, people chew betel and relax before turning to various arts and crafts. Late in the day, those who wish drift to informal assembly points on the beach, where older folk chat and gossip while younger ones, especially if they are unmarried, play games, wrestle, dance (Fig. 30–3), or make love. Many songs are composed and sung, most of which are timely and soon forgotten, but some of which are taken up and so frequently repeated that they become traditional. Everyone retires at will; there is no fixed bedtime.

As is to be expected, there is some sexual dichotomy, but it is not greatly marked on Tikopia, for cooperation is more important than separation. Besides bearing children and looking after households, females make bark cloth, plait mats, perform dyeing operations, help to grow or gather vegetal foods, and fish by hand along the reef. Men do the heavier farming tasks, climb coconut trees, work at carpentry, make all manner of cordage, serve as tattooers, conduct the major rituals, and fish in the open sea from outrigger canoes.

Respect and avoidance are important mechanisms of social control and make up an elaborate code of etiquette. Chiefs expect a great show of respect; all married women are supposed to be treated respectfully; restraint marks the reciprocal behavior of all cousins; personal body contact is generally avoided; and an individual's head, particularly that of a chief or parent, is never to be carelessly touched. So it is that the populace is ranked and differentiated, even though there is ample food for all, everyone dresses and lives alike on the surface, and matters of wealth, except for land containing coconut palms, are of little moment.

TIKOPIAN KINSHIP AND SOCIORELIGIOUS BEHAVIOR

Kinship plays an extremely important part in Tikopian social organization. Many aspects of the aboriginal religion are based on recognition of the fact that a kinship system continues to operate, even beyond the life spans of particular individuals. Each term employed may be regarded as a guide to a particular way of behaving, and children are taught how to address and act toward their various relatives. All natives of the island share a sense of kinship, and only those who come from elsewhere are considered to be true strangers. At the same time, not every inhabitant of Tikopia is regarded equally. Place of residence, age, sex, and social status, as well as the ties of "blood" or marriage, all make a great difference. Roughly speaking, the long axis of the island divides Tikopia into rival districts between which there is a great deal of distrust, competition, and slander, although the members of one unit are free to marry into the other.

Space and kinship are complexly interwoven on Tikopia. Large units of kin comprise *kainanga,* which may be equated with patrilineal clans. These are political and religious, in the sense that only the members of a *kainanga* may attend the rites performed by their leader; and the status of a group depends on the importance of the gods with which it is affiliated. In turn, each *kainanga* is subdivided into a number of *paito,* or households, whose inmates are determined by the combined workings of patrilineal descent and patrilocal residence. That is to say, each child finds itself born into a *paito* that contains as a nucleus his father's father, his father, and his father's brothers. All the females in the household would be either unwed or women who had moved in at marriage. Throughout their lives all men are expected to retain an interest in the women who once resided in their natal households. Each residence group has a headman, who speaks for it whenever necessary.

Strong links of kinship unite the males in every household, but on Tikopia, as elsewhere, relationship ties established involuntarily at birth are balanced by other links. Much is made of the affinal connections that develop at marriage. Although kin reckoning is entirely unilateral through males, the existence of the nuclear family is fully recognized. Furthermore, an infant is taught to show especially high regard for his mother's brother. On his part, a man will always befriend and help his sister's child. Very warm bonds also develop between a youngster and its grandparents. The formal relations of those in alternate generations are much less severe than the ones that prevail among those of successive generations.

A number of complicated ceremonies attend the birth of an infant. When a child reaches the age of three, its mother pierces its earlobes and nasal septum, usually a rather painless operation. Some years later, another milestone is passed when a boy, and once in a while a girl, is taken on his first fishing expedition by torchlight. This event is signalized by the wearing of a distinctive garment.

Adolescents of both sexes often band together for work or play. There is some resistance to parental authority, but there is no adolescent rebellion against established social practices. Children grow up in a permissive atmosphere and are even allowed to imitate sexual relations without much reproof. The onset of menstruation is not marked in any way, and among these people menstruants are neither isolated nor regarded as dangerous.[5]

Somewhere between the ages of 9 and 14, but not directly connected with the attainment of puberty, a few boys at a time are put through a tribal initiation. The principal feature consists of an operation on the foreskin of the penis, involving a cut that is a *superincision* rather than a circumcision. The whole affair is entrusted to a boy's mother's brothers, one of whom performs the superincision. Each youngster is smeared with turmeric and oil and dressed in a new waistband by his female relatives. The rites are said to have had a supernatural origin, but very little of a religious nature accompanies their performance. Instead, there is a great deal of feasting and gift exchanging. Failure to go through the rites makes a young man subject to teasing and taunting.

Not much serious attention is paid to premarital sexual experience, but virginity is known and a man who happens to marry a virgin is very proud of the fact. Despite the general absence of shame or punishment for youthful sexual intercourse, an unmarried girl who bears a bastard is sometimes regarded with contempt. Tikopians have no preferential marriages, and polygny is common, but the levirate is not practiced. Females usually want the security of marriage but males are less eager to settle down. A lover who makes a girl pregnant is expected to marry his partner, and elopements of sweethearts are not unknown. Most often, however, men capture their wives, sometimes by prearrangement, and sometimes by actual abduction.[6] As a rule, feasts and amicable exchanges

[5] This is by no means typical of primitive societies.

[6] It is often extremely difficult for an anthropologist to ascertain the true facts of a custom that may be described as "wife capture." On the island of Bali, Margaret Mead tells us (*And Keep Your Powder Dry,* New York, 1942, p. 42), no one but a neurotic would "abduct" a bride without first having obtained her consent.

of gifts between the households and kinsfolk involved follow soon after a capture. Within a short time after a marriage, too, a groom is expected to accompany his bride on a visit to her parents at her natal household.

If a new wife so resents a captor that she violently rejects his initial advances, his kinsmen may hold her by force until her husband enjoys her. Women are expected to remain true to their mates, but infidelities on the part of men are lightly treated. There is no formal mechanism of divorce, but separations for various reasons do take place.

Death removes a person to the supernatural realm, but it does not end his contacts with the world of the living. When someone dies, it is customary to light two ovens, which means that the pair of households which the deceased most frequented show their sympathy by serving feasts. Corpses are wrapped in mats or plain lengths of bark cloth, and burial takes place either within the confines of a house or in a designated sector just outside. Some houses have their floor space partitioned for use by males or females, or for other purposes. In such houses one portion may remain unoccupied except at funerals. Important spirits of the dead may be commemorated by special mats, and people are reluctant to abandon a house in which some of their ancestors are buried. Personal grief is often expressed by the bereaved, but some purely formal wailing is also prescribed.

On the whole, the island of Tikopia is quite isolated, and the abundance of its resources is sufficient to keep the inhabitants from wanting to leave. Nevertheless, objects of metal, obtainable only from outside sources, are greatly coveted, and other aspects of acculturation, notably Christian teachings, are known. As far back as 1928 Firth found that many young men tried to stow away on ships, but their purpose was not to escape but to acquire heightened prestige so that their status would rise when they returned.

MATERIAL CULTURE AND SOCIAL ORGANIZATION OF THE HOPI INDIANS[7]

Perched picturesquely on the flat tops of a trio of mesas in a semi-arid portion of northeastern Arizona are the nine traditional pueblos whose inhabitants comprise the core of the Hopi Indian tribe. As one approaches from the east, the only feasible way in the old days, he comes

7 This and the following section summarize material taken, by permission, from Mischa Titiev, "Old Oraibi: A Study of the Hopi Indians of Third Mesa," *Papers of the Peabody Museum of American Archaeology and Ethnology,* Vol. 22, No. 1, Cambridge, Mass., 1944.

successively to First, Second, and Third Mesa. Atop the Third Mesa is to be found the ancient village of Oraibi (Fig. 30–4), until September of 1906 the largest of the Hopi towns and unofficially known as the capital of Hopiland. In reality, the Oraibi chief never exerted political authority over the other pueblos, and each village is jealous of its autonomy.

In 1934 there were in all about 3000 Hopi Indians, but an exact count has never been made. The native language is a form of Shosho-

FIG. 30-4. Airview of Old Oraibi. With the possible exception of Acoma pueblo in New Mexico, Oraibi is the oldest continuously occupied village in the United States. It is located in northeastern Arizona, about 100 miles east of the Grand Canyon, and on the edge of the Painted Desert.

nean. Despite their lack of political unity and numerous local variations of custom, all the Hopi speak one language and share a way of life that is typified by the inhabitants of Oraibi.

Every pueblo is divided into a number of exogamous, matrilineal clans, from one of which town chiefs are regularly drawn, and each of which has the privilege of farming on a particular bit of land. Theoretically, a village chief owns all the land associated with his pueblo, but in practice every clan knows where its holdings lie, and hardly ever does a chief interfere with long-established customs of land use. Hopi men are diligent and expert dry farmers, and whenever they get sufficient rain they raise good crops of maize, beans, and squash. In addition, they grow a variety of such fruits as watermelon, peaches, and apricots, and they supplement these foods with meat from flocks of sheep or with rabbits killed by hunting. Because land is owned by clans and clans are matrilineal, a man is expected to farm for his mother or sister while he is unwed and for his wife after marriage.

In summertime men like to arise before daybreak so that they may finish their field work before the afternoon heat begins. They usually breakfast at home and take for lunch a few loaves of *piki,* a paper-thin bread, made from a cornmeal batter, that is quickly baked on a hot stone. *Piki* is customarily eaten with a liquid, perhaps plain water or the juice of a fruit. The big meal of a day is taken toward evening.

Men who herd sheep usually do so with partners. Each partner herds for two days and spends the intervening night at a sheep camp.

Hopi pueblos are built in terraced style of local stone and adobe mud. Structures are ordinarily two or three stories high, but each home, consisting essentially of a main room and a supplementary storage chamber, is privately held within the over-all ownership of a clan. A man may do the major work of building or repairing a house, but when he is through, the home belongs to his wife and her clan.

Both sexes have many duties. Women cook and run their households, carry water, nurse and rear children, tend small vegetable gardens, weave plaques and baskets of dried rabbitbrush, and occasionally make pottery. Men do the heavy work of farming and house-building, herd sheep, conduct most of the rituals, weave blankets and garments of all sorts, and make moccasins. Neither sex can get along well without the help of the other.

In addition to being matrilineal, these Indians are also matrilocal. This means that a man moves into his spouse's house when he marries and that his children belong to his wife's clan. The core of each household, accordingly, consists of an elderly woman and her spouse, together with their married daughters and the daughters' daughters and unwed sons. Nevertheless, each married man, though he moves in from the outside, is called "father" by his offspring, so that the nuclear family is adequately recognized even though the kinship system is rigorously unilateral. Warm affection often prevails between mates and between fathers and their offspring, and it is not unusual for a man to side with his family even if it means opposition to his clan. The friendliness of a father and his children is certainly aided by the Hopi convention that all discipline should be carried out by a mother's brother.

Apart from its household mates, a child, especially a boy, forms his warmest and dearest ties with the women of his father's clan (*ikya'am*).[8] Indeed, there is reason to believe that at one time a Hopi boy was expected to marry his father's sister's daughter, a custom that is consonant with one form of cross-cousin marriage.

A married woman is so firmly rooted in her natal household that a divorce is of relatively slight importance. Her father, unmarried brothers, brothers-in-law, or sons can always be relied upon to look after her material needs, and she always has a roof over her head. As for a man, if his wife asks him to leave, he is free to marry again, or he can go back to his mother's or sister's (that is, his natal) household. Under such conditions it is small wonder that there is a high divorce rate and that Hopi monogamy is very brittle indeed.

Everyone sleeps on sheepskins stretched out on the floor or ground. Small children lie close by their mothers, but adolescents sleep farther apart, and young men are free to roam about at will. Very often such youths call during the night on unmarried girls, and if they are favorably received, they indulge in sexual intercourse. This custom is known as *dumaiya*. It is found in all Hopi towns and is not uncommonly a preliminary to a wedding. Discovery of lovers is seldom taken seriously, and the bearing of a premarital bastard scarcely affects a girl's chances of marriage. Both boys and girls apparently grow tired of love affairs and eventually marry and settle down.

Nuptial ceremonies are long-drawn-out affairs, culminating in an act of union symbolized by the mingling or knotting of the couple's hair in a single washbasin. During the preliminaries, a bride lives at her groom's house and prepares much of the food for his household while her wedding outfit is being made. When the rites are concluded, the young wife proceeds to her permanent residence in her mother's house, and there later in the day her husband joins her.

Puberty receives no official recognition for either sex, and a menstruant continues to carry out all her customary obligations.

When a person dies, he is buried the same day by a kinsman, and only those who were present at the time of death are expected to weep. Spirits of the dead, except for witches, are supposed to travel quickly to the other world, where they live a shadowy replica of life on earth.

---

[8] In the Hopi language *ikya'am* means either "my father's sisters" or "women of my father's clan." Each infant belongs to its mother's clan, but is known as a child of its father's clan. It is named shortly after birth by its father's clanswomen, who name it in some fashion suggestive of their clan. Thus the child of a Sand clansman might be named by its father's clanswomen "Shifting Sand."

Witches make a slow and painful journey and are burned in ovens to emerge as beetles.

The word *Hopi* means peaceful, and these people are nonaggressive and strongly Apollonian in most of their behavior. They are prone, however, to much bickering and gossiping. Furthermore, their pueblos are so compact that privacy is virtually impossible to attain, and everyone's actions are subject to endless discussion. Yet, each Hopi is brought up to be a strong individualist, all decisions are left to the person most concerned regardless of sex or age, chiefs exert very little authority, and there are no agencies to enforce compliance with traditional mores or to punish those who refuse to conform. Under such a system of extreme *laissez faire* the native communities are always potentially disintegrative, and in each town the culture pattern must somehow achieve harmony to prevent collapse. Much of the cohesion that is so necessary for the maintenance of the Hopi way of life comes from religion, to which we now turn.

Hopi ceremonialism

In every pueblo the populace is organized into a number of secret societies, each of which is responsible for the conduct of a single ceremony. A particular clan is said to own each ceremony, but this only means that it has charge of some of the requisite sacred paraphernalia and that it has the added duty of supplying the ceremony's leader or chief. Even here the principle of *laissez faire* continues to operate, for should a headman refuse to perform his rites, no one could force him to do so. On the other hand, since lesser officials and ordinary participants are drawn from anywhere in the village, the ceremonies cannot help but pull together a number of people from various clans. In this way, participation in religious affairs, which is an important test of good Hopi citizenship, helps to weld together the inhabitants of each village.[9]

All important Hopi observances tend to be calendrical. Some may occur at any time within a given season, but others must be held at a precise time. A very small number of tribally significant rituals are held in houses, but an overwhelming majority of rites take place in kivas. These are underground chambers, roughly rectangular in shape, that

[9] It should not be forgotten that another tie arises from the fact that Hopi clans are exogamous. This forces each person to get a mate from an outside group and thus to establish affinal bonds and some cooperation with a clan other than his own.

can be entered only by climbing down a ladder. Each kiva has a slightly raised platform behind the ladder's base, regarded as a minor area for occasional spectators, and a lower main area in front of the ladder, where the important parts of an observance always take place.

Kiva rites vary from ceremony to ceremony, but they generally include the rearing of a temporary altar, brought piecemeal into the kiva at the proper time, the smoking of native tobacco, praying, singing to the accompaniment of shell or gourd rattles, and the manufacture of prayer offerings that are later deposited at appropriate shrines. Sometimes, too, a man and a woman dress in costume to represent a cult's hero and heroine, dancing takes place, and medicine is brewed.

As a rule, it is relatively simple to join any secret society. All one has to do is to locate a member of the group in question, give him a handful of sacred cornmeal, and ask him to serve as one's sponsor during initiation. Among the Hopi, participation is completely optional.

By far the greater share of the religious activities falls to the men, although both sexes begin their careers in the same way. Ceremonial life starts when a father and mother select ceremonial parents who will put a child of 8 or so into the Kachina society. The Kachina cult is open to all of the appropriate age, but parents decide if a child is to join the simple Kachina group, whose initiation procedure includes a whipping, or the more elaborate Powámu society, whose observances include admission to the Kachina cult and whose initiates are not whipped. Thereafter boys may dance as the masked figures known as *kachinas*, but girls may not. In fact, unless a female happens to be called upon to act as a cultus heroine, her later ceremonial life is limited to membership in one or more of the women's societies, named Marau, Oaqöl, and Lakon.

When a boy reaches adolescence, at an age of 12 to 15, he may join either of two Flute societies and he may also enter the Snake or the Antelope fraternity. Several years later, whether or not he has already married, a young man is expected to go through a tribal initiation by joining any one of four concurrently held observances. After that, his ceremonial career reaches a climax when he goes into the winter solstice, or Soyál society, whose leader at Oraibi is the village chief.

In addition to the formal, calendrical rituals just mentioned, the Hopi have an indeterminate number of critical rites that are held in case of emergency. Most of these are performed by shamans or medicine men and are designed to render a field fertile, to counteract witchcraft, or to cure a sick person.

The most fundamental concept of Hopi religion is a belief in the continuity of life after death. The Hopi have many myths which purport to tell how, in the beginning, all of mankind emerged from under the ground through a hole known as the *sipapu*. It is through the self-same *sipapu* that the spirits of the dead pass into the other world. There they live much as they did on earth, but on some occasions they may revisit their former homes in the shape of clouds or *kachinas*. It is in this way that the spirits of the dead may bring rain and other benefits to those who are still alive.

The Hopi keep careful track of the sun's apparent movements by having officials designated as *Sun Watchers* observe each day's sunrise from one spot. Long ago they noted that the sun each day comes up in the east and goes down in the west, and they believe that this is possible only because the sun journeys underground from west to east while it is dark on earth. Hence, daytime among the living is nighttime among the dead and vice versa. By analogy, too, winter in this world corresponds to summer in the other world, and in all regards death is looked on as the reverse of life. Yet, as day and night follow each other and as the seasons are regularly repeated, so does death follow life and life follow death. On the basis of such beliefs, the Hopi feel assured that their society and its culture will endure forever.

THE UNITED STATES[10]

All social scientists who have attempted to analyze contemporary life in America have invariably been struck by the historic influences exerted by the mingling of numerous cultural elements, originally brought into this country by various immigrants; and by the part played in the past by our frontier. As several writers have pointed out, the American frontier, unlike European frontiers, was not a barrier to movement but an invitation to get away from cramped quarters or confining customs. It seems safe to assume that the mingling of many different traits of culture, which is really diffusion in action, has done much to enrich and variegate our lives; and that the nature of our frontier has had a great deal to do with making us admire mobility, rugged individuality, self-reliance, and independence.

For the United States as a whole there is a marked need for bal-

10 Those who wish more data on how American anthropologists view life in the United States are advised to read C. Kluckhohn, *Mirror for Man,* New York, 1949, Chap. 9; and M. Mead, *And Keep Your Powder Dry,* New York, 1942. An interesting analysis of Americans, made by an English anthropologist, may be found in G. Gorer, *The American People:* A Study in National Character, New York, 1947.

Much that will be said about culture in the United States applies to other Euro-American nations whose ways of life are generally comparable to those of the United States.

ancing regional differences, as well as the distinctions that prevail between rural and urban centers. Although the countryside has made relatively little change in the natural environment, the city, except for parks and recreational areas, has almost completely altered its original physical setting. Urban dwellers live almost entirely within a man-made environment, and so much has the landscape been modified that cityfolk can neither raise their own food nor secure at first hand the raw materials needed for the erection of buildings and the manufacture of garments, utensils, and similar products. Each city's population must depend for vital supplies on rural sources beyond city limits, and the larger the city the bigger will be the district required to service it.

Because of the greater density of urban populations, the amount of their total knowledge is much greater than can be found within a rural area of comparable extent. This means that a higher degree of specialization must exist in the cities and that some country residents will be drawn cityward whenever they require the services of specialists or desire to learn a specialty. Some specialists will inevitably concentrate on arts and entertainments, which will exert another magnetic pull toward the city. Others will make improvements in housing and various material traits, which will prove attractive to Americans whose cultural values stress physical comforts, body cleanliness, and the use of devices that conserve time and human muscular energy. Then, again, since city dwellers must purchase raw materials and vital necessities, a pattern of exchanging work for money has to be formed. The accumulation of money thus becomes a compelling motive of American culture, and rural folk who want to increase their dollar earnings find themselves attracted to large cities.

America's trend toward urbanization cannot be understood in terms only of material culture. As an absolute minimum the members of each city must devise social legislation in order to ensure and facilitate the necessary cooperation without which large numbers of specialists cannot exist. Moreover, urban life offers more possibilities than rural residence for social mobility, and one of the strongest cultural motivations in America is the desire of parents to have their offspring do better than themselves. Coupled with this attitude is the lack of compulsion for children to take up the same occupations as their elders. If youngsters are to advance beyond their parents, they must be encouraged to follow pursuits that hold forth the promise of greater prestige, larger money rewards, or both. Cities offer better opportunities of this nature than do rural communities, where most people are farmers and a child has little alternative but to follow in the footsteps of the parent of his sex.

One of the most telling social effects of a city environment has been the decreasing reliance on kin (despite some effort to maintain ties of relationship), and the corresponding increase of dependence on strangers. This becomes most noteworthy after a child has begun to go to school. Thereafter, he will receive less and less of his education and training from kindred. As time goes on he will have to depend on nonrelatives to prepare his food, make his garments, protect his property, provide him with transportation, and afford him the pleasures of company and recreation. Residence in an urban setting rarely makes possible a concentration of kinfolk in one place and a distant relative who is seldom seen plays little effective part in a person's life. As in a primitive tribe, nearness of residence may provide a substitute for ties of kinship.

Although many vital aspects of interpersonal relations in the United States are directly connected with matters of urbanization and technology, there are other features of social organization that are only indirectly concerned with such factors. One of the most important of these pertains to the status of women. Because of the large number of wonderful inventions that have so greatly reduced the need for an outlay of human muscular strength and energy, women are able to do nearly anything nonbiological that men can do, and a high percentage of our labor force, estimated at about one third, is now feminine (Fig. 30–5).[11] As a result, our educational system fluctuates between training girls for crafts and business careers, and for motherhood and domestic tasks.

Equalization of women's status is directly interwoven with changes in American values. Only a few generations ago an American woman was not expected to have a career outside the home or to receive much formal schooling. In keeping with this situation high value was attached to being a good mother and housekeeper. Women took pride in keeping their children neat and their houses spic and span, and got much pleasure from being praised for their efforts. Nowadays, mechanical implements are capable of taking so much drudgery out of a housewife's duties that she can have extra time for outside work.[12] It is considered old-fashioned for a woman to have no interests outside her home and family. Social rewards go to those who play the most active parts in education and community affairs or who demonstrate the greatest skill in business or politics. Nor has increased education made women more content to be

---

[11] Readers are reminded that what is said here applies best to the United States and similar countries. In other parts of the world, as in the Soviet Union, India, and the Far East, women often work on a par with men, even though they have no access to "wonderful inventions."

[12] Reliance on servants may have been equally or, perhaps, even more effective in reducing a housewife's duties in times past, but mechanical appliances are much more readily available to all classes of American society than servants ever were.

housewives. After all, it is hardly to be expected that a young woman with a PhD degree in astrophysics will regard keeping her children neat as her chief mission in life. With the highest honors being won in activities outside the home, American women are refusing to restrict themselves to the lowly valued tasks of keeping house and children spotlessly clean.

As has already been indicated, the citizens of the United States, like members of any other large and far-flung national unit, do not

FIG. 30-5. American women at work. In the United States a high percentage of the work force is feminine. This figure shows a step in the processing of income tax returns. To the extent that American women hold outside jobs, they cannot limit themselves to their homes, husbands, and children. (Courtesy *U.S. News & World Report.*)

comprise a homogeneous society. What complicates the situation is the inconsistent way in which differences from an assumed norm may be used either to reward or punish. Yet, there is no absolute standard of behavior that can guarantee freedom from social displeasure to all who conform. In upper-class circles around Boston, a person who speaks English with Italian intonations might well be looked down upon, but one who speaks with an English accent might be admired. But in the Middle West, fun may be poked at anyone who affects English mannerisms of speech.

We are equally inconsistent in regard to differences of stock and race. Caucasoids who have one-sixteenth Negro ancestry may try to hide the fact, but those with the same amount of Indian "blood" may brag about it. Again, where a small percentage of Indian "blood" may be esteemed, a half-breed may be stigmatized. A similar lack of uniformity prevails in our attitudes toward religion. America is a Protestant Christian country, but in some districts Baptists are greatly respected and in others they are not.

Lack of consistent cultural values may lead to very tragic consequences. Throughout most aspects of American life there runs a current of emphasis on speed. "Time is of the essence," the lawyers say, and our children are frequently admonished to hurry up and not to waste time. Industrialists build automobiles capable of going faster and faster, and communities compete in building roads suitable for greater speeds. Yet, overtly, we are reluctant to admit that high speeds are connected with many traffic fatalities. Recently, a bright young woman who had survived the crash of a speeding car that had killed some of her companions was asked by a judge why she had consented to go on such a wild ride. "I like speed," she replied simply. No doubt the judge was so shocked that he failed to give the young woman credit for being honestly consistent.

Another outstanding problem of American society, related to the lack of fixed standards, is the speed and irregularity with which some cultural values change. As has already been said, a social subgroup which has adjusted itself to one set of cultural values is disorganized and bewildered during any period of transition. Children of immigrants, who reject the ideas of right and wrong that their parents brought from a foreign country, are particularly likely to feel uneasy until the whole family has absorbed the values of American culture.

Every student of modern American culture is struck by the lack of *reliance* on religion. Unquestionably, a good part of the reason for this situation lies in the high development of science. With few exceptions scientists, rather than priests, are called upon for help when people fall ill, crops fail, animals sicken, or mentalities break down. True *reliance* on religion is most manifest where controlled causation is most uncertain.

There is a strong possibility that the lack of deep religiosity in the United States is related to the fact that no national religion exists in our country. Apparently, religious systems are most powerful when they conform exactly to particular social structures. However, all of the prevailing nation-wide religions in this country were originally developed elsewhere and were tailored to fit societies different from our own. Only parts of these imported systems seem applicable to us.

American faith in science is coupled with a belief in the power of reason. In most areas of behavior we reject mysticism of any kind and make a veritable cult of being rational, according to our cherished principles of logic. Furthermore, since we like to moralize and to judge everything as good or bad, we have tended to combine moralization with our belief in rationality by making the assumption that whatever is reasonable is good and whatever is unreasonable is bad. On this basis we assume that people who are well-informed and reasonable are good. We are surprised and pained if a well-educated person turns out to be a scoundrel or a thief.

Education in America holds an ambivalent position. On the one hand, especially since the Russian advances into space, we admire science and technology; but on the other hand, we are likely to be suspicious of ideas as such. In fact, many Americans regard thinkers as loafers and condemn contemplation as a waste of time.

THE BIOCULTURAL TRIANGLE IN AMERICA

If we mentally project a model of American culture (Fig. 30–6) against a configuration of primitive ways of life, certain resemblances and differences immediately stand out. Sometimes our culture seems to hold together better, but at other times comparison reveals unsuspected weaknesses in our sociocultural structure. When flaws show up, they cannot be remedied by a simple return to primitive conditions. Defects brought out by comparative analysis should be regarded only as diagnostic. They serve to show social scientists where remedial action is necessary, but they do not of themselves suggest what that action should be.

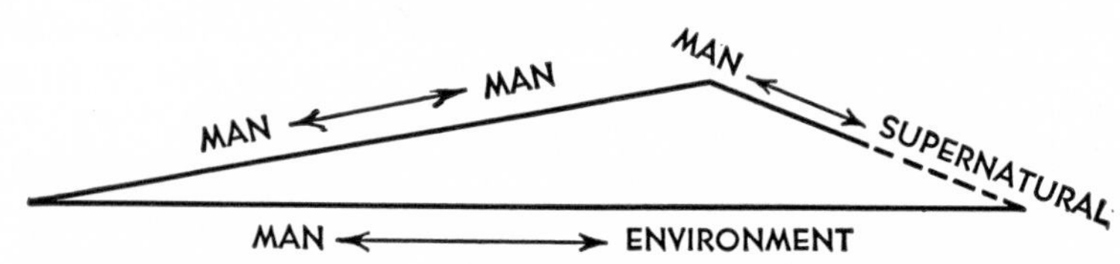

FIG. 30-6. The American way of life. The biocultural configuration that prevails in the United States appears unsymmetrical and disjointed. We seem to have overelaborated man's dealings with his environment, at the expense of man's relations with man and, particularly, of man's interplay with the supernatural.

Americans, like all other members of *Homo sapiens,* must develop satisfactory interrelationships with their physical setting. We are, however, changing our environments and expanding our use of natural resources so rapidly that we are in far greater danger than is any primitive group of exhausting what nature can provide. So far, constantly more effective ways of manipulating the environment and greatly improved means of communication have enabled us to keep going, but it is obvious that our way of dealing with our setting creates some difficult problems.

Our interpersonal relations, too, are vastly different from those found in numerous primitive societies. We do not segment our social structure into such unilateral groups as lineages and clans. Yet, though we reckon kindred bilaterally, we seldom expect direct help either from our mother's side or our father's. So much is this the case that parents may even bring up and train children in such a way as to show that they fully expect them to shift for themselves as soon as they can marry and move away from home. Ironically, we make fun of those who remain too long tied to parental apron strings, and at the same time we complain about the lack of strong family ties.

It is in the field of religion that some of the greatest differences exist. Like all other people, we have calendrical and unscheduled critical rites. Sometimes they appear related to other aspects of our ways of life, and sometimes they do not. To many Americans, supernatural practices lie outside their social structures, not within them. Above all, we lack anything corresponding to a tribal initiation. As Americans, we do not feel sufficiently integrated to make up a single, perpetually interacting society, and we would, moreover, be at a loss to know into what we were expected to initiate young people. If it were but a case of training them to follow in the footsteps of their parents or to play particular roles in society, that would be another matter. But we do not expect children to live like their parents, and we have neither fixed roles nor unchanging social statuses. Furthermore, we would find it hard to see what supernaturalism has to do with such matters in any event.

Compared to primitive ways of life, our culture seems to be terribly segmented and occasionally disjointed. In a primitive society it is easy to see the evenness and connections of all three sides of a biocultural triangle, but the American configuration sometimes appears to be uneven and disconnected. We have an excellent record in solving problems of material culture and technology, but we are woefully weak when it comes to dealing with social relations or religion.

Selected References

Beals, Ralph, "Urbanism, Urbanization, and Acculturation," *American Anthropologist,* Vol. 53, 1951, pp. 1–10.

Firth, Raymond, *We, the Tikopia,* New York, 1936.

Gorer, Geoffrey, *The American People,* New York, 1947.

Helm, June, "The Ecological Approach in Anthropology," *American Journal of Sociology,* Vol. 67, 1962, pp. 630–39.

Kluckhohn, Clyde, *Mirror for Man,* New York, 1949, Chap. 9.

Mead, Margaret, *And Keep Your Powder Dry,* New York, 1942.

Sahlins, Marshall D., and Service, Elman R., eds., *Evolution and Culture,* Ann Arbor, Mich., 1960, pp. 45–68.

Steward, Julian H., "Basin-Plateau Aboriginal Sociopolitical Groups," *Bureau of American Ethnology,* Bulletin 120, 1938.

———, "Ethnography of the Owens Valley Paiute," *University of California Publications in American Archeology and Ethnology,* Vol. 33, No. 3, 1933.

Thompson, Laura, and Joseph, Alice, *The Hopi Way,* Lawrence, Kans., 1944.

Titiev, Mischa, "Old Oraibi," *Papers of the Peabody Museum of American Archaeology and Ethnology,* Cambridge, Mass., Vol. 22, No. 1, 1944.

Warner, W. Lloyd, *American Life: Dream and Reality,* Chicago, 1953.

Ethnology Branches Out

CHAPTER 31

INTRODUCTION TO CULTURE CHANGE

Whatever patterns of culture a society develops never remain perpetually the same. Only as a kind of delusion, comparable to stopping a motion picture film on one frame so that it looks like a still, does a way of life appear to be static. There are, of course, periods when changes are more noticeable or more rapid than at other times. Even if a group lives in total isolation from the rest of mankind, however, the pressure of internal forces of culture inevitably brings about change. Many *internal changes* seem to arise simply as people add to their collective stockpile of knowledge. With the passage of time the members of any society are likely to learn more and more about the physical environment in which they live. The result is a different and usually wider and more efficient use of natural resources. Inevitably, this leads to some modification of technology. The technological shifts then impel some people to develop new skills, and very often to make novel tools. If the new devices are to become a permanent part of a society's culture pattern, their use must be taught to others. The resultant changes, therefore, may begin with man's dealings with his physical setting but are likely also to enter the zone of interpersonal relations.

The history of Japanese culture illustrates the principle of internal change at work. During the *Tokugawa* era, from about 1600 to the restoration of the Meiji emperor in 1859, the rulers of Japan employed every possible means of minimizing their country's contacts with the rest of the world. At the same time, they could not prevent the forces of internal change from operating. Consequently, as every student of Japanese culture knows, many customs and things current in early Tokugawa times became vastly different late in the Tokugawa period.

Much more striking than the alterations that arise internally are those external modifications that result from the contact of one group with another. Prerequisite to this kind of change is a breakdown of isolation. Most often this process is brought about by the building of a road, but any new form of transportation or communication may have the same effect. As long as a society lives in complete isolation, it cannot possibly receive any stimulus to *external changes* of culture; nor can it have the opportunity to compare its own customs with those of different people. However, just as soon as one society comes into contact with another, a potential for comparison arises. Without fail, through the operation of some process whose workings social scientists do not always understand, a comparable trait from one society comes to be more highly esteemed than its counterpart in another. When this happens a choice is made, and preference is given to that item which has come to be rated higher.

Ralph Linton has proposed a different way of analyzing contact situations. He differentiates *directed contacts,* in which the giving society insists that its patterns must be followed by the receiving society, from *undirected* contacts, in which the dominant group does not necessarily impose its ways on a subordinate unit. Linton has fully recognized that there are also cases when neither of two societies in contact becomes dominant over the other, and he also has noted instances in which some features are taken over while others are rejected. Modern scholars regard the whole question of culture contact to be full of complexities, and there is a growing feeling that what happens is really a complicated interweaving of several simultaneously ongoing processes and factors.

Acculturation and Problems of Culture Change

At present there is hardly any society that has not felt the impact of a culture different from its own. It is to the process of the intermingling of cultures that the name *acculturation* has been given.[1] Although inter-

[1] Those who wish to explore this topic further should consult M. J. Herskovits, *Acculturation,* New York, 1938; R. Linton, ed., *Acculturation in Seven American Indian Tribes,* New York, 1940; H. G. Barnett, *Innovation,* New York, 1953; F. M.

mingling may be studied together with diffusion or culture change, and acculturation can be used for designating whole or partial mixtures of any different ways of life, the latter term is most commonly applied to the study of the influence of a Euro-American culture on that of a primitive group.

The most obvious approach to research in acculturation is for an observer to list the kinds and numbers of recognizably foreign objects, such as sewing machines or cast-iron stoves, to be found in a primitive society. Considered by itself, a survey of this sort has only superficial value, but it can afford a basis for studying such things as migrations, the history of culture contacts, or the process of diffusion. Acculturation studies gain in value as they contribute to an understanding of cultural processes. Some ethnologists have begun to examine such dynamic aspects of acculturation and culture change as the differential emphases that the people of a lending society may give to various parts of their culture. Quite often representatives of a powerful society may want a weaker group to adopt their religious beliefs. In other cases, however, those who establish contact may strive to introduce instead such economic features as the use of power-driven tools or a system of working for cash rather than for goods. Other cultural anthropologists have begun to investigate the motives that may influence the adoption of some new items and the rejection of others. Valuable results likewise can be obtained from a study of the degree of compulsion that might have forced peoples to accept a foreign trait against their will. Students of culture are also inquiring into the ways that new features are modified or left intact and how they are fitted into a native culture pattern. Others are analyzing the effects of a borrowed item on individuals of different sex, age, education, occupation, or social standing. In addition, it has now become fully realized that the process of acculturation may cause changes in those who give as well as in those who take.

A few rules of general cultural behavior have already emerged from *acculturational* investigations, broadly considered. Unless there is a great deal of compulsion involved, a receiving society is likely to accept only items that fill a conscious need, particularly if the new things can be interpreted as no more than modifications of existing traits. Most readily borrowed are objects of material culture whose use will

---

Keesing, *Culture Change,* Stanford, Calif., 1953; H. G. Barnett, L. Broom, B. J. Siegel, E. Z. Vogt, and J. B. Watson, "Acculturation: An Exploratory Formulation," *American Anthropologist,* Vol. 56, 1954, pp. 973–1002; E. M. Bruner, "Differential Culture Change: Report on the Interuniversity Summer Research Seminar, 1956," *Social Science Research Council Items,* Vol. II, No. I, March 1957, pp. 1–3; and E. H. Spicer, ed., *Perspectives in American Indian Culture Change,* Chicago, 1961.

result in a large saving of time and human muscular energy and whose greater effectiveness can be most readily demonstrated, grasped, and accurately measured. Nonliterate people are rarely articulate about their motives for borrowing, but even a simple list of Euro-American things accepted by a number of primitive groups confirms such a conclusion. Metal tools and weapons seldom fail to supplant similar implements of stone or wood, especially if their use does not require long training and the acquisition of new motor habits. Also, factory-made garments can always be counted on to replace homemade clothes. Women are more likely than men to cling to native forms of dress, and religious personages are even more conservative. For the most part, though, "store-bought" clothing soon becomes the rule for those who have sufficient money. This demonstrates that the acceptance of new material traits cannot be considered apart from the degree of success with which individual natives accumulate cash, or otherwise come to participate in the money economy of the Euro-Americans with whom they have contact.

Nonmaterial traits are more likely to meet with widespread initial resistance, but even the acceptance of a purely technological trait is likely to alter a society's social and religious structure. Realization of this fact, though usually implicit rather than explicit, may lie behind the refusal of some "backward" nations to accept offers of material assistance. In the nonmaterial realm Euro-American forms of religion are apt to be rejected at first, although they may later be accepted in whole or in part[2] through missionary and other influences. Among other things, anthropologists have found Christianity to be surprisingly flexible. Sometimes it is deliberately molded to primitive shape by evangelists who hope by this means to gain ready converts, and sometimes it is given strange twists through the ignorance of native practitioners.[3]

One of the areas of resistance to acculturation is in the field of speech. Many a people, but not all tribes, who seem to be thoroughly acculturated in other respects continue to speak their native tongue in addition to a Euro-American language. At the present time, to cite a specific example, the Araucanian Indians are practically indistinguishable from their nearby Spanish-speaking Chilean neighbors in physical

---

[2] When elements from two or more different religions are combined they result in *syncretism*. Various anthropologists have studied syncretism. See, for example, M. J. Herskovits, "African Gods and Catholic Saints in New World Religious Belief," *American Anthropologist,* Vol. 39, 1937, pp. 635–43.

[3] A great many examples of this point can be found in E. Nida, *Customs and Cultures,* New York, 1955.

appearance, dress, occupations, and the use of material objects; but every person who considers himself an Indian speaks Araucanian at home. The Japanese provide an outstanding example of the same phenomenon. Throughout the course of centuries they borrowed all sorts of cultural items from China. They even began their system of writing by employing Chinese characters as a basis. Still, at no time did spoken Chinese offer the slightest challenge to the continued use of Japanese speech.

Food preferences also change slowly. People everywhere are reluctant to give up foods to which they have grown accustomed. Nevertheless, whether or not the individuals concerned like it, diets do change along with other aspects of culture. Inevitably, even the most conservative persons, or their offspring, find themselves unable to get the things that they once esteemed, and all that remains as they adjust their tastes to new menus is a vague longing for the foods that mother used to make.

As might be expected, and with some exceptions, a strong or an "advanced" group usually imposes its system of cultural outlooks or values on a weaker, "backward" one. If the difference of strength is very marked, the latter cannot resist; and if the stronger society appears to be better adjusted and more prosperous, the weaker one may actually show eagerness to accept the other's values. But a value system does not exist apart from an entire configuration of culture, and it is often impossible for the imitating society to take over the complete way of life of the dominant people.

Because biocultural forces usually maintain a dynamic equilibrium, some account must be taken of the differing rates of speed at which various parts of culture are likely to change. Also, pressures for modification must always be balanced against forces of stability or inertia. Without fail, in the course of acculturation, existing equilibriums become upset. It is when this happens that an era of uncertainty is most likely to set in and to endure until a new equilibrium has been established. Thus does a period of transition occur, during which the weaker society continues to lose its own traditional values, but has not yet completely adopted the new ones. At such times a marked feeling of *dysphoria* prevails, and the members of the society faced with prospects of a changeover appear to be disturbed, insecure, and unhappy. The values that had previously been affixed to all aspects of life are no longer applicable, and the new sets of values have not yet emerged with any degree of clarity or fixity. Moreover, it is not easy for an individual to readjust himself and to accept new values after he has already learned to live by a different set of standards. This difficulty of adjustment is perhaps the basis of the universal human tendency to look back nostalgically to the "good old days," when everything had its place in what seemed to be a permanent scale of values. By the same token this may be why oldsters everywhere tend to be conservative, to look askance at innovations and innovators, and to feel that the contemporary world is "going to the dogs."

THE STUDY OF VALUE SYSTEMS

There has been a long-standing belief among social scientists that one should not make value judgments because values are different from objective facts and cannot be treated by scientific methods. In recent years it has become recognized that this reasoning is fallacious. Even the selection of "facts" by a physical scientist implies the existence of a covert system of values that considers some things to be more significant than others. As for the social sciences, the notion of an entirely value-free discipline is now regarded as fantastic. The current tendency is to look upon a society's goals, objectives, or values as interdependent with its methods of achieving its ends. No longer are ultimate aims considered to be entirely separate from techniques, for every society recognizes right and wrong or improper and proper ways of acting.

An effort to make scientific studies of values[4] was begun by Clyde and Florence Kluckhohn. They believe that a society's values can be studied naturalistically by the same means as any other form of empirical knowledge.[5]

Students of values invariably come up against a troublesome problem. They are so fearful of being branded as ethnocentric that they

---

4 While he was directing the Laboratory of Social Relations at Harvard, Kluckhohn instituted a project that aimed to make a comparative study of values in various societies and cultures. A number of his efforts in this field were integrated with investigations of the Navaho. For a bibliography of writings on this topic see O. Von Mering, *A Grammar of Human Values,* Pittsburgh, 1961, p. iii and pp. 265–82; and W. Caudill and H. A. Scarr, "Japanese Value Orientations and Culture Change," *Ethnology,* Vol. 1, 1962, p. 91.

See also D. Bidney, "The Concept of Value in Modern Anthropology," in A. L. Kroeber, ed., *Anthropology Today,* Chicago, 1953, pp. 682–99; and F. R. Kluckhohn, "A Method for Eliciting Value Orientations," *Anthropological Linguistics,* Vol. 2, 1960, pp. 1–23.

5 C. Kluckhohn, "The Scientific Study of Values and Contemporary Civilization," *Proceedings of the American Philosophical Society,* Vol. 102, No. 5, 1958, p. 469.

have tended to shy away from setting up absolute standards (which might be interpreted as simply their own), by means of which any society's values could be measured and ranked.[6] Instead, as can be seen in the writings of Boas, most anthropologists are inclined to take a relativistic position, claiming that each culture's values should be judged not in terms of some absolute standard, but relative only to its own particular patterns of culture.

Strict adherence to cultural relativism would rule out all comparisons of one culture (or any part of it) with another. It would also make it impossible ever to set up any absolute concepts, such as normality, that one might wish to apply universally and across cultures. Luckily, wider knowledge of the way in which the forces of culture operate is making it possible to formulate new absolute standards. One can measure the comparative strengths of forces without reference to their goodness or badness, and without the danger of ethnocentricity.

Cultural dynamics or the study of forces of culture

A number of anthropologists have devoted themselves to what is called *cultural dynamics.* Invariably, they have dealt, in one way or another, with those repetitive ways of doing things that may be termed *cultural institutions,* but they have not dealt with *the forces of culture.* These are not the same thing. To take an analogy from physics, the force of electricity is not the same as an electric light bulb.

As far as culture is concerned, two pairs of forces must be recognized. Every pattern of culture originates because of the pressure of *forces of initiation.* The plural is used because initiatory forces may be of many kinds—somatic, environmental, and so forth. These forces of initiation, however, do not express themselves freely, but are counterbalanced, or held in check, by *forces of limitation.* Initially, every pattern of culture seems to take its distinctive shape from an interplay between forces of initiation and forces of limitation. Thus, for example,

[6] In *The Primitive World and Its Transformations,* Ithaca, N.Y., and London, 1953, Chap. 6, Robert Redfield, of the University of Chicago, raised the question whether it was either possible or desirable for an anthropologist to rid himself entirely of his own viewpoints and values while he was studying a culture that was entirely different from his own. According to Redfield, one's own culture might well provide a needed measuring rod for making comparisons.

forces of hunger initiate all food habits, but, since there are only about sixteen waking hours per day, the four-hour process of digestion serves to limit the possible number of full meals, or their equivalents, to four. It thus becomes possible, without ethnocentrism or moralizing, to predict that every ongoing society's way of life will make provision for the consumption of not less than one, and not more than four, "square meals" per day.

Once a pattern of culture has been formed, another pair of forces begins to operate. Now a balance must be achieved between *forces of stability* that work to maintain an established way of life, and *forces of instability* that make for breakdown or change. Analysts of cultural dynamics might well gain additional insights from a study of the forces of culture.

Some other approaches

Under Robert Redfield's leadership, a considerable amount of interest has been aroused in the ways of life that are to be found in what he termed *folk societies.* These are hard to define as they are neither primitive, as that word is customarily used, nor are they "advanced." They resemble most nearly those communities which are sometimes labeled "peasant societies." Generally, they are parts of a larger social group, such as a nation. They are almost invariably rural and have a subsistence economy, but they always maintain some contacts with their urban fellows.[7] In a sense folk societies comprise rural subcultures within larger units. An understanding of how they operate and change should be obtained by anyone who professes to deal with the whole species of *Homo sapiens.*

Other cultural anthropologists have recently been advocating the improvement of living conditions among various groups of aborigines who are still to be found in the New World. They call their program *action anthropology,* and their principal leader is Sol Tax, of the University of Chicago. *Action anthropologists* are concerned with such prob-

---

[7] Much information regarding folk societies may be found in R. Redfield, "The Folk Society," *American Journal of Sociology,* Vol. 52, 1947, pp. 293–308; R. Redfield, *The Little Community,* Chicago, 1955; and in R. Redfield, *Peasant Society and Culture,* Chicago, 1956.

See also H. M. Miner, "The Folk-Urban Continuum," *American Sociological Review,* Vol. 17, 1952, pp. 529–37; and G. M. Foster, "What is Folk Culture?" *American Anthropologist,* Vol. 55, 1953, pp. 159–74.

lems as the betterment of prevailing conditions on reservations, in terms of what the natives themselves want.[8]

ANTHROPOLOGY AND THE NONPRIMITIVE WORLD

Until about thirty-five years ago, anthropologists in America were neither expected nor trained to concern themselves with large, literate societies, including their own. It then occurred to some scholars that ethnologists working with primitive tribes had developed techniques that might successfully be applied wherever any groups of human beings habitually lived together. First in the field was Robert Lynd of Columbia who, with his wife, Helen, and a small staff, undertook an intensive study of the city of Muncie, Indiana, in 1924. Professionally Lynd was classed as a sociologist, but his methods combined features of sociology with those of ethnology. The Lynds resided in the community under observation, participated in its life, conducted interviews, distributed questionnaires, analyzed newspapers, and examined census data. Throughout their stay they tried to maintain the same objectivity that a cultural anthropologist seeks to achieve while he is living with a primitive tribe. When the results were published,[9] they created a furor that soon led others to enter the promising new field of study which Clark Wissler called, "the social anthropology of contemporary life." Within a period of less than four decades, a great number of anthropological studies have been made on various phases of life in contemporary America.[10]

Soon after the applicability of ethnological techniques to non-

[8] This approach is described and explained in S. Tax, "Action Anthropology," *Journal of Social Research,* Vol. 2, 1959, pp. 1–9.

A full account of an event that incorporated some of Tax's concepts is given in N. O. Lurie, "Report on the American Indian Chicago Conference," *Current Anthropology,* Vol. 2, 1961, pp. 478–500.

[9] R. S. and H. M. Lynd, *Middletown: A Study of Contemporary American Culture,* New York, 1929. The Lynds made a second study of Muncie during the great economic depression that swept the United States early in the 1930's. They found the inhabitants bewildered because many of the old American ideas, such as the belief that "you can't keep a good man down," no longer applied. The second visit is described in *Middletown in Transition,* New York, 1937.

[10] Only two works will be cited, but they contain many references to other studies. See C. Kluckhohn, *Mirror for Man,* New York, 1949, Chap. 9, and W. L. Warner, *American Life: Dream and Reality,* Chicago, 1953. For further studies see the selected references at the end of this chapter.

primitive societies had been demonstrated, cultural anthropology was drawn into the arena of practical affairs. During the 1930's the Commissioner of Indian Affairs, John Collier, began to rely increasingly on anthropologists to help him revise the workings of his Bureau. By the time that the United States entered World War II in 1941, a good number of anthropologists had had some experience in dealing with practical problems as they applied to primitive peoples. Within the United States many cultural anthropologists were called upon by numerous agencies including the Office of Strategic Services (OSS) and the Office of War Information (OWI). Others went to work for the War Relocation Authority, to help with programs that concerned the removal of Japanese inhabitants from the Pacific coast and the administration of various relocation centers that were established for them.[11]

Only a few years after the appearance of *Middletown*, a very interesting group of studies was being sponsored at Harvard University. Elton Mayo, who had worked at the Fatigue Institute in England during World War I, and who had become convinced of the biocultural nature of weariness, organized a research project that was carried out at the Hawthorne plant of the Western Electric Company in Chicago. The investigations were conducted jointly by representatives of the firm and members of the Harvard School of Business Administration. One of their immediate objectives was to study the output of six girls who assembled telephone relays in a small room. Production increased, as was anticipated, when physical improvements, such as improved lighting, were made in working conditions. Unexpectedly, however, when the working conditions were returned to the original level, there was no attendant drop in the number of relays assembled. Analysis showed that the girls had been organized into a team, whose pride in their work and loyalty toward each other continued to make them exert themselves, even when they were no longer pampered with physical comforts.[12] Other studies have supported the conclusion that working teams are sociocultural units, with integrated and cohesive elements and systems of values, such as exist in any society.

Mayo also exerted much influence on the career of W. Lloyd

[11] For an important work on this subject, see A. H. Leighton, *The Governing of Men,* Princeton, N. J., 1946.

[12] This experiment was fully described in F. Roethlisberger and W. J. Dickson, *Management and the Worker,* Boston, 1934. It had a profound effect on labor-management relations in many industries.

A fresh analysis of this experiment is given in G. C. Homans, "The Western Electric Researches," in H. S. Dean, ed., *Human Factors in Management,* rev. ed., New York, 1951.

Warner, who had recently returned to Harvard from a long ethnological sojourn among Australian aborigines. Warner was led to apply anthropological techniques to contemporary American society. With a large staff to assist him, he undertook an exhaustive study of a typical New England community in Massachusetts. The results were published, after Warner had transferred to the University of Chicago, in a number of volumes entitled *The Yankee City Series*. They represent the most intensive analysis ever made of an American city and its patterns of culture. It is impossible to single out the most important contribution resulting from this project, but one of its most telling consequences was the convincing proof that social classes exist in the United States, despite assertions of democracy and the overt belief that all men are equal. Warner and his associates found six classes in Yankee City: two lower, two middle, and two upper. They were clear-cut in terms of degree of prestige, occupation, place of residence, and membership in clubs and other associations. No one factor was all-important as a determinant of one's class. Doctors, for example, ranged from lower middle to upper upper; and the negative fact that money, in and of itself, did not determine one's assignment to a social class was thoroughly demonstrated.

At about the same time that these activities were going on, other anthropologists continued to apply their knowledge to American affairs, particularly in the field of industrial relations. Spearheaded by Eliot D. Chapple, much was done to supplement and expand the findings that had been made at the Hawthorne plant, and Chapple's scheme of analyzing social situations by determining which person initiates action whenever there is contact among individuals was made part of the conceptual framework.[13] Chapple states that his basic assumption for an understanding of human relations in industry is that attitudes, emotional reactions, and productivity are functions of the interactional situation, which represents an interplay of personality and culture. Improvements are made either by putting people with personality problems into different interactional systems or else by changing some aspect of the culture pattern within which a person works. Chapple's approach is based on his awareness that workers in a large industrial plant form a sociocultural unit with its own system of values, coupled with the knowledge that changes in one segment of a biocultural configuration

---

[13] A good summary and review of anthropological techniques used in studying industrial relations is to be found in E. D. Chapple, "Applied Anthropology in Industry," in A. L. Kroeber, ed., *Anthropology Today,* Chicago, 1953, pp. 819–31.

Chapple uses a machine, the Interaction Chronograph, which provides accurate statistical data. He is president and founder of the E. D. Chapple Company, which serves many business firms.

are likely to bring about alterations in the other parts. He thus finds it possible to introduce material innovations, such as modifying a layout, with the intention of causing subtle changes in an individual's personal relations, usually without the subject's knowing what has happened.

Another group of anthropologists, often under Warner's leadership, has also entered the field of industrial relations, chiefly in the Chicago area. They do not use Chapple's methods but they also base their work on anthropological concepts of social and cultural structure. Much of what they do is related to psychological techniques of interviewing and counseling. This branch of anthropology has become an integral part of what is known as *MR* or *motivational research.* In its practical form it seeks to uncover the hidden (covert) reasons why people purchase one product in preference to another, or why a given style of packaging is more attractive than another.[14] The underlying concept seems to be that buyers are motivated by deeply hidden systems of values that are implicit in their patterns of culture. In Chicago, Burleigh Gardner, initially trained as an anthropologist, heads Social Research, a concern whose clientele includes some of the biggest firms in the United States. A large number of industrial organizations have found the services of various kinds of applied anthropologists to be exceedingly valuable.

Selected References

Chapple, Eliot D., "Applied Anthropology in Industry," in A. L. Kroeber, ed., *Anthropology Today,* Chicago, 1953, pp. 819–31.

———, and Arensberg, Conrad M., "Measuring Human Relations: An Introduction to the Study of the Interaction of Individuals," *Genetic Psychology Monographs,* No. 22, 1940.

Kluckhohn, Clyde, "The Scientific Study of Values and Contemporary Civilization," *Proceedings on the American Philosophical Society,* Vol. 102, 1958, pp. 469 ff.

Kluckhohn, Florence R., and Strodtback, Fred L., *et al., Variations in Value-orientations: A Theory Tested in Five Cultures,* Evanston, Ill., 1961.

Leighton, Alexander H., *The Governing of Men,* Princeton, N.J., 1946.

[14] Most central to this approach is Ernest Dichter, head of the Institute for Motivational Research in New York State. Although Dichter has had phenomenal success, some social scientists are strongly opposed to motivational research. They fear that complete knowledge of hidden motives may enable manipulators to force people to do whatever the manipulator desires.

Lynd, Robert S., and Helen M., *Middletown: A Study of Contemporary American Culture,* New York, 1929.

———, *Middletown in Transition,* New York, 1937.

Malinowski, Bronislaw, *The Dynamics of Culture Change,* P. M. Kaberry, ed., New Haven, 1945.

Miner, Horace M., "The Folk-Urban Continuum," *American Sociological Review,* Vol. 17, 1952, pp. 529–37.

Redfield, Robert, "The Folk Society," *American Journal of Sociology,* Vol. 52, 1947, pp. 293–308.

———, *The Primitive World and its Transformations,* Ithaca, N.Y., 1953.

Roethlisberger, Fritz J., and Dickson, William J., *Management and the Worker,* Boston, 1934.

Seeley, R., *et. al., Crestwood Heights: A Study of Suburban Life,* New York, 1956.

Spicer, Edward H., ed., *Perspectives in American Indian Culture Change,* Chicago, 1961.

Tax, Sol, "Action Anthropology," *Journal of Social Research,* Vol. 2, 1959, pp. 1–9.

Vogt, Evon Z., "Navaho Veterans: A Study of Changing Values," *Papers of the Peabody Museum of Harvard University,* Vol. 41, No. 1, 1951.

Warner, W. Lloyd, *et al., Yankee City Series,* New Haven, Conn., 1941 ff.

West, James, *Plainville, U.S.A.,* New York, 1945.

Summary and Conclusion

CHAPTER 32

GLANCING BACKWARD AND FORWARD

Throughout the last century an impressive amount of work has been done in all branches of anthropology. When a massive stockpile of knowledge had been accumulated, an unfailing law of cultural growth went into effect and an increasing number of specialists arose. Much is to be gained from a situation of this kind. Specialists always refine existing techniques and learn to use them in ways that bring to light previously unsuspected facts, many of which make possible fresh interpretations of data and the formulation and testing of new hypotheses and theories. Counterbalancing the advantages is the great danger of fragmentation resulting from the threatened separation of parts that were once found together. Already there are archeologists and ethnologists who know little of each other's work, and physical anthropologists who cannot understand an essay on primitive linguistics. This book seeks, among other things, to demonstrate that all segments of the science of man belong together and contribute to a total understanding of the human species and its behavior.

No matter how one chooses to approach the study of anthropology, it soon becomes apparent that the thing called culture cannot exist without mankind. No other animal develops it, lives by it, or maintains its existence by transmitting it through education from one generation to another. It is true that for purposes of certain theoretical analyses one can separate culture from its carriers, but this does not apply to the study of its beginnings. There is no means of understanding how culture first arose without taking into account the ways in which the biology and capabilities of *Homo sapiens* differ from those of other animals, who are devoid of culture. And since man did not come by his body suddenly, it becomes necessary to examine the process of evolution by means of which *Homo sapiens* acquired its unique characteristics. Most of the biological material in this text has been included with a view to clarifying the steps by which man came to have a distinctive body, one capable of devising and continuing culture. Once that stage was reached, we also find all of *Homo sapiens'* various stocks and races, every one of which is equally capable of symbolic cultural behavior. As far as is known, *Homo sapiens,* in spite of its diversity of forms, is truly a single species within which interbreeding may take place without biologically harmful consequences.

Having brought the story of man to the point where culture begins, we next took up the record of cultural progress through time. Archeologists have been able to show that after a slow start in the Old Stone Age, there was a gradual speeding up of new developments in the Middle Stone Age, followed by rapid acceleration, which became the rule throughout the New Stone Age and the Metal Ages, and which has continued into our own day. Not until cultural progress had gone on for many millenniums did it mature enough to provide mankind with a reasonably satisfactory alternative to predominately biological behavior. From then on man came to rely increasingly on culture. It is true that *Homo sapiens* has had to continue obeying the biological imperatives, yet, whenever possible, he has everywhere chosen to convert biological activities to biocultural ones. This he has done by introducing symbolic cultural values, which call for the modification of actions that have remained essentially biologic among other creatures.

Although archeologists discover a great deal about past forms of material culture, they are prevented, by the very nature of their approach, from learning many things that are essential to an understanding of biocultural behavior. To find out more about this central aspect of human life it was necessary to turn to the findings of ethnologists. After many facts had been gathered from primitive societies throughout the world, comparative analyses revealed that beneath a bewildering profusion of differing details there were certain aspects that were universal. In the course of time it was found that most of the features of any society's design for group living fell into a configuration whose minimum essentials could be expressed as a triangle. It was also found that the various segments of the triangle were closely interrelated and that the entire figure might be said to have a distinctive slant or emphasis.

With this viewpoint as a common base, contemporary cultural anthropologists have branched out in various ways. A number continue to visit primitive societies yet unknown to science, and to describe and analyze their patterns of culture; some concentrate on the tasks of studying how cultural configurations are held together or changed; many try to find out how ways of life are taught and learned; others look into the consequences which demands for conformity to cultural values have on the personalities of individuals; and still others have begun to transfer ethnological techniques from the investigation of primitive tribes to peasant groups and to large, heterogeneous, literate societies such as those commonly found in the industrialized Western World. Increased understanding of the nature of man, society, and culture has resulted from the combined efforts of all these investigators.

An anthropologist would be unfaithful to his convictions if he feared to look ahead and make predictions. For all that has already been accomplished in the science of man, much more remains to be done. If the cultural activities of *Homo sapiens* are to be directed to socially desirable goals for all mankind, all of human behavior must be brought into the range of controlled causation. Before this can be done, greater knowledge will have to be obtained in several critical areas.

Future research will have to be directed in part, at least, to the problem of cultural origins. If it be true that man alone is capable of symbolic behavior, exactly what is there in his biophysicochemical composition that sets him apart from all other animals? At the moment we are forced to postulate that algebraic mentality is somehow a function of increased brain size. If that is so, what is the precise threshold below which symbolization is impossible? If factors other than size are involved, what are they and how do they work? And when the matter of origins has been settled, we would still like to know exactly why so many cultural values apparently run counter to biological necessities. Why should people everywhere, in varying degree, make efforts to conceal activities involving excretion or sexual relations? Why should an American who has dined well feel ashamed if someone tells him that he has crumbs on his lips? Why do members of many societies feel uneasy about eating in full view of others? It is simple enough to rationalize some of these attitudes, as by postulating that some things are good and others bad. To Euro-Americans, for instance, the odors of stale urine or fresh feces are offensive, but there is no universal agreement on what constitutes a bad smell, and numerous tribes are indifferent about handling the waste products of the human body.

Suppose we bypass these questions and simply assume that all normal humans have the capacity to symbolize and that all societies formulate biocultural standards for living together. We are then faced with a new set of questions which future investigators must try to answer. How does a configuration of culture acquire an emphasis—such as that which is called Dionysian or Apollonian by Benedict—which resembles the personality structures of certain kinds of individuals? What is the precise nature of the process of interiorization? What happens to a child's inherited biogenetic mechanisms as it learns to conform to the cultural values of its society?

Then again, other basic problems await solution in respect to many facets of individual and group behavior. What is the way by which a society arrives at a decision regarding values, or comes to express a preference? Exactly how are systems of values established or made to change? Why are some aspects of a foreign culture eagerly accepted while others are stubbornly resisted? Why are people more willing to develop the new motor habits required for the use of borrowed material objects than they are to change the motor habits involved in the acquisition of new forms of speech?

More basic still would be satisfactory answers to the questions of why mankind in general has preferred to make cultural rather than biological adjustments to many new situations, and why the species has so consistently favored the saving of time and the conservation of human muscular energy. Partial explanations for some of these matters are already available, but a great deal that is now uncertain will have to be clarified by future research workers.

An area that is badly in need of further work is the field of cultural dynamics. We know that there are forces of initiation and forces of limitation; and we know that some forces make for stabilization and equilibrium while others bring about disruption, change, or disintegration; but when it comes to understanding the nature of these forces and of measuring their strength, social scientists are no better off than were students of the processes of organic evolution before there was any knowledge of genetics.

Every person, as well as every social unit, is continuously subject to the pressure of shifting, and often conflicting, sociocultural forces. We take it for granted that an individual must be prepared to live by varying sets of cultural values as he grows from infancy to old age or enters on different marital or occupational statuses; and now that isolation is virtually impossible, we expect whole societies to be ready to confront the possibility of change. Yet, we neither teach nor train people to live in an ever-changing world; and we cannot claim to know how to control the processes of change, because we know pitifully little about how they work.

Anthropologists of the future may have to concern themselves with still another aspect of dynamics, the relations of cultural to biological forces. Both of these sets of forces may easily be seen operating together in the field of man's interplay with his physical environment. The needs for oxygen, food, drink, and shelter from the elements originate as biological imperatives, but since man does not satisfy them with the attributes of his body, the biological needs stimulate cultural responses and so serve as forces of culture. These forces press upon every society that seeks to survive, and they express themselves in the form of particular cultural adjustments or institutions. Most contemporary social scientists are concerned with institutions and pay scant attention to the forces that bring them into being.

Man's relations to man likewise consist of institutions, such as marriage or child raising, that may be interpreted as cultural responses to biological forces; but for the present, man's dealings with the supernatural can seldom be directly connected with his biology, and must be attributed, for the most part, to sociocultural pressures. Once cultural anthropologists begin to deal with basic forces as well as with institutions, they may find themselves in a better position to formulate scientific laws.

Conclusion

There are many reasons why a book of this kind should end on a note of optimism. Modern anthropology is only about a century old, has attempted to cover a diversified range of topics, and has dealt with a tremendously long span of time, but it has received professional attention from only a relatively small number of scholars. Nevertheless, it has aroused great interest and has had a valuable stimulating effect on other disciplines devoted to an understanding of man. Above all, cultural anthropologists have proved that it is possible for human beings to study their fellow men dispassionately, and they have shown that no generalizations about mankind are valid unless the entire species is taken into account. No longer can a few men and women of a single type, from a single region, or possessed of a single way of life, be regarded as the equivalent of *Homo sapiens.*

The anthropological view of man has served to call into question the claims of all those who would glorify one stock or race at the expense of another. Biological differences among various groups of mankind are self-evident, and have been more closely investigated by physical anthropologists than by any other scientists. Their conclusions are soundly based and positive. No race is known to be biologically better than any other; mixture between stocks or races is not biologically harmful; there are no sure differences of mental potential; no society of humans lives on a purely "animal" level; and any group of mankind has the capacity to learn any other unit's patterns of biocultural behavior.

In the study of man's behavior anthropologists have also made some outstanding contributions. Through the painstaking work of archeologists they have been able to show the great antiquity of human efforts to develop culture, the various stages through which it has passed, and the different combinations of traits that have developed in various localities. At the same time they have provided evidence of the existence of universal laws of culture growth whose operations override regional considerations. What archeologists dealing with extinct peoples and cultures have found out has been supplemented and expanded by ethnologists. They have shown how human beings as living organisms interact with all phases of their environments, fellow men, and cultures, and they have worked out some of the basic configurations that patterned ways of life seem to take in all societies.

Finally, a few aspects of cultural anthropology deserve special mention. Fieldworkers have demonstrated that ways of life must be studied as wholes, wherein each part is not only integrated with the others, but is also affected by them. Furthermore, they have shown that one must be cautious about measuring primitive cultures against ethnocentric, preconceived, and often arbitrary, notions of right and wrong. As a last word, anthropologists have found no barriers, in theory, to the establishment of a pattern of culture for human beings everywhere. There is a noteworthy trend nowadays for small social groups to amalgamate into larger units. Should this trend continue indefinitely it will lead to the formation of a universal society, and whenever the peoples of the world may require it, cultural anthropologists will be among those who can help fashion a diversified way of life that will suit the need of all mankind.

Selected References

Barnett. Homer G., "Culture Processes," *American Anthropologist,* Vol. 42, 1940, pp. 21–48.

———, *Innovation: The Basis of Cultural Change,* New York, 1953.

Benedict, Ruth F., "The Science of Custom: The Bearing of Anthropology on Contemporary Thought," in V. F. Calverton, ed., *The Making of Man,* New York, 1931, pp. 805–17.

Emerson, Alfred E., "Dynamic Homeostasis: A Unifying Principle in Organic, Social and Ethical Evolution," *Scientific Monthly,* Vol. 78, 1954, pp. 67–85.

Kroeber, Alfred L., "Evolution, History, and Culture," in S. Tax, ed., *Evolution after Darwin,* Chicago, 1960, Vol. 2, pp. 1–16.

———, *The Nature of Culture,* Chicago, 1952.

Linton, Ralph, "Present World Conditions in Cultural Perspective," in R. Linton, ed., *The Science of Man in the World Crisis,* New York, 1945, pp. 201–21.

Steward, Julian H., "Evolution and Process," in A. L. Kroeber, ed., *Anthropology Today,* Chicago, 1953, pp. 313–26.

———, *Theory of Culture Change: The Methodology of Multilinear Evolution,* Urbana, Ill., 1955.

Thompson, Laura, *Towards a Science of Mankind,* New York, 1961.

White, Leslie A., *The Evolution of Culture,* New York, 1959.

Appendixes

Appendix A

Miscellaneous extinct hominids

A number of extinct hominids, not all of which were described earlier in this text, are discussed here. Their significance varies, but in general they supplement the material given in Chapter 6.

1. *Pithecanthropus robustus*

This specimen is a mosaic of apish and hominid traits. It resembles *Pithecanthropus erectus* in some respects, but it has been named robustus because of its large size. For example, the teeth of *Pithecanthropus robustus* are hominid but extremely big, and the canines undoubtedly projected and interlocked because there is a clear diastema. Furthermore, the entire upper jaw is wider and longer than in any creature called *Homo;* and the brain case, though very low in elevation, is long and exceedingly broad. There also seems to have been a ridge of bone running from front to back along the mid-line of the skull's top (sagittal crest). This feature was once regarded as a badge of simian status, but the current tendency is to play down its diagnostic importance.

2. *Atlanthropus*

Atlanthropus was found in Algeria in 1954, in the early mid-Pleistocene levels of a pumped-out sand pit, much of which had been flooded. Camille Arambourg, a French paleontologist, was the discoverer. Among other finds were some unusual jaw bones. They were not identical, but they conformed in shape, though not in size, to Meganthropus. The molar teeth are taurodont and reminiscent of Sinanthropus. It is impossible to make a definitive classification of Atlanthropus, but

Arambourg's find seems to suggest that *Homo erectus* may have lived in Africa, as well as in eastern Asia. This possibility has been strengthened by some of Leakey's most recent discoveries in east Africa. There is also a possibility that Atlanthropus should be linked to *Telanthropus*, an African fossil that is sometimes classified with the Australopithecinae.

3. *The Kanam and Kanjera Relics*

Louis S. B. Leakey, who, in 1932, found the *Kanam* and *Kanjera* specimens close by Lake Victoria in Kenya, east Africa, is convinced they ought to be given *sapiens* status. He even goes so far as to claim that the Kanam find, known only from a single fragmentary mandible, is a Lower Pleistocene representative of modern man, which is more advanced than Swanscombe because it shows a chin.

As for Kanjera, it is represented by parts of four badly crushed skulls. Not everyone accepts Leakey's judgment that the Kanjera remains are mid-Pleistocene members of *Homo sapiens*.

Appendix B

Supposed links between extinct hominids and the living varieties of Homo sapiens

Many forms of Cro-Magnon are now known. All of them occur in the late Pleistocene, and all of them approach *Homo sapiens* far more closely than did their predecessors. Wherever their remains are found associated with tools, the implements turn out to be one or another of the styles that archeologists call Upper Paleolithic. These come after Neandertal Man's Mousterian culture, and indicate that Cro-Magnon people are later than the Neandertals.

It was once the fashion to regard some of the diversities of late Pleistocene hominids as indicating, or at least foreshadowing, living mankind's division into stocks, races. Today it is admitted that hominids were greatly diversified in late Pleistocene times, and that some of them were probably ancestral to some strains of *Homo sapiens,* but contemporary anthropologists hesitate to say that Cro-Magnon man was divided into the actual stocks and racial groups that we see at the present time.[1] Most of the relics involved, and their presumed connections with *Homo sapiens* are discussed below.

1. *Wadjak Man*

This specimen is not usually regarded as Cro-Magnon. Nevertheless, it is said to be of Upper Pleistocene date, and an effort has been made to link it with contemporary Australoids. The linkage is customarily made through a series of resemblances, including the *Keilor* and *Talgai* finds of Australia.

The *Wadjak* discoveries were made in Java by Eugene Dubois, finder of *Pithecanthropus erectus,* but were not announced for thirty

[1] C. S. Coon's, *The Origin of Races,* New York, 1962, provides a modern exception to the general rule.

years. By then it was far too late to check on the circumstances of their finding. The specimens consist of two skulls, one of which has a high cranium like Cro-Magnon man, whereas the other has a huge palate, comparable to that of Rhodesian man.

A close similarity has been noted by Weidenreich between Wadjak and Keilor. The Keilor skull was found in 1940 near Melbourne, Australia. Its geological age is uncertain, but it seems to be Upper Pleistocene or later, and it may be likened to a cross between a recent Tasmanian and a modern Australian aborigine.

The Talgai skull, which pertains to an adolescent youngster, was found in Queensland, Australia, in 1884. Like the Keilor skull, its exact geologic age cannot be established. The Talgai youth had an extremely large palate and big canine teeth, but the conformations of his face and head are typical of Australian aborigines. As has been said, some anthropologists think there is a possible tie between Wadjak man and Australian natives, through such intermediaries as Keilor and Talgai.[2]

2. *Upper Cave Men from Chou Kou Tien*

At Chou Kou Tien, where *Sinanthropus pekinensis* was found, but in an upper cave above the levels occupied by Sinanthropus, three skulls were discovered in 1938–39. They appear to be terminal Pleistocene in age, and may be on the border between *Homo modernus* and *Homo sapiens*. They are usually set apart from Cro-Magnon. Weidenreich fancied that one skull resembled a modern European, another an Eskimo, and the third skull a Melanesian. Present-day anthropologists go no further than to call attention to the great diversity indicated by the skulls from the Upper Cave, and to note their lack of resemblance to the contemporary Chinese.

3. *Supposed Caucasoid Types*

Some years ago a number of anthropologists, who were impressed by the diversity of late Pleistocene hominids, attempted to group them into the three great divisions that are most universally known today: White or Caucasoid; Black or Negroid; and Yellow or Mongoloid.

---

[2] Another famous Australian skull is called *Cohuna*. Much was once made of its primitive features by Sir Arthur Keith, who tried to relate it to the Talgai specimen. However, in geological age and appearance it seems to be no more than a contemporary, native Australian.

Since these classifications depend, in part, on skin color and other features that disappear from skeletons, modern anthropologists are understandably reluctant to make racial judgments of Upper Pleistocene men.

Many types of supposed Caucasoids have been found. The original Cro-Magnons are somewhat riskily held to belong to this category. In addition, it is occasionally claimed that there was a longheaded (dolichocephalic) variety, whose skulls were less than three quarters as broad as they were long; and a broadheaded (brachycephalic) type, with heads more than three quarters as broad as they were long.

Taken together, the so-called Caucasoids were once said to comprise a *"Brünn"* race. Many variants have been described, one of the best-known of which is *Předmost man.* About forty specimens of this type were found at Předmost, near Brünn in Czechoslovakia. All have large faces and massive brain cases. They generally show pronounced brow ridges, which used to be taken as a sign of intermixture with Neandertaloids.

Another variant of this kind comes from *Combe-Capelle* in France. Not much is known about this specimen. Yet, so able a scholar as Carleton S. Coon looks upon Combe-Capelle as the direct ancestor of some of the dolichocephalic, bigheaded, beetle-browed strains found among living Caucasoids.

Still other divergences are represented by finds made at Krapina in Yugoslavia, and Ofnet in Bavaria. Both of these types betray a tendency toward broadheadedness. *Krapina man* is much the older of the two. He was, possibly, a contemporary of Ehringsdorf, and he exhibits a combination of what appear to be Neandertal and *modernus* or *sapiens* traits. *Ofnet man* is quite late. This discovery, which comprised a diversified assortment of thirty-three skulls, has attracted wide interest because the skulls have been deliberately buried, and because they give every indication of beheading.

So-called Upper Pleistocene Caucasoids were not restricted to Europe. A north African variant of Cro-Magnon was encountered at Afalou in Algeria. No less than about fifty burials were found. Measurements made on the *Afalou* bones differ in some details from the averages shown by the European Cro-Magnons, but they are not sufficiently different to warrant a separate classification for the two sets of remains.

4. *The Chancelade Skull*

Just as efforts have been made to read Caucasoid characteristics into the remains of many late Pleistocene hominids, so have attempts been made to see certain Mongoloid traits in one specimen. This is the famous *Chancelade skull,* which looks like that of an Eskimo.

The Chancelade specimen was found in 1888 in Dordogne, France. The skull is narrow, with a broad face (disharmonic) and powerful jaws. It is the cheekbones, which jut forward strongly, that give the face a flat appearance, reminiscent of Mongoloid faces. Much of the supposedly Eskimo resemblance rests on a combination of short stature, disharmonic skull, narrow nasal opening, and, above all, a ridgelike elevation along the mid-line of the skull roof.

Although cultural evidence should not influence biological judgments, many observers point out that the tools found with Chancelade man are consonant with the implements used by Eskimos. Cautious anthropologists, however, refuse to accept the Eskimoid affiliations of Chancelade man; and it is obviously unwise to set up racial classification on the basis of a single specimen.

5. *Pseudo-Negroids from Grimaldi*

In a cave near Mentone on the Italian Riviera, an expedition financed by the then Prince of Monaco, discovered in 1901 two late Pleistocene skeletons. One was that of an adult female, and the other that of an adolescent boy. Almost at once Verneau, a leading anthropologist of the day, judged them to be Negroid. He stressed the facts that the skeletons were prognathous and had limb proportions like those found among living Negroes.

Current anthropologists have found that the totality of the traits of the *Grimaldi* skeletons are well within the ranges of other late Pleistocene hominids, and they point out that neither remnant has the kind of flat, low, broad nose that is so typical of contemporary Negroids. To repeat a rather fanciful phrase coined by Hooton, "The Grimaldi widow and her son were not as black as they have been painted."[3]

---

[3] E. A. Hooton, *Up from the Ape,* rev. ed., New York, 1946, p. 374.

Glossary

Glossary

Reference to pages where the terms here defined occur will be found in the index.

Abbevillian A stage of western Europe's culture. See *Paleolithic Age.*

acculturation The process of intermingling of cultural elements, in part or in their entirety. May result from the impact of a Euro-American group on a primitive society, but may also come about in other ways.

Acheulian A stage of western Europe's culture. See *Paleolithic Age.*

affinal Relationship established by marriage, as opposed to *natal* or consanguineal relationships.

age group A class or set of persons, ordinarily of the same sex, who are of approximately the same age. Where they are recognized to form a unit, they may be expected to cooperate in carrying out particular duties.

algebraic mentality The ability to assign or change non-sensory meanings or values ascribed to anything that is used as a *symbol.* This capacity seems limited to human beings with large, healthy, *Primate* brains.

allophones Different sounds to which the speakers of a language assign the same meaning.

alloy A fusion of two or more metals forming a substance with properties of its own.

amniote egg Egg in which a thin membrane forms a sac enwrapping an embryo; the type of egg from which an offspring develops in reptiles, birds, and mammals.

amulet Any object, usually worn by a person, to which supernatural power has been ascribed; commonly used as a defense against evil forces.

animatism Belief that inanimate or inorganic things may contain supernatural power.

animism The doctrine that all living things contain a supernatural element widely equated with the life principle, or soul.

Apollonian Descriptive of an individual whose temperament is shy and restrained, or else of a social group in which qualities such as self-control or sobriety are esteemed.

archeology A branch of general anthropology in America. Its practitioners discover, excavate where necessary, and interpret the remains of former cultures.

artifact Any object that is consciously manufactured for human use.

associations Social groups voluntarily formed or entered for some special purpose. In primitive societies they generally balance clusters of individuals linked together by involuntary bonds of relationship.

atlatl Originally a word in the aboriginal Aztec (Nahua) language of Mexico, but commonly used by American anthropologists to designate a *spear-thrower*. See *spear-thrower.*

Aurignacian A stage of western Europe's culture. See *Paleolithic Age.*

Australopithecinae A general term for the whole group of extinct man-apes recently discovered in Africa.

avunculocal A custom whereby a bridal couple takes up residence with a maternal uncle of the groom. Such a nephew frequently becomes his uncle's heir.

Azilian Name of a Mesolithic stage discovered in France. It is characterized by the presence of painted pebbles.

banner stone An American archeological artifact of stone now thought to have been a weight attached to a spear-thrower, but once taken to have been used as a standard or banner. It consists of two wings that extend in opposite directions from a central perforation.

basic personality type See *modal personality type.*

batons de commandement Objects of antler or horn now thought to have been used for straightening out the shafts of spears or arrows. Once interpreted to have been staffs of high office.

berdache A man who dresses and acts like a woman. Not all berdaches are biologically impelled to become transvestites, and they are not invariably homosexuals.

biocultural unconformity The situation that develops whenever a person is subjected at one and the same time to a conflict between biological and cultural forces, motivations, expressions, values, or objectives. Such situations are always potentially dangerous.

blade A parallel-sided, somewhat rectangular, blank or tool of a stone such as flint, usually made from a previously prepared core. Blade implements were commonly used only in the later or upper phases of the *Paleolithic Age.*

blue baby A child born with an oxygen deficiency. It is usually a second or later Rh-positive child with an Rh-positive father and an Rh-negative mother.

bolas An implement thrown to entangle small game. It consists of centrally attached thongs, each of which is weighted at the end.

botanical animism The belief that all things in the plant kingdom have a vital principle, life force, or soul, often equated with *mana.*

brachiating The method of progression whereby a creature swings by the hands and arms. Usually associated with tree life and best exemplified by gibbons and some species of American monkeys.

brachycephalic Broadheaded. A skull or head that is at least 80 per-cent as broad as it is long.

bulb of percussion A swelling on a piece of cryptocrystalline stone that occurs below the place (*striking platform*) where it is struck a smart blow.

calendrical rites Supernatural ceremonies scheduled in advance to be performed at certain times or seasons. They must be socially desirable, inasmuch as they take no account of individual wants.

carbon-14 A radioactive form of carbon in living organisms that disintegrates at known rates of speed after death. The fixed rates of disintegration are widely used by archeologists as a measure of time.

caste A group of persons, marked by a particular occupation, who are expected to marry only among themselves. Caste membership is usually hereditary and lifelong, and castes generally have a fixed status in a social hierarchy.

casting The pouring of molten metal into a heat-resistant form, so that it will take the shape of the form when it cools and hardens.

Catarrhini See *Cercopithecidae.*

Ceboidea Family of broad-nosed monkeys, sometimes known as *Platyrrhini,* that represents the highest Primates to have evolved in the Western hemisphere.

cell A unit of *protoplasm* consisting, in most cases, of a *nucleus* containing *genes* arranged in *chromosomes,* and surrounding material that is loosely called cytoplasm.

celt A polished stone tool, resembling a modern hatchet blade or ax-head. It was always attached to a handle and was widely used in the *Neolithic Age.*

cephalic index A traditional device used in classifying subdivisions of *Homo sapiens.* It expresses as a percentage the width of a person's head or skull in proportion to its length. The higher the cephalic index, the more broadheaded the person.

Cercopithecidae Narrow-nosed monkeys of the Old World, who are commonly known as *Catarrhini.*

cerebral cortex See *neopallium.*

Chalcolithic (Eneolithic) A disputed stage of the Old World's cultural development. It is supposed to follow the *Neolithic,* and to represent a time when pure copper was the only metal used by man.

charm An object thought to contain supernatural power; customarily worn to attract favorable forces.

Chellian A stage of western Europe's culture. See *Paleolithic Age.*

chromosome Most commonly understood to be a microscopic string of *genes.* Wherever reproduction is bisexual, each parent is believed to contribute one of every pair of chromosomes that is contained in the nuclei of an offspring's *cells.*

cire-perdue A method for manufacturing metallic objects by fitting clay over a wax model. When heated, the wax runs out and is replaced by molten metal.

clan A *unilateral* cluster of relatives, following along one sex line only, who are held together by the shared belief that they are descended from a common ancestor. Common in primitive societies, where it may have social, political, economic, artistic, and religious functions.

class As opposed to a *caste,* a class refers to a group of persons who have the same social status but who can move from class to class in keeping with their attainments.

classificatory A method of labeling kindred whereby a number of persons may share one term. Thus an individual may have a number of fathers, mothers, and so forth. This supports the contention that a kinship system is a sociocultural rather than a genetic phenomenon. Strictly speaking, a classificatory system merges collateral and lineal descent terms.

clitoridectomy An operation on the clitoris performed in some primitive societies. It is often regarded as the feminine equivalent of circumcision.

contagious Used, most often, in the phrase "contagious magic" to describe certain supernatural beliefs or practices. It refers to the flow or movement of power as the result of contact.

council of elders A form of political control, *gerontocracy,* in which authority is vested in a group of oldsters.

counting coup In several Plains Indian tribes, a systematic and carefully graded scheme for winning honors in war. Greatest prestige of all went to a warrior who touched an unwounded enemy. Claims had to be supported by oaths or witnesses.

couvade The practice of having husbands lie in, after their wives have given birth. In extreme form, found among several Amazonian tribes, men may mimic the pain and process of childbirth.

cranial capacity A measure of gross brain size expressed in cubic centimeters.

critical rites Practices, based on a belief in the supernatural, designed to help an individual or a society, only in time of crisis.

Cro-Magnon A type of *hominid* closely resembling modern man, dominant in western Europe during the later Pleistocene period.

cross-cousin marriage Union between the offspring of a brother and those of his sister. This kind of marriage is often preferred or prescribed in primitive societies. One of its effects is sometimes that of making children take mates from the same natal *household group* as did the grandparent of their sex, of making brothers and sisters the parents-in-law of one another's offspring, and, later, of making a brother and his sister the grandparents of the same youngsters.

cross-cousins The children of a man and those of his sister.

Crossopterygia A kind of truly vertebrate fish with muscular fins and a capacity for breathing atmospheric oxygen. Sometimes believed to be the forerunner of amphibians, and to foreshadow vertebrate life on land.

Crow kinship system A method of labeling kindred, widely found in *matrilineal* societies, which uses separate terms for mother's sister and father's sister—but which uses a single term, regardless of generation lines, for a woman and all her descendants through females.

cultural anthropology That branch of anthropology that specializes in studying the prevailing ways of life among all the living individuals who constitute a society. In the United States, it often overlaps, and is sometimes interchangeable with, *ethnology, social anthropology,* and *ethnography.*

cultural blindness A convenient phrase for a custom whereby an individual fails to note something glimpsed, because he regards it as unimportant or because his society thinks he ought not to have seen it.

culture The complete range of objects, values, symbolic meanings, and repetitive ways of behaving that guide the conduct of individual members of a society. No aspect of culture can be biogenetically transmitted, and each person must learn postnatally the features of culture that pertain to him. Patterns, or configurations, of culture may persist beyond the deaths of particular individuals.

culture area A region or territorial zone within which one way of life is predominant. There is usually a noticeable difference in important aspects between one culture area and another.

culture hero A figure, often glorified in folklore, who is supposed to have taught particular ways of life to ancient members of a society.

cuneiform A form of writing, employing wedge-shaped characters, that was used in Mesopotamia and in many other parts of the Near East during the Bronze Age.

dendrochronology Method of establishing dates by measuring tree-ring arrangements. Works best in places where annual rainfall is irregular, such as the southwestern United States.

descriptive A method of labeling kindred that, theoretically, is supposed to use a single term for each type of relationship. In practice, as our term "cousin" indicates, one term may cover a variety of relationships.

diastema A space in the jaw, usually interpreted to mean that it was meant for the accommodation of a projecting or interlocking canine tooth.

diffusion The spread of a cultural item from its place of origin to other places. Thus, the opposite of local, or *independent invention.*

Dionysian Descriptive of a person of outgoing and aggressive temperament, or else of a society whose members esteem daring, unrestrained, intemperate, and reckless behavior.

divination The act of finding out or foretelling the wishes or designs of supernatural powers. May also refer to methods of discovering hidden information, such as the whereabouts of lost objects.

DNA An abbreviation for deoxyribonucleic acid, which is thought to be the first substance to have had the capacity to duplicate itself.

doctrine of signatures Belief, sometimes found in primitive religions, that the appearance of a substance reveals how it was meant to be used.

dolichocephalic Longheaded. A skull or head the breadth of which is less than about 75 percent of its length. See *cephalic index.*

double descent The system of having two different *unilateral* groups of kindred in one society, as, for example, both a mother's and a father's units.

dysphoria A feeling of unrest, unhappiness, uneasiness, or dissatisfaction. It tends to prevail throughout a society when its culture is disintegrating or changing quickly.

emancipation of the forelimbs A phrase used to describe the anatomical freeing of the front appendages from any duties connected with the support or movement of the body.

enculturation (socialization) The universal process whereby every human being learns from birth on to adjust its behavior to the *culture* of its society.

endogamy The custom whereby approved marriages must always take place within the bounds of particular social units; generally contrasted with *exogamy.*

Eneolithic See *Chalcolithic.*

eolith A natural stone utilized as a tool, without having been consciously manufactured. Some people claim that the earliest of men must have used unworked stones, recognizable by the markings resulting from usage.

Ertebølle A stage of *Mesolithic* culture in Scandinavia, featuring *kitchen middens.*

ethnocentric Culture-bound, tending to interpret the cultures of other people in terms of one's own way of life. Ethnocentricism usually implies a tendency to regard as "bad" any deviations from one's own practices.

ethnography The description of ways of life. See *cultural anthropology.*

ethnology In the United States this term refers to the study and analysis of ways of life. It has the implication of giving greater attention to theory than does *ethnography.* See *cultural anthropology.*

ethnomusicology The study of music in all societies, including primitive ones.

Eutherian mammals That subclass of mammals whose females nourish their young during pregnancy by means of a deciduous placenta. *Homo sapiens* belongs to this subclass.

exogamy A sociocultural requirement that approved marriages must take place outside certain units of society. As in *endogamy,* it is the total society that determines what those units shall be.

family of orientation The family group within which a newly born child normally learns the first things about its culture.

family of procreation The family group in which a married Ego begets and rears children.

fetish Any inanimate object to which a society ascribes supernatural power.

fibula Anatomically, the larger of the two long bones that run from ankle to knee in man. Archeologically, a safety pin from the Copper-Bronze or Iron Ages.

first-fruit rites Usually these are harvest rituals, during which part of the first yield is dedicated as a thanksgiving offering to the divinities thought responsible for enabling a society to obtain food. May be applied to the first seasonal appearance of any kind of food.

fluorine dating A test for the amount of fluorine possessed by a bone. Developed by K. P. Oakley, this test assumes that bones are of the same approximate age if they have absorbed similar amounts of fluorine from similar surroundings.

fluting The production of a channel on the face of a stone implement by the removal of a suitable flake. Usually found on certain American projectile points.

folk society A peasantlike community. May be only a rural or "backward" portion of a highly modern nation.

foramen magnum The major opening of a vertebrate skull or head, through which the top of the spinal cord enters. In Primates the foramen magnum is at the base of the skull; and in those whose heads are well-poised, as in orthograde creatures, it is located near the center.

forging In metallurgy, the forming of an object by repeated heating and hammering.

geisha Professional female entertainers in traditional Japan. They were not the same as prostitutes. Often hired by men for private parties.

genes Tiny biochemical particles supposed to be the units of biogenetic heredity. Most scientists think of them as component parts of *chromosomes.*

genna taboo A period of time, often following the death of an important personage, during which it is forbidden to undertake any but the most essential of actions.

genotype An organism whose form, or any of its parts, is thought to result only from the workings of its intrinsic genetic or hereditary material.

gerontocracy See *council of elders.*

glottochronology A technique for determining the time when speakers of related languages first moved apart. Also called *lexicostatistics.*

grid A diagram, usually consisting of a succession of squares, that is customarily used by archeologists to guide and systematize many of their excavations.

grinding See *polishing.*

hafting Increasing the mechanical efficiency of a tool by affixing it to a handle. Believed to have been first employed during the *Mousterian* phase of the *Paleolithic Age.*

hemoglobin The red coloring matter of the corpuscles that carry oxygen in the blood stream.

heterodont Having teeth that vary in shape, size, and function.

heterosis The phenomenon of *hybrid vigor,* whereby the offspring of differing parents exhibit a tendency to gain in size and strength.

hieroglyphic A form of writing by arranging pictorial symbols in rows or columns.

hominid Manlike or mannish. Any creature whose anatomical structure approximates that of *Homo sapiens.*

homodont Having teeth that are all alike.

Homo erectus A term suggested as a designation for extinct hominids that walked upright but were otherwise far removed from *Homo sapiens.* Their remains usually occur in early or middle Pleistocene deposits.

Homo modernus A term proposed for describing extinct Pleistocene hominids that closely resemble *Homo sapiens.* Some of their remains are supposed to occur quite early.

Homo neandertalensis See *Neandertal man.*

household group As a unit of kindred, this term applies to all relatives in one sex line of descent, who customarily share a common residence.

hybrid vigor See *heterosis.*

idol A carving, usually three-dimensional, to which supernatural power is ascribed; often supposed to depict the appearance of the associated supernatural power.

imitation magic See *mimetic magic.*

incest Prohibited sexual relations between certain kin. Practically universal are taboos on relations between parents and offspring, and between brothers and sisters; but societies may forbid mating on many grounds other than consanguinity.

independent invention Any invention that is developed in a given locality and not borrowed from an outside source. It thus affords a contrast to *diffusion.*

institutions As used in this book, the term denotes socially approved and standardized or repetitive ways of behaving that are responses to various forces.

javelin-thrower See *spear-thrower.*

joking relationships Socially approved and usually standardized forms of familiarity that are expected to prevail between certain types of relatives.

kachinas Male dancers who become gods or spirits among the Hopi and other Pueblo tribes as soon as they don masks. Kachinas usually sing as they dance. Simple membership in the cult is tribal wide and open to members of both sexes, but only males may wear masks and dance.

kinship sets Clusters comprising kindred bound together by one or more ties of relationship.

kitchen middens Heaps or mounds of debris that often accumulate near human settlements. When excavated by trained archeologists, they yield valuable information about extinct cultures. See *Ertebølle.*

kiva A subterranean religious chamber, sometimes used by men for social purposes, that is typically found in the villages of the Pueblo Indians.

kris A short sword or dagger customarily worn by men in Malaysia.

La Chapelle-aux-Saints Place in France where the most widely described specimen of *Neandertal man* was found.

lanceolate This term is used for describing early American tools of stone that are pointed and have the general form of a lancehead.

law of controlled causation A law of cultural evolution, which states that as any problem comes under the certain control of a society, it is no longer left for solution to a supernatural agency. As an increase of knowledge brings more and more things within a society's control, it has the effect of reducing the society's *reliance* on the supernatural.

Levallois *Lower Paleolithic* technique for the manufacture of stone tools from flakes struck from a tortoise core.

levirate The custom that entitles a widow to marry one of her late husband's brothers. Note that it does not entail arrangements with a new *household group.*

lexicostatistics See *glottochronology.*

lineage A *unilateral* line of consanguineous kindred, whom a society believes to be closely and demonstrably related by virtue of descent from a common ancestor or ancestress.

lost-wax See *cire-perdue.*

Magdalenian A stage of western Europe's culture. See *Paleolithic Age.*

magic Rituals involving a belief in the supernatural, performed for the benefit of those who request them. Magicians tend to work by formulas that compel supernatural agencies to do their bidding if the formulas are properly executed. Most cultural anthropologists feel that there is a subtle distinction between magic and *religion,* but some scholars treat them as one. Magical rites are usually *unscheduled* and *critical* and are virtually never *calendrical.*

Maglemose A *Mesolithic* culture of Europe, which flourished along the Baltic Sea.

mana A general term for supernatural power. The word was first noted in Melanesia, but it is now used by cultural anthropologists who study supernaturalism anywhere in the world.

mano A stone held in the hand for rubbing against a *metate* while making flour or meal.

mantic "sciences" "Sciences" of prophecy, usually based on a determination by man of supernatural plans for the future. See *divination.*

marital frigidity The inability of a spouse, most often a wife, to enjoy sexual relations with a legal mate.

matrilineal Reckoning descent unilaterally only through one's mother. By this means, a *unilateral* descent group is formed by a woman and the offspring of her female descendants. Such groups may comprise matrilineal *lineages* or *clans.*

matrilocal A postmarital residence rule that requires a groom to live in or near his bride's natal household.

medicine man See *shaman.*

mesocephalic Medium-headed. Skulls which are 75 to 80 percent as broad as they are long.

Mesolithic That phase of cultural evolution that falls between the *Paleolithic* and the *Neolithic.* May refer either to the tools and other objects that were then current or to the time involved. For most of the Old World this would mean approximately from 12,000 to 8,000 B.P. Some anthropologists regard the Mesolithic as no more than an extension of the *Upper Paleolithic.*

metate A stone slab, often resembling a washboard in size and shape, on which flour or meal is produced by rubbing the appropriate material with a *mano.*

microlith An implement fashioned by man from a tiny bit of stone.

mimetic magic Efforts to influence supernatural powers to help the members of a society get what they desire by showing what is wanted. Thus, if more heat from the sun is desired, a fire might be built as part of a ceremony. Sometimes known, too, as *imitation magic.*

mixed farming This term is used, particularly for the Neolithic in the Near East, to indicate subsistence techniques that combine the domestication of animals with the domestication of plants (agriculture).

modal personality type Also known as *basic personality type.* Refers to the most common or average personality type that is supposed to prevail in a given social group.

moiety Each subdivision of a society that is divided into halves.

molding See *casting.*

morpheme The smallest unit of speech to which meaning is ordinarily attached.

mother-in-law taboo A sociocultural rule that forbids a man to look upon or converse with his mother-in-law. This is one form of avoidance.

motor habits Movements of the body or any of its parts in accord with cultural conventions. Motor habits are usually much the same for all persons of the same sex and age who occupy equivalent positions in a society.

Mousterian The middle phase of Paleolithic culture in western Europe, closely associated with *Neandertal man.* See *Paleolithic Age.*

multilocal household A social unit comprised of unilateral kin who would presumably have shared a common residence under earlier conditions, but who now occupy two or more houses.

natal kin Relatives automatically and involuntarily acquired by an infant at birth.

national character The kind of personality structure that is believed to be most typical of an entire nation. See *modal personality type.*

Neandertal man A variety of extinct *hominid,* linked to *Mousterian* culture, that lived through the middle phases of the Pleistocene. Those in western Europe are sometimes called "Classic," and had low skull vaults, outthrust faces, relatively chinless lower jaws, and short, thick necks.

Neolithic Age The New Stone Age, usually considered to have begun in the Near East about 6000 B.C. It is characterized by people who lived in permanent settlements, practiced agriculture, made polished stone tools, domesticated animals, fashioned pottery, and knew how to weave.

neolocal A postmarital residence custom that results in newlyweds living in new homes that are not necessarily near any of their kin.

neopallium Part of the brain that first appeared in reptiles and corresponds to the *cerebral cortex.*

new-fire rites Ceremonies that involve the kindling of fresh blazes. North of the equator such rites are generally *calendrical* and occur late in December, at the time of the winter solstice. The new-fire is usually an act of *mimetic magic,* designed to strengthen the power of the sun, and also to convey the implication of a fresh start, such as the beginning of a new year.

Omaha kinship system A method of naming relatives, widely found in *patrilineal* societies, that has separate terms for father's brother and mother's brother, but which uses a single term to designate, regardless of generation, a man and all his masculine descendants through males.

opposable thumb A *Primate* anatomical mechanism, whereby the ball of the thumb can be opposed to the balls of the other four fingers of each hand, making possible a prehensile grip.

orthograde Carriage of the body in an upright position. Among *Primates* man is the only creature that habitually carries the body upright, firmly supported on the hind legs.

osteodontkeratic R. A. Dart's term for an "industry" that made artifacts of teeth, bones, and sinews or leather. This "industry" supposedly comes before mankind's use of stone.

Paleolithic Age The Old Stone Age. Represents the time and type of man's earliest, clearly recognizable forms of culture. In western Europe it is conventionally arranged into the following subdivisions, during all of which man made stone tools by percussion or pressure, and failed to develop permanent settlements and methods of controlled food production:

A. *Lower Paleolithic*
   1. *Chellian (Abbevillian)*
   2. *Acheulian,* including the *Levallois* technique.
B. *Middle Paleolithic*
   1. *Mousterian*
C. *Upper Paleolithic*
   1. *Aurignacian*
   2. *Solutrian*
   3. *Magdalenian*

palstave A metal *celt* in which the sides rise up and meet to form an enclosed socket. Some have a ring for tying, in addition to wedging, a handle into the socket. Widespread in the Copper-Bronze Age.

parallel cousins The children of two brothers or of two sisters. In some societies, parallel cousins are forbidden to wed. In Moslem societies this type of wedding may actually be preferred.

patrilineal A *unilateral* group of kindred who trace their descent in the male line. Such groups may comprise patrilineal lineages or clans.

phenotype An organism, or any of its parts, whose form is presumed to result from the interplay of its inherited genetic material and such external forces as are in the environment. Often implies surface appearance as opposed to biogenetic inheritance.

phoneme The smallest identifiable or contrastive unit of sound that can be distinguished in any human language.

phratry In primitive societies, this is most commonly an unnamed *exogamic* unit, containing two or more *clans.* Authorities differ on whether phratries were formed by the segmentation of an original clan or by the amalgamation of originally distinct clans.

Pithecanthropus erectus Also known as Java man, and less widely as Trinil man. Found at Trinil, Java, by Eugene Dubois. Represents an early and archaic form of extinct *hominid* that is here called *Homo erectus.*

Platyrrhini See *Ceboidea.*

polishing The technique most widely used in the *Neolithic Age* for the manufacture of stone tools. Called for rubbing or grinding a tool to shape by moving it back and forth across a rough, abrasive material. The resulting tool is highly polished, and smooth to the touch.

polyandry A custom, quite rare throughout the world, that permits one woman to have two or more husbands at the same time.

polygamy Any form of having, simultaneously, multiple spouses.

polygyny The most widespread form of multiple mating, wherein one man takes two or more wives.

potassium-argon technique A method of dating based on the regular conversion of radioactive potassium to argon. Although not yet perfected, this means of dating is already being used by some archeologists.

Primate That order of *Eutherian mammals* to which belong lemurs, tarsiers, monkeys, apes, and men.

prognathism Protrusion of the face and jaws. Sometimes restricted to protrusion of the tooth-bearing portions of the jaws.

pronograde The method of progression on all fours, with the body carried horizontally.

protoplasm Living matter, making up the bodies of all plants and animals. Always divided into units or *cells.*

Protozoan A tiny animal, whose entire body consists of one *cell* of *protoplasm.*

quipu A knotted string used in aboriginal Peru as a reminding device. By means of various colors and knots, the Inca were capable of keeping track of complicated statistical data. Not a form of true writing.

race A subdivision of *Homo sapiens.* In this text the term is used to indicate a biological subsubspecies of *Homo sapiens.*

radiocarbon See *carbon-14.*

rites of passage Supernatural ceremonies designed to help individuals pass from one stage of a life cycle to another.

sagittal crest A crest of bone that rises upward from front to back along the mid-line of a skull.

samurai Japanese nobles and fighting men of the past, who were allowed to wear two swords as a token of their status.

seal An engraved or inscribed stamp used for identification or signature. In Copper-Bronze days seals were frequently pressed into a soft substance that later hardened.

secret societies *Associations* of people who keep at least some of their rites or activities secret from the nonmembers of their society.

sexual dichotomy The sociocultural assignment of tasks to one sex or the other.

shaman An individual, thought to be heavily endowed with *mana.* Since he customarily uses his supernatural power to cure the sick or to counteract witchcraft, he is often equated with a *medicine man.* Originally, the word was restricted to certain Siberian tribes, but today it is universally used.

shifting cultivators Farmers who move their farms from time to time.

siblings Children of the same parents, such as brothers or sisters. May be of one sex or both.

simian shelf A transverse plate or shelf of bone that occurs inside the lower jaws of apes, "opposite" the chin region in man.

Sinanthropus pekinensis A specimen of *Homo erectus.* Its name means "Chinese man from Peking." It was found in a limestone quarry at Chou Kou Tien, about forty miles from Peking.

slip Term used for a fine wash of clay that is applied to the surface of a pot. May be independently tinted.

social anthropology A phrase widely used by British anthropologists to connote very largely what American students of man call "*cultural anthropology.*"

socialization See *enculturation.*

sodality An *association* or group of people who may or may not be consanguineous kin. See *associations* and *secret societies.*

Solutrian A phase of western Europe's culture. See *Paleolithic Age.*

somatotyping Sheldon's method of classifying human bodies in terms of structural components rather than by virtue of racial traits.

song-tying The custom of trying to shame or defeat an opponent by means of a song contest.

sororate The cultural convention of expecting a widower to marry one of his late wife's sisters. See *levirate.*

spear-thrower An instrument for hurling a spear, which has the effect of extending the user's arm by the length of the spear-thrower. Often called an *atlatl* by American archeologists.

stereoscopic A type of vision in which the images entering from the left and right eyes overlap to produce a sense of depth. In the higher *Primates* the sense of depth may be produced even when the object that is seen is only a few inches away from the viewer.

stimulus diffusion The spread of an idea or stimulus from one place or culture area to another. The final products based on transmitted ideas or stimuli are not necessarily identical.

stock As it is used in this text, a biological subspecies of *Homo sapiens.*

stop ridge A raised horizontal or transverse bar, usually placed across a *celt,* to keep a handle from slipping downward.

striking platform A level place on a piece of stone that receives a sharp blow whenever a fragment is to be detached.

supernatural sanctions The concept that the mores of a society are backed up by supernatural powers.

supraorbital torus A bar of bone that runs across the upper margins of the eye sockets. Found in most species of apes and in some extinct *hominids.*

Swanscombe man An important type of extinct *hominid,* found in England. A number of anthropologists regard the remains as pertaining to a very early specimen of *Homo modernus.*

symbol Anything to which an extrasensory value or meaning is attached by the members of a society. See *algebraic mentality.*

taboo A prohibition or restriction, usually backed by the threat of supernatural punishment.

talisman An object of supernatural value, generally containing sacred writing, that is believed to help a person by defending him from forces of evil.

taxonomy The science of classifying together related organisms. Presumed relationships grow larger as the units become progressively smaller. The largest category is a kingdom, followed by phylum, class, order, family, genus, and species.

teknonymy The custom of identifying an individual by his relationship to another party. Usually applies to the identification of a parent through his child.

temper Coarse or gritty material that is worked into clay from which pottery is to be made. While the pottery is being fired, the temper provides tiny outlets for the escape of gases that might otherwise cause the clay walls of a pot to crack open.

territoriality The habit of many animals of keeping intruders out of any territory that they claim for themselves. Such behavior may possibly apply to *hominids* under certain circumstances.

thermoluminescence A method that archeologists may someday find useful for dating artifacts that have once been exposed to fire. It depends on accurate measures of glow curves.

torus See *supraorbital torus.*

totem An object, plant, or animal with which a social unit feels itself to be intimately connected. Sometimes, members of a *lineage* or *clan* may use art forms or engage in ceremonies that express their relationship to a totem.

tribal initiation One or more rituals that fit individuals for completely adult roles in their society. Frequently, but not invariably, tribal initiations are puberty ceremonies in *rites of passage.*

unilateral One-sided. Has reference to the tracing of relationship through one parent only, a common way of labeling kindred in primitive societies.

unilineal See *unilateral.*

unilocal household A unit of kinfolk formed when a newly wedded pair, and such offspring as may later be born to them, live in the natal *household* of either principal and are terminologically merged with the other kin who reside there.

unilocal residence The custom of postmarital residence wherein a bridal pair moves into a home already occupied by the relatives of either party to the marriage.

unscheduled rites Rituals that cannot be anticipated far in advance and that cannot be placed on a ceremonial calendar because they are usually of a critical or emergency nature. See *magic.*

uxorilocal residence The same as *matrilocal* residence.

value interiorization The presumed process by which a child takes into itself the cultural values of its society. See *enculturation.*

virilocal residence The same as *patrilocal* residence.

warp Those threads, used in weaving, that hang permanently downward on a loom. They are tied in place and can be moved only slightly up or down, usually with the help of a heddle, as weft elements pass over or under them at right angles. See *weft.*

weft (woof) Untied threads that move horizontally across a loom, over and under warp elements. For ease of movement the weft is usually attached to a shuttle. See *warp.*

weregild A custom that permits a murderer to escape further punishment by the payment of money to the surviving kin of his victim.

witch A person of either sex who uses supernatural power for harmful or antisocial purposes.

Würm The fourth extensive outflowing movement of ice during Europe's Pleistocene.

ziggurat An artificial hill of earth, on top of which public buildings were placed during Mesopotamia's Copper-Bronze Age.

zoological animism A belief in the supernatural power of animals. A cornerstone of primitive religion.

Index of Living Tribes, Societies, and Cultures

Numbers in italics refer to figures; the letter "n" following a page reference refers to the footnote(s) on that page.

Name Index

For additional names see the Selected References at the end of each chapter. Authors and editors are cited only in conjunction with the first reference to a given work. Numbers in italics refer to figures; the letter "n" following a page reference refers to the footnote(s) on that page.

Subject Index

Numbers in italics refer to figures; the letter "n" following a page reference refers to the footnote(s) on that page.